Genomic Essentials *for* Graduate Level Nurses

Genomic Essentials *for* Graduate Level Nurses

Edited by

Diane C. Seibert, Ph.D, WHNP-BC, ANP-BC, FAANP, FAAN

Professor and Interim Associate Dean, Academic Affairs
Daniel K. Inouye Graduate School of Nursing
Uniformed Services University of the Health Sciences
Bethesda, MD

Quannetta T. Edwards Ph.D, FNP-BC, WHNP-BC, AGN-BC, FAANP

Professor
College of Graduate Nursing
Western University of Health Sciences
Pomona, CA

Ann H. Maradiegue, Ph.D, FNP-BC, FAANP

James Madison University
Harrisonburg, VA

Susan T. Tinley, Ph.D, RN, CGC (RET)

Associate Professor Emerita
Creighton University College of Nursing
Omaha, NE

DES*tech* Publications, Inc.

Genomic Essentials for Graduate Level Nurses

DEStech Publications, Inc.
439 North Duke Street
Lancaster, Pennsylvania 17602 U.S.A.

Printed in the United States of America
10 9 8 7 6 5 4 3 2 1

Main entry under title:
    Genomic Essentials for Graduate Level Nurses

A DEStech Publications book
Bibliography: p.
Includes index p. 433

Library of Congress Control Number: 2016932489
ISBN: 978-1-60595-094-5

Table of Contents

Preface

The purpose of this book is to improve the genomic competency of nurses prepared at the graduate level. The more informed graduate level nurses are about the rapidly evolving field of genomics, the more likely they are to apply it at the point of care, and the more prepared they will be to engage in conversations about how, when and where genomic technologies should be used in healthcare systems.

In 2009, a group of fifteen graduate nurses with genetics/genomics expertise from around the U.S. began a 2-year process to develop 'The Essential Genetic/Genomic Competencies for Nurses with Graduate Degrees," an expanded set of genetic/genomic competencies tailored to meet the needs of nurses prepared at the graduate level. The competencies have two major domains, with each divided into seven major categories. The first domain, Professional Practice, includes (1) Risk Assessment & Interpretation; (2) Genetic Education, Counseling, Testing and Results Interpretation; and (3) Clinical Management. The second domain, Professional Responsibilities, comprises: (4) Ethical, Legal and Social Implications (ELSI); (5) Professional Role; (6) Leadership; and (7) Research.

The present volume evolved from and is based on constructs found in the graduate essentials mentioned above, and many of the chapters are authored by nurses who participated in developing the competencies. A number of chapters address the competencies in a clinical setting, while others, e.g., chapters 4 and 16, are focused exclusively on a single category within the competencies. The first five chapters provide the scientific underpinnings for genomic practice, which are Basic Genetic/Genomic Concepts, Risk Assessment, Genetic Testing and Counseling, ELSI and Pharmacogenomics. The next four chapters present genomic issues across the human lifespan: Preconceptual/ Prenatal, Newborn Screening, Pediatrics and

Aging. The following six chapters review genetic and genomic contributions to disorders of selected body systems: Respiratory, Cardiology, Hematology, Neurology, Endocrine and Cancer. The next two chapters discuss issues unique to nursing, Genomics in Nursing Research, Practice, Administration & Education and Genomics and Symptomatology. The final chapter, Genomic Technologies, offers a glimpse of genomic advances that are being translated into clinical application. Because genomic science is evolving so quickly, new information was emerging daily as this book was being prepared. Each chapter therefore should be considered an orientation and introduction to a topic, in contrast to a comprehensive resource.

We would like to thank the talented inter-professional team of nurses, physicians, researchers, scientists, geneticists and genetic counselors who worked with us to turn an idea into reality. Inter-professional education and collaboration, endorsed by the Institute of Medicine and the American Association of Colleges of Nursing are essential to improve outcomes in today's healthcare environment. This book's collaborating authors represent a highly experienced group of health care professionals from a number of different specialties, including: advanced practice registered nurses (many who have received post-doctoral training at the National Institutes of Health or National institute of Nursing Research), board-certified advanced genetics nurses, certified genetic counselors, physicians, nurse ethicists, molecular geneticists, nurse genetic scientists, nurse academicians, nursing leaders and administrators. Working in hospitals, specialty clinics, universities, laboratories and pharmacies throughout the world, these specialists devoted many hours to researching and writing chapters, sending references we may never have found otherwise, and furnishing valuable insight and support across the entire life of this writing project. We wholeheartedly thank each and every contributor.

We hope readers find this book useful, informative and interesting. In creating it our ultimate goal has been to produce a resource that will improve healthcare outcomes for individuals, their families and communities by moving nursing one step closer to the further goals of personalized healthcare and precision medicine.

DIANE C. SEIBERT
QUANNETTA T. EDWARDS
ANN H. MARADIEGUE
SUSAN T. TINLEY

List of Contributors

Sheila A. Alexander, Ph.D, RN

Bradley T. Andresen, Ph.D, FAHA

Edwarda M. Buda-Okreglak, MD, FACP

Yvette P. Conley, Ph.D

Jennifer R. Dungan, Ph.D, RN

Julia Eggert, Ph.D, GNP-BC, AOCN

Jeffery Fan, RN

Megan Grove, MS, LCGC

Ran He, Ph.D, AGN-BC

Ying Huang, Ph.D

Kory W. Jasperson, MS, CGC

Heather L. Johnson, DNP, FNP-BC, FAANP

Sara M. Jordan, BA, BSN, RN

Erica A. Julian, RN, BSN

Dana Knutzen, MS, CGC

Dale H. Lea, RN, MPH, CGC

Catherine Ling, Ph.D, FNP-BC, FAANP

Yu Liu, Ph.D, RN

Michelle Munroe, DNP, COL, AN, CNM

Lucia Novak, MSN, ANP-BC, BC-ADM

Sarah Race, RN, MSN, CNS

Debra L. Schutte, Ph.D, RN

Joanna Spahis, RN, CNS, APNG

Kathleen Sparbel, Ph.D, RN, FNP-BC

Martha Turner, Ph.D, RN-BC

Allison A. Vorderstrasse, DNSC, APRN

Karen L. Zanni, MSN, ARNP-BC, RN

June Zhang, Ph.D, RN

Chapter 1

Introduction to Basic Genetics and Genomics

SUSAN T. TINLEY, Ph.D, RN, CGC (RET)

Objectives:

- Describe the difference between "genetics" and "genomics".
- Explain the similarities and differences between mitosis and meiosis.
- Discuss normal and abnormal chromosome structure.
- Explain how DNA and RNA function in creation of gene products.
- Describe various alterations in the genetic code and their functional effects.
- Discuss details of each of the patterns of inheritance.

1.1. INTRODUCTION

Basic genetic/genomic concepts need to be understood to meet competencies outlined in the *Essential Genetic and Genomic Competencies for Nurses with Graduate Degrees* (Greco, Seibert & Tinley, 2012). This chapter provides a foundation for the remaining chapters in this book by offering a review of the basic principles of "genetics," and introduces the concept of "genomics." The traditional science of "genetics" is focused on exploring and explaining the impact of individual (or single) gene or chromosome changes, most of which are individually quite rare, on health. The broader term, "genomics," considers the interactions between and within genes, regulatory sequences, and the environment. Genomics research is improving our understanding of genetic disorders, common complex health problems such as diabetes and heart disease, and disease prevention and treatment response. The basic science of "genetics" has evolved into "genomic healthcare." For simplicity and continuity, the term genomics will be used throughout this book except when addressing specific genetic concepts or conditions. Because the genomics education of our readers may vary substantially, there are references at the end of the chapter to resources that can provide additional information. The reader is encouraged to refer back to these resources in the future, to stay current with the rapidly changing field of genomics and its impact on specific areas of nursing practice, administration, research, and education.

1.2. DNA STRUCTURE AND REPLICATION

1.2.1. Structure of DNA and Chromosomes

Deoxyribonucleic acid (DNA) is the molecule that provides the genetic instructions for the development, growth, and ongoing functioning of any human being. There are two different cellular locations for DNA, in the nucleus (nuclear DNA [nDNA]) and in the mitochondria (mitochondrial DNA [mtDNA]). The nucleus is the location for the vast majority of human DNA; except in areas where both types of DNA are being discussed, it can be assumed that DNA is used to refer to DNA in the nucleus.

DNA is composed of two strands of polynucleotides. Each nucleotide is made up of a five carbon sugar, a phosphate, and a nitrogenous base. The appearance of DNA has been compared to a ladder which is coiled around core units of eight histones to provide support and stability to the structure.

The two sides of the ladder are composed of the alternating sugar and phosphate, and each sugar phosphate unit has a base attached. Hydrogen bonding between the bases holds the two strands together, forming the rungs of the ladder. One of the bases in a pair is larger, a purine, and the other is smaller, a pyrimidine. The purines

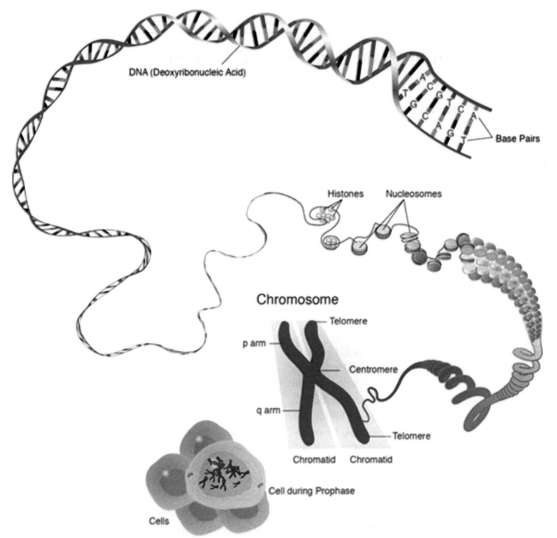

FIGURE 1.1. Chromosome. (Figure from the National Institutes of Health. National Human Genome Research Institute. Digital Media Database. Darryl Leja/NHGRI/NIH. Available at: http://www.genome.gov/dmd/img.cfm?node=Photos/Graphics&id=85281.)

are adenine and guanine (A and G) and the pyrimidines are cytosine and thymine (C and T). The pyrimidine thymine always pairs with the purine adenine (A and T) and the pyrimidine cytosine always pairs with the purine guanine (C and G). This consistent pairing is essential when the DNA replicates itself during cell division and during transcription and translation of the DNA code into proteins. A gene is a unit of the DNA that provides the code for a protein (Figure 1.1).

The nuclear DNA, which will be the primary focus of this chapter, is packaged into 23 pairs of chromosomes. Within each pair, 1 chromosome is maternally derived and the other is pater-

nally derived. Of the 23 pairs of chromosomes, 22 are the same for males and females and are called autosomes, numbered "1 to 22," with 1 being largest and 22 the smallest. The 23rd pair of chromosomes determines the sex of the individual: XX for females and XY for males. The Y chromosome carries approximately 50 genes (National Library of Medicine [NLM] [U.S.], 2014a), whereas the X chromosome, which is much larger, carries approximately 2,000 genes (NLM [U.S.], 2014b).

The chromosome consists of two arms joined at a constriction point called the centromere. The shorter of the two arms is the p arm (for "pe-

FIGURE 1.2. Acrocentric, Metacentric, and Submetacentric Chromosomes. (Figure adapted from U.S. Department of Energy Genomic Science Program's Biological and Environmental Research Information System (BERIS). Individual chromosome illustrations available at: https://public.ornl.gov/site/gallery/default.cfm?restsection=.)

tite") and the longer arm is the q arm. Some of the pairs of chromosomes are the same size, but the centromeres are located in different positions on the chromosome. Chromosomes with centromeres located in the center (chromosomes 1, 3, 16, 19, and 20) are called metacentric; those with off-center centromeres (chromosomes 2, 4 to 12, 17, 18, X, and Y) are called submetacentric; and those with centromeres at the tip of the chromosome (chromosomes 13, 14, 15, 21, and 22) are acrocentric (Figure 1.2).

Another way of differentiating the chromosome pairs, in addition to their size and centromere placement, is by the distinctive patterns of

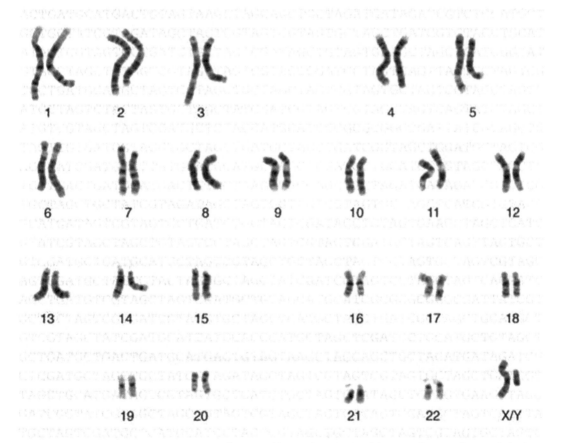

FIGURE 1.3. Chromosomes of the Human Genome. (Figure from National Human Genome Research Institute. Digital Media Database. Darryl Leja/NHGRI/NIH. Available at: http://www.genome.gov/dmd/img.cfm?node=Photos/Graphics&id=85175.)

light and dark bands (Figure 1.3). The tips of the chromosomes (similar to shoelace tips) are called telomeres (Figure 1.1), which act as a cap to prevent the chromosome from unraveling. Telomeres are made of many repeats of the sequence "TTAGGG," and each time a cell divides, 20 to 30 of these TTAGGG repeats are lost. When all the telomere repeats are completely gone, the cell dies. Germ cells produce an enzyme called "telomerase," which restores the telomeres to their original length so that at fertilization, there are sufficient repeats for the new individual's lifetime (Read & Donnai, 2011).

1.2.2. The Cell Cycle

Each somatic cell goes through a cycle from its formation to its division into two daughter cells. There are four phases in each cell cycle: Gap1 (G1), S, Gap2 (G2), and M (Figure 1.4). During G1, the longest phase, individual chromosomes cannot be distinguished, because the DNA is unwound (extended) to allow easy access to the genetic code for protein production.

During the "S" phase, the DNA is reproduced in the process of replication (Figure 1.5) so that each daughter cell receives an exact copy of the DNA from the original cell. During replication, the hydrogen bonds between the bases break so that the two strands of the DNA can separate. The bases of each strand attract new nucleotides with complementary bases, and hydrogen bonds form between the bases to hold the new strand to the old strand. Replication does not occur at the same time in all of the chromosomes or even within any given chromosome, but by the end of the S phase, all of the chromosomes are completely reproduced. Each of the original two DNA strands have been a template for a new complete molecule of DNA that is an exact copy of the original. The two identical copies of the chromosome are called sister chromatids, and they are held together at the centromere.

In the G2 phase, any replication errors that occurred during the S phase are detected and repaired. If the errors are too numerous or severe, programmed cell death (apoptosis) occurs. Malfunction in the process of apoptosis can lead to the development of cancer, which is discussed in greater depth in Chapter 15.

1.2.3. Mitosis

The M phase of the cell cycle is the phase in which the cell divides, forming 2 new cells. In somatic cells, this phase is called mitosis (Figure 1.6). During the first stage of mitosis (prophase), the chromosomes become tightly coiled and visible under a microscope. The nuclear membrane disappears and spindle fibers develop at the centrioles at either side of the cell, and the free end of the spindle fibers attach to the centromeres. During the second stage (metaphase), the chromosomes are highly condensed and most easily visualized under the microscope. During metaphase, the chromosomes are arranged along the equatorial plane of the cell, and the spindle fibers begin to contract, pulling the sister chromatids apart. During the third phase (anaphase), all the centromeres divide and the spindle fibers pull one sister chromatid to one side of the cell and the other to the opposite side. At the end of anaphase, there should be 92 chromosomes, with 46 on either side of the cell. During the next phase (telophase), a nuclear membrane develops around each group of 46 chromosomes, which are beginning to extend into indistinguishable

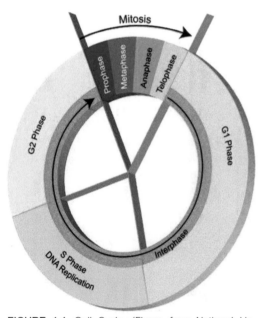

FIGURE 1.4. Cell Cycle. (Figure from National Human Genome Research Institute (NHGRI) Digital Media Database. Darryl Leja/NHGRI/NIH. Available at http://www.genome.gov/dmd/img.cfm?node=Photos/ Graphics&id=85276.)

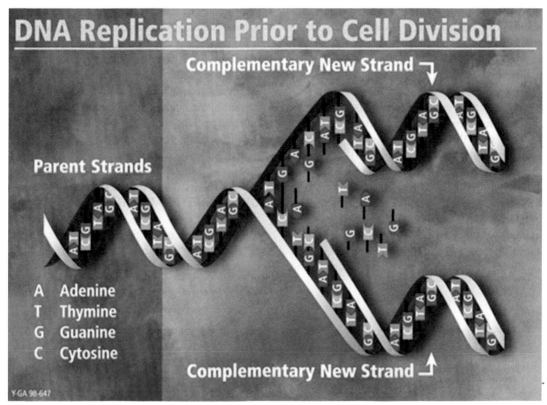

DNA Replication Prior to Cell Division

Complementary New Strand ⌐

Parent Strands

A   Adenine
T   Thymine
G   Guanine
C   Cytosine

Complementary New Strand ⌐

Y-GA-98-647

FIGURE 1.5. DNA Replication Prior to Cell Division. (Figure from Human Genome Program, U.S. Department of Energy, *Genomics and Its Impact on Science and Society: A 2008 Primer*, 2008. [Original version 1992, revised 2001 and 2008.] Available at: https://public.ornl.gov/site/gallery/detail.cfm?id=393&topic=&citation=&general=DNA%20 replication&restsection=all.)

structures again. The division of the cytoplasm (cytokinesis) follows, forming two daughter cells which are identical to the original cell. These two daughter cells then enter interphase, which corresponds to G1, S, and G2 of the cell cycle.

1.2.4. Meiosis

A different series of cell division steps occurs during meiosis, ultimately reducing the number of chromosomes in germ cells (sperm and ova) from 23 pairs (46 individual chromosomes) to 23 single chromosomes (Figure 1.7). To accomplish this, two cell divisions are required. As in mitosis, during meiosis, DNA replicates during prophase I, which occurs prior to the first meiotic division. In meiosis, prophase I is divided into five periods:

Leptokene: DNA becomes condensed, but the two chromatids are so tightly associated, they cannot be distinguished.

Zygotene: Chromosomes pair up (e.g., maternal chromosome 12 pairs up with paternal chromosome 12) and are held tightly together by the synaptical complex.

Pachytene: Chromosomes condense even further and some genetic material from one chromosome trades places with genetic material of the other chromosome, creating four unique chromatids. This exchange is called crossing over or recombination.

Diplotene: The synaptical complex disappears and the chromosomes in each pair start to separate. The two chromatids of each chromosome are still held together at the centromere.

Diakenesis: The chromosomes reach maximum condensation.

After prophase, the division steps proceed as in mitosis: the nuclear membrane dissolves, and the chromosome pairs align along the cells equatorial plane (metaphase I). Each pair then splits, and the individual chromosomes assort randomly, with some paternally derived chromosomes going to one pole and others to the other side, and similarly with the maternally derived chromosomes (anaphase I). Because of random assortment of maternally and paternally derived chromosomes, there are 2^{23} or > 8 million possible chromosomal combinations. This tremendous potential for diversity is further increased by the crossing over that occurs during the pachytene period of prophase 1 (Clancy, 2008). The chromosomes group at either pole during telophase I and then the cell divides. The cell enters into a short interphase prior to beginning meiosis II.

During prophase of meiosis II, the nuclear membrane disappears and the spindle apparatus forms. In metaphase II, the chromosomes line up in the center of the cell, and in anaphase II, the centromeres of the chromosomes separate as the spindle fibers pull the sister chromatids apart toward opposite poles. In telophase II, the nuclear membrane reforms and cytokinesis occurs so that there are now four cells, each having 23 chromosomes with a single chromatid. At the time of fertilization, the nuclei of the sperm and ovum join into one nucleus with 23 pairs of chromosomes, a unique combination of genetic information from mother and father.

1.3. NUMERICAL AND STRUCTURAL CYTOGENETIC ABNORMALITIES

Cytogenetics is the field that focuses on the examination of chromosomes for correct number and structure. A basic understanding of chro-

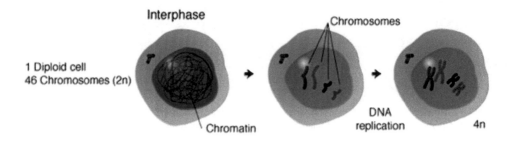

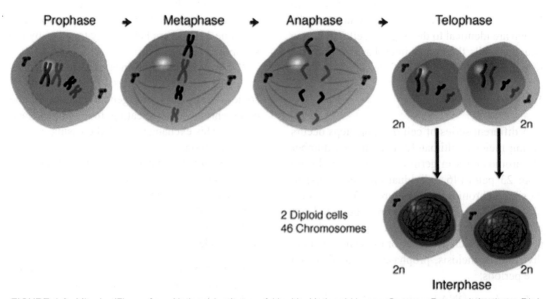

FIGURE 1.6. Mitosis. (Figure from National Institutes of Health, National Human Genome Research Institute. Digital Media Database. Darryl Leja/NHGRI/NIH. Available at: http://www.genome.gov/dmd/img.cfm?node=Photos/Graphics&id=85204.)

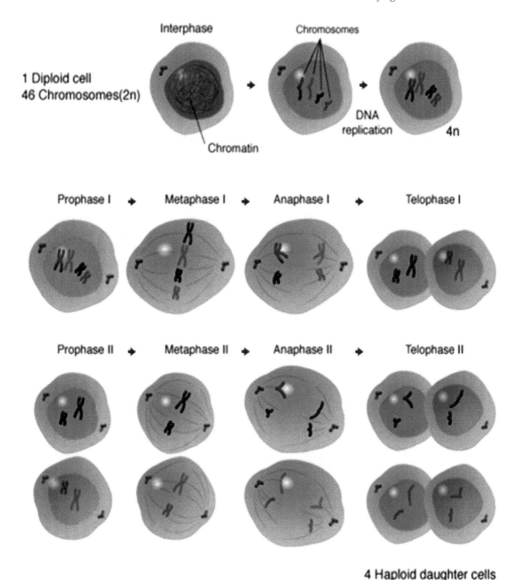

FIGURE 1.7. Meiosis. (Figure from National Institutes of Health. National Human Genome Research Institute. Digital Media Database. Darryl Leja/NHGRI/NIH. Available from; http://www.genome.gov/dmd/img.cfm?node=Photos/Graphics&id=85196.)

mosomal abnormalities is particularly important when caring for prenatal and pediatric populations and in oncology settings, because chromosomal abnormalities occur during reproduction and may arise in malignant cells, particularly those found in leukemia, lymphoma, and some solid tumors.

1.3.1. Nondisjunction

Meiosis usually produces germ cells with 23

chromosomes ready for fertilization with another germ cell with its own 23 chromosomes. Occasionally, however, a nondisjunction error occurs and chromosomes or chromatids fail to separate. Nondisjunction errors can occur either during the first or second meiotic division. If the nondisjunction occurs in the first meiotic division, one daughter cell receives an extra chromosome and the other is missing one, and when these cells go through the second meiotic division, the error is passed on to their respective daughter cells.

If nondisjunction occurs during the second division, the chromatids of one chromosome fail to separate, and two copies go to one cell and none to the other.

If a germ cell with 24 chromosomes is fertilized, it will contain three copies of one chromosome (trisomy). Conceptuses with Trisomy 13, 18, and 21 may survive to birth, whereas trisomies of other autosomes are lethal. Chromosome 13 has approximately 300 to 400 genes that code for proteins (NLM, 2014c). chromosome 18 has approximately 200 to 300 genes (NLM, 2014d), and chromosome 21 has approximately 200 to 300 genes (NLM, 2014e), fewer than any of the other autosomes. If a germ cell with 22 chromosomes is fertilized (monosomy), the embryo rarely survives because too little genetic information is usually lethal. The one monosomy that is compatible with survival is Monosomy X (Turner syndrome [TS]), although it is estimated that up to 99% of Monosomy X conceptuses miscarry in the first or second trimester. It is theorized that those that survive to term have a mosaicism (Wolff, Van Dyke, & Powell, 2010).

1.3.2. Genetic Mosaicism

Genetic mosaicism is the result of a chromosomal nondisjunction or DNA mutation that develops during a very early mitotic division after fertilization. The individual develops with both normal and abnormal cell lines. Individuals affected with a chromosomal mosaicism usually are more mildly affected (milder phenotype) than someone with a meiotic nondisjunction, because at least some of their cells have a normal chromosomal complement. Females with TS (45 X) often have a mosaic form of the disorder.

1.3.3. Translocations

Some chromosomal abnormalities are due to translocations of which there are two major

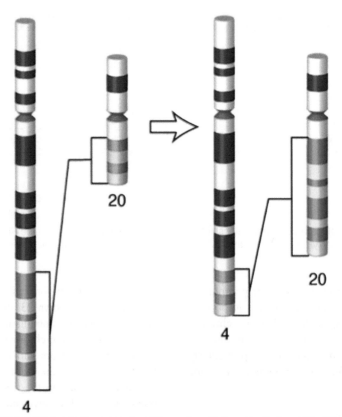

FIGURE 1.8. Reciprocal translocation. (Figure from National Institutes of Health. National Human Genome Research Institute. Digital Media Database. Daryl Leja/ NHGRI/NIH. Available at http://www.genome.gov/dmd/img.cfm?node=Photos/Graphics&id=85253.)

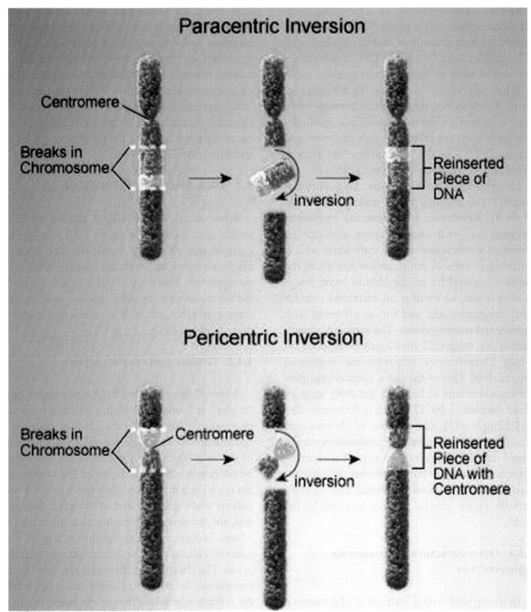

FIGURE 1.9. Chromosomal Inversion. (Figure from United States National Library of Medicine. Genetics Home Reference. Available at http://ghr.nlm.nih.gov/handbook/illustrations/inversion.)

types, Robertsonian and reciprocal. Robertsonian translocations develop when the centromere of one acrocentric chromosome fuses with the centromere of another acrocentric chromosome. The two most common types are Robertsonian and reciprocal translocations.

Robertsonian translocations should be considered when a couple has more than one child with Down syndrome (DS). Although DS is most frequently due to a nondisjunctional error, about 5%

of DS is the result of an unbalanced Robertsonian translocation. In an unbalanced Robertsonian translocation of chromosomes 14 and 21, the offspring inherits the translocated chromosome as well as two normal 21s and one normal 14. The embryo has a normal number of chromosomes (46), but because of the fused 21 and 14, it inherits three copies of chromosome 21 and manifests the typical DS phenotype.

Standard nomenclature for translocation DS in

a male would be as follows: 46 XY + t(14q, 21q); 46 chromosomes, male gender "XY," translocation of the long arms of 14 and 21 "t(14q 21q)." If his mother has a balanced 14/21 translocation, she would have all the essential genetic material, but only 45 chromosomes: 45 XX + t(14q, 21q). Robertsonian translocation carriers often have a history of infertility, multiple spontaneous abortions, and offspring with chromosomal abnormalities like DS (Keymolen, Van Berkel, Vorsselmans, Staessen, & Liebaers, 2011).

In reciprocal translocations, two chromosomes break and the pieces trade places (Figure 1.8). Reciprocal translocations can occur between any two chromosomes and can be balanced or unbalanced. An individual with a balanced reciprocal translocation has all of the genetic material he or she should have, but it is rearranged, so there is an increased risk for early pregnancy loss and for an offspring with unbalanced rearrangement. The standard nomenclature for reciprocal translocation depends on which chromosomes (chromosome segments) are involved. One of the more common reciprocal translocations is between the long arms of chromosomes 11 and 22, which is documented as t(11;22)(q24;q12). The number of chromosome structures in an unbalanced translocation varies. There may be monosomy of part of a chromosome and trisomy of part of another. The phenotype for an unbalanced reciprocal translocation depends on the genetic material received by the child.

1.3.4. Other Structural Chromosome Abnormalities

Deletion refers to a part of a chromosome missing, such as in 5P–, in which a portion of the short arm of chromosome 5 is missing. Duplication refers to an extra copy of part of a chromosome. Duplications and deletions generally result from uneven crossing over or abnormal segregation during meiosis from a translocation carrier. The clinical impact of these structural changes depends on the genetic material deleted or duplicated.

Inversions involve breakage of a chromosome at two points and the intervening piece being reinserted in reverse order. If the inversion includes the centromere, it is called a pericentric inver-

sion, and if the centromere is not included, it is a paracentric inversion (Figure 1.9). Inversions interfere with the pairing of homologous chromosomes and crossing over during meiosis. A helpful resource for additional information about chromosome abnormalities in prenatal and pediatric populations is found in the publication by Gardner, Sutherland, and Shaffer (2011) and in oncology populations in the publication by Heim and Mitelman (2009).

1.4. DNA AND RNA FUNCTION

Ribonucleic acid (RNA) is similar to DNA in that it is made up of bases held together by a sugar and phosphate backbone, but RNA is single stranded and contains ribose rather than deoxyribose. There are 4 RNA bases. Three of the bases, adenine, cytosine, and guanine, are the same as in DNA, but in RNA uracil replaces thymine found in DNA.

1.4.1. Genetic Code to Polypeptide

A unit of three DNA or RNA bases makes up a "triplet" or "codon." DNA triplets code for complementary RNA codons that, in turn, code for a specific amino acid. The potential combinations of the four bases into three base codons would be 64 possible codons. Three of the codons do not code for amino acids; they function as "stop" codons that signal the end of the gene. One codon, for the amino acid methionine, functions as a "start" codon, signaling the start of a gene. The other 60 codons code for the remaining 19 amino acids. The discrepancy between the number of codons and the number of amino acids represents the redundancy within the genetic code, which is a safeguard against harm from accidental alterations in the genetic code.

The order of the DNA bases determines the order of amino acids in production of a protein. Two major steps, transcription and translation, are needed to create a protein. During transcription, the two strands of DNA separate in the area of the gene. One strand is referred to as the "sense" strand, and the other, the "antisense" strand, serves as a template for the synthesis of a strand of messenger RNA (mRNA). Once the mRNA is created, it carries the instructions for linking amino acids together in the correct order

TABLE 1.1. DNA and RNA Coding for Amino Acids.

Amino Acid	DNA sense strand	Anti-sense strand	mRNA
Met*	ATG	TAC	AUG
Iso	ATT ATC ATA	TAA TAG TAT	AUU AUC AUA
Thr	ACT ACC ACA ACG	TGA TGG TGT TGC	ACU ACC ACA ACG
Asp	AAT AAC	TTA TTG	AAU AAC
Lys	AAA AAG	TTT TTC	AAA AAG
Ser	AGT AGC TCT TCC TCA TCG	TCA TCG AGA AGG AGT AGC	AGU AGC UCU UCC UCA UCG
Arg	AGA AGG CGT CGC CGA CGG	TCT TCC GCA GCC GCT GCC	AGA AGG CGU CGC CGA CGG
Val	GTT GTC GTA GTG	CAA CAG CAT CAC	GUU GUC GUA GUG
Gly	GGT GGC GGA GGG	CCA CCG CCT CCC	GGU GGC GGA GGG
Leu	CTT CTC CTA CTG TTA TTG	GAA GAG GAT GAC AAT AAC	CUU CUC CUA CUG UUA UUG
Pro	CCT CCC CCA CCG	GGA GGG GGT GGC	CCU CCC CCA CCG
His	CAT CAC	GTA GTG	CAU CAC
Gln	CAA CAG	GTT GTC	CAA CAG
Asp	GAT GAC	CTA CTG	GAU GAC
Ala	GCT GCC GCA GCG	CGA CGG CGT CGC	GCU GCC GCA GCG
Glu	GAA GAG	CTT CTC	GAA GAG
Cys	TGT TGC	ACA ACG	UGU UGC
Phe	TTT TTC	AAA AAG	UUU UUC
Tyr	TAT TAC	ATA ATG	UAU UAC
Trp	TGG	ACC	UGG
Stop	TGA TAA TAG	ACT ATT ATC	UGA UAA UAC

*Start Codon; Met = Methionine; Iso = Isoleucine; Thr = Threonine; Asp = Asparagine; Lys = Lysine; Ser = Serine; Arg = Arginine; Val = Valine; Gly = Glycine; Leu = Leucine; Pro = Proline; His = Histidine; Gln = Glutamine; Asp = Aspartic Acid; Ala = Alanine; Glu = Glutamic acid; Cys = Cysteine; Phe = Phenylalanine; Tyr = Tyrosine; Trp = Tryptophan.

to make a new protein. For decades, the central dogma in genetics was that one gene encoded one protein. It is now known that some genes are nested within other genes and that both strands of the DNA can serve as the sense strand or antisense strand producing different protein products (Feero, Guttmacher, & Collins, 2010). Table 1.1 illustrates the sense and antisense strands of DNA, complementary codons for mRNA and respective amino acids.

1.4.2. Transcription

An enzyme called RNA polymerase initiates transcription of DNA. There are three major types of RNA polymerase: Type I initiates transcription of ribosomal RNA (rRNA); Type II initiates transcription of most genes; and Type III initiates transcription of transfer RNA (tRNA). Type II binds to the promoter region upstream from the gene to be transcribed. The RNA polymerase causes the antisense and sense strands in the region of the gene to separate, exposing the

bases of the antisense strand, forming a template for creating a complementary strand of mRNA (Figure 1.10). The mRNA sequence, therefore, is the same as the sense strand of DNA, other than having uracil in the place of thymine.

Soon after the initiation of transcription, the end of the mRNA is capped by a chemically altered guanine to provide stability and indicate the start of translation into a protein. When a termination or stop codon is reached, transcription is stopped and a poly-A tail composed of repeated adenine bases is added to the end for stability of that end of the mRNA. The mRNA has to go through additional processing prior to leaving the nucleus of the cell, including splicing out sections of mRNA called introns (Figure 1.11). Although these introns are not used to code for the protein, they contain regulatory sequences. The sections that remain, called exons, are spliced together to form the mature mRNA that codes for the protein. Splicing errors can be the cause of some cases of genetic disorders such as hereditary breast/ovarian cancer, Pick disease,

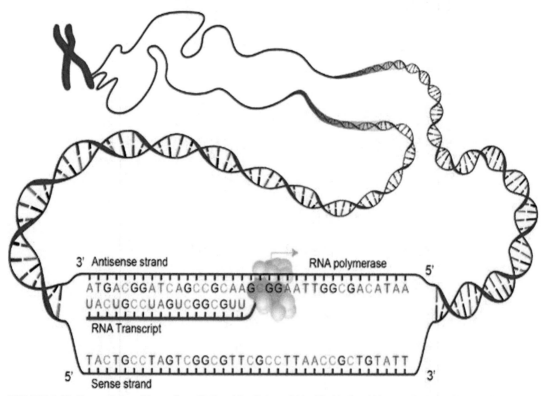

FIGURE 1.10. Transcription (Figure from National Institutes of Health. National Human Genome Research Institute. Digital Media Database. Darryl Laja/NHGRI/NIH. Available at http://www.genome.gov/dmd/img.cfm?node=Photos/Graphics&id=85249.)

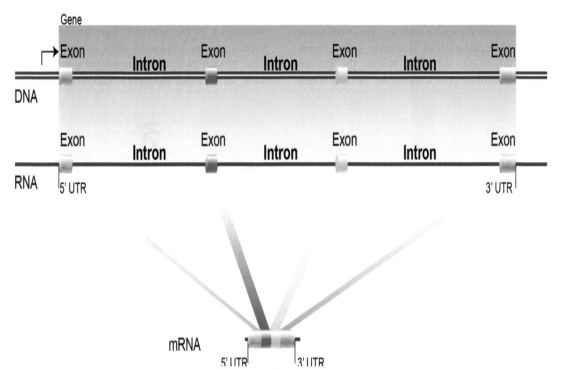

FIGURE 1.11. Splicing RNA to Produce mRNA. (Figure from National Institutes of Health National Human Genome Research Institute. Digital Media Database. Darryl Leja/NHGRI/NIH. Available at: http://www.genome.gov/dmd/img. cfm?node=Photos/Graphics&id=85171.)

cystic fibrosis, myotonic dystrophy, and retinitis pigmentosa (Faustino & Cooper, 2003).

1.4.3. Translation

Once splicing is completed, the mature mRNA moves out of the nucleus and into the cytoplasm, where translation of the mRNA into a polypeptide chain can occur. The small subunit of a ribosome attaches to the mRNA just upstream from the start codon, and as the ribosome moves along the mRNA, the larger ribosomal subunit attaches at the start codon. Ribosomal RNA (RNA) promotes the pairing of transfer RNA (tRNA) with the mRNA. Each unit of tRNA has an anticodon at one end and its respective amino acid at the other end. To build the protein, first a tRNA with the anticodon UAC and the amino acid methionine (the start codon) must pair with the AUG codon of the mRNA. A complementary tRNA unit pairs with the next mRNA codon, and the amino acid of the second tRNA binds with the methionine. Once these two amino acids are bound, the first tRNA dissociates and a third tRNA pairs with the third mRNA codon, and its amino acid binds with second amino acid (Figure 1.12). This process continues until a stop codon is reached, at which time the chain of amino acids dissociates from the tRNA and the ribosome. The amino acid chain goes through additional processing, sometimes attaching to another amino acid chain or breaking into more than one chain before folding into a functional protein product. Several good animations of transcription/translation can be found on the DNA Learning Center site published by Cold Spring Harbor Laboratory at http://www.dnalc.org/resources/animations/.

1.4.4. Regulation of Gene Expression

Some genes, known as housekeeping genes, are expressed in all cells (Eisenberg & Levanon, 2013), but most genes are only transcribed in certain types of tissues and only when their proteins are needed. A number of processes, called epigenetics, such as histone modification and methylation, can modify DNA without altering the DNA code, controlling gene expression and affecting when, how, or if a particular gene is expressed. Some genes have alternative splice sites, allowing them to create different gene products depending on the splice sites that are used. Some of the noncoding DNA (formerly called "junk DNA") between genes or within the introns helps to regulate gene expression. Several forms of RNA, such as microRNA (miRNA) and short interfering RNA (siRNA), have recently been shown to play important roles in gene expression. MicroRNA directly regulates gene expression, and siRNA interferes with translation by

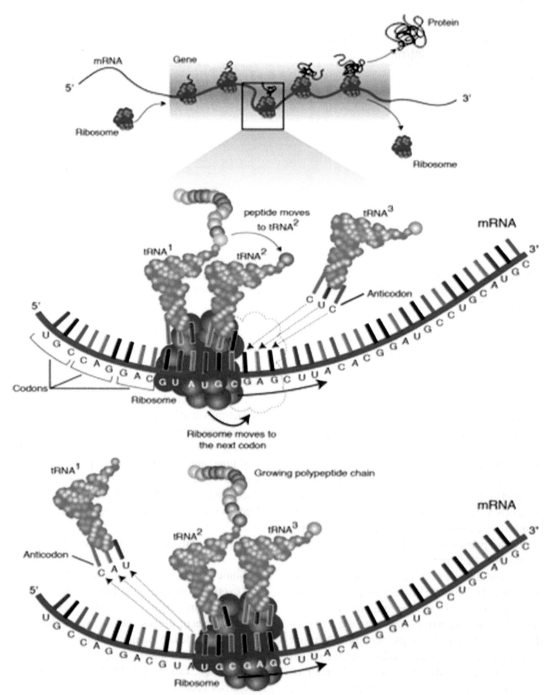

FIGURE 1.12. Translation (Figure from National Human Genome Research Institute, Digital Media Database. Darryl Leja/NHGRI/NIH. Available at: http://www.genome.gov/dmd/img.cfm?node=Photos/Graphics&id=85191.)

binding to complementary mRNA. Overexpression or interference with miRNAs or siRNAs can have negative consequences for the immune system and may play a role in carcinogenesis (Feero, Guttmacher & Collins, 2010). See Chapter 15 for more discussion of the role of miRNA and siRNA. The various mechanisms for regulation of gene expression and their relationship to health and illness are promising areas of research that may ultimately lead to new and more effective means of disease prevention and treatment.

1.5. MUTATIONS IN THE GENETIC CODE

Overall, the process of DNA replication is amazingly precise. Occasionally, however, spontaneous alterations (mutations) occur during replication, and environmental exposures can damage DNA. When a mutation in a somatic cell occurs, and the cell is not destroyed, the mutation is passed along to successive generations of that cell (cell line). For example, if a mutation occurs in a colon cell, it is reproduced in all new colon cells produced from that one. Most somatic mutations have no practical implication for the organism, but if the gene that acquires the mutation is involved in regulating cell growth or differentiation, it could be the first step toward cancer,

discussed further in Chapter 15. If a mutation occurs in a germ cell that is fertilized, the mutation is present in all the cells of the offspring and will be passed on to the next generation.

Several examples of "spelling errors" are provided below in two sets of instructions. The first set shows the normal spelling, and the second set shows what happens when a mutation disturbs the spelling. The first two lines of each example represent the sense and antisense strands of the "wild type" DNA (the most common sequence in a population) of a gene. The third line is the mRNA, and the fourth line is the string of amino acids that is ultimately built during translation. The changes are indicated in bold and underlined to help identify them and their effect on transcription and translation of the rest of the gene.

1.5.1. Polymorphism

In the first example (Table 1.2), a spelling error occurs (GCA → GCT), in which an A is replaced by a T in the sense strand, causing a complementary change in the antisense strand (CGT → CGA). During transcription, mRNA changes from GCA → GCU, but no change occurs in the amino acid because of the inherent redundancy in DNA code. This simple alternative spelling change is often called a single nucleotide poly-

TABLE 1.2. *Example of Wild Type Compared with Polymorphism on DNA Sense and Antisense Strands, mRNA, and Amino Acids.*

Wild Type							
DNA sense strand	ATG	ACT	GCA	CCC	TAT	TGT	TAG
	↓	↓	↓	↓	↓	↓	↓
Anti-sense strand	TAC	TGA	CGT	GGG	ATA	ACA	ATC
	↓	↓	↓	↓	↓	↓	↓
mRNA	AUG	ACU	GCA	CCC	UAU	UGU	UAG
	↓	↓	↓	↓	↓	↓	↓
Amino acids	Met	Thr	Ala	Pro	Tyr	Cys	*Stop*
Polymorphism							
DNA sense strand	ATG	ACT	GC**T**	CCC	TAT	TGT	TAG
	↓	↓	↓	↓	↓	↓	↓
Anti-sense strand	TAC	TGA	CG**A**	GGG	ATA	ACA	ATC
	↓	↓	↓	↓	↓	↓	↓
mRNA	AUG	ACU	GC**U**	CCC	UAU	UGU	UAG
	↓	↓	↓	↓	↓	↓	↓
Amino acids	Met	Iso	**Ala**	Pro	Tyr	Cys	*Stop*

TABLE 1.3. *Example of Wild Type Compared with Missense Mutation on DNA Sense and Antisense Strands, mRNA, and Amino Acids.*

Wild Type							
DNA sense strand	CTG	ACT	CCT	GAG	GAG	AAG	TCT
	↓	↓	↓	↓	↓	↓	↓
Anti-sense strand	GAC	TGA	GGT	CTC	CTC	TTC	AGA
	↓	↓	↓	↓	↓	↓	↓
mRNA	CUG	ACU	CCU	GAG	GAG	UGU	UCU
	↓	↓	↓	↓	↓	↓	↓
Amino acids	Leu	Thr	Pro	Glu	Glu	Lys	Ser
Missense Mutation							
DNA sense strand	CTG	ACT	CCT	G**T**G	GAG	AAG	TCT
	↓	↓	↓	↓	↓	↓	↓
Anti-sense strand	GAC	TGA	GGT	C**A**C	CTC	TTC	AGA
	↓	↓	↓	↓	↓	↓	↓
mRNA	CUG	ACU	CCU	G**U**G	GAG	UGU	UCU
	↓	↓	↓	↓	↓	↓	↓
Amino acids	Leu	Thr	Pro	**Val**	Glu	Lys	Ser

morphism (SNP). There is a great deal of variation in the genetic code from one individual to another because of these small spelling changes. SNPs are often used during forensic DNA testing, such as DNA fingerprinting.

1.5.2. Missense Mutation

Another example of a common mutation is that of missense mutation. In a missense mutation (Table 1.3) another single spelling change occurs, but this time, the mutation results in a change of the 3rd amino acid from glutamine to valine. This type of substitution or missense mutation may or may not alter the protein product. Sickle cell anemia, for example, results from a missense mutation in the construction of hemoglobin molecules caused by the substitution of

TABLE 1.4. *Example of Wild Type Compared with Nonsense Mutation on DNA Sense and Antisense Strands, mRNA, and Amino Acids.*

Wild Type							
DNA sense strand	ATG	ACT	TAT	CCC	TAT	TGT	TAG
	↓	↓	↓	↓	↓	↓	↓
Anti-sense strand	TAC	TGA	ATA	GGG	ATA	ACA	ATC
	↓	↓	↓	↓	↓	↓	↓
mRNA	AUG	ACU	UAU	CCC	UAU	UGU	UAG
	↓	↓	↓	↓	↓	↓	↓
Amino acids	Met	Thr	Tyr	Pro	Tyr	Cys	*Stop*
Nonsense Mutation							
DNA sense strand	ATG	ACT	TA**A**	CCC	TAT	TGT	TAG
	↓	↓	↓	↓	↓	↓	↓
Anti-sense strand	TAC	TGA	AT**T**	GGG	ATA	ACA	ATC
	↓	↓	↓	↓	↓	↓	↓
mRNA	AUG	ACU	UA**A**				
	↓	↓	↓	↓	↓	↓	↓
Amino acids	Met	Thr	***Stop***				

TABLE 1.5. Example of Wild Type Compared with Frameshift Mutation from a Deletion on DNA Sense and Antisense Strands, mRNA, and Amino Acids.

Wild Type							
DNA sense strand	ATG	ACT	TTT	CCC	TAT	TGT	TAG
	↓	↓	↓	↓	↓	↓	↓
Anti-sense strand	TAC	TGA	AAA	GGG	ATA	ACA	ATC
	↓	↓	↓	↓	↓	↓	↓
mRNA	AUG	ACU	UUU	CCC	UAU	UGU	UAG
	↓	↓	↓	↓	↓	↓	↓
Amino acids	Met	Thr	Phe	Pro	Tyr	Cys	*Stop*
Frameshift Mutation (deletion)							
DNA sense strand	ATG	ACT	TTT	CC**T**	**ATT**	**GTT**	**AGA**
	↓	↓	↓	↓	↓	↓	↓
Anti-sense strand	TAC	TGA	AAA	GG**A**	**TAA**	**CAA**	**TGT**
	↓	↓	↓	↓	↓	↓	↓
mRNA	AUG	ACU	UUU	CC**U**	**AUU**	**GUU**	**ACA**
	↓	↓	↓	↓	↓	↓	↓
Amino acids	Met	Thr	Phe	**Cys**	**Ile**	**Val**	**Thr**

valine for glutamic acid in the beta globin gene (*HBB*), producing the "S" version of hemoglobin rather than the normal "A" version.

1.5.3. Nonsense Mutation

The mutation in Table 1.4 shows what happens when a substitution of one base results in a premature stop codon. This mutation causes a truncated chain of amino acids to be produced, which cannot be processed into normal protein.

1.5.4. Frameshift Mutation

Deletions or insertions of bases can cause all the bases to shift to the right or left. In Table 1.5, the deletion does not alter the order of amino acids immediately, because of the redundancy of

TABLE 1.6. Example of Wild Type Compared with Frameshift Mutation from an Insertion on DNA Sense and Antisense Strands, mRNA, and Amino Acids.

Wild Type							
DNA sense strand	ATG	ACT	GCA	CCC	TAT	TGT	TAG
	↓	↓	↓	↓	↓	↓	↓
Anti-sense strand	TAC	TGA	CGT	GGG	ATA	ACA	ATC
	↓	↓	↓	↓	↓	↓	↓
mRNA	AUG	ACU	GCA	CCC	UAU	UGU	UAG
	↓	↓	↓	↓	↓	↓	↓
Amino acids	Met	Thr	Ala	Pro	Tyr	Cys	*Stop*
Frameshift Mutation (insertion)							
DNA sense strand	ATG	ACT	GC**G**	**ACC**	**CTA**	**TTG**	**TTA**
	↓	↓	↓	↓	↓	↓	↓
Anti-sense strand	TAC	TGA	CG**C**	**UGG**	**GAT**	**AAC**	**AAT**
	↓	↓	↓	↓	↓	↓	↓
mRNA	AUG	ACU	GC**G**	**ACC**	**CUA**	**UUG**	**UUA**
	↓	↓	↓	↓	↓	↓	↓
Amino acids	Met	Thr	Ala	**Thr**	**Leu**	**Leu**	**Leu**

TABLE 1.7. Example of Wild Type Compared with an Expansion Mutation on DNA Sense and Antisense Strands, mRNA, and Amino Acids.

Wild Type							
DNA sense strand	ATG	ACT	**CAG**	**CAG**	**CAG**	TGT	GCT
	↓	↓	↓	↓	↓	↓	↓
Anti-sense strand	TAC	TGA	**GTC**	**GTC**	**GTC**	ACA	CGA
	↓	↓	↓	↓	↓	↓	↓
mRNA.	AUG	ACU	**CAG**	**CAG**	**CAG**	UGU	GCU
	↓	↓	↓	↓	↓	↓	↓
Amino acids	Met	Thr	**Gln**	**Gln**	**Gln**	Cys	Ala
Repeat Expansion							
DNA sense strand	ATG	ACT	**CAG**	**CAG**	**CAG**	**CAG**	**CAG**
	↓	↓	↓	↓	↓	↓	↓
Anti-sense strand	TAC	TGA	**GTC**	**GTC**	**GTC**	**GTC**	**GTC**
	↓	↓	↓	↓	↓	↓	↓
mRNA	AUG	ACU	**CAG**	**CAG**	**CAG**	**CAG**	**CAG**
	↓	↓	↓	↓	↓	↓	↓
Amino acids	Met	Thr	**Gln**	**Gln**	**Gln**	**Gln**	**Gln**

the genetic code, but ultimately a major alteration occurs; instead of a stop codon, the string of bases elongates. Frameshift mutations are usually very deleterious, because often no normal protein is produced.

Table 1.6 shows another frameshift mutation, this time caused by an insertion between the G and the C of the 3rd codon. Although the change does not alter that particular amino acid, it shifts the reading frame to the right and alters the order of all amino acids from that point on.

1.5.5. Expansion Mutation

Some genes normally contain multiple repetitions of a particular codon, but additional expansion in the number of repeats can result in abnormal protein products. In the example below, there is an area where the codon CAG is repeated. In reality, the normal repeats are generally longer than three codons. Examples of disorders due to repeat mutations include myotonic dystrophy and Huntington disease (HD). Table 1.7 gives an example of an expansion mutation.

1.6. FUNCTIONAL EFFECTS OF MUTATIONS

A number of different functional effects can be caused by mutations. Some result in a loss of function, such as repeats in the *G6PD* gene on the X chromosome, which decreases the activity of glucose-6-phosphate dehydrogenase (G6PD), causing hemolytic anemia in males and to a lesser extent, females exposed to certain drugs or fava beans. *G6PD* mutations are found more frequently in Mediterranean, African, Asian, and Middle Eastern populations, and it is estimated that approximately 10% of the population worldwide has G6PD deficiency. Other mutations cause a gain of function, where the protein product takes on a new or enhanced function (Guttmacher & Collins, 2002). HD is an example of a gain of function mutation. HD is caused from an expansion of a CAG repeat in the *HD* gene from the normal 10. People with 40 or more repeats invariably develop a neurodegenerative disorder that usually manifests in adulthood. More information about HD can be found in Chapter 13.

Some mutations are in regulatory regions and result in a functional change downstream. The mutation for Fragile X syndrome is an expansion of a repeat that interferes with expression of the *FMR1* gene, which is downstream from the repeat. Some mutations can decrease the disease risk as well. For example, a frameshift mutation in one allele of the *CCR5* gene slows the progression of human immunodeficiency virus (HIV) to acquired immunodeficiency syndrome (AIDS) and individuals with mutations in both alleles are resistant to HIV type 1 infection. Some mutations confer protection if one copy is inherited and disease if two copies are present. The missense mutation for the *HBB* gene discussed above causes sickle cell disease if two copies are present, but malaria immunity if only one copy is present.

1.7. MENDELIAN PATTERNS OF INHERITANCE

Single gene patterns of inheritance, often called "Mendelian inheritance patterns" in recognition of Gregor Mendel's sentinel work on the genetics of garden peas, explain the inheritance and expression of single gene traits within families. Single gene inheritance patterns include autosomal dominant (AD), autosomal recessive (AR), X-linked recessive, and X-linked dominant. It is important to recognize that although the term "pattern of inheritance" is most often associated with a genetic disorder, normal traits are also inherited via these pattern. In this chapter, the discussion focuses on inheritance patterns associated with genetic disorders.

Each gene in the human genome can be found in a specific location (locus) on a particular chromosome, and except for male sex chromosomes, every individual inherits two copies of each chromosome, one maternal chromosome and one paternal chromosome. Although the gene locus is the same on both chromosomes, the genetic code may differ between the two chromosomes, giving rise to different "alleles" (different coding of the same gene). If the two alleles are the same (which can be either normal or altered) they are homozygous *alleles*. If the alleles have different codes (one normal, one altered), they are heterozygous *alleles*. If the alleles have different codes but neither is normal, the alleles are compound heterozygotes. Single gene traits or disorders are determined by the genetic code of the two alleles at a single locus.

Many genetic disorders are heterogeneous, meaning similar clinical characteristics and inheritance pattern may be present, but different genes and/or mutant alleles may be involved. Hereditary breast/ovarian cancer (discussed in greater detail in Chapter 16) is an example of heterogeneity, because mutations in either *BRCA1*, located on the long arm of chromosome 17, or *BRCA2*, found on the long arm of chromosome 13, can significantly increase the risk for herediary breast and ovarian cancer (HBOC). Hundreds of deleterious variants have been identified in both *BRCA1* and *BRCA2*.

1.7.1. Characteristics of Autosomal Dominant (AD) Inheritance

A gene located on one of the numbered (1 to 22) chromosomes is called "autosomal." Because autosomes are not associated with sex (not located on the X or the Y chromosome), males and females are equally likely to inherit an autosomal mutation and are equally likely to pass the mutation on to either a son or daughter. A dominant allele produces the same phenotype regardless of the code of the other allele at that locus. Vertical transmission means that a disorder has affected family members across multiple successive generations (e.g., grandparents, parents, children, etc.). Each time an individual with an AD disorder reproduces, there is a 50% recurrence risk (meaning 50% chance of passing along the mutated allele/50% chance of passing on the normal allele) (Figure 1.13). Because gene alleles assort randomly with each meiotic event, each offspring has a 50% risk for inheriting the mutation. Recognizing an AD disorder within a family may be complicated because of factors such as nonpenetrance, variable expressivity, or the emergence of a new (de novo) mutation in the family.

Some genes have more than one allele that is dominant. If an individual happens to inherit two different dominant alleles, one from each parent the alleles are said to be codominant and both are expressed. The most common example of codominant alleles is in the ABO blood types (Figure 1.14). Both A and B are dominant, whereas O is recessive. If an individual inherits both an A allele and a B allele, he will have AB blood type with both alleles being expressed.

1.7.2. Penetrance

Nonpenetrance occurs when someone who has a mutation does not exhibit the expected phenotype. Penetrance rates are expressed as a percentage of individuals in a population who have a particular genotype and express the expected

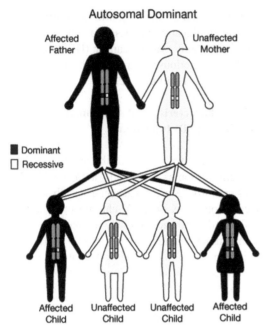

FIGURE 1.13. Autosomal Dominant Inheritance. Illustration by Mark Wieber, R.N., M.S.

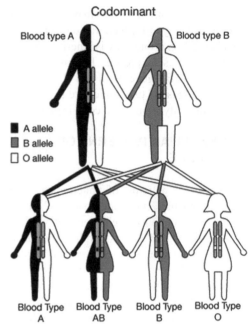

FIGURE 1.14. Co-Dominant Inheritance. Illustration by Mark Wieber, R.N., M.S.

phenotype. Retinoblastoma is a good example of variable penetrance. Retinoblastoma develops when an individual with an inherited germline mutation in an *Rb1* allele develops a somatic mutation in the corresponding allele later in life. Although nearly 90% of people born with an *Rb1* mutation will develop retinoblastoma, those with the *V654L* allele have a much lower penetrance (Hung *et al.*, 2011).

1.7.3. Expressivity

Variable expressivity refers to differences (severity, age of onset, etc.) in the way a disease presents in individuals who have identical mutations. Neurofibromatosis 1 (*NF1*) is a good example of a genetic disease that exhibits significant variations in expressivity. Clinical features of NF1 include a number of different skin findings, such as café-au-lait spots, inguinal and axillary freckling, as well as many other manifestations, such as scoliosis, learning disabilities, neurofibromas, and a variety of malignant tumors, including carcinomas and sarcomas. Family members with identical *NF1* mutations may have vastly different expression of the mutation. Some may have mild skin findings, whereas others have hundreds of neurofibromas, and still others have brain or

spinal cord tumors. Research to identify factors that alter the transcription of the mutant *NF1* is underway to explain some of the variability in *NF1* expression (Sabbagh *et al.*, 2009).

1.7.4. De novo (new) Mutations

When an AD condition appears suddenly in a family with no family history of that condition, a de novo, or "new," mutation is suspected. It has been estimated that almost twothirds of the cases of tuberous sclerosis (TS) are the result of new mutations (Au, Williams, Gambello, & Northrup, 2004). Generally, the TS de novo mutations occur in the ovum or sperm involved in the conception of the first affected family member, and therefore the parents can be reassured that future children are not at increased risk for having the same disorder. Sometimes TS mutations develop during gametogenesis, resulting in a germline mosaicism, which increases the risk for having more than one offspring with TS, depending on the proportion of gametes with the mutation. Another type of de novo mutation is a somatic mutation that occurs early in embryonic development, affecting a significant proportion of the body, and causing TS mosaicism, which is often associated with a milder phenotype (Crino, Nathanson, &

Henski, 2006). The parents of a child that develops somatic mosaicism are not at increased risk for having additional affected children.

1.7.5. Autosomal Recessive (AR) Inheritance

In autosomal recessive genetic disorders, both alleles in a gene pair must have a mutation before the phenotype is expressed, because a single copy of the normal allele is sufficient to produce adequate amounts of gene product. Usually the parents of an individual with an AR condition have one normal allele and one allele with a deleterious mutation. The parents themselves are healthy, because their one normal allele produces enough gene product (Figure 1.15). With every pregnancy, the allele contributed by each parent is random and one of three combinations is possible. There is a 25% probability that both parents pass on the normal allele and the child will be phenotypically and genotypically normal. There is a 50% probability that one parent will pass along the mutation and the other parent will pass on the normal allele, and the child will be a carrier like the parents and phenotypically normal. Finally, there is a 25% probability that both parents will pass on the mutation and no allele capable of producing the normal gene product will be present, and the child will have disease phenotype.

1.7.6. Consanguinity

Most AR disorders are very rare metabolic disorders. The more unusual the disorder, the more likely that an affected child's parents share a common ancestor. The likelihood that two carriers of the same rare allele mate is increased with non-random mating through consanguinity or assortative mating. Consanguinity is a mating between relatives who have at least one common ancestor no more remote than a great-great-grandparent such as third cousins. The more closely they are related, the more likely they are to have a common genetic mutation and, thus, they are at greater risk to have a child with an AR disorder. In some Middle Eastern cultures, marriage of first, second, or third cousins is a relatively common occurrence. Assortative mating occurs in populations that are physically, culturally, or religiously isolated, leading to intermarriage within that isolated population.

1.7.7. Carrier Rate

The more carriers for a recessive disorder there are in an "isolated" population, the greater the likelihood that two carriers will mate and have an affected child. The higher the carrier rate, the greater the incidence of a particular AR disorder in that population. Sickle cell disease and thalassemia are much more common in African and Mediterranean populations; cystic fibrosis is more common in northern European communities; and several disorders including Tay Sachs, Gaucher, and Canavan disease are much more common among the Ashkenazi Jewish (Center for Jewish Genetics, 2014). Because there is such a high carrier rate in these populations, carrier screening is often offered to identify carriers, providing individuals with the opportunity to make reproductive decisions if the prospective mate is also a carrier. Additional information about carrier screening is provided in Chapter 3.

1.7.8. X-linked Recessive

X-linked refers to genes located on the X chromosome so there is no male to male transmission of an X-linked allele (males give their male offspring a Y chromosome). All female offspring of

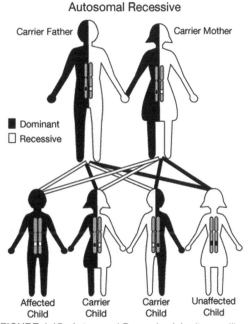

FIGURE 1.15. Autosomal Recessive Inheritance. Illustration by Mark Wieber, R.N., M.S.

an affected male will receive his X and are, therefore, obligate carriers of anything on his single X. Because a male has only one copy of the X chromosome, he will express all of the genes on that chromosome whether dominant or recessive. In the typical inheritance pattern of an X-linked recessive disorder, affected males appear in alternate generations, and carrier mothers are present in the intervening generations. Diseases such as hemophilia and Duchenne muscular dystrophy (DMD) have an X-linked recessive pattern of inheritance. In Figure 1.16, the X-linked, recessive, carrier mother has one allele with the mutation and one normal allele; each of her daughters has a 50% chance of being a carrier, and each of her sons has a 50% chance of being affected. In the same figure (Figure 1.16) depicting an X-linked recessive, affected father, the mother has two normal alleles, but the father is affected. Because he only passes on his Y chromosome to his sons, none of them will be affected, but because his X chromosome has the mutation, all of his daughters will be carriers.

1.7.9. Pseudoautosomal Regions

An exception to the usual X-linked pattern of inheritance is found in the pseudoautosomal re-gions, PAR1 and PAR2, which are short regions of homology on the X and the Y chromosomes. PAR1 is found in the terminal regions of the short arms of the X and Y chromosomes, and PAR2 is located at the tips of the long arms of the X and the Y. A deletion of PAR1 on the Y chromosome prevents the X and Y chromosomes from pairing up during meiosis, resulting in male sterility. PAR1 mutations have also been implicated in manifestations associated with TS, bipolar affective disorder, and asthma (Mangs & Morris, 2007)

1.7.10. X-inactivation

Soon after fertilization, as early as the 8 cell stage of embryogenesis, one of the X chromosomes in each cell of a female embryo is inactivated. X-inactivation is essentially random, but in most embryos roughly half of the maternal and half of the paternal Xs are inactivated. The inactive X (the "Barr body") remains condensed throughout most of the cell cycle. Inactivation is occasionally unequal, either due to chance, or because one of the X chromosomes has a structural abnormality. The single X in females with monosomy X (TS) remains active in all cells. In all of these scenarios, if the active X contains

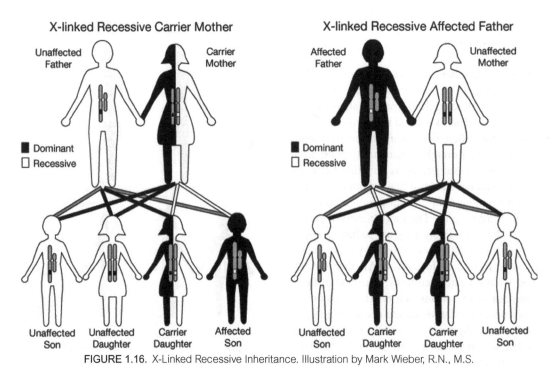

FIGURE 1.16. X-Linked Recessive Inheritance. Illustration by Mark Wieber, R.N., M.S.

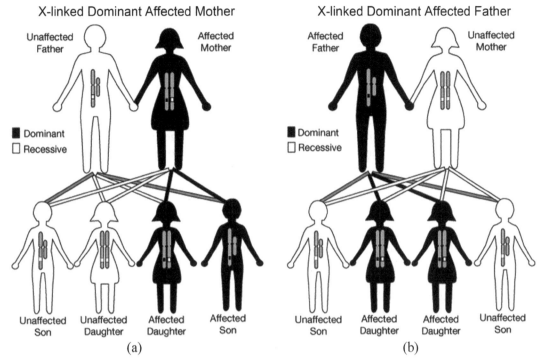

X-linked Dominant Affected Mother

Unaffected Father

Affected Mother

■ Dominant
☐ Recessive

Unaffected Son

Unaffected Daughter

Affected Daughter

Affected Son

(a)

X-linked Dominant Affected Father

Affected Father

Unaffected Mother

■ Dominant
☐ Recessive

Unaffected Son

Affected Daughter

Affected Daughter

Unaffected Son

(b)

FIGURE 1.17. X-Linked Dominant Inheritance. Illustration by Mark Wieber, R.N., M.S.

a deleterious mutation, an affected female may manifest symptoms of an X-linked disorder typically affecting only males.

1.7.11. De novo (new) X-linked Mutation

It is estimated that nearly 33% of all cases of DMD are the result of a de novo (new) mutation (NLM [U.S.], 2014f). If the new mutation occurs in just one ovum, there is no greater risk for the parents to have another affected or carrier child. However, DMD has also been the result of the mother having a germline mosaicism, which increases the risk for other offspring to be affected or be carriers.

1.7.12. X-linked Dominant

There are very few X-linked dominant disorders, but Fragile X, the most common cause of inherited cognitive dysfunction, is one of them. In Figure 1.17(a), the affected mother has a 50% probability of passing on the mutation to each child (male or female) who would also be affected. In Figure 1.17(b), the affected father cannot pass on the mutation to any of his sons because they get his Y chromosome. All of his daughters

will receive the mutation and be affected. Females with Fragile X often have a milder phenotype of Fragile X than males. Some X-linked dominant conditions, such as X-linked ichthyosis (XLI) and Rett syndrome (Smith & McLean, 2011; Weaving, Ellaway, Gecz, & Chritodoulou, 2005), are almost universally lethal in males, so only affected females survive.

1.8. ALTERATIONS TO MENDELIAN PATTERNS

1.8.1. Epigenetics

Epigenetic changes are alterations in gene expression caused by chemical processes that do not change the DNA coding sequence, such as DNA methylation or histone processing (Figure 1.18). Epigenetic modification can be triggered by genetic influences, such as a high concentration of the cytosine-guanine dinucleotides (sometimes referred to as CpG islands), and proximity to repetitive elements of DNA or environmental factors. Xchromosome inactivation, discussed previously, is the result of an epigenetic process known as DNA methylation. Epigenetic modifications can occur during prenatal and postnatal development and are an "important pathway by which environmental factors influence disease risks, both within individuals and across generations" (Cortessis *et al.*, 2012, p. 1565), and are thought to be important in the etiology of diverse diseases such as asthma, cancer, and metabolic disorders. Epigenetic modifications are reproduced within cell lineages and, therefore, are usually permanent changes within one individual, but these modifications may be erased in ovum and sperm at the time of fertilization.

1.8.2. Imprinting

One exception to the epigenetic reprogramming described above involves genomic imprinting. Imprinted genes have only one working allele; in some genes, the maternal allele is silenced through imprinting and in others the paternal copy is inactivated. Because there is normally only one active copy of an imprinted gene, if the normally active allele is accidently deleted as in uniparental disomy, no normal gene product will

be produced. Uniparental disomy usually occurs during meiosis or embryogenesis, and two copies of a particular chromosome are inherited from one parent but no copy of that chromosome from the other parent is present. The child has 2 copies of each chromosome and has a total of 46 chromosomes and a normal appearing karyotype. If there are imprinted genes on that particular chromosome, some gene products may not be made, because the chromosomes originated from one parent.

A group of genes on the long arm of chromosome 15 (15q11-q13) provide a good example of imprinting. Paternal uniparental disomy or a deletion of the maternal genes in that region of chromosome 15 causes a loss of function of the *UBE3A* gene and the development of Angelman syndrome (AS), a neurogenetic disorder resulting in severe mental retardation and ataxia. Because the *UBE3A* gene is only expressed by the maternal allele in the brain, mutations in the paternal allele do not alter the normal phenotype. Maternal uniparental disomy or deletion of the

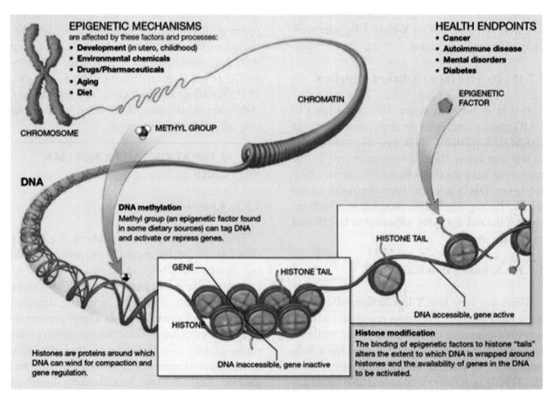

FIGURE 1.18. Epigenetic Mechanisms and How They Can Affect Health. (Figure from U.S. Department of Health and Human Services, National Institutes of Health, Division of Program Coordination, Planning and Strategic Initiatives (DPSPSI). Available from http://commonfund.nih.gov/epigenomics/figure.aspx.)

paternal chromosome at 15q11-q13 results in PraderWilli syndrome (Buiting, 2010) which is associated with mental retardation, significant hypotonia, and feeding difficulties in infancy, followed by insatiable appetite and severe morbid obesity later in life.

1.8.3. Anticipation

Some genetic disorders manifest symptoms progressively earlier, because they are passed down through the generations. This characteristic, a phenomenon referred to as "anticipation," is most commonly associated with disorders caused by triplet repeat expansion mutations discussed above. The larger the size of the repeat, the more unstable it becomes and the more likely it is to increase even more in the next meiotic event. Fragile X syndrome, for example, is caused by an expanded CGG repeat upstream of the *FMR1* gene on chromosome X. The expansion from premutation to a full mutation occurs when the X passes through female meiosis but remains stable, or may occasionally contract, during male meiosis. HD is another disorder caused by expansion of a CAG repeat in the *HTT* gene located on chromosome 4. In HD, expansion occurs during male meiosis and is stable in female meiosis (Everitt & Wood, 2004).

1.8.4. Modifier Genes

The variability in phenotypes seen in many genetic disorders is increasingly thought to be caused by changes in genes that modify the action of a particular gene, rather than in changes to the genes themselves (Cutting, 2010). For example, some polymorphisms have been shown to modify cancer risk in individuals with cancer syndromes, such as hereditary breast/ovarian cancer and Lynch syndrome (Antoniou & Chenevix-Trench, 2010). Lung disease severity in people who are homozygous for the cystic fibrosis p.Phe508del mutation may vary due to polymorphisms in *SNAP23, PPP2R4, PPP2R1A*, and *KRT19* (Gisler, von Kanel, Kraemer, Schaller, & Gallati, 2013). Modifier genes are also being studied in relation to common complex disorders, such as hypertension and isolated birth defects, including cleft lip and palate. As more is learned about the genomics of modifier genes and their

effect on disease expression, more personalized risk assessment and disease management become possible.

1.9. NON-MENDELIAN PATTERNS OF INHERITANCE

1.9.1. Mitochondrial Inheritance

Mitochondria are organelles in the cytoplasm (Figure 1.19) and are frequently referred to as the cell's "powerhouse," because they are the primary source of adenosine triphosphate (ATP). Depending on a cell's function, it may contain hundreds to thousands of mitochondria. Mitochondria have their own unique DNA in the form of a small circular chromosome, and each mitochondrion contains several copies of the chromosome.

Each mitochondrial chromosome includes DNA that encodes 13 proteins, 2 rRNAs, and 22 tRNAs (Koopman, Willems & Smeitink, 2012). During cell division, the mtDNA replicates and sorts randomly among the multitude of copies of mitochondria, which then sort randomly among the two daughter cells. Because of this random assortment, daughter cells may have very different proportions of mitochondria with a specific allele compared to the parent cell, and compared to one another. At conception, the egg contains thousands of mtDNA, but the sperm's mtDNA are actively ejected from the egg, creating the unique inheritance pattern of the mtDNA, in which mtDNA mutations are passed on to the next generation only by an affected female (Figure 1.20). Because of random assortment and varying proportions of normal vs mutant DNA, symptoms can vary widely among affected offspring. Some may have a very mild presentation, some may have a very severe presentation, and some may not have any symptoms at all (Nussbaum, McInnes, & Willard, 2007). MtDNA disorders include mitochondrial encephalopathy with lactic acidosis and strokelike episodes (MELAS) and myoclonic epilepsy with ragged red fibers.

DNA found in the nucleus is sometimes referred to as nuclear DNA (nDNA) to differentiate it from mtDNA. Approximately 1000 nDNA genes coded for mitochondrial proteins have been identified. Mutations in approximately a quarter

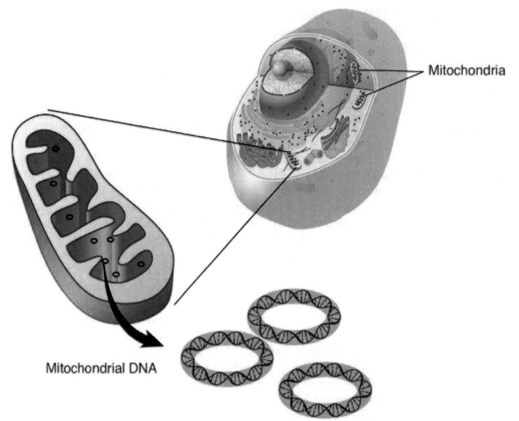

FIGURE 1.19. Mitochondrial DNA. (Figure from the National Human Genome Research Institute, Digital Media Database, Darryl Leja NHGRI. Available from http://www.genome.gov/dmd/img.cfm?node=Photos/Graphics&id=85203.)

of those nDNA genes and 13 mtDNA genes have been linked to human diseases (Koopman *et al.*, 2012), some of which are single gene diseases and individually rare. Others such as Alzheimer's disease and Parkinson disease (Coskun *et al.*, 2011), diabetes (Sleigh *et al.*, 2011), heart disease (Hoppel, Tandler, Fujioka, & Riva, 2009), and obesity (Tseng, Cyprus, & Kahn, 2010) are multifactorial and very common. A progressive decline in mitochondrial gene function has also been linked to normal aging (Bishop, Lu & Yankner, 2010).

1.9.2. Multifactorial Inheritance

Many congenital anomalies, such as neural tube defects, facial clefting, and congenital heart disease, are considered "multifactorial," because they are not caused by changes in single genes, but develop in response to a combination of genetics, lifestyle, and/or environmental factors. Neural tube defects (NTDs), such as anen-cephaly and spina bifida, are some of the most clearly described multifactorial disorders. Folic acid deficiency prior to and/or during very early pregnancy, particularly in genetically susceptible women, has been shown to contribute to the development of NTD. As a result, 0.4 mg folic acid has been added to all prenatal vitamins. In addition, many grain products, such as cereals and breads, are supplemented with folic acid. Research has revealed that the 677 C > T variant of *MTHFR*, a gene involved in folate metabolism, is associated with NTDs in non-Hispanics. Interestingly, however, this variant is not associated with NTDs in Hispanics who are at high risk for having babies with NTDs, and folic acid supplementation in these women is not as protective. It is speculated that Hispanic women are more likely to have chronic folate deficiency and, therefore, may require a higher dose of supplementation (Marini *et al.*, 2011).

Virtually all common complex medical disorders are now thought to be multifactorial in that they develop as a result of the combined influence of both genes and environment. Multifactorial diseases are considered "threshold traits," because the disorder does not usually manifest unless an individual with risk alleles is exposed to specific environmental insults; the amount of exposure needed to create a particular disorder will vary depending on the number and type of genetic factors as well. In diabetes, for example, multiple family members may be affected, because of either shared genes or common environmental exposures, such as high carbohydrate diet.

1.10. ADVANCES IN GENOMICS AND PHARMACOGENOMICS

A major thrust of recent genomic research has been to identify the genes associated with common complex disorders. Genome wide association studies (GWASs) have identified many single nucleotide polymorphisms (SNPs), normal variations in a single nucleotide, associated with several common complex conditions. Most of these SNPs reside outside of the protein coding regions. Individually, most SNPs explain only a small portion of the heritability of the associated conditions, making it currently impractical to use them in assessing risks. Copy number variations (CNVs) caused by insertions or deletions of large DNA segments are fairly common throughout the genome, and some have been associated with disorders such as autism and schizophrenia. Many of the chapters that follow in this book are focused on the genomics of common complex disorders.

Pharmacogenomics, the study of genomic variations affecting individual response to drugs, is another rapidly expanding area. Researchers are particularly interested in identifying genetic variations associated with significant side effects, genes that alter the effectiveness of particular drugs, or genes that regulate drug metabolism. Improved understanding of these genes offers the promise of truly personalizing drug therapies. Chapter 5 includes a detailed discussion of pharmacogenomics.

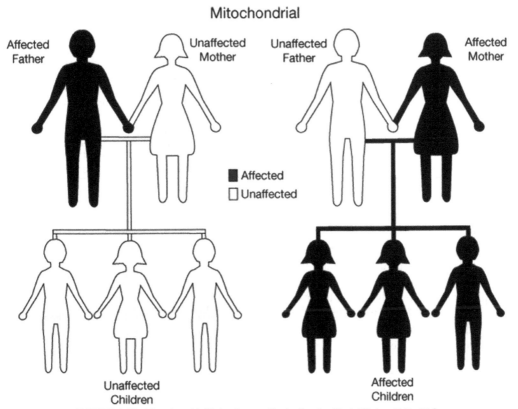

FIGURE 1.20. Mitochondrial Inheritance. Illustration by Mark Wieber, R.N., M.S.

TABLE 1.8. Example of Online Resources for Understanding Common Genetic/Genomic Concepts Used in this Chapter.

Talking Glossary of Genetic Terms	http://www.genome.gov/Glossary/	Web site by the National Human Genome Research Institute (NHGRI) to assist learners at any level with better understanding of genetic terms; guided by national science standards and explained by scientists at the National Institutes of Health (NIH).
Human Epigenome Project	http://www.epigenome.org	Collaboration that aims to identify and catalogue Methylation Variable Positions in the human genome.
Genetics Home Reference (U.S. National Library of Medicine)	http://ghr.nlm.nih.gov	Consumer friendly information on genetic disorders. Includes information on genetic conditions, diseases and syndromes, genes, chromosomes, glossary of medical and genetic definitions, resources and handbook regarding mutations, inheritance, genetic counseling, testing, genome research, and more.
Public Health Genomics Centers for Disease Control and Prevention (CDC)	http://www.cdc.gov/genomics/	Provides information for the translation of genomics into population health to improve the health of all people.
Genetics and Genomics for Health Professionals	http://www.genome.gov/27527599	NHGRI—provides reliable up-to-date genetics/ genomics information related to patient management, curricular resources, new NIH and NHGRI research activities, and ethical, legal, and social issues.
NIH Genetic Testing Registry	http://www.ncbi.nlm.nih.gov/gtr/	Central location for voluntary submission of genetic test information by providers, including the test's purpose, methodology, validity, evidence of the test's usefulness, and laboratory contacts and credentials.
Gene Reviews®	www.ncbi.nlm.nih.gov/books NBK1116 *http://www.ncbi.nlm.nih.gov books/NBK5191/	Expert-authored, peer-reviewed disease descriptions presented in standardized format focusing on clinical relevant and medically actionable information on diagnosis, management, and genetic counseling of patients and families with inherited diseases. *Includes link for Illustrated Glossary. (Pagon, R. A., et al., eds. 1993–2014) GeneReviews® Seattle (WA): University of Washington, Seattle).

The overarching goal of applying genomic knowledge to healthcare is to improve health outcomes. This can be accomplished by identifying high-risk individuals, understanding the interaction of environment with genetic make-up, and applying this knowledge to better manage or prevent disease. Each of the following chapters provides more in-depth coverage of what is known and yet to be learned related to single gene disorders, isolated birth defects, specific common complex disorders, and pharmacogenomics. A list of resources for this chapter can be found in Table 1.8.

1.11. REFERENCES

Antoniou, A. C., & Chenevix-Trench, G. (2010). Common genetic variants and cancer risk in Mendelian cancer syndromes. *Current Opinion in Genetics & Development, 20*(3), 299–307.

Au K. S., Williams, A. T., Gambello, M. J., & Northrup H. (2004). Molecular genetic basis of tuberous sclerosis complex: from bench to bedside. *Journal of Child Neurology, 19*(9), 699–709.

Bishop, N. A., Lu, T. & Yankner, B. A. (2010). Neural mechanisms of ageing and cognitive decline. *Nature, 464*, 529–535.

Buiting K. (2010). Prader-Willi syndrome and Angelman syndrome. *American Journal of Medical Genetics, Part C Seminars in Medical Genetics, 154C,* 365–376.

Center for Jewish Genetics. (2014). Ashkenazi genetic traits. Retrieved from https://www.jewishgenetics. org/ashkenazi-genetic-traits

Clancy, S. (2008). Genetic recombination. *Nature Education, 1*(1), 40. Retrieved from http://www. nature.com/scitable/topicpage/genetic-recombination-514.

Cortessis, V. K., Duncan, C. T., Levine, A. J., Breton, C. V., Mack, T. M., Siegmund, R. W., . . . Laird, P. W. (2012). Environmental epigenetics: prospects for studying epigenetic mediation of exposure-response relationships. *Human Genetics, 131,* 1565–1589.

Coskun P., Wyrembak, J., Schriner, S. E., Chen, H., Marciniack, C., LaFerla, F., & Wallace, D. C. (2011). A mitochondrial etiology of Alzheimer and Parkinson disease. *Biochimica et Biophysica Acta—Molecular and Cell Biology of Lipids, 1820,* 553–564.

Crino, P.B., Nathanson, K.L., & Henski, E.P. (2006). Medical progress: The tuberous sclerosis complex. *New England Journal of Medicine, 355,* 1345–1356.

Cutting, G.R. (2010). Modifier genes in Mendelian disorders: the example of cystic fibrosis. *Annals of New York Academy of Science, 1214,* 57-69. doi: 10.1111/j.1749-6632.2010.05879.x.

Eisenberg, E. & Levanon, E. (2013). Human housekeeping genes revisited. *Trends in Genetics, 29*(10), 569–554. doi:10.1016/j.tig.2013.05.010.

Everett, C. M., & Wood, N. W. (2004) Trinucleotide repeats and neurodegenerative disease. *Brain, 127,* 2385–2405. doi:10.1093/brain/awh278.

Faustino, N. A., & Cooper, T. A. (2003). Pre-mRNA splicing and human disease. *Genes & Development, 17*(4), 419–437. doi:10.1101/gad.1048803.

Feero, G.W., Guttmacher, A.E., & Collins, F.S. (2010). Genomic medicine—An updated primer. *New England Journal of Medicine, 362,* 2001–2011.

Gardner, R., J., Sutherland, G., R., & Shaffer, L., G. (2011). *Chromosome abnormalities and genetic counseling: Oxford monographs on medical genetics (4th ed)* New York: Oxford Press.

Gisler F. M., von Kanel T., Kraemer, R., Schaller, A., & Gallati, S. (2013). Identification of SNPs in the cystic fibrosis interactome influencing pulmonary progression in cystic fibrosis. *European Journal of Human Genetics, 21* (4), 397–403. DOI: 10.1038/ejhg.2012.181

Greco, K. E., Tinley, S., & Siebert, D. (2012). *Essential Genetic and Genomic Competencies for Nurses with Graduate Degrees.* Silver Spring, MD: American Nurses Association and International Society of Nurses in Genetics.

Guttmacher, A. E., & Collins, F. S. (2002) Genomic medicine—A primer. *New England Journal of Medicine, 347*(19), 1512–1520.

Heim, S., & Mitelman, F. (Eds). (2009). *Cancer Cytogenetics: Chromosomal and Molecular Genetic Aberrations of Tumor Cells.* 3rd ed. New York: Wiley Blackwell.

Hoppel, C. L., Tandler, B., Fujioka, H., & Riva, A. (2009) Dynamic organization of mitochondria in human heart and in myocardial disease. *International Journal of Biochemistry and Cell Biology, 41,* 1949–1956.

Hung, C., Lin S., Lee C., Chen, C., Lin, S., Chao, M., Chiou, S., & Su, N. (2011). Low penetrance of retinoblastoma for p.V654L mutation of the RB1 gene. *BioMed Central Medical Genetics, 12,* 76. Retrieved from: http://www.biomedcentral.com/1471-2350/12/76

Keymolen K., Van Berkel K., Vorsselmans A., Staessen C., & Liebaers I. (2011). Pregnancy outcome in carriers of Robertsonian translocations. *American Journal of Medical Genetics, 155A*(10), 2381–2385. doi: 10.1002/ajmg.a.33941

Koopman, W. J., Willems, P. H., & Smeitink, J. A. (2012). Monogenic mitochondrial disorders. *New England Journal of Medicine, 366,* 1132–1141.

Mangs, A. H., & Morris, B. J. (2007). The human pseudoautosomal region (PAR): Origin, function and future. *Current Genomics, 8*(2), 129–136.

Marini, N., Hoffmann, T., Lammer, E., Hardin, J., Lazaruk, K., Stein, J., . . . Rine, J. (2011). A genetic signature of spina bifida risk from pathway-informed comprehensive gene-variant analysis. *PLoS One, 6*(11), e28408. doi:10.1371/journal.pone.0028408.

National Library of Medicine (U.S.). (2014a). Genetics Home Reference [Internet] Bethesda (MD): The Library; Chromosome Y. [reviewed 2010, Jan; cited 2014, Apr 14]. Available from http://ghr.nlm.nih.gov/chromosome/Y

National Library of Medicine (U.S.). (2014b). Genetics Home Reference [Internet] Bethesda (MD): The Library; Chromosome X. [reviewed 2012, Jan; cited 2014, Apr 14]. Available from http://ghr.nlm.nih.gov/chromosome/X

National Library of Medicine (U.S.). (2014c). Genetics Home Reference [Internet] Bethesda (MD): The Library; Chromosome 13. [reviewed 2013, Jul; cited 2014, Apr 14]. Available from: http://ghr.nlm.nih.gov/chromosome/13

National Library of Medicine (U.S.). (2014d). Genetics Home Reference [Internet] Bethesda (MD): The Library; Chromosome 18. [reviewed 2012, Mar; cited 2014, Apr 14]. Available from: http://ghr.nlm.nih.gov/chromosome/18

National Library of Medicine (U.S.). (2014e). Genetics Home Reference [Internet] Bethesda (MD): The Library; Chromosome 21. [reviewed 2013, Nov; cited 2014, Apr 14]. Available from: http://ghr.nlm.nih.gov/chromosome/21

National Library of Medicine (U.S.). (2014f). Genetics Home Reference [Internet]. Bethesda (MD): The Library; Duchenne and Becker muscular dystrophy; [reviewed 2012, Feb; cited 2014, Apr 14]. Available from: http://ghr.nlm.nih.gov/condition/duchenne-and-becker-muscular-dystrophy

Nussbaum, R. L., McInnes, R. R., & Willard, H. F. (2007). *Thompson & Thompson genetics in medicine, (7th ed.)*. Philadelphia, PA: Saunders.

Read, A., & Donnai, D. (2011). *New Clinical Genetics, 2nd ed*. Banbury, UK: Scion Publishing.

Sabbagh, A., Pasmant, E., Laurendeau, I., Parfait, B., Barbarot, S., Guillot, B., . . . Wolkenstein, P. (2009). Unravelling the genetic basis of variable clinical expression in neurofibromatosis 1. *Human Molecular Genetics, 18*(15), 2768–2778.

Sleigh A., Raymond-Barker, P., Thackray, K., Porter, D., Hatunic, M., Vottero, A., . . . Savage, D. B. (2011). Mitochondrial dysfunction in patients with primary congenital insulin resistance. *Journal of Clinical Investigation, 121*, 2457–2461.

Smith, F. J. D., & McLean, W. H. (2011). Genodermatoses: inherited diseases of the Sskin. In M. J. Murphy (Ed.), *Molecular diagnostics in dermatology and dermatopathology* (pp. 379–409): New York: Humana Press.

Tseng, Y. H., Cyprus A. M. & Kahn, C.R. (2010). Cellular bioenergetics as a target for obesity therapy. *Nature Reviews Drug Discovery, 9*, 465–482.

Weaving, L.S., Ellaway, C.J., Gecz, J., & Chritodoulou, J., (2005). Rett syndrome: clinical review and genetic update. *Journal of Medical Genetics, 42*, 1–7.

Wolff, D. J., Van Dyke, D. L. & Powell, C. M. (2010) Laboratory guidelines for Turner syndrome: ACMG standards and guidelines. *Genetics in Medicine, 12* (1), 52–65.

Chapter 2

A Primer: Risk Assessment, Data Collection, and Interpretation for Genomic Clinical Assessment

ANN H. MARADIEGUE, Ph.D, FNP-BC, FAANP
QUANNETTA T. EDWARDS, Ph.D, FNP-BC, WHNP-BC, AGN-BC, FAANP

Objectives:

- Discuss the essential components of a risk assessment and its significance to genetics/genomics.
- Apply information from a family history to construct a three-generation pedigree on the maternal/paternal lineage using standardized pedigree symbols and terminology.
- Interpret selected three-generation pedigrees to assess for red flags that indicate disease risk.
- Describe different clinical settings (e.g., adult and pediatric) and how they influence the family history information collected.
- Distinguish between commonly used genetic terms of expressivity and penetrance and how each of these terms may impact the family history.
- Differentiate between personal, familial, and environmental factors that could be considered red flags in the three-generation-pedigree.
- Explain behavioral factors and their impact on disease development.
- Analyze a genomic selected case(s) and the role of the advanced practice nurse with regards to risk communication and management of risk.
- Utilize the five-step risk assessment approach (RAPID) to analyze data for disease risk.

2.1. DEFINITION OF TERMS IMPORTANT FOR THIS CHAPTER

Ancestry of Origin   Belonging to a social group that has common national or cultural traditions; characteristics of a people or a group who share a common and distinctive culture, religion, and language. Certain diseases are more prevalent among specific ethnic groups.

Autosomal Dominant   One mutated copy of the gene in each cell is sufficient for a person to be affected by an autosomal dominant disorder. Each affected person usually has one affected parent. Autosomal dominant disorders tend to occur in every generation of an affected family.

Autosomal Recessive   Two mutated copies of the gene are present in each cell when a person has an autosomal recessive disorder. An affected person usually has unaffected parents who each carry a single copy of the mutated gene (and are referred to as carriers). Autosomal recessive disorders are typically *not* seen in every generation of an affected family. Consanguinity is a risk for autosomal recessive disorders.

Anticipation   A phenomenon whereby the symptoms of genetic disorders for individuals in successive generations present at an earlier age and/or with more severe manifestations. This is often observed in disorders resulting from the expression of a trinucleotide repeat mutation in diseases such as Huntington's disease and myotonic dystrophy. Trinucleotide repeats tend to increase in size and have a more significant effect when passed from one generation to the next. For example, a grand-child may have earlier onset and more severe symptoms than the parent, who had earlier on-set than the grandparent.

Carriers   An individual with a genetic muta-tion associated with a disease that may or may not display disease symptoms. Carriers are as-sociated with diseases inherited as recessive traits. In order to have the disease, the indi-vidual must have inherited the mutated alleles from both parents. For recessive disorders, an individual having one normal allele and one mutated allele does not have the disease. Two carriers may produce a child with the disorder.

Common Complex Diseases   Term used to de-scribe diseases or disorders, also known as multifactorial disorders. These disorders are associated with the effects of multiple genes in combination with lifestyle and environmen-tal factors. Although complex disorders often cluster in families, they do not have a clear-cut pattern of inheritance.

Consanguinity   Genetic relatedness between in-dividuals descended from at least one common ancestor, for example when first cousins have a child.

Consultand   The individual seeking medical at-tention.

De novo Mutation   An alteration in a gene that is present for the first time in one family mem-ber as a result of a mutation in a germ cell (egg or sperm) of one of the parents or in the fertil-ized egg itself.

Dysmorphology   An abnormality in fetal devel-opment; refers to a difference of body struc-ture that is suggestive of a congenital disorder, genetic syndrome, or birth defect.

Family History   Consists of medical informa-tion about disorders that are present or have occurred in the patient and direct blood rela-tives of the patient. Psychosocial information (relationships, demographics, occupation, be-havioral factors, and environmental factors) is also collected as part of the family history. This information can help the provider iden-tify any predisposition to illnesses and enable education and prevention strategies to avoid behavioral and environmental triggers.

Horizontal Transmission   Individuals affected with a disorder in a single generation vs every generation.

Karyotype   The chromosomes of a cell dis-played as a systemized arrangement of chro-mosome pairs in descending order of size.

Mendelian Inheritance   An inheritance pattern for autosomal gene pairs. The genetic trait dis-played results from one parent's gene domi-nating over the gene inherited from the other parent.

Pedigree   A graphic description of biological relationships within a family, from one genera-tion to the next using standardized symbols.

Penetrance   The proportion of individuals with a particular genetic mutation who exhibit signs and symptoms of a genetic disorder. If some people with the mutation do not develop features of the disorder, the condition is said to have reduced (or incomplete) penetrance. Reduced penetrance probably results from a combination of genetic, environmental, and lifestyle factors, many of which are unknown. This phenomenon can make it challenging for professionals to interpret a person's family medical history and predict the risk of passing a genetic condition to future generations.

Personal History   An account of the personal and social details of a person's life that in-cludes place of birth, religion, race, marital status, number of children, military status, oc-cupational history, place of residence, educa-tion, current living situation, and smoking, al-cohol, and drug habits. The personal and social history is obtained at the initial interview and becomes a part of the permanent record.

Phenotype   A set of observable characteristics as a result of gene-environment interaction.

Precision Medicine   Offering medical treatment that is specifically tailored to that individual based on their genomic characteristics, This healthcare model proposes customized care in-cluding diagnostic tests, treatments, and drugs based on an individual's genomic profile.

Probability   The process to estimate the nature of adverse health effects in humans who may be exposed to genomic, environmental, and behavioral factors, now or in the future.

Proband   The family member through whom a family's medical history comes to attention.

For example, a proband might be a baby with Down's syndrome. The proband may also be called the index case.

Presymptomatic Testing   Testing of an asymptomatic individual in whom the discovery of a gene mutation indicates certain development of findings related to a specific diagnosis at some future point.

Risk Assessment   Identifying potential health threats and determining the disease probability influenced by genomic, familial, behavioral, and environmental determinates enabling personalized care.

Risk Communication   Discussing quantitatively and qualitatively the probability of a disease event occurring and the strategies available to ameliorate the disease. This is an interactive process of sharing risk and benefit information in order for individuals, families, and communities to make informed decisions.

Risk Management   Set of activities used to identify and evaluate strategies to deal with risks characterized in the risk assessment and involves a decision-making process in response to the hazards or threats.

X-Linked Inheritance   Single gene disorders associated with defective genes on the X-chromosome, making the disease more common in males.

Variable Expressivity   Refers to the range of signs and symptoms that can occur in different people with the same genetic condition. Variable expressivity is probably caused by a combination of genetic, environmental, and lifestyle factors, most of which have not been identified. If a genetic condition has highly variable signs and symptoms, it may be challenging to diagnose.

Variant of Unknown Significance   A variance in a genetic sequence with an unclear disease significance.

Vertical Transmission   Multiple generations affected within the pedigree, seen in autosomal dominant disorders.

Whole Exome Sequencing   The part of the genome primarily responsible for protein coding.

Whole Genome Sequencing   A laboratory process that sequences an organism's entire DNA genome.

2.2. INTRODUCTION

This chapter focuses on the important role that advanced practice nurses (APRNs) play in applying genomic information in healthcare throughout the life span. Specifically, the chapter focuses on the *elements of risk assessment* including (1) data collection, (2) identification of red flags, (3) probability of risk, (4) assessment of the data for risk communication, and (5) assessment of the data for risk management in order to identify genomic diseases. The components of the personal and *family history* are provided as one major component of the data collection process. The manner of formulating these components into a generational pedigree are explained, including interpretation of data that may be indicative of red flags, emphasizing the assessment of *risk* for hereditary (single gene) diseases and syndromes, as well as those defined as *complex or genomic disorders* due to interaction of multiple genes and environmental and behavioral factors.

The concept *genomic* assessment rather than *genetic* assessment is used because the emphasis is moving towards the understanding that an individual's genes themselves are not acting in isolation; many factors impact overall health of an individual. Scientists are learning that an individual's genome is flexible and changes take place throughout the life span (Khanherkar, Bhatia-Dey, & Csoka, 2014). The term *genomic* assessment captures not only the evaluation of single gene disorders, but also an individual's overall health, including diseases spanning infancy to geriatrics. Single gene disorders play a small role in the health of the public, and genomic discoveries are being applied to common diseases such as cancer and diabetes (Nicol, Skirton, Feero, & Green, 2013). Testing strategies that are faster, less expensive, and more accurate have the potential to change health care delivery (Khoury, Cashion, & Billings, 2015).

APRNs must understand genomics well enough to be aware of and appreciate the wide variety of diseases and single gene disorders that might be encountered in primary care and other healthcare settings. Briefly, the public expects APRNs to recognize genomic diseases, assess individual risks for acquiring or developing genomic disorders, implement primary and secondary preventive measures, including surveillance as indicated and refer for consultation when needed. Nurse leaders play major roles in helping to ensure that the genomic information needed to assess risk is integrated into the workplace by developing and implementing policies and providing appropriate resources (e.g., electronic medical records with *family history*, research) to assist in translating the genomic information consistent with the ethical, cultural, legal, and social considerations of the individual, family, and community. Leaders in nursing education will play key roles in training APRNs who understand and use advances in genomic sciences to communicate and manage disease risk to promote the health of clients and the public. Nurse researchers are designing innovative studies using genomics to improve healthcare outcomes of importance to nursing practice. Summarily, nurses play critical roles in assessing behavioral, social, and physiologic factors that impact the genomic risk of individuals, families, and communities. *Risk assessment*, therefore, is an important concept for all the various nursing roles, including practice, education, research, and leadership.

Assessment is an ongoing continuous process that contains multiple components, including the *risk assessment* process and interpretation of the findings. Health assessment is a systematic, deliberative, and interactive process based upon data collection, validation, analysis, and synthesis for making decisions about health status of individuals, families, and/or communities (Benner, Hughes, & Stuphen, 2008; Bickley & Szilagyi, 2013). It is an essential function of APRNs to identify clients' needs and clinical problems and to evaluate health problems and employ interventions. *Risk assessment* provides additional information, enabling APRNs to make an informed decision based upon specific characterizations of potential risk. A genomic *risk assessment* is an important component of the overall assessment and management of clients. *Risk assessment* focuses on collection of data to identify an individual's potential disease risk so that appropriate measures can be implemented early to mitigate or, when applicable, eliminate the risk. Genomic *risk assessment* enables the use of a wide range of assessment tools for identifying risk *probability* (e.g., personal, *family history*, pedigree, empiric risk models), implementation of appropri-

ate screening or genetic testing when applicable, and the application of preventive measures and targeted therapy based upon individuals risks and disease occurrence as a means of *precision medicine*. *Precision medicine* provides not only personalized treatments to meet the needs of the individual, but uses genomic, epigenomic, exposures, and other data to define individual patterns of disease, leading to a more accurate, person-centered, and multifaceted diagnosis (Insel, 2011). *Precision medicine* entails identifying clients suspected to have an inherited disease, estimating risk for Mendelian and multifactorial disorders, and providing appropriate management of care and/or referral (Greco, Tinley, & Seibert, 2012).

One of the first places that *precision healthcare* is having an impact is in the area of pharmacogenomics. Individual responses to pharmacotherapy are beginning to play a major role in clinical practice, and APRNs will be expected to provide the right therapeutic agent based upon individual gene variations related to drug actions, absorption, distribution, metabolism and excretion (European Commission, DG Research, 2010; Tanaka, 2010; United States [U.S.] Food and Drug Administration, 2014).

Risk assessment and interpretation is central to APRN practice. It is one of seven major categories in the *Essential Genetic and Genomic Competencies for Nurses with Graduate Degrees*, established by a National Consensus Panel and endorsed by the American Association of Nurses (Greco *et al.*, 2012). These current genomic competencies focus on assessment, identification, referral, and provision of education, care, and support as it relates to genomics (Greco *et al.*, 2012). Examples of specific following:

- *Nursing Assessment*—demonstrating the relationship of genetics/genomics to a wide range of areas, including health, prevention, screening, diagnostics and prognostics, treatment, and monitoring treatment effectiveness; applying and integrating genetic and genomic knowledge, including but not limited to, eliciting a three-generation family health history and construction of a pedigree.
- *Identification*—of clients with genomic information based upon assessment as well as

other issues that may impact this information, including ethical, cultural, religious, fiscal, and societal issues.

* *Referral*—to genomic services when applicable.
* *Provision of Care and Support*—Services, decision making, risk-assessment, and interventions to improve genomic outcomes; collaborative care; evaluation of genomic outcomes (Greco *et al.*, 2012). For more information on these competencies, nurses are referred to the website: http://www. nursingworld.org/MainMenuCategories/ EthicsStandards/Genetics1/EssentialNursing-CompetenciesandCurriculaGuidelinesforGe-neticsandGenomics.pdf.

Understanding the key concepts related to genomics is an important skill when conducting an individual *risk assessment*. *Genetics* is the study of single genes and their effects on the body, whereas *genomics* examines the functions and interactions of *all the genes in the genome* (Guttmacher & Collins, 2002). *Genomic medicine* is an emerging discipline that involves the use of an individual's genomic information to make decisions about diagnostics, prognostics, prevention, or therapeutic decision-making (Manolio *et al.*, 2013). Genomic science has expanded to include a wider range of information, including concepts such as germline differences (polymorphisms), the genome, interactome (totality of molecular interactions in an organism), and the proteome (all the proteins) (BioLicense, 2013; Khoury *et al.*, 2007). The sciences related to genomics facilitate an improved understanding of disease processes and advance disease prediction, prognosis, drug response (pharmacogenetic/pharmacogenomics), and personalized management of care (Redekop & Mladsi 2013; Tanaka, 2010). These scientific advances have been integrated into an evidence based framework for the integration of genomic testing in public health by the Office of Public Health Genomics, an arm of the Centers for Disease Control and Prevention, and this trend is continuing to grow across other institutions making APRNs participation crucial in promoting the health of the public (Centers for Disease Control and Prevention [CDC], 2013).

One way to begin adoption of the science is through understanding the process of *risk assess-*

ment. In this chapter, we present one approach, a *Rapid Approach* when conducting a genomic assessment to ensure an accurate and appropriate assessment of risk. This approach uses an acronym, *RAPID*, which stands for **R**isk Assessment (Communication and Management) based upon the **P**robability of risk **I**dentified through **D**ata Collection (Figure 2.1). This chapter provides an overview of each of these elements: (1) data collection, (2) risk identification, (3) determination of risk *probability*, (4) *risk communication*, and (5) *risk management* and how each of these elements are important in the overall genomic assessment.

2.3. RISK ASSESSMENT RAPID APPROACH—STEP 1 DATA COLLECTION

Risk assessment begins with data collection. Data collection includes an in-depth history to identify familial and personal data and, when applicable, laboratory, ancillary, and environmental data. The physical assessment is also a part of the data collection process and is integral to the genomic assessment.

2.3.1. Familial Risk History

The *family history*, collecting a minimum of three generations to assess both the maternal and paternal lineage, should be part of an initial *risk assessment* for all clients. Collection of *family history* data is not a one time event but should be a continuous process, evaluated and updated during each client contact. The *pedigree* has many functions, including use as a tool for diagnosis, testing strategies, determining patterns of disease, identifying individuals and families 'at risk' for disease or susceptible to injury, and determining reproductive options (Bennett, 2010). The *pedigree* is useful in determining if patterns of disease are present suggestive of conditions that indicate single gene disorders/syndromes that may warrant genetic testing, as well as the recognition of chronic diseases associated with genomic and environmental factors (Weitzel, Blazer, MacDonald, Culver, & Offut, 2011). The *pedigree* can aid in determining genetic *probability for disease*, calculating *disease risk*, confirming *risk probability*, and recognizing potential red

FIGURE 2.1. Risk Assessment based upon Probability of risk Identified through Data collection (RAP-ID Approach). Five steps of Risk Assessment including: (1) data collection; (2) identification of data for red flags; (3) probability (calculation of risk); (4) communication of risk; and (5) risk management.

flags that may be suspect for disease. Decisions regarding management of care and surveillance, as well as developing rapport and educating the client and family members, are also important functions of the *pedigree* (Bennett, 2010).

New genetic/genomic technologies have increased the importance of the *pedigree* as this information assists with the genetic testing accuracy. In *genetic panel testing* used in cancer, heart disease, and reproductive health the *pedigree* plays an important role in narrowing the list of candidate genes for testing based on the *phenotype* of disease presentation noted within the individual and family members (Singleton *et al.*, 2014). *Whole genome (WGS)* and/or *whole exome sequencing (WES)* is currently used primarily in research settings and is considered to have potential for the future of *precision medicine*. *WES* and *WGS* may not provide full cov-

erage of critical genes, the *family history* in the form of a *pedigree* provides a clearer picture of the disease presentation, thereby assisting the genetic team in generating a differential diagnosis and ordering of more sensitive testing. Finally, the *family history* may provide a roadmap when segregating *variants of unknown significance* within a family (Ormond, 2013). The *pedigree*, therefore, is an essential method for presenting the *family history* and is crucial to the *risk assessment* process. Chapter 17 provides a more in depth discussion of other emerging genomic technologies.

Use of the *pedigree* for *risk assessment* requires the knowledge of standardized human *pedigree* nomenclature and symbols important in ensuring consistent history data for interprofessional collaboration and referral and to communicate accurate information to reduce errors in interpretation (Bennett, 2010; Bennett, French, Resta, & Doyle, 2008). The *pedigree* can serve to clarify any genetic tests that were found to be positive (e.g., *autosomal dominant, autosomal recessive, X-linked*), including the carrier status of an individual and whether the status of the individual or family member is asymptomatic or *presymptomatic*. When possible, health care providers (HCPs) should obtain pertinent laboratory, ancillary, or pathology data, as well as genetic test results, to confirm diagnosis or disease state that may influence the disease risk of the client and the management of care strategy (Bennett, 2010).

Family history, particularly when presented as a three-generation pedigree, is one of the most important indicators of disease risk currently available and is an important component of the *Essential Genetic and Genomic Competencies for Nurses*. Family history is important to obtaining an accurate genomic assessment. In the future, it is likely that medical and *family history* will be used to help the clinician better understand variants and their *penetrance* within the family and individual with a disorder (Hooker, Ormond, Sweet, & Biesecker, 2014). There are several tools available for obtaining a *family history* (see Table 2.1).

Notably, the *family history* is a cost-effective approach to health care that can be used to initiate health interventions (Bennett 2010; Heald, Edelman, & Eng, 2012; Ouakrim, Boussioutas, Lockett, Hopper, & Jenkins, 2014; Ramsey, Wilschut, Boer, & van Ballegooijen, 2010). Whenever possible, this information should be recorded in the form of a three-generation pedigree, using standardized symbols, as displayed in Table 2.2, so that interpretation is consistent across HCPs and practices (Bennett, 2010; Bennett *et al.,* 2008). Use of a three-generation pedigree when conducting a *family history* provides a depiction of family members by sex, across generations (e.g., three generations), enabling visualization of patterns and traits that cluster around the family (Bennett *et al.,* 2008; Jorde, Carey & Bamshad, 2010). This depiction provides useful information in determining *Mendelian patterns of inheritance* associated with hereditary disorders, as well as enabling HCPs to begin to assess risk for disease; identifies at-risk family members; distinguishes genetic from other risk factors; and aids HCPs in making care and surveillance management deci-

sions (Bennett, 2010). Further, the *pedigree* provides a means for *risk assessment* and can serve to identify medical screening needs for healthy individuals. The use of the *pedigree* also aids in establishing client rapport and decision-making and is useful in clarifying client's misconceptions. Thus, the *family history* serves not only as a valuable diagnostic tool but also an important educational tool (Bennett, 2010).

2.3.2. Clinical Setting and *Family History*

The type of clinical setting and situation may influence the *family history* information collected and the application of the *family history*. Although it is the hope that every individual will have a comprehensive three-generation pedigree as part of his or her medical record that is updated regularly, certain clinical settings may require a more focused approach to the *family history*. For example, a preoperative screening would require a targeted approach focusing on risk due to complications that can occur during surgery (e.g., a *family history* of blood clots or bleeding disorders) and with anesthesia. A preconception counseling or prenatal clinic visit, however, requires an in-depth family history to identify patterns in the family that may be suggestive of potential single gene disorders warranting possible genetic screening and counseling. A *family history* is also essential in primary care and specialized clinic settings (e.g., internal medicine, cardiology) to determine risk for disease, early diagnosis, and *personalized/precision* management of care. In fact, the Surgeon General, in cooperation with other agencies with the U.S. Department of Health and Human Services, launched a national public health campaign called the *Surgeon General's Family History Initiative*, to encourage all American families to learn more about their family health history (National Human Genome Research Institute, 2012). It is up to HCPs, including APRNs, to ensure that this *family history* is incorporated into the medical record and updated during the individual's clinic or hospital visit. Regardless of the setting, genomic principles such as the pedigree collection need to be put into practice and integrated across clinical situations (Greco *et al.,* 2012). Incorporating this information is important since *family history* is often referred to as the

TABLE 2.1. Selected Family History Tools, Resources, Online Genetic Referral Consultation, and Selected Nursing Genetic Educational Resources.

Resources	Purpose	Website
Family History		
American Medical Association	Family medical history tools: Prenatal providers; prenatal genetic screening; adult family history	http://www.ama-assn.org/ama/pub/physician-resources/medical-science/genetics-molecular-medicine/family-history.page
U.S. Department of Health & Human Services, U.S Surgeon General's Family History Initiative	Surgeon General's Family History Initiative, to encourage all American families to learn more about their family health history	http://www.hhs.gov/familyhistory/
March of Dimes	Information on pregnancy and health profile-risk assessment and screening tool	http://www.marchofdimes.org/pregnancy/your-family-health-history.aspx
Power Lineage	Pedigree tools for providers: prenatal, oncology, generic	https://www.powerlineage.com/
Progeny	Advanced pedigree software used by genetic specialists. Has videos and free demonstrations	http://www.progenygenetics.com/
Genetic Referral		
National Society of Genetic Counselors	Information for healthcare providers; resources for finding a genetic counselor	http://nsgc.org/p/cm/ld/fid=164
Practice Guidelines		
National Comprehensive Cancer Network	Guidelines on risk reduction for selected cancers and hereditary cancers (e.g., colorectal; breast)	http://www.nccn.org/professionals/default.aspx
National Cancer Institute PDQ©	Expert-reviewed information summary of hereditary cancer and other cancer genetics; expert-reviewed information summary in which cancer risk perception, risk communication, and risk counseling is explained	http://www.cancer.gov/cancertopics/pdq
Nursing Genetics		
International Society of Nurses in Genetics (ISONG)	Global nursing specialty organization dedicated to fostering scientific and professional growth of nurses in genetics and genomics worldwide	http://www.isong.org/
Cincinnati Children's Hospital	Genetic education programs for Nursing	http://www.cincinnatichildrens.org/education/clinical/nursing/genetics/default/

first genetic test, because it is used to guide the diagnosis of *presymptomatic* individuals with a genetic disorder (single gene) who may warrant further diagnostic or genetic testing or referral to specialists for management of care. For *common complex disorders* (e.g., diabetes, hypertension), *family history* informs individuals about needed screening, testing, and targeted interventions for prevention, early treatment, and education. *Family history* also helps the clinician build rapport

with the patient to identify the shared environment and behaviors that might place the individual at higher risk for disease. The Centers for Medicare and Medicaid Services determined that the *family history* is a crucial component of the physical examination visit and is required for reimbursement of the patient encounter (Department of Health and Human Services/Centers for Medicare and Medicaid Services, 2010).

Family history is an essential tool to be used

throughout the life span and in specialized settings. In the prenatal clinical setting, assessment often focuses on single gene disorders, chromosomal abnormalities, congenital malformations or other genomic conditions, in which, based on the *family history* or other information, a myriad of invasive and/or noninvasive procedures (e.g., chronic villus sampling, maternal serum alpha fetal protein, ultrasound) may be warranted for appropriate and early prenatal diagnosis (Mari-

TABLE 2.2. *Standardized Pedigree Symbols and Relationship Lines Commonly Used in Family History. Symbols Adapted from Bennett et al., (1995). Recommendations for Standardized Human Pedigree Nomenclature. Am. J. Hum. Genet., 56: 745–52. Adapted with permission from the copyright center (Bennett, French, Resta, & Doyle, 2008).*

no, 2012). *Family history* during the prenatal visit not only assesses genetic risk to the offspring, but also establishes disease carrier status of the parents. Once a parent is identified as a carrier of a genetic disorder (e.g., sickle cell, cystic fibrosis), this becomes useful data in determining disease risk to the newborn and determining other 'at-risk' family members. The information is also important for reproductive counseling and family planning (Dolan & Moore, 2007). Multiple birth defects are often associated with chromosome abnormalities, particularly where there is a *family history* of miscarriages, infertility, mental disability, or delay, all of which are important to record on the *family history*, including the pedigree (Bennett 2010). Further, newborn screening at time of the infant's birth provides an array of measures to detect potentially fatal or disabling conditions in newborns due to single gene disorders, and the *family history* may provide additional information to aid in obtaining these screening tests. Whole genome and other sequencing strategies during the newborn phase, in addition to the *family history*, may identify important information for future health care needs (Connolly & Hakonarson, 2012).

During the pediatric visit, *family history* guides the diagnosis of both singlegene disorders and common chronic conditions. Many single gene disorders first become evident during childhood, and common chronic diseases that run in families often have preclinical signs in children and adolescents (Colvin & Bower, 2009; Tarini & McInerney, 2013; Valdez, Greenlund, Khoury, & Yoon, 2007). For example, children with a strong *family history* of coronary artery disease may show early signs of atherosclerosis, such as elevated markers for inflammation and high cholesterol level (Kelishadi, Sabri, Motamedi, & Ramezani, 2009; Solini, Santini, Passaro, Madec, & Ferrannini, 2009).

Family history is useful in the adult health care setting for diagnosing adult onset single gene disorders (e.g., hemochromatosis, Huntington disease) and common chronic disease predisposition (e.g., genomic disorders) that have complex etiology, such as cancer, cardiovascular disease, hyperlipidemia, and diabetes. The bulk of *family history* in the adult primary care setting focuses on the genomics of common chronic diseases, which is becoming increasingly important in

the era of personalized healthcare (Chen *et al.*, 2014). The collection of the *family history* in this age group can be used to motivate patients to make healthier life style choices and undergo recommended screenings for disease prevention and health promotion. Evidence from the United States Preventive Services Task Force (2011) found the *family history* is an important clinical consideration for issuing screening and prevention recommendations for breast cancer, colorectal cancer, lipid disorders, coronary heart disease, and abdominal aortic aneurysm. Although single gene disorders in the general population are rare, the *family history* is critical to identification of the rare, single gene cancer syndromes and other single gene etiologies that often present in adulthood, in order to refer these high risk individuals for the proper disease management and in some cases disease prevention.

Utilization of the *family history* in the acute care setting assumes an important role in safety of the hospitalized patient. A *family history* of blood clots (e.g., Factor V Leiden) can require aggressive interventions for the patient undergoing surgical procedures. Dosing and medication choice, for example, warfarin for deep venous thrombosis, may require pharmacogenomic testing for proper disease management for individuals carrying the specific polymorphisms for Factor V Leiden (Cremin *et al.*, 2010; Thalji & Camire, 2013). A *family history* of malignant hyperthermia, a potentially fatal pharmacogenomic disease, is triggered by several anesthetics and should always be included as part of the perioperative *family history* (Glahn *et al.*, 2010). Although the settings differ, these scenarios underscore the importance of the personal and *family history*. Many of the previous examples focused on single gene disorders, which cannot be ignored but are rare in the general population. As science moves into the genomic era, the *family history* is still considered very important as a screening tool for chronic disease, behavioral and environmental risks, as well as a potential aid in pharmacogenomics and disease management (Doerr & Teng, 2012).

Behavioral and environmental histories are also an important part of risk assessment, because these elements in some circumstances may contribute to disease risk. The behavioral component of risk assessment should entail documentation of any elements that can increase the individual's risk for disease, injury, or harm, including drug, nicotine, and alcohol abuse. Further, documentation of medication history, including over-the-counter drugs, is an essential part of risk assessment in identifying potential agents that can affect the action and interaction of genes increasing the risk for birth defects and potentially impacting risk of drug interactions. The inclusion of medication history is particularly important in maternal and newborn risk assessment for women receiving preconception counseling.

The majority of *common complex diseases* have been associated with the interaction of genomic and environmental factors. Whether by chance encounter or planned or systematic exposure, gene-environmental interactions influence disease risk (Nussbaum, McInnes, & Willard, 2015). For example, individual and familial risk for *common complex diseases*, such as type 2 diabetes, heart disease, obesity, psychiatric disorders, and cancer, have been associated with genomic and environmental factors (McDermott, Downing, & Stratton, 2011; Nussbaum *et al.*, 2015; Peay, Hooker, Kassem, & Biesecker, 2009; Wynne *et al.*,2006). Overexposure to chemical, radiation, or other hazardous agents also has the potential to impact health and increase disease risk, particularly many types of cancer. Lifestyle behaviors and genomic and environmental interactions, such as frequent sun exposure and avoidance of sun protection agents, increase the risk for skin cancers. Behavioral factors, such as lack of exercise, overweight and obesity due to poor nutritional habits, and exposure to secondhand smoke all impact disease risks. The value and utility of assessing behavioral and environmental elements should therefore be an integral part of risk assessment and be included in the personal and *family history* (Bennett, 2010).

2.3.3. Personal Risk History

The personal health history of the individual interviewed is also a part of the pedigree data collection process. This individual can be the one who has a specific health history, or the affected individual (*proband*), or the individual without a medical problem but whose *family history* is significant for a disorder (*consultand*). Therefore, the purpose of conducting a *personal history* in risk assessment is to identify factors within an individual's health history that contribute to disease susceptibility, to identify disease characteristics, to facilitate treatment and prognosis of genomic conditions, and to identify environmental risks. This information is then constructed into a pedigree from the collected *family history* information, using standardized symbols and terminology (Bennett, 2010). A quick reference is provided in Table 2.2.

Personal risk assessment includes a detailed medical, surgical, behavioral, and environmental history; along with information obtained from the physical assessment, and any ancillary, laboratory, and/or pathology data that are important to determining health, disease, and overall disease risk (Goetzel *et al.*, 2011; Whelan *et al.*, 2004). The physical examination and/or laboratory and ancillary data may indicate disease risks not apparent in the *family history*. Early age of onset of disease or abnormal pathology results might indicate single gene disorders that could be masked by the *family history* due to adoption, death of family members due to non-genetic causes, or limited family structure. For example, a female diagnosed with breast cancer at age 40, with tumor characteristics of triple negative disease (hormonal receptors negative for estrogen and progestin and negative for human epidermal growth factor receptor 2 [*HER2*]) and unknown *family history* due to her adopted status, represents a *personal history* of *red flags* for hereditary breast cancer syndromes, such as hereditary breast and ovarian cancer syndrome (HBOC) due to mutations in *BRCA1*, *BRCA2* and other genes. (Robertson *et al.*, 2012; Suba, 2014). This history warrants genetic referral, counseling, and consideration for genetic testing. Refer to Chapter 15 in the text on the genetics and genomics of cancer for further discussion regarding HBOC, including risk assessment and identifying red flags associated with the syndromes. Other disorders such as coronary heart disease, detailed in Chapter 11, can be caused by numerous factors, including single gene disorders (e.g., familial hypercholesterolemia), or a combination of genomic and environmental factors, including familial or behavioral determinants (e.g., *family history* of heart disease, obesity, and inactivity). A thorough personal, family, laboratory, and behavioral assessment may provide the clues to the individual's disease risk so that strategies can be implemented to reduce that risk.

Personal history encompasses the individual's medical, surgical, and social history, whereas the *family history* assessment gives insight into the medical history of blood relatives and, thus, provides a picture of inherited disease susceptibility, as well as complex disorders related to genomic and environmental factors. For all individuals, basic demographic information in the personal and *family history* should include the date the history was taken and updated; current age; race/ethnicity; ancestry-of-origin of the maternal and paternal lineage; pertinent medical and surgical data, including psychiatric illnesses and age of onset of the condition; cause(s) of death and age of occurrence; and behavioral history (e.g., tobacco and alcohol use). Pertinent reproductive history (e.g., history of stillborn, congenital anomalies, spontaneous abortions [miscarriages], pregnancy complications, infertility) should also be a part of the assessment. In addition, data obtained from the history should be depicted in the pedigree, as well as any *consanguinity*. Stage of life often determines the generalized areas of focus during the data collection process, including physical assessment. For example, in infants and children, the focus is on proper growth and development. During the teen and young adult years, the focus is on behavioral risks and any known diseases that will influence their transition to adulthood (e.g., sickle cell disease or carrier state), as well as stages of development (e.g., Tanner stage) and reproductive history. In adults, besides the basic health history information, the *personal history* may focus more on the reproductive history and gynecologic/obstetrical history. If the individual (or couple) is of reproductive age and they do not have children, it is important to establish and document if this is by choice or if there is a biological cause for the infertility (e.g., azoospermia, multiple miscarriages, or endometriosis).

During the reproductive years, preconceptual counseling maximizes the chances of a healthy pregnancy, in which, based on the individual and *family history*, recommended genetic screening tests can be ordered on the parents so that appropriate counseling can take place prior to conception. Once the child is born, infants and pediatric patients require a detailed birth history that includes any gestational problems or illness-es experienced by the mother, *family history* of birth defects, and gestational age at birth. In the geriatric population or older adult, personal and *family history* includes much of the same data as the adult history but differs because it usually focuses on elderly individuals with complex problems, and the emphasis is on functional disabilities and potential risk for harm (e.g., fall risk). A complete geriatric assessment may be warranted and performed by multiple personnel (e.g., medical, social work) over many encounters and is best suited for elders with multiple medical problems and significant functional limitations (Elsawy & Higgins, 2011). An important part of the personal medical history data collection process includes documentation of laboratory values (e.g., complete blood count and indices, cholesterol), pathology and radiographic reports, and a complete review of systems. An example of a list of questions that should be included as part of the review of systems in the genomic *family history* assessment is located in Table 2.3. In addition, other attributes should also be considered in the *personal history* (e.g., culture), as well as pertinent social data that may impact overall health and risk for disease (e.g., occupation and/or hazardous exposures).

Assessment of the *ancestry of origin* of the individual comprising the maternal and paternal lineage should be an integral part of the personal and *family history*. This contains not only race/ethnicity but also constitutes the 'ethnic origin' of the family. This is important because certain racial/ethnic groups are at higher risk for hereditary, as well as complex, disorders. For example, African-Americans and those of Hispanic origin are at greater risk for sickle cell disease.

Cultural background, religious practices, and personal beliefs are intertwined in the *personal history*. Cultural and religious beliefs influence dietary practices and behaviors. Among some cultures (e.g., Middle East, Africa, India), marriage of close relatives is commonplace, referred to as *consanguinity* or the genetic relatedness between individuals descended from at least one common ancestor. *Consanguineous unions* have a higher risk for inherited *autosomal recessive* gene mutations. Counseling for consanguineous couples focuses on risks to their offspring; however, *family history* of adult disorders such as cancer syndromes needs to be considered as part

TABLE 2.3. *Example of Questions for the Genomic Family History Based Upon Review of Systems.*

System	Questions
General	• Ask about current and past occupations. • Does anyone have anything unusual about their appearance?
Head, Face, and Neck	• Anyone have an unusually large or small head? • Are there any problems in the family with vision, blindness, cataracts, or glaucoma? (If yes, at what age did the problem begin, the severity, and any treatment). • Does anyone in the family have a cleft lip or palate? • Anyone with unusual problems with their teeth? (e.g., missing, extra, misshapen, fragile, early teeth loss). • Any problems with hearing or speech? • Anyone with a short or webbed neck?
Skeletal	• Is any family member unusually tall or short? • Anyone with curvature of the spine? • Anyone with multiple fractures? (How many, at what age, how the breaks occurred, what bones were broken.) • Anyone with an unusual shape to their chest? • Anyone with unusually formed bones? • Anyone with unusually shaped hands or feet, such as extremely short or long fingers or toes, missing or additional fingers or toes? • Anyone with joint problems, such that they are stiff or unusually flexible, or dislocate frequently?
Skin	• Anyone with unusual bumps, lumps, or birthmarks? If so give a detailed description. Were they ever treated or biopsied? • Any problems with healing or bruising? • Any unusual problems with their fingernails or toenails, such as absent nails or growth under the nails?
Respiratory	• Any family members with lung disease? (smoking history) • Were they treated for the lung disease, and how?)
Cardiac	• Anyone with heart disease? (If so at what age, and how were they treated?) • Was anyone born with a heart defect? (If so did they have birth anomalies or intellectual delay?) • Anyone with heart murmurs? • Anyone with high blood pressure? • Were there any heart surgeries? (If so, what was done, and at what age?)
Gastrointestinal	• Anyone with stomach or intestinal problems? (If so were they treated and how?)
Renal	• How old were they when the symptoms presented? • Anyone with kidney disease? (If so were they treated for the problem, and how? How old were they when the symptoms presented?)
Hematologic	• Anyone with bleeding, clotting, or healing problems? • Have any relatives told you they were anemic? • Have any relatives told you they have high iron levels? • Have there been any relatives who needed blood transfusions or phlebotomy?
Endocrine	• Anyone with thyroid problems? • Anyone with diabetes? • Anyone who is overly heavy or thin?
Immune	• Anyone with frequent infections or hospitalizations, or difficulties healing?

(continued)

TABLE 2.3 (continued). Example of Questions for the Genomic Family History Based Upon Review of Systems.

System	Questions
Reproductive	• Have any relatives had miscarriages or babies who died, severe pregnancy complications, or infertility?
Neurological/Neuromuscular	• Anyone with muscle weakness, or problems with walking? • Do any family members use a cane or wheelchair? (If there are muscle problems inquire about the age of onset, any testing such as muscle biopsy, nerve conduction studies, or brain imaging.) • Anyone with strokes or seizures? (If so, age of onset and any medications.) • Anyone with uncontrolled movements, tics, difficulty with coordination, or spasticity? (If so, what was the age of onset and any medications given?) • Anyone with slurred speech?
Mental	• Anyone in the family with mental or intellectual impairment or severe learning disabilities? Did anyone attend special classes, or need help to finish school? If the answer to the above questions is yes, describe the level of functioning and any dysmorphic features. • Does anyone have a diagnosis of autism or autistic like features? • Are there any relatives with problems in thinking and judgment, mental illness, or severe depression? (If so, describe the relatives symptoms, age of onset, and any known medications.) • History of alcohol/substance abuse?

Adapted with permission from Bennett, R. L. (2010). *The practical guide to the genetic family history, 2nd ed.* Hoboken, New Jersey: John Wiley & Sons.

of the risk profile in adult members as well as the offspring of consanguineous marriages (Bennett, 2010; Read & Donnai, 2012). Education level and other sociodemographic characteristics may impact health literacy, often affecting the accuracy of the *family history*. Some conditions may be more known by certain family members, particularly those with the disease or disorder. For example, breast cancer is usually more accurately reported than uterine cancer in the *family history* report (Wilson *et al.*, 2009). Talking with multiple family members, with the client's permission, increases the accuracy of the *family history* information. In some cases, where accurate *family history* is important for genetic testing, confirmation of history using medical or surgical records may be warranted, or in some cases death certificates, when family members are deceased, may be required to validate a diagnosis.

Once the *personal history* is complete, information about family members is another crucial part of the history collection process. Family and medical history of blood relatives, both living and deceased, is part of the health and risk assessment and best depicted using a pedigree as discussed previously. The *pedigree*, unlike writ-ten information, provides a visual display of the health history of the *proband* or consultand as well as other family members and includes information from both the maternal and paternal lineage if known. It also provides a visualization of disease patterns that may exist among multiple members and generations. When using the *pedigree*, the *family history*, like that of the *personal history*, should include current age of all members, sex, medical history and age of onset, surgeries if applicable, and any significant data regarding behaviors and environmental exposures that impact the overall health status of the family (e.g., smoking and history of lung cancer). The *family history* should include members who have died and the age and cause of death (if known). Additional information regarding family members may warrant laboratory values, depending on the condition, and if applicable previous medical records, pathology reports, and genetic test results to confirm disease or existing health status. These data can aide in filling in the missing pieces of a *family history* or be used to verify diagnoses that are questionable or unclear; however, obtainment of this data may warrant informed consent to adhere to the guidelines of the

Health Insurance Portability and Accountability Act (HPAA) of 1996, and respect ethical, legal, and cultural considerations.

Family histories at times may be perplexing to the HCP and even among family members. For example, a specific syndrome may present with varied diseases among family members, and details of the disease presentation among family members may differ, or not be understood. For example, in a family with a Lynch syndrome (a hereditary colon cancer syndrome manifesting with colon and various other cancers), some of the individuals may present with colon cancer, whereas women within the same family may present initially with endometrial cancer. Family members, as well as some HCPs, may be unaware that these presentations are linked to the same inherited cancer syndrome. Thus, it is important for HCPs to understand genetics and genetic syndromes in order to educate families appropriately when diagnosed or suspected for a genetic syndrome. Chapter 15 provides more information about the presentation of cancer syndromes.

Common chronic diseases are influenced by complex gene-gene and gene-environment interactions. The presentation of heart disease and age of onset may differ among family members, making it important to collect information on three generations of relatives to obtain a full picture of the disease risk and occurrence within the individual and the family. Collecting the personal and *family history* information may require multiple visits and some detective work on the part of the HCP and the client. Most Americans know that *family history* is important to health, and a recent survey found that 96% of Americans believe that knowing their *family history* is important. However, despite this high percentage, the same survey found that only one-third of Americans have ever tried to gather and write down their family's health history (CDC, 2012). Patience and encouraging the individual to contact family members will assist the provider in obtaining the necessary information. The Surgeon General designated Thanksgiving as an opportunity for families to gather together and share their family health history. This information can help family members work with their providers to decide the appropriate tests and screenings to assist with identifying health risks. *My Family Health Portrait* is a tool developed by the Surgeon General

and can be found online (https://familyhistory.hhs.gov/fhh-web/home.action) to help families collect and organize the family health history (United States Department of Health and Human Services, 2013). *Family history* and appropriate care management, regardless of the setting, requires accurate documentation of medical information. Abnormal results of the family member should be reported; for example, the result of an abnormal electrocardiogram (ECG), laboratory value, or ancillary finding that documents the type of cardiac disorder should be noted on the pedigree for the affected family member.

2.3.4. Pedigree Construction

A basic pedigree usually includes a minimum of three generations. This includes the individual seeking consultation or care and his/her firstdegree relatives (i.e., parents, children, siblings), second degree relatives (i.e., half siblings, grandparents, aunts and uncles, grandchildren), and third degree relatives (i.e., cousins, great-grandparents, great-grandchildren). The three-generation pedigree provides a graphic picture of how family members are biologically related to each other, from one generation to the next. This depiction utilizes a variety of standardized figures that illustrates sex, family relationships, status (alive/deceased), and medical history displayed and described by Bennett, French, Resta, and Doyle (2008) in Table 2.2. Adding a legend to the pedigree as seen in Figure 2.2 that details a description of the disease abbreviations makes the pictorial representation easy to understand. Drawing pedigrees may become time consuming, particularly when there are large numbers of individuals within the family, and may be challenging to complete when there are complex familial, social, or medical issues occurring in the family (e.g., multiple marriages, divorces, large number of children, out of wedlock or with multiple paternities, *consanguinity*, gamete donor). Challenges in interpretation of the *family history* can also occur when there is uncertainty in the health history or the history of family members is unknown; there are adopted family members, and/or the family structure is limited by sex, particularly when assessing for gender related disorders (e.g., Duchenne Muscular Dystrophy, Fragile X syndrome).

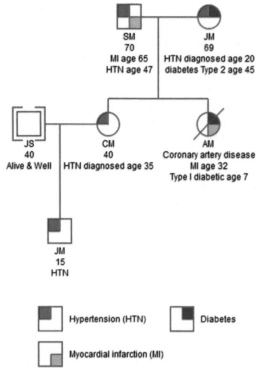

FIGURE 2.2. Three-generation pedigree in a family with many chronic disorders. Based on the information in this chapter, what are the missing elements of the pedigree? What are the red flags?

There are several standardized terms when conducting a pedigree that define the individual who is undergoing the *family history*. As stated previously, the *consultand* or *proband* are terms used to define the individual who is presenting for the appointment. More specifically, the *consultand* is the person with the appointment in the clinical setting; this person is seeking genomic health information but does not have a known diagnosis of the disorder for which he or she is seeking consultation. This person is identified on the pedigree with an arrow but is not identified in the pedigree legend with the medical disease/disorder. The *consultand* can be healthy or a person with medical conditions but not currently diagnosed with a condition warranting evaluation. In contrast, the *proband* is the affected individual that brings the family to medical attention (National Library of Medicine, 2014). Besides recording who is the *proband* or *consultand*, it is also helpful to record the person in the family who is the historian, for example, the parent of a minor or the guardian of a disabled person.

Standardized symbols should always be used when constructing a pedigree. The pedigree should clearly provide information on social and legal relationships (e.g., adoption, divorce), deaths, pregnancy, pregnancy termination, and use of assistive reproductive technologies if applicable (see Table 2.2). Each family member within the pedigree is recorded using the appropriate symbol noted as a square (male) or a circle (female) to depict sex and connect these gender-related symbols, using the appropriates line to each symbol to display the relationship between each member to that of the family. If a female is pregnant, a pregnancy is represented as a box or circle depicting sex of the fetus if known with a letter '*P*' inside. A diamond can also be used when sex of the pregnancy is unknown or noted by placing an n inside. The diamond symbol on the pedigree can also be used for a transgendered person or persons with congenital disorders of sexual development (e.g., chromosomal, gonadal, or anatomic). In chromosomal abnormalities the *karyotype* is placed below the diamond symbol, for example, 46XY. The various pedigree symbols related to pregnancy, spontaneous abortion, termination of pregnancy, and infertility are also depicted in Table 2.2.

A relationship in a pedigree is depicted by *a horizontal line* between two individuals. This relationship is used most often to denote marital status. A slash or break in that line indicates separation or divorce. A consanguineous couple should be connected by a double relationship line. The sibship line is depicted as a horizontal line that connects siblings, brothers and sisters. The difference between sibship and partner relationship lines is that each sibling has a vertical individual line attached to the horizontal line above the individual's symbol. Examples of family relationships within the *pedigree* and relationship lines are depicted in Figure 2.3.

Generations are displayed on the pedigree vertically. The line of descent is a vertical bridge connecting the horizontal sibship line to the horizontal relationship line (Brock, Allen, Kieser, & Langlois, 2010). A minimum of three generations for both the maternal and paternal lineage should be drawn to provide a thorough *pedigree* that can be useful in identifying patterns of Mendelian disorders or familial related disorders associated with chronic diseases indicating genetic and environmental factors. It also may be important to record the 'spouse' of a family member who is not a part of the kinship in the *family history*, because this information may be pertinent when attempting to establish a medical history of their offspring. This is particularly important when a *family history* of a medical condition is identified based upon a single gene disorder to aid in determining the family lineage of inheritance. When drawing the *pedigree* (or using computer programs), each generation should be on the same horizontal plane. For example, an individual's siblings and cousins should be on the same horizontal axis. For clarity, each generation can also be defined by designating it with a Roman numeral (Table 2.2) that is often placed on the left of the pedigree; however, the number of generations can be displayed without the Roman numerals if the pedigree is clearly constructed us-

ing appropriate symbols and placement of family members with proper relationships and a clear arrow noting the *consultand* or *proband*. First names or initials, without last names, are generally recorded by the symbol for each individual to meet privacy standards. It is important to note adoption as someone who is *adopted in* (a couple adopts a non-biological relative) from someone who is *adopted out* (a biological relative who is put up for adoption by a couple). If the person is adopted by an individual or a couple, a straight line is used to indicate a non-biological relationship, as noted in Table 2.2. It is not uncommon for family member to adopt a relative; for example, if a sibling adopts his or her niece or nephew, a dotted line extends from the parents to the biological relative adopting the individual to show the relationship within the family.

Documenting who is affected and who is un-

First degree Relatives   **Second degree Relatives**

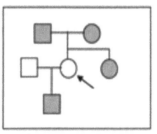

Parents
Full Siblings
Children

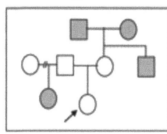

Grandparents
Half Siblings
Aunt/Uncle

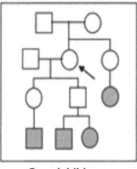

Grandchildren
Niece/nephew

Third degree Relatives

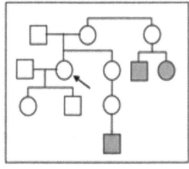

First cousins
Great niece/nephew

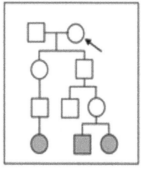

Great grandchildren

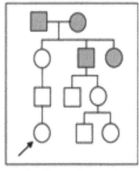

Great grandparents
Great aunt/uncle

FIGURE 2.3. Relationship lines used in constructing a three-generation-pedigree. Copyright reprinted with permission from the Journal of Obstetrics and Gynaecology Canada, copyright center (Brock, Allen, Kieser, & Langlois, 2010).

affected with a disorder is a crucial for risk assessment and interpretation of the pedigree. Pedigree symbols should be shaded only for affected individuals. Different shading can be used to identify separate diseases on the pedigree. For example, when documenting a *family history* of heart disease, shading in the various quadrants of each square (male) and each circle (female) demonstrated in Figure 2.2 is a way to symbolize different presentations of heart disease within the family. An optional way to provide clarity of individuals and family members who are disease free is to document A&W (alive and well) under each healthy individual on the pedigree. Pertinent information about unaffected members of the family may be important when interpreting the *family history*. For example, individuals who are *carriers* of a single gene disorder but will not manifest the disease, as is the case for many recessive disorders, should be depicted on the pedigree with a symbol indicating carrier status despite the individual currently being A&W. *Family history* information is important when assessing the spouse's or partner's status to determine potential genetic risk to an off-spring. These data can also provide information that may be shared by the *proband* or consultant to other family members (e.g., siblings) who may be unaffected with the disease but who also may be *carriers*; knowledge of this status can be useful regarding testing and reproductive decisions prior to conception.

Pedigrees should include ancestry of origin for both lineages, as well as information on pertinent medical and surgical conditions. Many genetic disorders, due to single gene mutations, are found to occur at higher rates among certain racial/ethnic groups, and the sensitivity of genetic tests depends on the correct ethnic information (Feuchtbaum, Carter, Doway, Currier, & Lowry, 2012; Maradiegue & Edwards, 2006). For example, sickle cell anemia is more common in people of African, African American, or Mediterranean heritage, and TaySachs disease is more likely to occur among people of Ashkenazi (eastern and central European) Jewish or French Canadian ancestry (Maradiegue & Edwards, 2006). Understanding the role of ethnicity or ancestry-of-origins in disease occurrence within certain populations is important, but does not completely eliminate the disease risk in other ethnicities. For

instance, *HFE*-hemochromatosis, an inherited disorder that can result in iron storage disease, is more common in white populations of northern European ancestry and is highest in those of Irish *ancestry of origin*. Although *HFE*-hemochromatosis is exceedingly rare in some races, such as Asians, Hispanics, African Americans, and Pacific Islanders, it has been found to occur in individuals with these ancestry-of-origins (Adams *et al.*, 2005; Crownover & Covey, 2013; Emanuele, Tuason, & Edwards, 2014).

There may be 'uncertainty' when medical information is reported on an individual by family members. Maintaining HIPAA privacy regulations, this can be addressed by confirming the family member's medical history through death certificates, pathology reports, test results, or medical records. When critical information is required and the history is unknown, it is best to document this in the pedigree by denoting 'history unknown' or using a question mark above the pedigree with a comment reflecting the uncertainty. Sometimes little information is known about the *family history*. Placing a question mark above the pedigree symbol shows that someone inquired about the person's medical history and the information is unknown (Bennett, 2010).

The pedigree provides essential information while displaying this information in a visual format that can aid in assessing for patterns, traits, and relationships and diseases that may be associated with *Mendelian inheritance*, as well as chronic conditions that are familial, or 'exist in multiple' members or generations. As previously discussed, using standardized pedigree nomenclature with documentation of a minimum of three generations is essential for accurate pedigree interpretation. Some additional general guidelines when drawing a pedigree to provide clarity and standardization for interpretation include the following:

- Depicting male partners to the left of female partners
- Siblings drawn from oldest to youngest with the oldest listed on the left and the youngest on the right (see Figure 2.4, for example)
- Distinct and clear measures used to identify multiple disorders or diseases, (i.e., quadrants or different shading [solid, cross-hatching] to indicate each disease) (Figures 2.2, 2.4 and 2.5)

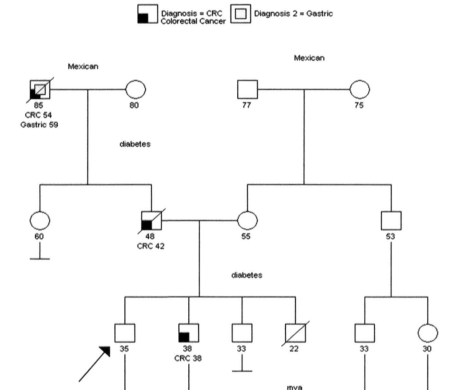

FIGURE 2.4. Four-generation pedigree with of a 35-year-old consultand with a family history of colorectal and gastric cancers.

- Record pertinent information on unaffected and affected relatives.

Information that must be included in a pedigree:

- Date of the pedigree when first initiated
- Limitation of identifying information as much as possible to be compliant with HIPAA guidelines
- First name or initials of relatives (i.e., use first names only or initials of relatives)
- Affected status (i.e., who in the family has disease) for each individual in the family
- Age of all family members, or age at death (do not submit a full birth date at this time to be compliant with HIPAA guidelines)
- Status of members (i.e., living or deceased and age at death and cause of death, if known, should be indicated below the symbol)
- Brief description of a family member with a

disorder or behavior (e.g., smoker) that is important but not displayed on the legend (key)
- Legend (key) for relevant disorders, shading symbols for diseases
- Adoption status
- *Consanguinity* (i.e., parents are related)
- Ancestry-of-origin/ethnicity of each side of the paternal lineages if known (e.g., French, African-American)
- Genetic test results if conducted, include findings if known. An example of genetic test results included in a pedigree can be found in Figure 2.5.

This information for pedigree construction can be done by hand or by computerized programs especially adapted to construct a standardized pedigree. There are several commercial products available for constructing a pedigree. In addition, some facilities have implemented the pedigree as part of the health records. Regardless of how the pedigree is constructed, the importance of using standardized symbols and recording pertinent data are essential for accurate *family history* and *risk assessment*.

Because of the importance of complete and accurate pedigree information, we have provided a pedigree for analysis in this chapter (Figure 2.2) with some questions to prompt discussion about the elements that should be included as part of the history. Given the information learned thus far in this chapter, what additional information might be needed given the *family history* displayed in Figure 2.2?

To further illustrate the importance of the personal and *family history* and use of the pedigree, risk assessment was conducted on a white female of Northern European ancestry presenting in a primary care clinic with overwhelming fatigue and joint disorder. After a thorough assessment by the APRN, using a *RAPID* approach to guide the risk assessment process, she was found to have *HFE*-associated hereditary hemochromatosis via genetic testing. The five-generation pedigree of this individual (Figure 2.5) provides detailed *family history* data to aid in the assessment process. Specifically noted are detailed information on *ancestry of origin*, symptoms consistent with hemochromatosis, and the skip in generations of diagnosed disease characteristic of the *horizontal transmission* pattern associated with *autosomal recessive* disorders due to carrier status required for both parents for transmission of disease occurrence to the offspring. Knowledge of the disorder, while essential in diagnosis, was greatly enhanced by an in-depth personal and *family history*, including the use of a five-generation pedigree and identification of 'red flags' based upon symptoms stated by the family (e.g., fatigue, muscle discomfort). The collection of data from the personal and *family history*, and laboratory and genetic tests, enabled the APRN to identify the red flags associated with disorder and determine qualitatively the *probability* that the individual was suspect for iron overload due to the singlegene disorder of *HFE*-hemochromatosis. The findings were communicated to the individual, resulting in referral to a genetic counselor for further counseling, and to the appropriate HCP provider for risk and disease management. Other aspects of the RAPID approach, specifically identification of red flags, *probabil-*

ity, *risk communication*, and *risk management*, are described later in this chapter.

The *family history*, including the use of a *pedigree*, is a continuous process. Once the *pedigree* has been initiated, the personal and *family history* should be revisited and updated routinely at each visit with the HCP. Merely asking the individual, *"Has the family history changed since last visit?"* (e.g., new illnesses, surgeries, births, deaths) provides the process for updating the *pedigree* when applicable. Any updates in the *family history* should include the date of modification or change in the history.

In summary, the *family history* provides essential information that may be useful in assessing risk for disease as well as disease diagnosis, and provides important insights into the individuals' health and predisposition to disease. This information is integral to providing health promotion, disease prevention, and treatment. Failure to collect complete *family history* information from an individual may compromise the HCP's ability to appropriately conduct an adequate disease *risk assessment*, recognize patterns of disease inheritance or chronic disorders that manifest in the family, and properly diagnose and manage the disorder Most importantly, failure to obtain an appropriate and accurate *risk assessment* may result in delayed preventive or enhanced surveillance that may result in adverse outcomes, including morbidity and mortality. Despite these benefits, genetics alone is not singularly responsible for disease risk. Environmental and behavioral factors also play a major role in the development of many chronic diseases and are part of the genomic assessment process.

2.3.5. Multifactorial Assessment: Environmental/Behavioral

Assessments of environmental and behavioral factors as part of the personal medical history are integral to the individual's overall risk for disease. Growing up in the same household often exposes individuals to the same environmental risk factors, for example, secondhand smoke and pesticides. Environment and behavior play a significant role in the cancer *family history*. For example, a 70-year old individual with a 50-pack-a-year smoking history who develops lung cancer is not surprising, but lung cancer in a 30-year-old

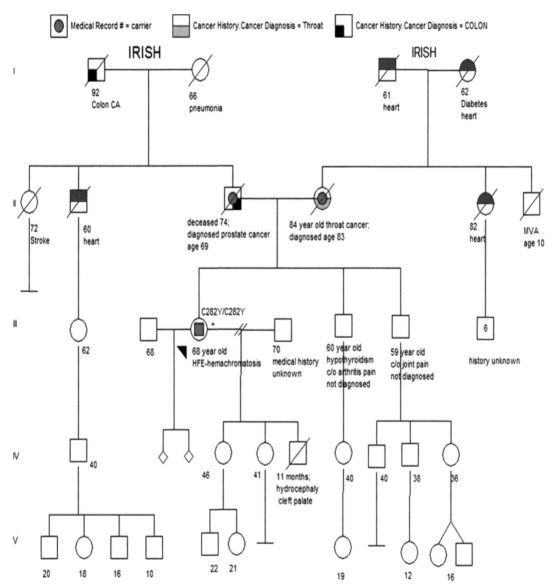

FIGURE 2.5. Five-generation pedigree of a history of 68-year-old female (proband) with HFE-hemochromatosis indicating an autosomal recessive pattern of inheritance.

nonsmoker is noteworthy and may be due to an inherited disorder or syndrome (Bennett, 2010). Occupational environment is another element that should be considered when conducting the history, particularly in the cancer and reproductive *family history*. Examples of substances that are known carcinogens and teratogens include asbestos, benzene, pesticides, and radon. A complete list of carcinogens can be located on the National Institute for Occupational Safety and Health web site: http://www.cdc.gov/niosh/topics/cancer/npotocca.html

Health behaviors including alcohol use, exercise, methods of coping with stress, exposure to sexually transmitted disease, and the use of herbal and dietary supplements can significantly impact health and should be a part of *risk assessment* and the health history. During pregnancy, it is important to explore the mother's occupation; prescription drug, alcohol, and street drug use; and exposure to infectious agents, in order to assess any threats to healthy fetal development. Assessment of risky sexual behaviors identifies individuals predisposed to sexually transmitted, chronic diseases (e.g., hepatitis B and HIV) and viral and bacterial infections that lead to the development of certain cancers. Human papilloma virus, for example, increases the likelihood of cervical, anal, and head and neck carcinomas. Hepatitis B and C infections are implicated in liver carcinoma. HIV infection increases the risk of Kaposi sarcoma and Non-Hodgkin lymphoma. Assessment of the individual's racial/ethnic background also helps identify exposures to certain infectious agents. Persons from Japan are at particularly high risk for *Helicobacter pylori* (*H. pylori*), which increases the risk for stomach carcinoma (Bennett, 2010; Shiota, Murakawi Suzuki, Fuijioka & Yamaoka, 2013). Although the rates of *H. Pylori* in Japan are gradually decreasing, having this information in the *family history* can allow for early identification and treatment that can eradicate *H. pylori* and significantly decrease cancer risk (Shiota *et al.*, 2013).

2.3.6. Physical Examination

The physical examination conducted as part of the genomic assessment provides an objective approach for healthcare providers, including APRNs, regarding clinical decision making, diagnosis, prognosis, counseling, and management of patient care (American Board of Medical Genetics [ABMG], 2014; Falk & Robin, 2004). Personal and *family history*, including *pedigree* analysis and interpretation, all serve to guide healthcare providers towards a targeted physical examination based upon recognition of patterns of inheritance, familial clustering of disease, symptomatology, clinical presentation, and/or analysis of laboratory and other diagnostic studies. Information from prenatal and birth histories, and behavioral and environment assessments are also frequently used to determine the direction of the physical evaluation, because congenital anomalies are often part of a genetic/genomic work-up. The primary objective of the physical examination within the context of genomics is to incorporate the health and risk histories with physical assessment findings, and applicable diagnostic studies, for early recognition of genomic disorders so that personalized/precision management of care can be implemented, including diagnosis, prognosis, and therapeutic management for individuals across the life span.

The genomic physical assessment requires basic physical examination skills, as well as knowledge of genetics/genomics and an understanding of clinical features found in inherited conditions. In addition, skilled assessment techniques in *dysmorphology* assessment, defined as the *study of atypical anatomical development resulting in abnormal physical feature* (Aase, 1990; ABMG, 2014) may also be warranted based upon history and clinical presentation. *Dysmorphologic* evaluation assesses unusual physical or behavioral characteristics that often occur during embryologic or fetal development (Falk & Robin, 2004; Solomon & Muenke, 2012). In this type of assessment, general physical examination techniques are used in conjunction with detailed observation of physical features, including analysis of body stature and structure; precise measurement of specific body structures entailing form, size, proportion, positioning, spacing, and symmetry, analysis of growth parameters; Tanner stage; and patterns of anomalies if present (Falk & Robin, 2004; Nussey & Whitehead, 2001; Solomon & Muenke, 2012). Structural defects assessed during the *dysmorphology* evaluation are considered to be either *major anomalies* (resulting in severe medical or cosmetic alterations, such as congenital heart defects or cleft lip or palate, and often requiring medical or surgical intervention) or *minor anomalies* (defects with medically little difference from normal development, requiring no surgical or medical interventions, and posing no added health risks) (Falk & Robin, 2004; Solomon & Muenke, 2012). Chapter 8 provides further detailed information regarding the topic of *dysmorphology* and the pediatric physical assessment.

If anomalies are present during the physical examination, careful documentation and recording of the number and pattern of defects are warranted, because these signs may be indicative of a multiple defect syndrome associated with a myriad of disorders, including genomic or gene/environmental conditions, chromosomal abnormalities, and behavioral, environmental, infectious, or chemical/drug responses (Falk & Robin, 2004; Solomon & Muenke, 2012). Specifically, multiple anomalies often represent *syndromes*, defined as the collection of anomalies occurring in a consistent pattern representing common pathogenic genetic etiology (Falk & Robin,

2004; Solomon & Muenke, 2012). Thus, it is important in the genetic assessment of patients with multiple anomalies to obtain a careful, detailed obstetrical history and prenatal and fetal evaluation of growth, environmental and chemical exposures, multiple births, and other relevant prenatal outcomes that could impact fetal growth and development (Stillerman, Mattison, Giudice, & Woodruff, 2008). Further, analysis of postnatal data for growth and development should also be a part of the genomic assessment for patients with congenital anomalies (Stillerman *et al.*, 2008).

Evaluation for *intellectual disability* (ID) based upon the personal, family, and risk assessment histories of the patient, as well as the clinical presentation, should also be assessed and documented when applicable as part of the *dysmorphology* examination. Intellectual disability is used for a wide range of symptoms, including severe deficits or limitations in developmental skills for the following functional domains: cognitive, language, motor, auditory, language, psychosocial, moral judgment, and activities of daily living (Moeschler, 2008; Flore & Milunsky, 2012). This form of disability is associated with a wide range of maladaptive behaviors, limited functioning, and poor academic performance occurring prior to age 18 (Moeschler, 2008; Flore & Milunsky, 2012). Clients presenting with a learning disability, delayed development, or significant behavioral problems often have an underlying genetic disorder or syndrome attributed to single gene alterations, chromosomal defects, or genetic and environmental factors (Nussbaum *et al.*, 2015). Using the personal, family, and risk assessment histories and physical examination findings, the genomic assessment may warrant evaluation of the mental status and psychosocial skills. Fetal alcohol syndrome (FAS), for example, a disorder associated with prenatal alcohol exposure, is a complex genetic-environmental disorder presenting with *dysmorphologic* features, including distinct craniofacial alterations, microcephaly, and growth deficiencies on weight and height, as well as behavioral, emotional, and mental health problems (Mattson, Crocker, & Nguyen, 2011; Pei, Denys, Hughes, & Rasmussen, 2011). Individuals who are suspect for FAS warrant a targeted genomic assessment, including a detailed prenatal, personal, and familial history; *dysmorphologic* and physical examina-

tion; and mental and behavioral health evaluation with intellectual disability evaluation. In another example, an adult female presenting with breast cancer due to a genetic mutation in the phosphatase and tensin homolog (*PTEN*) gene may present with *dysmorphology* as denoted by macrocephaly, increased head circumference ($\geq$ 97th percentile), and other clinical features (Shiovitz *et al.*, 2010). These findings may represent clues of the syndrome, warranting the need for evaluation of the *family history* and possibly genetic testing facilitating diagnosis so that enhanced surveillance, chemoprevention, and/or risk-reduction strategies can be implemented to improve outcomes for the individual and affected family members.

Because of the myriad of genomic disorders and heterogeneity of outcomes that may be present in children or adults, the genomic physical examination should be focused on the diagnosis of the genomic disorder with a personalized examination based upon the patient's age, personal and *family history*, presenting physical features, and mental and risk assessment status . The genomic examination may require interprofessional collaborative teams (e.g., geneticist, genetic counselor, physician, and physician specialist) and a systematic approach due to the complexity of many diseases/syndromes, pitfalls in the history (e.g., adoption), knowledge and skills of the healthcare provider, lack of diagnostics to confirm the disorder and the ambiguous presentation of clinical symptoms. Because the physical examination findings are often targeted based upon the underlying genomic condition, a more detailed discussion of the physical examination is presented throughout this book pertinent to the genomic condition presented in subsequent chapters.

2.4. RAP*I*D RISK ASSESSMENT APPROACH—IDENTIFICATION OF RED FLAGS

Personal and *family history*, once obtained, are used to determine if there are *red flags* suggestive of increased risk for disease occurrence or risk for an inherited disorder/syndrome. Red flags found in the early assessment process encompass health occurrences outside of the norm. For example, a disease that presents at an earlier age than is normally seen in the general population (e.g., heart disease in the 30s) may be suggestive of a single gene disorder. Table 2.4 provides examples of red flags that may be suspect for genomic disorders.

The *pedigree* of family members, including the *consultant* or the *proband*, is analyzed and interpreted to assess for red flags that warrant increased risk for disease. Red flags, while not totally sensitive or specific for an individual's risk of disease occurrence, can suggest that further evaluation, testing, follow-up, or genetic counseling/testing may be indicated for identification of hereditary, multifactorial, complex, or chronic diseases and the implementation of appropriate care management.

2.4.1. Interpreting the Pedigree

Considering all of the information (e.g., environment, ethnic background, and medical history) is the basis for constructing a detailed *pedigree*. Once the information is collected and the *pedigree* drawn, the information must be interpreted. Interpretation is the beginning of assessing disease risk, as well as aiding in the diagnosis and management of care. Interpretation of the *pedigree* provides a means of personalized care and can be the basis for determination of inherited single gene disorders, as well as for the risk for chronic disorders manifesting themselves in the family (*familial disorders*). Individuals with a *family history* of many disorders

TABLE 2.4. Red Flags in the Family History.

Red Flag	Description with Example
Early Age of Onset	Common disorder with earlier age of onset than expected: • Heart disease at age 32 • Breast cancer at age 28
Gender	Disease in the less-often-affected sex: • Breast cancer in a male • Stuttering in a female
Multiple Family Members	Disease in more than one close relative: • Parent • Sibling
Combination of Diseases	Multiple affected family members with same or related conditions: • Breast and ovarian cancer • Diabetes and heart disease
Reproductive	• 3 or more pregnancy losses • Babies who died • Severe pregnancy complications • Infertility
Disease in the Absence of Known Risk Factors	Genetic predisposition leading to disease occurrence in the absence of environmental factors: • Hyperlipidemia with an ideal diet and exercise routine
Abnormalities in Growth	Within an individual: • Dysmorphic features especially with a learning disorder • Learning disabilities or behavioral problems • Congenital/juvenile deafness, blindness or cataracts
One or More Major Malformations	• Heart defects • Underdeveloped or absent organs • Cleft lip and/or palate
Ethnic Predisposition	Some genetic disorders are more common in certain ethnic groups: • Hereditary breast and ovarian cancer syndrome in Ashkenazi Jews • Sickle cell disease in African Americans

Nussbaum, R.L., McInnes, R. R., & Willard, H.F. (2015). Patterns of single-gene inheritance, Chapter 7. *Genetics in Medicine*. Philadelphia, PA: Saunders Elsevier.

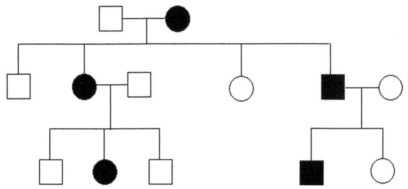

FIGURE 2.6. Three-generation-pedigree demonstrating autosomal dominant disorder. The blackened circles and squares represent affected individuals.

are at increased risk for developing a condition because of genetic, behavioral, and environmental factors. For example, African Americans are 40% more likely to have high blood pressure and 30% more likely to die from heart disease compared with Caucasian Americans (CDC, 2012). A strong *family history* of parents and siblings who developed heart disease or a stroke before they were age 55 years in male relatives or before age 65 years in female relatives increases an individual's personal risk for heart disease (CDC, 2012).

Completed *pedigrees* should be carefully reviewed and assessed for patterns and traits that may indicate Mendelian disorders that may be *autosomal dominant* (AD) or *autosomal recessive* (AR) or *X-linked* diseases, as well as scrutinized for familial risk due to genetic and environmental factors. For example, disorders with a *vertical transmission* appearing to occur in every generation as seen in Figure 2.6 might be indicative of an AD inheritance pattern like that of an inherited colon cancer syndrome (Lynch) noted in the ped-

igree depicted in Figure 2.4, whereas disorders that appear to skip generations might indicate AR disorders like that of *HFE*-hemochromatosis illustrated in the pedigree in Figure 2.5. AR disorders may be challenging to interpret because the disease/disorder will generally not manifest itself in every generation (Figure 2.7). AR traits require a gene copy of the mutation from each parent, both *carriers* of the gene, but neither of whom manifests symptoms of the disorder. The pedigree will often show unaffected parents, with an affected offspring and the disorder may not be seen for multiple generations unless other *carriers* in the family have children with a known mutation carrier. AR disorders occur equally in both sexes, as noted in Figure 2.7. Further, an analysis of the pedigree indicating disorders found only in males may be suggestive of *X-linked* trait disorders such as that of Fragile X. *X-linked* disorders predominantly affect males, with transmission coming from mothers who are usually *carriers* of the condition as noted in Figure 2.8. All females

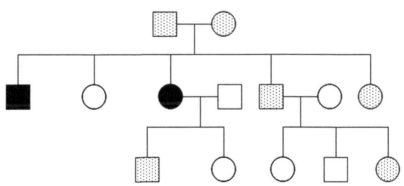

FIGURE 2.7. Three-generation pedigree demonstrating autosomal recessive disorder. The dotted circles and squares represent carrier status, and the blackened circles and squares represent affected individuals.

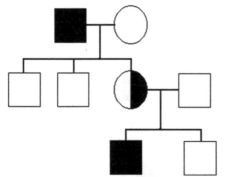

FIGURE 2.8. Three-generation pedigree demonstrating X-linked disorder. The dotted blackened circles and squares represent carriers. The completely blackened square represent affected individual.

of affected males will be *carriers* of the mutation. In general, men are affected and women are *carriers*, because men are likely to express the mutation since they have only one X chromosome, whereas women are protected by having two X chromosomes. A review of the sections on *Mendelian inheritance* in Chapter 1 is recommended for a further explanation of AD, AR, and *X-linked* traits.

AD disorders/syndromes require a gene copy of the mutation from only one parent and occurs equally in both sexes. Because AD disorders/syndromes require only one copy of the gene for transmission to the progeny, the disorder/syndrome tends to present on the *pedigree* in a "vertical" manner observed in every generation. However, this *vertical transmission* may not always be present due to complexities or challenges in the *family history*. Factors affecting the presentation of AD disorders include *penetrance* and *expressivity*, inaccurate or unknown *family history*, adoption, early age of onset of death of family members who may not live long enough to manifest the disorder, or limited family structure (e.g., paternal transmission with limited number of females with gender-related disorders such as hereditary breast and ovarian cancer syndrome). It is worth noting that the current parameters used to assign risk in single gene disorders are evolving because of genomic technologies and sophisticated bioinformatics filtering processes. Evaluations of clients will require the use of classic molecular biological principles, as well as an understanding of genomic technology, to interpret gene variants (Hooker *et al.*, 2014). The

sophisticated sequencing techniques described in Chapter 17 are already being used in clinical practice to identify unknown phenotypes and are being studied as a screening tool to identify disease predisposition (Facio, Lee, & O'Daniel, 2014).

2.5. PEDIGREE CHALLENGES— CONFOUNDING FACTORS IN INHERITANCE PATTERNS

The first and most important fact to remember is that incomplete or inaccurate *family history* information from a patient may compromise the ability to recognize patterns of disease within individuals and families (Bennett, 2010). Information about unaffected relatives is just as important as information in affected individuals to establish patterns of inheritance. Several factors may make the *family history* difficult to interpret, including *variable expressivity*, reduced *penetrance, anticipation*, and *de novo mutations*. Family members with mild disease may be missed as being an affected individual because of *variable expressivity*. *Variable expressivity* refers to the range of signs and symptoms that can occur in different people with the same genomic condition. *Variable expressivity* is likely due to a combination of genetic, environmental, and lifestyle factors (Nussbaum *et al.*, 2015). If a genetic condition has highly variable signs and symptoms, it may be challenging to diagnose. One example of a genetic disorder that may manifest itself with *variable expressivity* is neurofibromatosis type 1 (*NF1*). In this disorder, family members and individuals who carry the same mutated gene can exhibit a wide range of symptoms and clinical features. Some individuals may have café-au-lait spots, whereas others may have optic nerve gliomas, spinal cord tumors, scoliosis, vascular lesions, and long-bone abnormalities (Sabbagh *et al.*, 2009).

Another confounding factor in determining disease patterns within the *family history* is reduced *penetrance*. *Penetrance* refers to the proportion of people with a particular genetic mutation who exhibit signs and symptoms of a genetic disorder. People with the mutation who do not develop features of the disorder are said to have reduced or incomplete *penetrance* (Nussbaum *et al.*, 2015). More specifically, when the frequency of *expression* of the disorder is less than 100%, it is considered a gene with reduced *penetrance* (Nussbaum, *et al.*, 2015). Reduced *penetrance* often occurs with hereditary cancer syndromes. For instance, individuals predisposed to hereditary breast and ovarian cancer due to mutations in the *BRCA1* gene or *BRCA2* gene have a higher lifetime risk of developing breast and ovarian cancer than the general population. As an example, women who are *carriers* of the *BRCA1* gene mutation have up to an 80% lifetime risk of developing breast cancer and approximately a 50% lifetime ovarian cancer risk. Although individuals carrying this *BRCA* mutation have a significantly higher lifetime risk for breast and ovarian cancer than the general population, it is still not 100% because of decreased *penetrance* (Evans *et al.*, 2008). Reduced or incomplete *penetrance* is believed to result from a combination of genetic, environmental, and lifestyle factors, making it challenging to interpret a patient's family medical history and predict the risk of passing a genetic condition to future generations. More specific information on the genomics of cancer is provided in Chapter 15.

The next factor to consider within a *family history* of known genetic disorders is *anticipation*. *Anticipation* is the tendency in certain genetic disorders for individuals in successive generations to present at an earlier age and/or with more severe manifestations. This is often observed in disorders resulting from the expression of a trinucleotide repeat gene mutation that tends to increase in size and have a more significant effect when passed from one generation to the next. This is commonly seen in disorders with neurologic symptoms. For example, Huntington's disease, a single gene AD brain condition, results in progressive failure in cognitive function, chorea or uncontrolled movements, and emotional problems, with an average age of disease onset between 35 and 45 years. However, subsequent generations may reveal family members with the disorder at even earlier ages (e. g., before the age of 20) because of *anticipation* (Nussbaum *et al.*, 2015).

Many cases of severe genetic disease are the result of a new mutation referred to as *de novo mutation*. *De novo mutations* are due to an alteration in a gene that is present for the first time in one family member, as a result of a mutation in a germ cell (egg or sperm) of one of the parents or in the fertilized egg (Nussbaum *et al.*, 2015;

Veltman & Brunner, 2012). *De novo mutations* occur without warning in a family with no previous history of the disease. Thus, the condition may not appear at all in the *family history*, with the exception of the one individual diagnosed with the *de novo* or new mutation. There is some evidence that the father's age may play a role in *de novo mutations* (Kong *et al.*, 2012). Examples of conditions that may manifest as *de novo* include achondroplasia, a form of short-limbed dwarfism; Von Hippel-Lindau syndrome, which causes tumor formation and is associated with pheochromocytomas; and Kallmann's syndrome, which is characterized by absent puberty and an impaired sense of smell (Nussbaum *et al.*, 2015; Veltman & Brunner, 2012). Once all of the information is gathered, the physical examination can provide additional clues.

Pedigree information is then incorporated into both the medical and physical assessment data, in order to further analyze contributions to disease and health risks in the evaluation of common acute and chronic diseases, as well as indicators of disease susceptibility or any genomic condition. The medical history may identify potential *red flags*, such as extreme or unusual laboratory (e.g., iron overload) values or unusual disease presentation (e.g., emphysema in a non-smoker). The physical exam coupled with all of the previous information lends further support to the potential for genetic disorders (e.g., enlarged liver in a patient with hemochromatosis). Suspicious findings will warrant further evaluation and testing to rule out genetic risks (e.g., single gene disorders), including surveillance, genetic testing, and treatment and management of potential or current disease entities. Thus, the personal and *family history* serves as a means of identifying current health issues, as well as potential "risk" for disease, in order that health promotion and disease prevention measures can be implemented to improve health outcomes. Consideration of all of these elements is part of the risk assessment process, so that personalized plans for health care can be developed.

2.6. RAPID 2.3: STEP 3— DETERMINATION OF RISK PROBABILITY

Establishing a *probability* estimate for disease

occurrence is an important part of *risk assessment* and is integral in stratifying individuals regarding appropriate screening, testing, and treatment options based upon one's level of disease risk (i.e., low, average, high). The *personal history*, *family history*, and additional data are analyzed for genomic and environmental influence, and additional tools such as *probability* models may be used to facilitate decision-making toward diagnosis and, if applicable, genetic testing, as well as preventive measures such as enhanced screening and chemoprevention if available.

Effective *risk assessment* incorporates data collection to identify *elements of uncertainty* followed by the determination of how likely the uncertainty is to occur, or the risk *probability*. Risk *probability* is an important part of *risk assessment*, resulting in the patient's determination of risk based upon a criterion or standard, in many cases a comparison of the patient's risk to that of a population risk estimate. Empiric risk models and prediction tables are available for a wide range of diseases and many of them can be useful in predicting outcomes, including the *probability* of disease occurrence, prognostic information, and responses to medications, particularly adjuvant therapy used in oncology (Isariyawongse & Kattan, 2012). For example, there are several evidence based cardiovascular clinical risk prediction models, including the Framingham model, adult treatment panel III model (ATP III), and systematic coronary risk evaluation model (SCORE), enabling healthcare providers to obtain empiric risk estimates for cardiovascular disease, including patients with other chronic diseases such as diabetes (Mathney *et al.,* 2011).

The Gail Model, another empiric risk assessment tool designed for women ages 35 years and older meeting specific criteria, can be used by HCPs to estimate the quantitative *probability* for a woman's risk of developing breast cancer (National Cancer Institute, [NCI] 2011). The Gail Model assesses several risk elements: age, *family history* (first-degree relative with breast cancer), *personal history* (history of ductal hyperplasia), ethnicity, and surgical history (breast biopsy) to estimate a woman's 5-year and lifetime (to age 90 years) risks of developing invasive breast cancer (NCI, 2011). Another breast cancer prediction tool, the Tyrer-Cuzick model, incorporates familial and personal risk factors to establish a personalized breast cancer risk estimate for women. The model takes into account the *family history* and personal factors, including medical and reproductive history in the *probability* risk estimate (Tyrer, Duffy, & Cuzick, 2004). Assessment of *probability*, integral to risk assessment, provides another means of providing personalized healthcare. Although the focus here is on *risk assessment* as it relates to genomic diseases, including *common complex disorders*, the use of *risk assessment* models and *probability* estimates have also been conducted to assess risk for falls (Harrington *et al.,* 2011; McWilliams, 2011), pressure ulcers (Braden & Maklebust, 2005), and other medical issues and disorders in a variety of settings, including home health, inpatient and outpatient settings, and community health. Further information regarding detailed *risk assessment* tools for specific disorders is presented throughout this book, including the appropriate measures for data collection, risk identification, and risk *probability* assessment using the RAPID approach.

2.6.1. Pitfalls of Risk Probability

Although risk *probability* enables HCPs to communicate the likelihood or odds of developing disease, it is not 100% sensitive or specific. Further, empiric risk estimate tools that provide 'quantifiable' risk *probability* scores and are evidence based, validated, and population tested (e.g., Gail for breast cancer risk and Framingham for cardiovascular disease risk) are available for some, but not all, diseases/disorders. Although disease *probability* is obtained from an accurate and comprehensive personal and *family history*, interpretation of data can be limited by family structure, lack of information, variability of genetic expression, death due to nonmedical reasons and limited disease *penetrance*, risk reduction surgeries, de novo genetic conditions, and faulty/inaccurate patient information resulting in the potential to underestimate or overestimate risk (Weitzel *et al.,* 2011).

Assessment of genomic risk and therapeutic management will be further enhanced not only for risk assessment via the personal and *family history*, but also by newer and validated risk assessment models and advanced technologies, including molecular analysis and genomic markers

(Diamandis, White & Yousef, 2010). Thus, HCPs must have the knowledge, skills, and self-efficacy to effectively utilize risk assessment in practice and provide appropriate management of care based upon their patient's personalized risks.

Risk assessment requires that HCPs are knowledgeable about genomics and behavioral and environmental factors that impact individual and familial health risks. This includes incorporating an accurate and thorough personal and *family history*, including utilization of a minimum of a three-generation *pedigree*, *pedigree* interpretation, identification of risk elements, and determination of risk *probability*. The RAPID tool provides a structural approach towards data collection, recognition of risk, and risk *probability* so that individuals susceptible to genetic or complex diseases can be managed appropriately with enhanced surveillance, chemoprophylatic agents, or risk reduction surgical measures, if applicable.

Unusual disease presentations, multiple diseases within an individual, unusual pathology, or surprising laboratory values are *red flags*, suggesting a need for client referral for further evaluation. Table 2.4 provides a list of *red flags* that require further evaluation and collaboration with a genetic counselor or geneticist. It is important to recognize that a family member may have information he or she is reluctant to share, requiring patience and understanding on the part of the provider. A genetic counselor, geneticist, or APRN in genetics can aid in the *family history* and risk assessment process. Specific information regarding location of genetic counselors by geographic area or disorder can be found by going to the National Society of Genetic Counselors web site *www.nsgc.org*

2.7. RAPID 2.4: STEP 4—RISK ASSESSMENT—REVIEW DATA AND COMMUNICATE RISK TO CLIENT/FAMILY

Individuals and families require attention to their health needs, and the same care plan will not be appropriate for everyone. A recent report on chronic disease released by the Institute of Medicine recommends disease evaluation is based on a personalized plan of care (Harris & Wallace, 2012). The *family history* provides a basic and fundamental tool in the communication of risks to patients and families. These data collected from the *family history* allow for individualizing and selecting management of care strategies to reduce the risk of disease occurrence or recurrence and to promote overall health and quality of life. Utilizing the *family history* is a cost-effective tool that enables HCPs to establish rapport, communicate and educate patients, and evaluate understanding of disease risk (Bennett, 2010). Further, because the *family history* identifies at-risk family members, it aids in identifying the need for medical screening in healthy individuals, promoting health and preventing disease (Bennett, 2010). An accurate *family history* enables HCPs to relay correct information to patients and families, particularly when they have altered perceptions of disease risks that may be in contrast to actual empiric risks, often resulting in individual and/or familial anxiety and stress.

Communicating risk in a culturally sensitive way is central to establishing patient rapport and facilitating decision making (Bennett, 2010). Important elements of the communication process include the assessment of social and psychosocial histories of patients, including an appraisal of support systems, perceived health beliefs, and cultural influences that might impact management of care (Weitzel *et al.*, 2011). Communicating information that is patient/family centered and culturally relevant further incorporates a personalized management of care and facilitates provider/patient rapport, trust, and decision-making.

Personal beliefs may alter the health information individuals are willing to share with the HCP. It is important to listen and respect an individual's cultural beliefs, while avoiding stereotypes by assuming that all persons from a specific culture share the same views. Regardless of culture, important *family history* information may be withheld by an individual due to guilt or shame about the disease. A new genomic diagnosis can have profound effects on family dynamics and interpersonal relationships, both positive and negative. Individuals may feel their confidentiality is threatened due to the medical information that is requested about them and other family members. Reproductive plans may be altered due to genomic risk factors that affect both the parents and other family members. Knowledge that a genomic disorder may cause increasing disability throughout the lifespan may lead to despair. Recent miscarriage or the loss of a loved one that is disclosed during the history collection process needs to be acknowledged. These issues are important, and although there are increasing legal protections for affected individuals, many fear that the label of having a genomic disorder will impact their ability to obtain health insurance and employment (Bennett, 2010).

2.8. *RAPID 2.5*: STEP 5—RISK MANAGEMENT

Communicating risk to individuals also includes management of care strategies to reduce the risk for disease occurrence, promote health, and improve health outcomes. *Risk management* should be a mutually agreed (e.g., HCP, healthcare team, and patient and/or family) process that takes into account personal, cultural, spiritual/religious, and quality of life factors. Management of risk depends upon the diagnosed entity and may include enhanced surveillance, chemoprevention, risk-reduction surgery (e.g., discussion of bilateral mastectomy for individuals with hereditary breast cancer syndromes), and specific interventions, including medications and behavioral strategies, or other interventions to reduce disease risk and improve outcomes.

Common risk reduction strategies for individuals at risk for heart disease include, for example, diet, weight control, and exercise, as well as medications, if applicable. However, stress-reduction strategies (e.g., yoga, biofeedback) and other complementary alternative measures may also be warranted based upon mutually agreed upon *risk communication*. The use of support groups may be an important factor in aiding individuals to adhere to behaviors warranting change or may provide a means for dealing with newly diagnosed conditions (e.g., breast cancer). A checklist to aid in the *RAPID Approach* process for conducting a risk assessment is located in Table 2.5.

Scientific and technological advances are revolutionizing healthcare practice, shifting the focus from the management of acute problems to promoting, preventing, and maintaining health. Advances in genomic science are providing important new insights into disease pathogenesis and variation among patients, expanding knowledge and practice beyond standard health as-

sessment, to include a risk assessment process. Health assessment focuses on the physical examination and health history to determine overall health and wellness (Mosby, 2009). *Risk assessment* identifies potential health risks, focusing on uncertainty of disease and the determination of disease *probability* influenced by genomic, familial, behavioral, and environmental determinates enabling personalized/precision care. Assessing risk requires that HCPs, including APRNs, understand the way heredity, genetics/genomics, and environmental factors contribute to disease risk in order to appropriately assess individuals, families, and aggregates regarding disease susceptibility.

Unlike health assessment, *risk assessment* focuses on potential hazards or threats that can compromise health or cause injury or harm. By applying *risk assessment* in clinical practice, HCPs can appropriately implement a personalized management of care to patients based upon their disease risk. A RAPID approach enables HCPs to assess patients risk and *probability* of disease occurrence so that effective, culturally sensitive *risk communication* and *risk management* can be implemented to patients and families at risk for developing disease, injury, or harm. Because the health and illness spectrum is broad and influenced by genomic and environmental factors, the use of *risk assessment* in clinical practice should be an ongoing, continuous, and personalized process based upon the healthcare needs of the patient.

2.9. NURSING IMPLICATIONS OF THE GENOMIC FAMILY HISTORY AND RISK ASSESSMENT

Genomics is applicable to the entire spectrum of health care, as are the roles for nurses. APRN educators, researchers, practitioners, nurse leaders, managers, and nurse administrators all play key roles in ensuring that evidence based approaches are used to improve outcomes, are implemented into practice and are used to determine the overall success of risk-reduction strategies. Nurse leaders play pivotal roles in transforming healthcare because nurse administrators and managers provide direction for new generations of nurses. The cultivation of new nursing leaders therefore is imperative for societal health.

TABLE 2.5. Checklist for the RAPID Approach when Conducting Risk Assessment.

RAPID Process	Risk Assessment Elements	Results	
Step 1. Data Collection			
• Personal history indicative of disease risk?	Personal History	❑ Yes	❑ No
• Family history-patterns of Mendelian Inheritance?		❑ Yes	❑ No
• Multiple family members with an affected disorder or clusters of diseases representing hereditary syndromes? Is there a limited family structure?	Family History (three-generation pedigree)	❑ Yes	❑ No
• Abnormal physical findings of unusual presentation? Neurodevelopmental or neurologic deterioration with early age onset?	Physical Assessment	❑ Yes	❑ No
• Does laboratory, ancillary or radiographic data shows surprising or extreme results?	Laboratory Data	❑ Yes	❑ No
• Chemicals, pollutants, occupational hazards or environmental risks exposures?	Radiographic and/or Ancillary Data	❑ Yes	❑ No
• Is there substance, alcohol, drug, nicotine or chemical abuse? Suicide? Cutting?	Environmental	❑ Yes	❑ No
Step 2. Risk Identification			
• Identified risk for disease related to personal/family history? Behaviors? Environment?	Behavioral Assessment Biologic/Genetic Behavioral Environmental	❑ Yes	❑ No
Step 3. Probability Assessment			
• Is there a validated evidence-based probability tool? Is it quantitative or qualitative model?		❑ Yes	❑ No
• What is the risk estimate?		❑ Yes	❑ No
Step 4. Risk Communication			
• Was risk communicated?		❑ Yes	❑ No
Step 5. Risk Management			
• Management based on risk?		❑ Yes	❑ No

Nurse leaders can be particularly helpful in supporting the acquisition and implementation of new technology systems, ensuring that genomics is integrated into the healthcare lexicon and through their advocacy for policy that supports genomic healthcare (O'Grady, 2008). Nurse educators should weave the elements from the guidelines included in *Essential Genetic and Genomic Competencies for Nurses with Graduate Degrees* (Greco *et al.*, 2012) into graduate nursing education so the next generation of nurses is prepared to deliver safe, effective patient care. Nurse researchers can improve the quality of health care for patients, their families, and communities by exploring the impact of genomics on outcomes that are important to nursing. APRNs working in direct patient care are responsible for diagnosing, evaluating, educating, and prescrib-

ing treatments, and should be using personal and *family history* to tailor their care to truly deliver *precision health care*; and the American Nursing Credentialing Center (2015) is now offering certification specifically for genetics. Genomic information has already been integrated into standard patient care; new treatment guidelines include genotypic testing as the preferred resistance testing to guide therapy in antiretroviral-naïve (ARV-naïve) patients (AidsInfo, 2013; Department of Health and Human Services, 2009); use of tumor marker tests in the prevention, screening, treatment, and surveillance of breast cancer (Harris *et al.*, 2007); and testing for *KRAS* gene mutations to predict response to treatment response in patients with metastatic colon cancer (Allegra *et al.*, 2009). As the list of genomic guidelines continues to grow, it is imperative that

APRNs not only routinely use the three-generation *pedigree*, but also be skillful in carrying out all five steps of the RAPID approach to risk assessment for personalized care and in implementing the standards of care. For example, a *family history* of arthritis, cirrhosis unrelated to alcohol, and diabetes in an individual presenting with vague complaints of joint pain, fatigue, general weakness, weight loss, and stomach pain should be suspicious for *HFE*-hemochromatosis, particularly is the patient who has high iron levels.

Family health history is different from other health information, because it contains information not only about the individual, but also about family members, which has ethical, legal, and social and health care policy implications. Individuals may respond differently to the information *family history* provides (Calzone *et al.*, 2010; Clayton, 2003); one individual within a family may decide to make lifestyle and behavioral changes to modify risk, whereas another may choose not to have any testing done at all. Risk probability is an important part of patient care and protecting the client's privacy is part of this process. Refer to Chapter 4 for further discussion on the ethical, legal, and social issues (ELSI) related to genomics.

2.10. REFERENCES

Aase, J. M. (1990). *Diagnostic dysmorphology.* New York, New York: Plenum Publishing.

Adams, P. C., Reboussin, D., Barton, J., McLaren, C., Eckfeldt, J., McLaren, G., . . . Sholinski, P. (2005). Hemochromatosis and iron-overload screening in a racially diverse population. *New England Journal of Medicine, 352*(17), 1769–1778.

AidsInfo, Service of U.S. Department of Health and Human Services. (2013). *Guidelines for the use of antiretroviral agents in HIV-1-infected adults and adolescents.* Retrieved from http://aidsinfo.nih.gov/guidelines/html/1/adult-and-adolescent-arv-guidelines/6/drug-resis tance-testing

Allegra, C., Jessup, J. M., Somerfield, M., Hamilton, S., Hammond, E., Hayes, D., . . . Schilsky, R. (2009). American Society of Clinical Oncology Provisional Clinical Opinion: Testing for KRAS Gene Mutations in Patients With Metastatic Colorectal Carcinoma to Predict Response to Anti–Epidermal Growth Factor Receptor Monoclonal Antibody Therapy. *Journal of Clinical Oncology, 27*(12), 2081–86.

American Board of Medical Genetics. (2014). *Clinical Genetic Competencies.* Retrieved from http://www.abmgg.org/pdf/LEARNING%20GUIDE-Clinical%20Genetics-2014%20final.pdf

Amercian Nurses Credentialing Center. (2015). Advanced Genetics Nursing. Retrieved from http://www.nursecredentialing.org/AdvancedGenetics

Benner, P., Hughes, R., & Stuphen, M. (2008). Clinical reasoning, decision making, and action: Thinking critically and clinically for nurses. In R. Hughes (Ed.), *Patient safety and quality: An evidence based handbook for nurses.* Rockville, MD: AHRQ. Retrieved from http://www.ncbi.nlm.nih.gov/books/NBK2643/

Bennett, R. L. (2010). *The practical guide to the genetic family history, 2nd ed.* Hoboken, New Jersey: John Wiley & Sons.

Bennett, R. L., French, K. S., Resta, R. G., & Doyle, L.D. (2008). Standardized human pedigree nomenclature: Update and assessment of the recommendations of the National Society of Genetic Counselors. *Journal of Genetics Counselors, 17*, 424–433.

Bickley, L. S., & Szilagyi, P. (Eds.). (2013). Bates' guide to physical assessment and history taking, (11th ed.). *Foundations in health assessment* (pp. 3-96). Philadelphia, PA: Lippincott, Williams & Wilkins.

BioLicense (2013). Omes and Omics. Retrieved from http://omics.org/index.php/Omes_and_Omics

Braden, B., & Maklebust, J. (2005). Preventing pressure ulcers with the Braden Scale. *American Journal of Nursing, 105*(6), 70–72.

Brock, J. K., Allen,V. M., Kieser, K., & Langlois. S. (2010). Family history screening: Use of the three generation pedigree in clinical practice. *Journal of Obstetrics and Gynaecology Canada, 10*(32), 663–672.

Calzone, K. A., Cashion, A., Feetham, S., Jenkins, J., Prows, C. A., Williams, J. K., & Wung, S. F. (2010). Nurses transforming health care using genetics and genomics. *Nursing Outlook, 58*(1), 26–35.

Centers for Disease Control and Prevention. (2012, January). Summary Health Statistics for U.S. Adults: National Health Interview Survey 2010, 10(252). Retrieved from http://www.cdc.gov/nchs/data/series/sr_10/sr10_252.pdf

Centers for Disease Control and Prevention. (2013). Office of Public Health Genomics. *Identifying opportunities to improve and transform healthcare.* Retrieved from http://www.cdc.gov/genomics/gtesting/file/print/EGAPP_factsheet.pdf

Chen, E., Carter, E., Winden, T., Sarkar, I., Wang, Y. & Melton, G. (2014, November). Multisource development of an integrated model for family health history. *Journal of the American Medical Informatics Association* (online). doi:10.1136/amiajnl-2014-003092 Retrieved from http://jamia.oxfordjournals.org/content/jaminfo/early/2014/11/07/amiajnl-2014-003092.full.pdf

Clayton, E. W. (2003). Ethical, legal and social implications of genomic medicine. *New England Journal of Medicine, 349*(6), 562–9.

Colvin, L., & Bower, C. (2009). A retrospective population-based study of childhood hospital admissions with record linkage to a birth defects registry. *BMC Pediatrics, 9*(32), doi:10.1186/1471-2431-9-32

Connolly, J.J., & Hakonarson, H. (2012). The impact of genomics on pediatric research and medicine. *Pediatrics, 129*(6), 1150-60. DOI: 10.1542/peds

Cremin, C., Carroll, J. C., Allanson, J., Blaine, S. M., Dorman, H., Gibbons, C. A., . . . Wilson, B. J. (2010). Genetics: Factor V Leiden. *Canadian Family Physician, 56*(4), 353.

Crownover, B. K., & Covey, C. J. (2013). Hereditary hemochromatosis. *American Family Physician, 87*(3), 183–190.

Department of Health and Human Services. Centers for Medicare Medicaid Services. (2010). *Guidelines for evaluation and management services.* Retrieved from http://www.cms.hhs.gov/MLNProducts/downloads/eval mgmt serv guide.pdf

Department of Health and Human Services. (2009). Panel on antiretroviral guidelines for adults and adolescents. *Guidelines for the use of antiretroviral agents in HIV-1 infected adults and adolescents.* Retrieved from http://aidsinfo.nih.gov/contentfiles/lvguidelines/adultandadolescentgl.pdf

Diamandis, M., White, N.M.A., & Yousef, G.M. (2010). Personalized medicine: Marking a new epoch in cancer patient management. *Molecular Cancer Research, 8,* 1175.

Doerr, M., & Teng, K. (2012). Family history: Still relevant in the genomic era. *Cleveland Clinic Journal of Medicine, 79*(5), 331–336. doi:10.3949/ccjm.79a.11065

Dolan, S.M., & Moore, C. (2007). Linking family history in obstetric and pediatric care: assessing risk for genetic disease and birth defects. *Pediatrics, 120*(Suppl. 2), S66–70.

Elsawy, B., & Higgins, K. (2011). The geriatric assessment. *American Family Physician, 83*(1), 48–56.

Emanuele, D., Tuason, I., & Edwards, Q. T. (2014). HFE associated hemochromatosis: overview of genetics and clinical implications for nurse practitioners in primary care settings. *Journal of the American Association of Nurse Practitioners, 26*(3), 113–22. doi: 10.1002/2327-692

European Commission, DG Research (2010). Summary report—Omics in personalized medicine. Retrieved from http://ec.europa.eu/research/health/pdf/summary-report-omics-for-personalised-medicine- workshop_en.pdf

Evans, D., Shenton, A., Woodward, E., Lalloo, F., Howell, A., & Maher, E. (2008, May). Penetrance estimates for *BRCA1* and *BRCA2* based on genetic testing in a clinical cancer genetics service setting: Risks of breast/ovarian cancer quoted should re-flect the cancer burden in the family. *BMC Cancer, 8*(155). Retrieved from http://www.biomedcentral.com/content/pdf/1471-2407-8-155.pdf

Facio, F., Lee, K., & O'Daniel, J.M. (2014). A genetic counselor's guide to using nextgeneration sequencing in clinical practice. *Journal of Genetic Counseling, 23*(4), 455462. DOI 10.1007/s10897-013-9662-7

Falk, M.J., & Robin, N.H. (2004). The primary care physician's approach to congenital anomalies. *Primary Care, 31*(3), 605–619.

Feuchtbaum, L., Carter, J., Dowray, S., Currier, R. J., & Lorey, F. (2012, November). Birth prevalence of disorders detectable through newborn screening by race/ethnicity. *Genetics in Medicine, 14*(11), 937–45.

Flore, L. A., & Milunsky, J. (2012). Updates in the genetic evaluation of the child with global developmental delay or intellectual disability. *Seminars in Pediatric Neurology, 19*(4), 173–180.

Glahn, K. P., Ellis, F. R., Halsall, P. J., Müller, C. R., Snoeck, M. M., Urwyler, A., . . . European Malignant Hyperthermia Group. (2010). Recognizing and managing a malignant hyperthermia crisis: guidelines from the European Malignant Hyperthermia Group. *British Journal of Anaesthesia, 105*(4), 41720.

Goetzel, R.Z., Staley, P., Ogden, L., Stange, P., Fox, J., Spangler, J., . . . & Taylor, M.V. (2011). A framework for patient-centered health risk assessments – providing health promotion and disease prevention services to Medicare beneficiaries. Atlanta, GA: US Department of Health and Human Services, Centers for Disease Control and Prevention. Retrieved from http://www.cdc.gov/policy/opth/hra/

Greco, K., Tinley, S., Seibert, D. (2012). *Essential genetic and genomic competencies for nurses with graduate degrees.* Retrieved from http://nursingworld.org/MainMenuCategories/EthicsStandards/Genetics-1/Essential-Gene tic-and-Genomic-Competencies-for-Nurses-With-Graduate-Degrees.pdf

Guttmacher, A. E., & Collins, F. S. (2002). Genomic medicine—a primer. *The New England Journal of Medicine, 347*(19):1512–20.

Harrington, L., Luquire, R., Vish, N., Winter, M., Wilder, C., Houser, B., . . . Qin H. (2011). Meta-analysis of fall risk tools in hospitalized adults. *Journal of Nursing Administration, 40*(11), 4830488. doi: 10.1097/NNA.0b013e3181f88fbd

Harris J. R., & Wallace R. B. (2012). The Institute of Medicine's new report on living well with chronic illness. *Prevention Chronic Disease, 9,* 120–126. doi: http://dx.doi.org/10.5888/pcd9.120126

Harris, L., Fritsche, H., Mennel, R., Norton, L., Ravdin, P., Taube, S., . . . Bast, R. (2007). American Society of Clinical Oncology 2007 update of recommendations for the use of tumor markers in breast cancer. *Journal of Clinical Oncology, 25*(33), 5287–5312.

Heald, B., Edleman, E., & Eng, C. (2012). Prospective comparison of family medical history with personal genome screening for risk assessment of common cancers. *European Journal of Human Genetics, 20*(5), 547–51.

Hooker, G.W., Ormond, K.E., Sweet, K., & Biesecker, B.B. (2014). Teaching genomic counseling: Preparing the genetic counseling workforce for the genomic era. *Journal of Genetic Counseling, 23*(4), 445-451. doi 10.1007/s10897-014-9689-4

Insel, T. (2011). Director's blog: improving diagnosis through precision medicine. National Institute of Mental Health. Retrieved from http://www.nimh. nih.gov/about/director/2011/improving-diagnosis-through-precision-me dicine.shtml

Isariyawongse, B. K., & Kattan, M. W. (2012). Prediction tools in surgical oncology. Surgical Oncology *Clinics of North America., 21*(3), 439–447.

Jorde, L. B., Carey, J. C., & Bamshad, M. J. (2010). Autosomal dominant and recessive inheritance (Chapter 4). In Jorde, Carey & Bamshad *Medical Genetics*, 4th ed. Philadelphia: Mosby.

Kelishadi, R., Sabri, M., Motamedi, N., & Ramezani, M.A. (2009). Factor analysis of markers of inflammation and oxidation and echocardiographic findings in children with a positive family history of premature coronary heart disease. *Pediatric Cardiology, 30*, 477–81.

Khanherkar, R., Bhatia-Dey, N., & Csoka, A. (2014). Epigenetics across the human lifespan. *Frontiers in Cell and Developmental Biology, 2*(49). doi: 10.3389/fcell.2014.00049 Retrieved from http:// www.ncbi.nlm.nih.gov/pmc/articles/PMC4207041/

Khoury, M., Cashion, A., & Billings, P. (2015). Evaluating the clinical utility of genomic variants derived from next-generation sequencing for opportunistic disease screening and risk assessment: Evidence gaps and priorities. Discussion paper. Institute of Medicine: Washington, DC. Retrieved from http:// www.iom.edu/DiseaseScreening

Khoury, M.J., Gwinn, M, Yoon, P. W., Dowling, N., Moore, C. A., & Bradley, L. (2007). The continuum of translation research in genomic medicine: How can we accelerate the appropriate integration of human genome discoveries into health care and disease prevention. *Genetics in Medicine, 9*(10) 665–674.

Kong, A., Frigge, M., Masson, G., Besenbacher, S., Sulem, P., Magnusson, G., . . . Stefansson, K. (2012). Rate of de novo mutations, father's age, and disease risk. *Nature, 488*(7412), 471–475.

Manolio, T. A., Chisholm, R. L, Ozenberger, B., Roden, D. M., Williams, M. S., Wilson, R., & Ginsburg, G.S. (2013). Implementing genomic medicine in the clinic: the future is here. *Genetics in Medicine, 15*(4), 258–267.

Maradiegue, A., & Edwards, Q. (2006). An overview of ethnicity and assessment of family history in primary care settings. *Journal of the American Academy of Nurse Practitioners, 18*(10), 472–480.

Marino, T. (2012). Prenatal diagnosis for congenital malformations and genetic disorders. Retrieved from Medscape [online], http://emedicine.medscape.com/article/1200683-overview

Mattson, S., Crocker, N., & Nguyen, T. (2011). Fetal alcohol spectrum disorders: Neuropsychological and behavioral features. *Neuropsychological Review, 2*(12), 81–101.

McDermott, U., Downing, J., & Stratton, M. (2011, January). Genomics and the continuum of medicine. *New England Journal of Medicine, 364*(4), 340–350. Doi:10.1056/NEJMra0907178

McWilliams, J.R. (2011). An evidenced-based pediatric fall risk assessment tool for home health practice. *Home Healthcare Nurse, 29*(2) 98–107.

Moeschler, J. (2008). Genetic evaluation of intellectual disabilities. *Seminars in Pediatric Neurology, 15*(1), 2–9.

National Cancer Institute. (2011). Breast cancer risk assessment tool. Retrieved from http://www.cancer.gov/bcrisktool/

National Human Genome Research Institute. (2012, December). The U.S. Surgeon General's Family History Initiative. Retrieved from: http://www.genome.gov/17516481

National Institute for Occupational Safety and Health. (2012). Workplace safety and health. Retrieved from http://www.cdc.gov/niosh/topics/cancer/

National Library of Medicine. (2014). *Genetics Home Reference* [Internet]. Your guide to understanding genetic conditions. Retrieved from http://ghr.nlm. nih.gov/glossary=consultand

Nicol, N., Skirton, H., Feero, W. G., & Green, E. (2013). Relevance of genomics to nursing practice. *Journal of Nursing Scholarship, 45*(1), 1–2.

Nussbaum, R.L., McInnes, R. R., & Willard, H.F. (2015). Patterns of single gene inheritance, Chapter 7. *Genetics in Medicine*. Philadelphia, PA: Saunders Elsevier.

Nussey, S., & Whitehead, S. (2001). *Endocrinology: An Integrated Approach.* Chapter 6, the gonad. Oxford: BIOS Scientific Publishers. Retrieved from: http://www.ncbi.nlm.nih.gov/books/NBK29/

O'Grady, E.T. (2008, April). *Advanced Practice Registered Nurses: The Impact on Patient Safety and Quality.* In: Hughes RG, editor. Patient Safety and Quality: An Evidence-Based Handbook for Nurses. Rockville (MD): Agency for Healthcare Research and Quality, Chapter 43. Retrieved from http:// www.ncbi.nlm.nih.gov/books/NBK2641/

Ormond, K.E. (2013). From genetic counseling to genomic counseling. *Molecular Genetics & Genomic Medicine*, 189–193. doi: 10.1002/mgg3.45 Retrieved from: http://www.ncbi.nlm.nih.gov/pmc/articles/PMC3865587/pdf/mgg30001-0189.pdf

Ouakrim, D.A., Boussioutas, A., Lockett, T., Hopper, J. L., & Jenkins, M.A. (2014). Cost effectiveness of family history-based colorectal cancer screening in Australia, *BMC Cancer, 14*, 261. doi: 10.1186/1471-2407-14-261

Peavy, H.L., Hooker, G.W., Kassem L., & Biesecker, B.B. (2009). Family risk and related education and counseling needs—Perceptions of adults with bipolar disorder and siblings of adults with bipolar disorder. *American Journal of Medical Genetics, 149A*(3), 364–371. doi. 10.1002/ajmq.a.32696.

Pei, J., Denys, K., Hughes, J., & Rasmussen, C. (2011). Mental health issues in fetal alcohol spectrum disorder. *Journal of Mental Health, 20*(5), 438–48. doi: 10.3109/09638237.2011.577113

Ramsey, S.D., Wilschut, J., Boer, R., & van Ballegooijen, M. (2010). A decision-analytic evaluation of the cost-effectiveness of family history-based colorectal cancer screening programs. *American Journal of Gastroenterology, 105*(8), 1861-9.

Read, A., & Donnai, D. (2012). What can be offered to couples at (possibly) increased genetic risk? *Journal of Community Genetics, 3*(3), 167–174.

Redekop, W. K., & Mladsi, D. (2013). The faces of personalized medicine: a framework for understanding its meaning and scope. *Value Health, 16*(6 Supplement), S4–S9.

Robertson, L., Hanson, H., Seal, S., Warren-Perry, M., Hughes, D., Howell, I., . . . TNT Trial TMG, BCSC (UK). (2012). *BRCA 1* testing should be offered to individuals with triple-negative breast cancer diagnosed below 50 years. *British Journal of Cancer, 106*(6), 1234–1238. doi: 101038/bjc.2012.31

Sabbagh, A., Pasmant, E., Laurendeau, I., Parfait, B., Barbarot, S., Guillot, B., . . . Wolkenstein, P. (2009). Unveiling the genetic basis of variable clinical expression in neurofibromatosis1. *Human Molecular Genetics, 18*(15), 2768–78.

Shiota, S., Murakawi, K., Suzuki, R., Fujioka, T. & Yamaoka, Y. (2013). *Helicobacter pylori* infection in Japan. *Expert Review in Gastroenterology Hepatology, 7*(1), 35–50. doi: 10.1586/egh.12.67

Shiovitz, S., Everett, J., Huang, S., Orloff, M., Eng, C., & Gruber, S. (2010). Head circumference in the clinical detection of PTEN hamartoma tumor syndrome in a population of high-risk breast cancer. *Breast Cancer Research and Treatment, 124*(2):459–65. doi: 10.1007/s10549-010-0839-6.

Singleton, M. V., Guthery, S. L., Voelkerding, K.V., Chen, K., Kennedy, B., Margraf, R. L., . . . Yandell, M. (2014). Phevor combines multiple biomedical ontologies for accurate identification of disease-causing alleles in single individuals and small nuclear families. *American Journal of Human Genetics, 94*(4), 599–610.

Solini, A., Santini, E., Passaro, A., Madec, S., & Ferrannini, E. (2009). Family history of hypertension, anthropometric parameters and markers of early atherosclerosis in young healthy individuals. *Journal of Human Hypertension, 23*, 801–7.

Solomon, B., & Muenke, M. (2012). When to suspect a genetic syndrome. *American Family Physician, 86*(9), 826–833.

Stillerman, K., Mattison, D., Giudice, L., & Woodruff, T. (2008). Environmental exposures and adverse pregnancy outcomes: A review of the science. *Reproductive Science, 15*(7), 631–650. doi: 10.1177/1933719108322436

Suba, Z. (2014). Triple-negative breast cancer risk in women is defined by the defect of estrogen signaling: preventive and therapeutic implications. *Onco Targets and Therapy, 7*, 147–164. Retrieved from http://www.ncbi.nlm.nih.gov/pmc/articles/PMC3905095/

Tanaka, H. (2010). Omics-based medicine and systems pathology. *Methods of Information in Medicine, 49*(2), 173–185. Retrieved http://dx.doi.org/10.3414/ME9307

Tarini, B. A., & McInerney, J, D. (2013). Family history in primary care pediatrics. *Pediatrics, 132*(Suppl. 3), S203-10. doi: 10.1542/peds.2013-1032D

Thalji, N., & Camire, R.M.(2013). Parahemophilia: new insights into factor v deficiency. *Seminars in Thrombosis and Hemostasis, 39*(6), 607–12.

Tyrer, J., Duffy, S. W., & Cuzick, J. (2004). A breast cancer prediction model incorporating familial and personal risk factors. *Statistics in Medicine, 23*, 1111–1130.

United States Department of Health and Human Services (2013). *My Family Health Portrait*. Retrieved from https://familyhistory.hhs.gov/fhh-web/home.action

United States Food and Drug Administration. (2014). Table of pharmacogenomic markers in drug labeling. Retrieved from http://www.fda.gov/drugs/scienceresearch/researchareas/pharmacogenetics/ucm083378.htm

United States Preventive Services Task Force. (2011). Agency for Health Care Quality and Research: National Guidelines Clearinghouse. Retrieved from http://www.guideline.gov/search/search.aspx?term=three+generation+pedigree

Valdez, R., Greenlund, K.J., Khoury, M.J., & Yoon, P.W. (2007). Is family history a useful tool for detecting children at risk for diabetes and cardiovascular diseases? A public health perspective. *Pediatrics, 120*(Suppl. 2), S78–86

Veltman, J., & Brunner, H. (2012). De novo mutations in human genetic disease. *Nature Reviews Genetics, 13*(8), 565–575.

Weitzel, J. N., Blazer, K. R., MacDonald, D. J., Culver, J.O., & Offut, K. (2011). Genetics, genomics, and cancer risk assessment—State of the art and future directions in the era of personalized medicine. *CA: A Cancer Journal for Clinician, 61*(5), 327–259.

Whelan, A. J., Ball, S., Best, L., Best, R. G., Echiverri,

S. C., Ganschow, P., . . . Stallworth, J. (2004). Genetic red flags: Clues to thinking genetically in primary care practice. *Primary Care: Clinics in Office Practice, 31*, 497–508.

Wilson, B. J., Qureshi, N., Santaguida, P., Little, J., Carroll, J. C., Allanson, J., & Raina, P. (2009). Systematic review: family history in risk assessment for common diseases. *Annals of Internal Medicine, 151*(12), 878–886.

Wynne, L. C., Tienari, P., Sorri, A., Lahti, I., Moring, J., & Wahlberg, K. E. (2006). II. Genotype-environment interaction in the schizophrenia spectrum: qualitative observations. *Family Process, 45*(4), 435–4.

Chapter 3

Testing and Counseling for Genetic and Genomic Conditions

SUSAN T. TINLEY, Ph.D, CGC, RN (RET)

Objectives:

- Differentiate among genetic/genomic testing modalities in terms of their purpose and the benefits and limitations of each.
- Appreciate and act on the need to remain current with genetic and genomic testing modalities, especially in one's specialty area.
- Apply client-focused counseling to interactions with clients needing information and support related to genetic and genomic conditions.
- Consult and collaborate with genetic specialists in the provision of testing, counseling, and management of genomic concerns.
- Support client coping and use of genomic information.

3.1. INTRODUCTION

This chapter addresses various aspects of testing and counseling for genetic and genomic conditions. Although the chapter is presented in two sections, it is important to keep in mind that in reality there is not and should not be such an artificial division between testing and counseling; they need to be seamlessly interwoven with each other and with the assessment activities addressed in the previous chapter.

3.2. GENETIC TESTING

Recent scientific and technical advances in genomic testing are transforming clinical care. Genomic tests are used for a variety of purposes that may include screening, diagnosis, risk stratification, and therapeutic management. In oncology, genomic tests are also used as a clinical decision making tool and to aid disease monitoring and prognosis of patients (Raman, Avendano, & Chen, 2013). Because genetic testing is different from other types of medical testing, it comes with increased responsibilities, particularly for nurses working in advanced practice nursing (APRN) roles. Genetic testing is different from other medical tests in several important ways.

(1) Most medical tests provide information only about the individual being tested. Genetic tests provide information about genes passed down through generations of family members and results provide information about the entire family. If one individual has a genetic variant associated with disease, it is likely that other family members (and/or future family members) may have the variant as well. The problem is that family members may not agree on the usefulness of genetic information; some may not want to share it with other family members and some may not want information shared with them.

(2) Genetic discrimination can be a real concern, despite protections provided by both the Health Insurance Portability and Accountability Act (HIPAA) and the Genetic Information Nondiscrimination Act (GINA). GINA, passed in 2008, specifically protects against employment and health insurance discrimination based on genetic information.

(3) Genetic testing done for medical purposes may cause rifts in family relationships if results illuminate information that would otherwise be private. One example is if a genetic test reveals non-paternity, i.e., the individual assumed to be the father of an individual is not the biological father.

(4) Medical records may be naively provided by

an uninformed client who otherwise would not have released genetic information. The unique vulnerabilities associated with genetic information should be discussed with clients to determine if and under what circumstances they want their genetic information to be released. Notes regarding these preferences should be placed in a prominent place on the records so the client's wishes are honored.

3.3. CYTOGENETICS

The branch of genetics that studies DNA at the chromosomal level is referred to as cytogenetics. This type of testing is indicated when there is suspicion of an abnormality in chromosome number or structure. There are traditional approaches to cytogenetic testing and more recent approaches to testing which are greatly enhanced with new technologies.

3.3.1. Karyotype

A karyotype is an image depicting the number and appearance of chromosomes that is produced during cytogenetic testing, as in Figure 1.3. Karyotypes are most commonly ordered in prenatal, pediatric, and oncology settings. Specimens are collected differently, depending on the setting. In the prenatal setting, fetal cells are obtained via amniocentesis or chorionic villi sampling (CVS). Postnatally through adulthood, lymphocytes are extracted from a 5 to 10ml sample of peripheral blood. In the oncology setting, the cells are taken from tumor tissue. Cells are grown in a culture medium; colchicine is added to arrest cell division at prometaphase, and then hypotonic saline is applied to swell and separate the chromosomes. The cells are dried, affixed to glass slides, geimsa stain is applied, and the chromosomes are photographed. The entire process takes approximately one week and although many of the preparation steps have been computerized, final analysis is done by a cytogeneticist (Tobias, Connor, & Ferguson-Smith, 2011). Indications for a karyotype vary by disease and life stage.

During the prenatal period
- Advanced maternal age (≥ 35 years)
- Fetal anomalies detected on ultrasound
- Maternal serum screening results indicating an increased risk for chromosomal abnormalities
- Parental carrier of balanced chromosome rearrangement

Pediatric
- Hypotonia
- Small for gestational age
- Failure to thrive
- Developmental delay
- Congenital structural anomalies

Adolescence through adulthood
- Infertility
- Amenorrhea or premature menopause
- Failure to develop secondary sex characteristics
- Multiple pregnancy losses
- Structural chromosome error in family

Oncology and hematology settings
- Testing of tumor tissues to confirm a diagnosis
- Classifying a disease
- Determining treatment regimens
- Monitoring disease status and recovery

3.3.2. Fluorescent in situ Hybridization (FISH)

This is a technique used to identify the presence of specific chromosomes or chromosomal regions through attachment (hybridization) of DNA probes to denatured chromosomal DNA. The probe is a fluorescently labeled segment of DNA complementary to the chromosomal region of interest. The probe can be for an entire chromosome or for a segment of a chromosome, as shown in Figure 3.1.

3.3.3. Chromosomal Microarray (CMA)

Also known as cytogenomics, CMA is replacing other technologies as a first-tier test for individuals with unexplained developmental disabilities, autism spectrum disorders, or multiple congenital anomalies (Miller *et al.*, 2011). CMA can detect unbalanced rearrangements, aneuploidy, small deletions, and/or duplications and copy number variants (CNVs). A CNV has been defined as "a DNA segment that is 1 kb or larger and present at variable copy number in com-

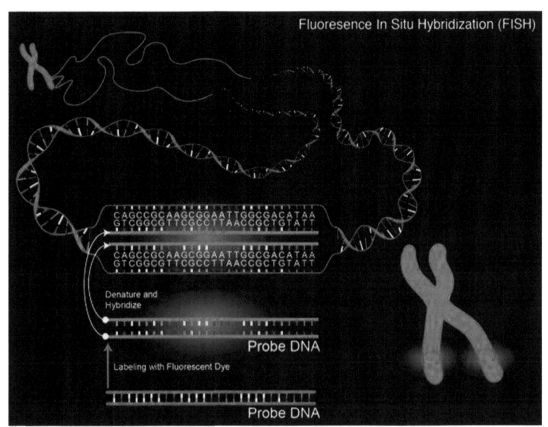

FIGURE 3.1 Fluoresence in situ hybridization (FISH). (Figure from the National Institutes of Health. National Human Genome Research Institute. "Digital Media Database." Darryl Leja/NHGRI/NIH, http://www.genome.gov/dmd/img.cfm?node=Photos/Graphics&id=85167.)

parison with a reference genome" (Redon *et al.*, 2006, p. 444). CNVs have been found throughout the genome and can be benign or pathogenic, requiring an extensive database for interpretation of findings such as the International Standard Cytogenomic Consortium. Unusual CNVs are particularly problematic, because many have yet to be defined and are reported as "variants of unknown significance." An additional limitation of CMA is the inability to identify many single-gene disorders and balanced chromosome rearrangements (Palmer, Peters, & Mowatt, 2012).

The use of CMA in prenatal settings has been controversial (Wapner, *et al.*, 2012). The test may identify variants in fetal cells that are associated with disorders that manifest in adulthood (incidental findings) and alleles with variable expressivity or decreased penetrance or whose impact is unknown. There are concerns about parents' abilities to understand the risks and limitations to provide truly informed consent (Dondorp, Sikke-

ma-Raddatz, de Die-Smulders, & de Wert, 2012). However, some providers are of the opinion that the benefits of CMA should not be denied to patients in the prenatal setting if supported with adequate information for clinicians and parents and an innovative approach to informed consent (Stark, Gillam, Walker, & McGillivray, 2013).

3.4. MOLECULAR OR DNA TESTING

There are a variety of testing methods that fall under the umbrella of molecular or DNA testing. In a clinical setting they all involve tests to identify variation in an individual's genomic makeup.

3.4.1. Targeted Mutation Analysis

Targeted mutation analysis is used to identify disorders caused by a well-defined mutation in a single gene, such as testing for sickle cell anemia, which is consistently associated with a point mutation in the beta globin gene. Targeted analysis may also be used to test family members after a specific mutation has been identified in an affected family member. Interpretation of a targeted mutation analysis is straight forward, because the individual either has (positive) or does not have (negative) the mutation.

3.4.2. DNA Sequence Analysis

DNA sequence analysis is used to determine the exact sequence of bases in a DNA molecule and is often more extensive (and expensive) than a targeted mutation analysis, because it provides detailed information on a larger section of nuclear material. Sequence analyses are done when family history and/or clinical findings suggest the presence of a mutation that has not yet been identified in the family. Interpreting sequence analysis results can be straightforward when a pathogenic mutation is identified. When the sequence analysis result fails to identify a pathogenic mutation, the results may be considered uninformative if the family and clinical history are clearly consistent with the disorder in question. The mutation detection rate (the likelihood of a mutation being identified when the clinical and family history are consistent with a disorder) needs to be included as part of the informed consent process and again when providing an uninformative result.

A third type of result is the presence of a variant of unknown significance. The American College of Medical Genetics and Genomics and the Association of Molecular Pathologists have developed guidelines for the terminology used in interpretation of sequence variants in genes for Mendelian disorders. These terms include pathogenic, likely pathogenic, uncertain significance, likely benign, and benign and are meant to reflect the level of evidence that exists for the identified variant (Richards, *et al.*, 2015). Additional samples from other family members may be requested to determine if the variant segregates with the disorder, which might resolve the issue. If the significance of the variant becomes clear as more families are tested, laboratories attempt to contact the referring clinician. Patients should be encouraged to remain "connected" to their provider, updating contact information as needed if

they wish to re-engage in a conversation about their test results if the significance of a currently unknown variant becomes clearer in the future. Clinicians in turn are responsible for informing their patients as updated information becomes available.

Hereditary breast and ovarian cancer (HBOC) provides a good example of some of the challenges in interpreting sequence analyses. *BRCA1* and *BRCA2* are two genes in which mutations have been shown to significantly increase risk for the development of breast and ovarian cancer. Both genes are large and hundreds of different mutations have been identified on each of them. Some mutations have been associated with an increased risk for cancer; others have not been associated with cancer; the significance of some is still unknown, and still others have not yet been identified. If no mutation is identified in sequence analysis, the result is qualified with a statement about the possible presence of a mutation that is currently unidentifiable.

3.4.3. Massive Parallel Sequencing

Also called next generation sequencing, massive parallel sequencing (MPS) supports simultaneous sequencing of large amounts of DNA. MPS is used in conditions such as isolated congenital deafness, which has considerable locus heterogeneity (different genes throughout the genome) and for simultaneous analysis of DNA from multiple individuals. MPS is a more efficient approach to examining the genetic underpinnings of diseases with locus heterogeneity or large testing programs such as newborn screening and will likely replace the evaluation of individual genes or gene panels (Bick & Dimmock, 2011).

Exome sequencing and genome sequencing are forms of MPS that are now available for clinical testing in some situations. Exome sequencing analyzes all of the coding regions of the DNA (exons). Genome sequencing is more comprehensive, analyzing the noncoding regions between genes and in the introns as well as the coding sequences. Neither approach will provide coverage for all mutations. Clients need to be informed of the coverage rate for the candidate genes for the individual's phenotype. As with CMA, incidental findings are possible. The clinician ordering the test and the client need to be informed of the laboratory's policy about revealing incidental findings (Korf & Rehm, 2013). As newer technologies become part of health care, it will be important for all nurses to be familiar with the technology and the appropriate approach to the client (Conley *et al.*, 2013).

3.5. PURPOSE OF TESTING

3.5.1. Diagnostic Testing

The most obvious purpose of genetic testing is to diagnose a condition that is suspected based on clinical findings and/or family history. All of the types of testing described above can be utilized to make or confirm a diagnosis, provide prognostic information, identify the inheritance pattern, inform risk assessment, and assist with management.

3.5.2. Screening

As with other types of screening tests, genetic screening tests lack the sensitivity or specificity of diagnostic tests and require further testing for confirmation of results. The following criteria for genetic screening have been identified by Grossea *et al.*, (2010):

- The disease is an important health problem
- Evidence-based treatment is available and positively alters outcome
- A suitable test with high predictive value exists
- Participation is voluntary
- Social and psychological harm is negligible
- Informed consent is provided
- Access is available throughout the population to be screened
- There is oversight of quality
- Benefits balance with cost

Three major types of genetic screening tests are available: prenatal screening (described in Chapter 6), newborn screening (described in Chapter 7), and carrier screening. Traditionally, carrier screening has identified carriers of autosomal recessive disorders in high-risk populations based on ethnicity to inform reproductive decision-making. A carrier may choose to avoid marriage with another carrier, not have children,

adopt, use assisted reproductive technologies, use prenatal diagnosis, or facilitate early diagnosis and treatment of an affected infant.

Carrier screening was initiated in the 1970's for Tay Sachs disease among individuals of Ashkenazi Jewish descent and for sickle cell among African Americans. Tay Sachs screening was successful because of support from the Jewish community. Sickle cell screening has been less successful because of poorly planned screening programs, inadequate education, and distrust of the medical community, leading to a lack of support from the African American community. In 2001, the American College of Obstetricians and Gynecologists (ACOG) and the American College of Medical Genetics (ACMG) recommended that cystic fibrosis and spinal muscular atrophy carrier screening be offered to all patients being seen preconceptually or prenatally regardless of ethnic origin (Strom *et al.*, 2011), in addition to ethnic specific tests.

Carrier screening for the Ashkenazi Jewish population has expanded to include eight or more conditions for which the population has a high risk. Research programs are reporting the feasibility and accuracy of applying next generation sequencing to carrier screening for a large number of recessive and x-linked conditions (Lazarin *et al.*, 2013; Umbarger *et al.*, 2013). However, this expansion requires careful consideration of the disorders to be included and their phenotype, penetrance, and age of onset (Grody *et al.*, 2013). As with previously discussed uses of next generation sequencing, clinicians and consumers will need to be educated and consumers should have the right to opt out of receiving certain results.

Regardless of the testing technology and the number of disorders included in the screening, the accuracy of prenatal carrier screening for autosomal recessive conditions is dependent on correct identification of paternity. Preconceptual and prenatal screening can be offered to both partners simultaneously or sequentially. In simultaneous screening, the results will be available for both partners at the same time, but if done sequentially the second partner is only tested if the first partner's result is positive. Both options have their advantages and disadvantages. Simultaneous testing is more expensive since both partners are tested, and sequential testing is less expensive but takes more time because the male partner is not tested until the female partner's result is known. If the female has a negative result, the male will not be tested and thus not know his carrier status. If he is an unidentified carrier, he will not be able to inform his family members of their potential risk. In practice, more couples opt for sequential screening because of cost.

3.5.3. Predictive or Presymptomatic Testing

Predictive testing is used to identify mutations that increase an individual's risk for developing a disorder later in life. The predictive power of the test is based on the penetrance of the mutation. For example, a positive result for predictive testing for Lynch syndrome indicates that someone has a mutation for the syndrome, but his chance of developing a syndrome cancer is approximately 80%. Predictive testing for Huntington's disease is virtually 100% predictive in the presence of a sufficient expansion of the CAG nucleotide repeat associated with the disease.

Predictive testing is preceded by testing with DNA sequence analysis of an affected family member to determine if the mutation in the family is identifiable. If no mutation can be identified with current testing capabilities, predictive testing cannot be performed. If the pathogenic mutation is identified, family members will be offered targeted mutation analysis and a negative result is a true negative. A negative result to sequence analysis for an unaffected family member without knowing the mutation in the family is an uninformative result because there may be a mutation that currently is unidentifiable. As genetic discoveries and technology advance, this is becoming less of an issue.

3.5.4. Testing to Guide Therapy

The greatest strides in knowledge and ability to utilize genetic testing to impact treatment have occurred in oncology and pharmacogenomics. Oncology specialists use genetic testing technologies to identify people with hereditary cancer syndromes, identify genetic changes that increase the risk for developing nonhereditary cancers, and profile the mutations within tumors to improve prognostic accuracy and guide therapeutic interventions. The pharmacology community has been actively engaged in genomic

research for over two decades, focusing on the genes involved in drug metabolism, adverse reactions, and effectiveness, with the goal of ending the current "trial and error" approach to drug therapy. A table published by the United States Food and Drug Administration (FDA) lists all the currently approved drugs that include pharmacogenomic information in their labeling (2015).

Sequencing advances have also stimulated advances in the understanding of the role of the microbiome (genetic make-up of the micro-organisms that reside on and in our bodies (Konkel, 2013) in health and illness as seen in such diverse areas as treatment of inflammatory bowel disease (Damman, Miller, Surawicz, & Zisman, 2012) and Methicillin-resistant Staphylococcus aureus (MRSA) in a neonatal nursery (Köser *et al.*, 2012).

3.5.5. Direct to Consumer Testing

Within a few years of the completion of the Human Genome Project in 2003, a number of laboratories began offering genetic testing directly to consumers. The tests have been marketed on television and the internet, test kits ordered and results provided via the internet, all without input from health care professionals. The envisioned benefits of this approach were to increase access to testing, empower consumers to take a proactive role in their health, and increase privacy. However, the lack of regulation of the laboratories and input from health care professionals has resulted in misleading claims by some direct to consumer (DTC) testing companies (Government Accountability Office, 2006).

In addition to the issue of education and counseling for individuals undergoing DTC testing, there are significant concerns about the validity of DTC results. Some tests have both clinical and analytical validity, while others have one or the other and still others have neither. The last two groups have the potential for not just misleading consumers, but creating harm. Weaver and Polin (2012) reported that all of the DTC testing companies they reviewed were providing genome testing for type 2 diabetes (T2D). At the time, there were 40 loci known to be associated with only 10% of the heritability of T2D, calling into question the clinical utility of genetic testing for

T2D and highlighting the potential for harm if a consumer assumes that he has little or no genetic risk based on his DTC test result.

Tests with both analytic and clinical utility also present the potential for harm without adequate education and counseling. Weaver and Polin (2012) provided the example of *BRCA1/2* testing, which was offered by at least one DTC company. This testing requires extensive counseling for a positive result in terms of the medical management of the associated risk and psychosocial support. Even in the presence of a true negative result, there should be counseling to help the consumer assimilate the reduction in risk but also understand the presence of the residual risk as a member of the general population. Yet, none of this was provided by the DTC company.

The Federal Trade Commission in cooperation with Centers for Disease Control and Prevention (CDC) and the FDA published a statement recommending that consumers consult with a health care provider prior to testing, seek assistance in understanding the results, avoid making health related decisions without consultation with a health care practitioner, and check the laboratory's policies to protect their privacy (Hudson, Javitt, Burke, Byers, & ASHG Social Issues Committee, 2007). In 2012, 23andME, a DTC company, announced that they had submitted the first documents for FDA review in the process of achieving FDA approval for their testing practices. However, controversy continues, as the FDA sent 23andME a letter on 22 November 2013 warning the company to discontinue marketing the Personal Genome Service (PGS) until it receives FDA approval (Annas & Elias, 2014).

Nurses have an essential role in helping clients identify the risks, limitations, and potential benefits of genetic testing, because consumers often seek counsel from nurses about the advisability of testing or health care decisions based on their results. Although, non-genetic specialists may not have the background to answer some specific questions, nurses should be generally informed about the pros and cons and able to refer the specific questions they cannot address to a genetic specialist.

3.6. GENETIC COUNSELING

The National Society of Genetic Counselors (NSGC) has defined genetic counseling as "the process of helping people understand and adapt to the medical, psychological and familial implications of genetic contributions to disease. This process integrates the following: interpretation of family and medical histories to assess the chance of disease occurrence or recurrence; education about inheritance, testing, management, prevention, resources and research; counseling to promote informed choices and adaptation to the risk or condition." (NSGC Definition Task Force, 2006, p. 77). All of this fits within the scope of graduate level nursing practice, although genetic counselors have a greater breadth and depth of knowledge in these areas than the majority of nurses. It is imperative for nurses to be aware of their limitations in knowledge and to form collegial relationships with counselors and other genetic professionals on behalf of their clients. The American Nurses Credentialing Center (ANCC) offers a genetic certification for advanced practice nurses with this specific training.

Counseling patients and families about genetic or genomic conditions may include several components that are interwoven and provided concurrently. The information that follows addresses those components.

3.6.1. Genetic Risk Assessment

Genetic risk assessment may include information obtained from any combination of family history, genetic test results, behavioral and environmental factors. Calculation of recurrence risks for Mendelian disorders may be straightforward based on the family history. Other calculations may include Hardy Weinberg calculation and Baye's Theorem. Hardy Weinberg calculations are utilized in estimating the frequency of autosomal recessive carrier status based on the incidence of the disease state in a given population. Baye's theorem is another calculation used to estimate the probability of genetic risk based on family history and genetic testing. The theorem states that the probability is based on the test characteristics of sensitivity and specificity and the probability of the disease or condition prior to the test, i.e., the prior probability (Ogino & Wilson, 2004) These are concepts that may be familiar to graduate nurses and risk calculations may be straightforward in some situations, but in other situations calculation of risk can be very complex and referral to a genetic specialist is indicated.

3.6.2. Client Focused Counseling

In a discourse analysis of genetic counseling sessions with parents of children with a newly diagnosed genetic disorder, Babul-Hirji, Hewson, and Frescura (2010) found that counselors tightly controlled the medical history phase and dominated the scientific information phase of the counseling. Similarly, a critical review of studies of genetic counseling found that the majority of providers were dominant and spoke more than their clients. The focus of the content was biomedical rather than psychosocial. Yet, clients had more positive outcomes if the provider was more empathic and less verbally dominant (Meiser, Irle, Lobb, & Barlow-Stewart, 2008). Clients need to be provided opportunities to be active in the communication so rapport can be established and communication can be more effective and meet the client's needs.

It is insufficient to obtain the medical history of the client and his family without including the impact that history has had on the individual and family functioning and cohesion, as well as the influence that the ethnic, cultural, and social background may have had on motivation to seek and receptivity to genetic information. Construction of a pedigree while interviewing the client provides a prime opportunity for the nurse to assess the influence of the client's experiential background that may impact the attitudes, values, beliefs, and emotions and receptivity of genetic/genomic information. While obtaining the family history, the nurse can also begin to get a sense of the client's understanding of the disorder under question and his or her view of how it is being passed on in the family. Family myths may need to be addressed and dispelled prior to the client being open to incorporate new information.

3.6.3. Literacy and Numeracy

If genetic counseling is to be effective, providers must accurately assess the client's levels of literacy and numeracy. Even individuals with normally high literacy levels may become lost when scientific and/or medical concepts are discussed. Because genetic counseling often includes information about risks which are presented numerically, it may be difficult to predict who walks away from a counseling session with more understanding, the college philosophy professor with low numeracy or the bookie with an eighth grade education who works with probabilities every day. There is evidence to suggest that people with high numeracy better understand genetic concepts even when literacy is low (Portnoy, Roter, & Erby, 2010). Low literacy can also be compensated for by making the dialogue more interactive and personally contextualized (Roter, Ebby, Larson, & Ellington, 2009). Low numeracy can also be offset by converting numbers into qualitative explanations or providing a contextualized narrative. Genetic risk can be compared to more commonly encountered events, such as being involved in a car crash, and narratives may help patients personalize the risk decision (Gordon-Lubitz, 2003). Flexibility in presenting information and frequent comprehension checks are essential when providing difficult-to-understand information.

3.6.4. Ethnic, Religious, and Cultural Background

As in many other areas of health care, ethnic minorities tend to be disproportionately less likely to receive genetic services. Obstacles for minorities identified through multiple studies include socioeconomic barriers, low awareness of potential risk, religious/spiritual beliefs, concern for social stigma and shame if found to be a mutation carrier, language and geographic barriers, and mistrust of the medical community, specifically genetic professionals (Forman & Hall, 2009). Because fewer minorities have had genetic testing, less is known about the specific variants they might have and the more likely they are to have a variant of uncertain significance, frequently resulting in persistent distress (O'Neill *et al.*, 2009) These issues call for nurses to be advocates for their clients by exploring their beliefs, values, and feelings related to genetic services and supporting them when they choose to pursue counseling and/or testing.

Studies exploring what clients of various ethnic backgrounds expect from a genetic evaluation provide insight into how genetics services can be improved to meet the needs of diverse communities. Caucasian, Asian, and Hispanic parents of deaf infants want to know why their infant is deaf. Asian and Hispanic parents expect the same information but also to use genetic information to assist with family planning, guide their child's medical care, and help other family members (Palmer *et al.*, 2008). While ethnicity has been shown to influence expectations and motivations for genetic testing, it is only a starting point for a discussion. Assumptions about how a specific individual, couple or family will respond cannot be made because attitudes and values may differ from the stereotype in significant ways. For example, native Palestinians and first generation Palestinian-Americans were markedly different in their approaches to information provided during prenatal genetic counseling. The investigators attributed the similarities to the common cultural roots and the differences to acculturation of the first generation Palestinian-American (Awwad, Veach, Bartels, & Leroy, 2008). Although ethnic, cultural, and religious backgrounds can heavily influence responses to genetic information, there may also be striking differences among individuals within the same group. Assessment and validation of values, beliefs, and feelings with the individual should always be the primary informer of the nurse's approach in counseling.

3.6.5. Experiential Background

Individual interpretation of and adjustment to genetic risk is influenced by past experiences, family history, and relatives' experiences with illness (Sivell *et al.*, 2008). Encouraging clients to describe their experiences, emotional responses, and coping strategies and those of their families can provide insights that help providers better understand the patient context, allowing them to more effectively guide the counseling approach. Sharing family stories occasionally reveals unmet psychosocial needs that may be far more important than the genetic information. Paying attention to these and other details may encourage clients to be more open and ready to absorb information. Nurses have an excellent opportunity to build this relationship and set the stage for more effective discussions throughout their encounters with their clients.

3.6.6. Family Relationships and Communication Patterns

Passing on genetic information can be affected by the social relationships within the family. In some families genetic information is freely shared, and in others it may be shared on a perceived need to know basis. In still other families, rifts and feuds can prevent communication to some individuals or whole branches of the family despite their high-risk status. The first member of the family to learn about a high risk may find himself or herself in a very stressful position as he or she negotiates the task of passing on information to others. This was exemplified in one family in which the grandparents and siblings on both sides ostracized a couple with two boys who had an X-linked lethal genetic disorder. The paternal side of the family blamed the mother for passing on the disease. The maternal side of the family blamed the parents for bringing home the bad news shortly before her sister was to get married and, "taking the joy out of the wedding." Strategies such as coaching about breaking bad news and providing written material or a videotape of the counseling session to share with family members can facilitate these difficult discussions. (Roshanai, Rosenquist, Lampic, & Nordin, 2009).

3.7. ELEMENTS OF INFORMED CONSENT FOR GENETIC TESTING

Signing consent forms is a common occurrence in a litigious society. The vocabulary of the forms often reflects a greater intent to protect the provider than to educate the one providing the consent. Because of these factors, it is common practice for many to sign consent forms without reading them. Due to the many personal and family issues that can arise from genetic testing, it is imperative that the client's consent is truly informed.

3.7.1. Client Characteristics for Informed Consent

Informed decision making about genetic testing requires that the individual be competent and the decision be voluntary. Evolving technologies make discussions and decisions regarding predictive screening of minor children difficult. Testing of newborns and children with physical, developmental, or behavioral abnormalities is common and less fraught with controversy. Predictive screening of an asymptomatic minor child for a familial disorder that does not manifest until adulthood is more complicated. If the family history is significant for a specific genetic condition and early surveillance or treatment can reduce morbidity or mortality, predictive testing may be recommended. When no benefit is to be derived from early detection, consideration must be given to the potential harms that may ensue. Physical harms could result from initiating ineffective or harmful treatments. Psychological harm could include parental guilt and anxiety, altered self-image/expectations, or increased family stress. Social harms could include difficulty obtaining life and/or disability insurance, detection of misattributed parentage, and family-planning decisions based on misunderstanding of the test result. Although predictive testing in minor children may be appropriate in some situations, the general consensus is to discourage it for late-onset conditions because early testing preempts the child's opportunity to make an informed decision later as an adult. (Ross, Saal, David, & Anderson, 2013).

It is inappropriate for a health professional to recommend one choice over another when working with an adult. It is the competent adult making the decision who can best predict his response to the various potential results and what the best course of action is for him. Sometimes, family members put pressure on the individual in favor of or against testing. For example, one young woman sought predictive testing after her maternal grandmother's mutation for HBOC was identified. The mother of the counselee had chosen not to seek testing for herself. It was explained that a positive result for the daughter would reveal her mother's status as an obligate carrier. The daughter insisted that she be tested and that she would never tell her mother she was tested. Within a week of the daughter's blood draw, the nurse received a call from the mother who was concerned about her daughter's decision to be tested. The mother requested testing, but wanted to be informed of her own results before her daughter received her results. If her result was positive, the mother wanted time to

adjust to the news to be in a better position to support her daughter with her result. The daughter agreed to have the laboratory postpone analysis of her sample. Fortunately for both of them, the mother's result was negative. Providers can support a client's independence, but the client has to decide if family pressures and relationships are sufficient reason for a decision that otherwise would not be made.

3.7.2. Content of Informed Consent

The informed consent for genetic testing is a process, not just a signature on a form that the client has not read or does not understand. This consent goes beyond the medical information and the risks and benefits of procedures or tests. For the consent to be truly informed, there has to be full disclosure of the alternatives to testing, the potential for noninformative results, unanticipated emotional responses, and discrimination. This counseling process is extensive, and the counselor spends a great deal of one-on-one time with the patient to communicate this information. The following are several content areas to be discussed as a part of the consent process.

3.7.2.1. Alternatives

The primary alternative to predictive testing is risk estimation and medical management based on family history and pedigree. An individual family member's risk can be estimated based on their position in the family related to affected family members. A first degree relative of someone affected with an autosomal dominant disorder will have a 50% chance of having the mutation. In many situations, the options for the medical management of risk are the same for someone with a 50% risk as for a known mutation carrier. The client should be encouraged to anticipate his responses to the outcomes of each alternative when deciding whether to proceed with testing.

3.7.2.2. Potential for a Noninformative Result

As noted above, clients have a right to know the accuracy and positive predictive value of the test for the laboratory that will be performing it. Pretest counseling should include the potential for an uninformative result or an indeterminate allele and the uncertainty these results might create. Studies have indicated that without such counseling, these results can be especially difficult for clients to understand and come to terms with in HBOC testing (van Dijk, Otten, Tollenaar, van Asperen, & Tibben, 2008) and Huntington disease testing (Semaka, Balneaves, & Hayden, 2013).

3.7.2.3. Emotional Impact

Relief from the uncertainty about their genetic status is often a motivator for those seeking predictive testing. However, negative emotions such as sadness, fear, and worry about the future may accompany a positive result and survivor guilt may follow a negative result. One of the most consistent responses from identified carriers is worry or guilt related to what they may have passed on to their children and grandchildren. Being forewarned about unanticipated responses to the results may help ameliorate the negative emotions. In addition, family relationships can be altered as a result of genetic testing; informing clients that this may be problematic may help them to discuss their feelings with other family members in order to safeguard relationships.

3.7.2.4. Discrimination

GINA is a federal law passed to protect individuals from discrimination by health insurers and employers based on genetic information. The law prohibits discrimination in premiums, eligibility, or coverage; requirement to undergo genetic testing; and requesting or requiring genetic information by group or individual health insurers. The protections of GINA do not extend to life and disability insurers so clients need to be forewarned of the limitations of the law. Most states have laws that reinforce or extend the Federal law. A table of state statutes related to the genome is regularly updated by National Human Genome Research Institute (2013).

3.7.2.5. Incidental Findings

With the advent of next generation sequencing and expanded newborn screening, much discussion has gone into policies concerning the revelation of secondary or incidental findings. The American College of Medical Genetics and Genomics (ACMG) has developed a table of 56 genes for 24 conditions for which incidental finding of a pathogenic mutation should be revealed in the circumstance of otherwise clinically indicated testing, regardless of the age of the person tested. The ordering clinician has the responsibility to ensure that genetic counseling is provided (Green *et al.*, 2013) to the client or parents. For all the conditions on the list, there is essential medical management that has the potential to alter the outcome. but for some, that medical management is not needed or appropriate until adulthood (Green *et al.*, 2013). The authors also recommend that the patient or parents who consent to the testing for the primary indication not be allowed to opt out of the analysis of the additional genes. The American Academy of Pediatrics Committee on Bioethics, Committee on Genomics and the American College of Medical Genetics and Genomics Social, Ethical and Legal Issues Committee (2013) published a separate document that supports traditional practice of not testing children for adult onset disorders when there is not an advantage to be gained for the child. Clayton *et al.* (2014) have reviewed these two policy documents and found them to be "in tension" in their recommendations related to testing for adult onset disorders in children, and these authors have recommended additional research in this area. It is essential for graduate level nurses to be aware of the issues and conflicting views that arise and to take part in the discussions and research aimed at their resolution.

3.8. SUPPORT OF CLIENT COPING AND USE OF GENETIC/GENOMIC INFORMATION

Nurses especially nurse practitioners who have an ongoing relationship with their patients have a major role in supporting their coping with and use of genetic/genomic information.

3.8.1. Client Coping

Genetic counseling, whether it be that provided at the initial evaluation, at time of diagnosis, or in follow-up, is often associated with a change in selfperception and perception of the well-being of close family members. Information presented in counseling can be the source of anxiety and/or depression. Studies that have assessed client well-being after predictive testing for hereditary cancer syndromes have revealed that distress, anxiety, and depression may be temporarily heightened, but resolve over time (Bjorvatn, Eide, Hanestad, & Havlik, 2008; Shiloh, Koehly, Jenkins, Martin, & Hadley, 2008; Mikkelsen, Sunde, Johansen, & Johnson, 2009; Werner-Lin, 2008; Smith et al., 2008) Those identified as being at greater risk for ongoing distress include those with inadequate support (Bjorvatn et al., 2008; Werner-Lin, 2008), those with high monitoring coping styles (Shiloh et al., 2008), and those who elected not to be tested (Smith et al., 2008).

3.8.1.1. Social Support

Social support can buffer post-counseling anxiety and depression (Bjorvatn et al. 2008). Some clients have reported inadequate informal support and formal support services to be unavailable or not utilized (Werner-Lin, 2011). Clients who lack a strong support network should be provided additional support and referred to appropriate support services, including support organizations targeted to specific genetic disorders. The Genetic Alliance is a nonprofit health advocacy organization with over 1,200 disease-specific member groups or organizations. The Alliance provides a search engine for these organizations http://www.diseaseinfosearch.org.

3.8.1.2. Interventions for High Monitors

Shiloh et al. (2008) provide interventions to prevent distress among those who have a high monitoring coping style. One suggested approach is to encourage the client to anticipate their reaction to potential test results to help ameliorate distress associated with a positive result. Another is to provide enhanced information in a reassuring way, de-emphasizing the negative aspects of a positive result and stressing an optimistic outcome with a focus on prevention or surveillance.

3.8.1.3. Risk Management After Genetic Testing

Individual and family past experiences with illness can outweigh actual risk in decision-mak-

ing about medical management of risk (Sivell et al., 2008). For example, prophylactic mastectomy and/or oophorectomy were chosen significantly more by women whose mother or first and second degree relatives died of breast cancer or pelvic cancer (Singh et al., 2013). Making a decision about prophylactic surgery is not an easy decision for most women, and many report a general lack of knowledge among health care providers about the decisional journey they were trying to navigate (Leonarczyk & Mawn, 2014). Women need to be well informed about their options. Opportunities should be made available for discussions with a knowledgeable and compassionate surgeon, as well as other women who have chosen surgery and those who have not, and they should be encouraged to discuss the options with their respective spouses. Anticipation of the likely physical and emotional outcomes of each option can help the woman to make a decision with which she will be comfortable in the long term.

3.8.1.4. Those Who Decline Testing

Clients who decline testing typically do not receive further genetic services. Yet, this group has been shown to be at higher risk for distress (Heiniger, Butow, Price, & Charles, 2013) and deserves further study. Nurse practitioners are in a prime position to assess the level of distress among decliners as they return for routine care and provide additional support as indicated.

3.8.1.5. No Answers

Uninformative results may be a relief to a few, but many experience frustration and at least a temporary increase in distress. Parents of children with disabilities are often physically, emotionally, and financially drained after years on a diagnostic odyssey. These families can share common experiences and provide/receive reassurance and support in an online support group, http://www.undiagnosed-usa.org/. A booklet, Living without a Diagnosis, has been developed in the United Kingdom (UK) based on the literature about the experience and interviews with parents and has been evaluated by additional parents and professionals. The book is available on the internet at http://www.geneticalliance.org.uk/docs/living-without-a-diagnosisprint.pdf.

TABLE 3.1. Examples of Resources to Aid in Understanding Testing and Counseling for Genetic and Genomic Conditions.

Organization/Title of Site	Description	URL
Genetic Alliance	Umbrella organization for over 1,200 disease-specific support organizations. The Alliance provides a wealth of information about advocacy for genetic conditions, newborn screening, translational research for advances in genomic discoveries, and a host of other topics related to genetics and genomics as applied to health care.	http://www.geneticalliance.org
American College of Medical Genetics and Genomics (ACMG) Genetics Clinics Database	Clinic database can be searched without login to identify clinical genetic services throughout the country.	http://www.acmg.net/GIS/Default.aspx
Genetic Counseling Cultural Competence Toolkit	"A public forum for learning about the critical, current, and ongoing problem of health disparities in health care, which supports our commitment to reducing and eliminating them."	http://www.geneticcounselingtoolkit.com/
Transcultural nursing	Provides basic concepts and case studies.	http://www.culturediversity.org/index.html
EGAPP	The EGAPP Working Group was established in 2005 to support the development of a systematic process for assessing the available evidence regarding the validity and utility of rapidly emerging genetic tests for clinical practice. This independent, multidisciplinary panel prioritizes and selects tests, reviews CDC-commissioned evidence reports and other contextual factors, highlights critical knowledge gaps, and provides guidance on appropriate use of genetic tests in specific clinical scenarios.	http://www.egappreviews.org/
Genome Statute and Legislation Database	Provides the total number of states that have enacted legislation on each topic in the database. Clicking on the number leads to another table listing each of those states, a link to full statute for each state and a summary of each statute.	http://www.genome.gov/27552194
Food and Drug Administration Table of Pharmacogenomics biomarkers in drug labels (2015)	"Lists FDA-approved drugs with pharmacogenomic information in their labeling. The labeling for some, but not all, of the products includes specific actions to be taken based on the biomarker information. Biomarkers in the table include germline or somatic gene variants, functional deficiencies, expression changes, and chromosomal abnormalities."	http://www.fda.gov/drugs/scienceresearch/researchareas/pharmacogenetics/ucm083378.htm
Gene tests	"A Laboratory Directory of over 600 international laboratories offering molecular genetic testing, biochemical genetic testing, and specialized cytogenetic testing for more than 3000 inherited disorders. A Clinic Directory of over 1000 international genetics clinics providing diagnosis and genetic counseling services to patients and their families with known or suspected inherited disorders."	http://www.genetests.org
National Human Genome Research Institute's Issues in Genetics	Provides links to a variety of sites that address policy, legal and/or ethical issues in genetic research.	http://www.genome.gov/PolicyEthics/

3.9. GENOMICS AND GENETIC COUNSELING

Next generation sequencing and other new technologies pose significant questions about the applicability of past genetic counseling experience and research findings obtained prior to the development of this new technology. Literacy and numeracy pose challenges when educating clients about single gene disorders; the complexity of genomics will be even more challenging. Can research findings from genetic counseling be translated to genomic counseling? Will clients be able to make sense of the findings and incorporate them into positive health behaviors? At least one study has demonstrated that we have much to learn about how to translate genomic findings into positive outcomes for the client. Grant, *et al.* (2011) conducted a randomized trial of genetic diabetes risk counseling among obese individuals. They found that the group that received diabetes risk counseling after genetic testing did not make a significant difference in their health behaviors compared with a control group without testing and counseling.

3.9.1. Expectations and Understandings of the Public

Individuals with serious mental illness were interviewed about what they know and expect of genomic testing for psychiatric illness (Potokar, Stein, Darrah, Taylor, & Sponheim, 2012). Although the majority were aware of basic genetics and were interested in genomic psychiatric testing for the sake of their families and society as a whole, many had unrealistic expectations of what such testing could do for them. They were unaware of genetic counseling and said they would prefer to receive any genetic test results from their personal mental health provider. Psychiatric nurse practitioners need to prepare themselves to help their clients understand the risks and benefits of psychiatric genomics and to work with researchers in exploration and development of counseling interventions.

3.9.2. DTC Whole Genome Testing

Some individuals have or are seeking whole genome sequencing from DTC companies. Interpretation of the results of such testing requires knowledge of the complexities of gene/gene and gene/environment interactions and the ability to integrate that with the test results, the client's personal and family history, behaviors, and environmental exposures to provide an accurate risk assessment and medical recommendations (O'Daniel, 2010). Without graduate or post graduate education in genetics and genomics, most graduate nurses are not prepared to deal with the complexities of genomic counseling for DTC testing. Nurses DO play a role in advocating for the client, providing psychosocial support, making appropriate referrals, reinforcing information provided in the formal genetic counseling session, and collaborating with genetic professionals.

3.10. CONCLUSION

The impact of genomics on disease prevention, diagnosis, and treatment are creating completely new ways of preventing disease and caring for the ill. Although few nurses are currently ordering genetic tests for their clients, that will be changing for nurse practitioners. Staying current with genomic advances supported by solid evidence will be essential.

3.11. REFERENCES

American Academy of Pediatrics Committee on Bioethics, Committee on Genomics and the American College of Medical Genetics and Genomics Social, Ethical and Legal Issues Committee (2013). Policy statement: Ethical and policy issues in genetic testing and screening of children. *Pediatrics, 131*(3), 620–622.

Annas, G, J,. & Elias, S. (2014). 23andMe and the FDA. *New England Journal of Medicine, 370*(11), 985-988. doi;10.1056/NEJMp1316367

Awwad, R., Veach, P. M., Bartels, D., M., & LeRoy, B. S. (2008). Culture and acculturation influences on Palestinian perceptions of prenatal genetic counseling. *Journal of Genetic Counseling 17*(1), 101–116.

Babul-Hirji, R., Hewson, S., & Frescura, M. (2010). A sociolinguistic exploration of genetic counseling discourse involving a child with a new genetic diagnosis. *Patient Education and Counseling, 78*(1), 40–45.

Bick, D., & Dimmock, D. (2011). Whole exome and whole genome sequencing. *Current Opinion in Pediatrics, 23*(6), 594-600. doi: 10.1097/MOP.0b013e32834b20ec

Bjorvatn, C., Eide, G. E., Hanestad, B. R., & Havlik,

O. E. (2008). Anxiety and depression among subjects attending genetic counseling for hereditary cancer. *Patient Education and Counseling, 71*(2), 234–243.

Clayton, E. W., McCullough, L. B., Biesecker, L. G., Jofie, S., Ross, L. F., & Wolf, S. M. (2014). Addressing the ethical challenges in genetic testing and sequencing in children. *American Journal of Bioethics, 14*(3), 3–9.

Conley, Y. P., Biesecker, L. G., Gonsalves, S. Merkle, C. J., Kirk, M., & Aouizerat, B. E. (2013). Current and emerging technology approaches in genomics. *Journal of Nursing Scholarship, 45*, 5–14.

Damman, C.J., Miller, S.I., Surawicz, C.M., & Zisman, T.L. (2012). The microbiome and inflammatory bowel disease: is there a therapeutic role for fecal microtia tansplantation? *American Journal of Gastroeneterology, 107*, 1452–1459.

Dondorp, W., Sikkema-Raddatz, B., de Die-Smulders, C., & de Wert, G. (2012). Arrays in postnatal and prenatal diagnosis: an exploration of the ethics of consent. *Human Mutation, 33*, 916–922.

Forman, A. D., & Hall, M. J. (2009). Influence of race/ethnicity on genetic counseling and testing for hereditary breast and ovarian cancer. *The Breast Journal, 15*(Suppl 1), S56–62.

Government Accountabilty Office. (2006). Nutrigenetic testing: tests purchased from four websites mislead consumers. http://www.gao.gov/new.items/d06977t.pdf

Grant, R. W., Meigs, J. B., Florez, J. C., Park, E. R., Green, R. C., Waxler, J. L., . . . & O'Brien K. E. (2011). Design of a randomized trial of diabetes genetic risk testing to motivate behavior change: the Genetic Counseling/Lifestyle Change (GC/LC) Study for Diabetes Prevention. *Clinical Trials, 8*(5), 609–15.

Green, R.C., Berg, J.S., Grody, W.W., Kalia, S.S., Korf, B.R., Martin, K., . . . & Biesecker, L.G. (2013). ACMG recommendations for reporting of incidental findings of clinical exome and genome sequencing. *Genetics in Medicine, 15*(7), 565–574. doi:10.1038/gim.2013.73

Gordon-Lubitz, R. J. (2003). Risk communication: Problems of presentation and understanding, *Journal of American Medical Association, 289*(1), 95. doi:10.1001/jama.289.1.95

Grody, W. W., Thompson, B. H., Gregg, A. R., Bean, L. H., Monaghan, K. G., Schneider, A, & Lebo, R.V. (2013). ACMG position statement on prenatal/preconception expanded carrier screening. *Genetics in Medicine, 15*(6), 482-3. doi: 10.1038/gim.2013.47.

Grossea, S.D., Rogowskic, W.H., Rossd, L.F., Cornele, M.C., Dondorpf, W.J., & Khoury, M.J. (2010). Population screening for genetic disorders in the 21st century: evidence, economics, and ethics. *Public Health Genomics, 13*, 106-115. DOI: 10.1159/000226594

Heiniger L, Butow PN, Price MA, & Charles M.

(2013). Distress in unaffected individuals who decline, delay or remain ineligible for genetic testing for hereditary diseases: a systematic review. *Psycho-Oncology, 22*(9), 1930–1945

Hudson, K., Javitt, G., Burke, W., Byers, P., & ASHG Social Issues Committee. (2007). ASHG statement on direct-to-consumer genetic testing in the United States. *American Journal of Human Genetics, 81*(3), 635–637. DOI:10.1002/pon.3235.

Konkel, L. (2013). The environment within: exploring the role of the gut microbiome in health and disease. *Environmental Health Perspectives, 12*(9), A276–A281.

Korf, B.R., & Rehm, H.I. (2013). New approaches to molecular diagnosis. *Journal of American Medical Association, 309*(14), 1511–1521.

Köser, C.U., Holden, M.T., Ellington, M.J. Cartwright, E.J., Brown, N.M., Ogilvy-Stuart, A.L., . . . Peacock, S.J. (2012). Rapid whole-genome sequencing for investigation of a neonatal MRSA outbreak. *New England Journal of Medicine, 366*, 2267–2275. DOI: 10.1056/NEJMoa1109910

Lazarin G.A., Haque I.S., Nazareth S., Iori K., Patterson A.S., Jacobson J.L., . . . & Srinivasan B.S. (2013). An empirical estimate of carrier frequencies for 400+ causal Mendelian variants: results from an ethnically diverse clinical sample of 23,453 individuals. *Genetics in Medicine, 15*(3), 178–86; doi:10.1038/gim.2013.83

Leonarczyk, T. J., & Mawn, B. E. (2014) Cancer risk management decision making for BRCA women. *Western Journal of Nursing Research*, doi: 10.1177/0193945913519870

Retrieved from: http://wjn.sagepub.com.cuhsl.creighton.edu/content/early/2014/01/23/ 0193945913519870.full.pdf+html

Meiser, B., Irle, J., Lobb, E., & Barlow-Stewart, K. (2008). Assessment of the content and process of genetic counseling: a critical review of empirical studies. *Journal of Genetic Counseling, 17*(5), 434–451

Mikkelsen, E.M., Sunde, L., Johansen, C., & Johnsen, S.P. (2009). Psychosocial consequences of genetic counseling: a population-based follow-up study. *Breast Journal, 15*(1) 61–68.

Miller, D.T., Adam, M.P., Swaroop, A., Biesecker, L.G., Brothman, A.R., Carter, N.P., . . . & Ledbetter, D.H. (2010). Consensus statement: chromosomal microarray is a first-tier clinical diagnostic test for individuals with developmental disabilities or congenital anomalies. *The American Journal of Human Genetics, 86*, 749–764 DOI 10.1016/j.jahg.2010.04.006.

National Human Genome Research Institute. (2013). Table of state statutes related to genomics. http://www.genome.gov/27552194

National Society of Genetic Counselors' Definition Task Force, Resta, R., Biesecker B.B., Bennett, R.L., Blum, S., Hahn, S.E., . . . Williams, J.L. (2006).

A new definition of Genetic Counseling: National Society of Genetic Counselors' Task Force report. *Journal of Genetic Counseling, 15*(2), 77–83.

O'Daniel, J. (2010). The prospect of genome-guided preventive medicine: A need and opportunity for genetic counselors. *Journal of Genetic Counseling, 19*(4), 315–327.

Ogino, S., & Wilson, R.B. (2004). Bayesian analysis and risk assessment in genetic counseling and testing. *Journal of Molecular Diagnosis, 6*(1), 1–9.

O'Neill, S.C., Rini, C, Goldsmith, R.E., Valdimarsdottir, H., Cohen, L.H., & Schwartz, M.D. (2009). Distress among women receiving uninformative BRCA1/2 results: 12 month outcomes. *Psychonocology, 18,* 1088-1096. DOI:10.1002/pon.1467

Palmer, C.G., Martinez, A., Fox, M., Sininger, Y., Grody, W.W., & Schimmenti, L.A. (2008) Ethnic differences in parental perceptions of genetic testing for deaf infants. *Journal of Genetic Counseling, 17*(1), 129–138.

Palmer, E. E., Peters, G. B., & Mowatt, P. (2012). Chromosome microarray in Australia: A guide for paediatricians. *Journal of Paediatrics and Child Health, 48,* E59-E67.

Portnoy, D.B., Roter, D., & Erby, L.H. (2010). The role of numeracy on client knowledge in BRCA counseling. *Patient Education and Counseling, 81*(1), 131–136.

Potokar, D.N., Stein, C.H., Darrah, O.A., Taylor, B.C., & Sponheim, S.R., (2012) Knowledge and attitudes about personalized mental health genomics: narratives from individuals coping with serious mental illness. *Community Mental Health Journal, 48,* 584–591 DOI:10.1007/s10597-011-9400-2.

Raman, G., Avendano, E.E., & Chen, M. (2013, July). Update on Emerging Genetic Tests Currently Available for Clinical Use in Common Cancers. Evidence Report/Technology Assessment. (AHRQ Report No. 290-2007-10055-I). Retrieved from: http://www.cms.gov/Medicare/Coverage/DeterminationProcess/Downloads/id92TA.pdf

Redon, R., Ishikawa, S., Fitch, K.R., Feuk, L., Perry, G., Andrews, T.D., . . . Hurles, M.E. (2006) Global variation in copy number in the human genome. *Nature 444,* 444–454 doi:10.1038/nature05329.

Richards, S., Aziz, N., Bale, S., Bick, D., Das, S., Gastier-Foster, J., . . . Rehm, H.L. (2015) Standards and guidelines for the interpretation of sequence variants: A joint consensus recommendation of the American College of Medical Genetics and Genomics and the Association for Molecular Pathology. Genetics in Medicine, Advance online publication, DOI: 10.1038/gim.2015.30.

Roshanai, A.H., Rosenquist, R., Limpic, C. & Nordin, K. (2009) Does enhanced information at cancer genetic counseling improve counselees' knowledge, risk perception, satisfaction and negotiation of information to at-risk relatives? A randomized study. *Acta Oncologica, 48*(7), 999–1009.

Ross, L.F., Saal, H.M., David, K.L. & Anderson, R.R. (2013). ACMG Policy Statement: Technical report: ethical and policy issues in genetic testing and screening of children, *Genetics in Medicine, 15*:234–245, doi: 10.1038/gim.2012.176

Roter, D.L., Ebby, L., Larson S., & Ellington, L. (2009) Oral literacy demand of prenatal counseling dialogue: predictors of learning. *Patient Education and Counseling, 75*(3), 392–7.

Semaka, A., Balneaves, L. G., & Hayden, M. R. (2013). "Grasping the grey": patient understanding and interpretation of an intermediate allele predictive test result for Huntington disease. *Journal of Genetic Counseling, 22,* 200–217. DOI 10.1007/s10897-012-9533-7

Shiloh, S., Koehly, l., Jenkins, J., Martin, J., & Hadley, D. (2008). Monitoring coping style moderates emotional reactions to genetic testing for hereditary nonpolyposis colorectal cancer: a longitudinal study. *Psycho-oncology, 17*(8) 746–755.

Singh, K., Lester, J., Karlan, B., Breese, C., Geva, T., & Gordon, O. (2013). Impact of family history on choosing risk-reducing surgery among BRCA mutation carriers. *American Journal of Obstetrics and Gynecology, 208,* 329.e1-6. Doi.org/10/1016/jajog2013.01.026

Sivell, S., Elwyn, G., Gaff, C.L., Clarke, A.J., Iredale, R., Shaw, C., . . . & Edwards, A. (2008). How risk is perceived, constructed, and interpreted by clients in clinical genetics, and the effects on decision making: systematic review. *Journal of Genetic Counseling, 17,* 30-63. DOI 10.1007/s10897-007-9132-1

Smith, A.W., Dougall, A.L., Posluszny, D.M. Somers, T.J., Rubinstein, W.S., & Baum, A. (2008). Psychosocial distress and quality of life associated with genetic testing for breast cancer risk. *Psycho-Oncology, 17*(8), 767–773.

Stark, Z., Gillam, L., Walker, S.P., & McGillivray, G. (2013). Ethical controversies in prenatal microarray. *Current Opinion in Obstetrics and Gynecology, 25,* 133–137 DOI:10.1097/GCO.0b013e32835ebb67

Strom, C. M., Crossley, B., Buller-Buerkle, A., Jarvis, M., Quan, F., Peng, M., . . . & Sun W. (2011). Cystic fibrosis testing 8 years on: lessons learned from carrier screening and sequencing analysis. *Genetics in Medicine, 13*(2), 166–72.

Tobias, E.S., Connor, M., & Ferguson-Smith, M. (2011) *Essential Medical Genetics,* 6th Edition. Hoboken, NJ: Wiley-Blackwell.

Umbarger M.A., Kennedy C.J., Saunders P., Breton B., Chennagiri N., Emhoff J., . . . Porreca G.J. (2013). Next generation carrier screening. *Genetics In Medicine,* Jun 13, Advance Online.

United States Food and Drug Administration. (2015) Table of pharmacogenomics biomarkers in drug labels. http://www.fda.gov/drugs/scienceresearch/researchareas/pharmacogenetics /ucm083378.htm

van Dijk, S., Otten, W., Tollenaar, R.A., van Asperen,

C.J., & Tibben, A. (2008). Putting it all behind: long-term psychological impact of an inconclusive DNA test result for breast cancer. *Genetics in Medicine, 10*(10), 745–750. doi:10.1097/GIM.0b013e318185213e

Wapner, R.J, Martin, C.L., Levy, B., Baliff, B.C., Eng, C.M., Zachary, J.M., . . . & Jackson, L. (2012). Chromosomal microarray versus karyotyping for prenatal diagnosis. *New England Journal of Medicine, 367* (23), 2175–2184. DOI:10.1056/NEJMoal1203382.

Weaver, M., & Polin, T.I. (2012). Direct to consumer genetic testing: what are we talking about? *Journal of Genetic Counseling, 21*(3), 361–366. DOI:10.1007/s10897-012-9493-y

Werner-Lin, A. (2011). Formal and informal needs of young women with BRCA mutations. *Journal of Psychosocial Oncology, 26*(4), 111–133.

Chapter 4

Ethical, Legal, and Social Implications in Genomic Advanced Practice Nursing

KATHLEEN SPARBEL, Ph.D, FNP-BC
MARTHA TURNER, Ph.D, RN-BC

Objectives:

- Discuss the differences between Principalism and the virtue approach.
- Describe how nursing ethical standards and competencies evolved.
- Identify the important ELSI concepts in a selected clinical scenario.

4.1. INTRODUCTION

Incorporation of genetics and genomics into practice by nurses with graduate degrees, especially those in advanced practice roles, requires consideration of ethical foundations, exploration of moral decision-making models, and standards of genetic/genomic competencies for advanced practice. Across the globe, ethics guides nursing practice. According to the International Council of Nurses (ICN), "the nurse, in providing care, ensures that use of technology and scientific advances are compatible with the safety, dignity and rights of people" (ICN, 2012). An overview of ethics provides the context for the understanding and practice of clinical genetics and genomics. Ethics also informs the discussion of individual, organizational, and societal issues, although it is important to remember that not all difficult issues are ethical issues. Advanced practice nurses (APRNs) frequently confront situations requiring reflection and use of a decision-making model, which specifies that the interests of all stakeholders must be identified and balanced. Ethics suggests reflection and influences both decisions and actions. It also helps APRNs meet their ethical obligations. The nature and types of ethical challenges APRNs encounter vary and will be highlighted in relationship to genetic conditions addressed in the following chapters. The purpose of this chapter is not to develop expert nurse ethicists; instead, it is to assist APRNs to develop an awareness of the ethical, legal, and social implications (ELSI) of rapidly evolving genetic knowledge and application of that knowledge in the care of patients and families. A knowledge base of ethical principles and models for decision-making along with a heightened personal awareness facilitates approaching clinical situations with the ethical perceptual 'lens' needed to achieve genetic and genomic competencies in practice.

4.2. APPROACHES IN BIOETHICS

Although many approaches are commonly cited in bioethics, five approaches are especially useful when applied to the ethics of genetics and genomics in clinical care. The most familiar is the principles approach or *Principalism*. This approach emerged from the Belmont report (The National Commission for the Protection of Human Subjects of Biomedical and Behavioral Research, DHEW, 1979). Autonomy, beneficence, nonmaleficence, and justice are the principles identified in that report. Beauchamp and Childress (2009) argued that health care ethics can be built upon these and other relevant principles that include privacy, safety, trust, and truth or veracity. In Bok's (1999) classic book Lying: Moral Choice in Public and Private Life, she describes truth telling and its variations and exceptions. Chapters titled, "Truthfulness, deceit, and trust," "White lies," "Excuses," "Lies for the public good," "Paternalistic lies," "Lies to the sick and dying," and "Is the whole truth attainable?" all provide familiar examples for those in health care. Although not sufficient to achieve ethical competence, understanding these ethical principles provides initial guidance for APRNs in clinical practice when encountering ethical situations. Dahnke and Dreher (2006, pp. 12, 13) provide brief definitions of many principles. Each principle is fundamental and requires special attention in the context of genetic technology and science. Their definitions and examples of related issues illustrate each principle (Table 4.1).

The *Virtue approach* has been described since the time of Aristotle and is best articulated in the work of Pellegrino and Thomasma (1993). They state that virtues or character traits require practice and enable us to achieve our highest potential. Once individuals have acquired a virtue, their actions will reflect it; thus, a virtuous person is an ethical person. Examples of virtues include intellectual honesty, compassion, humility, trust, compassion, benevolence, justice, and integrity. This approach should be considered in addition to the principles approach or rules approach, when making decisions, not instead of them (Velasquez, Andre, Shanks, & Meyer, 1996). The value of integrating personal virtuous characteristics with principles of duty towards the patient is illustrated in the following quote by Fowler:

> "Both a virtue and a duty-based approach to ethics is essential if duties are to have any power and if virtues are to have any direction. The problem of a duty-based ethics is that obligations are empty if the person does not possess the moral character to meet those obligations. The problem of a virtue-based ethics is that it runs the risk of abuse through unwarranted intrusion into the private life of the individual." (Fowler, 2010)

Another way of integrating virtues and values into action is seen in nurses' "ways of being" described by Pavlish *et al.* (2011). These "ways of being" with clients include being present, empathetic, supportive, and sincere. Some "ways of being" appropriate for clients and for collegial relationships are being courageous, respectful, open to multiple perspectives, and proactive.

Three additional bioethics approaches are particularly relevant to genomic nursing practice. The *Deontologic approach* judges the morality of an act by the rightness or wrongness of the act itself, not by the outcomes. This approach sug-

gests to do it because it is the right thing to do. Duties, obligations, and rights are addressed in this approach; dilemmas may result from conflicts between two competing rights or two competing duties. Embedded in this approach is the understanding that when one has a right, there is a corresponding duty or obligation on the part of another (Alexander & Moore, 2012). Thus, if a client has a right to information then the APRN has an obligation to provide the information. In this approach equal respect is given to everyone and this question is asked, "Which actions consider the rights of all those involved?" In the *Caring approach*, the focus is on the ethics of relationships while including themes from both the principles based approach and the virtue based approach. Taylor (1993) lists several characteristics of this approach; they include "centrality of the caring relationship, promotion of the dignity and respect of patients and colleagues as people, attention to the particulars of individual patients and colleagues and the context in which we find ourselves and a redefinition of fundamental moral skills to include virtues like kindness, attentiveness, empathy, compassion and reliability" (Taylor, 1993; pp. 552–560). By contrast, using the approach of *Consequentialism* dictates the rightness or wrongness of actions or intentions should be judged on the outcomes they achieve. The utilitarian approach is one kind of consequentialism and proposes that the morally right thing to do is that which produces the greatest happiness for the greatest number of people (Boylan, 2000). One example is telling the truth; it is considered the right thing to do unless it brings about distress or suffering in another. Another example would be unauthorized use of funds specified for one purpose to help a client who otherwise would not have access to test or services.

A simple decision-making model uses these bioethics approaches and aids in making ethical decisions in genomic clinical practice. There are four steps in the model: Act, Intention, Context, and Consequences. In Step 1, Act, the emphasis is on asking about the "rightfulness" or "wrongfulness" of the act itself. The Bioethics approaches considered are the deontological, rights-based, rule based approach and consequentialism. Questions asked in this step include the following: "What makes an act right? What is the right thing to do? Is there a rule? Is there a right action (or, a

TABLE 4.1. *Definitions of Ethical Principles.*

Principle	Dahnke and Dreher's Definition	Related Genetic/Genomic Issues
Autonomy	"the right to self-determination; being one's own person without constraints by another's actions or psychological and physical limitations."	• Ownership of genetic information • Difficulty of truly informed consent with novel genetic/genomic clinical applications, • Right to know and right to not know.
Confidentiality	"holding information entrusted in the context of special relationships as private"	• Disclosing genetic information to others • De-identification of materials • Discrimination based on disclosed genetic information in the workplace • Dissemination of genetic information if participants or group membership could be identified (e.g., ethnicity or geographic origin) • Breaching confidentiality in order to access needed consultation
Fidelity	"duty to keep one's promise or word"	• Competing loyalties to patient vs. employers • Requests for access to information from the funding organization
Beneficence	"the duty to do good"	• Risks and benefits of genetic testing • Risk communication and informing of genetic results to family members if they want to know • Maintaining confidentiality of genetic information if the client doesn't want family members informed vs. potential good of providing family members with genetic risk information which could affect their own decision-making • Providing resources and support for patients and families to interpret genetic information
Nonmaleficence	"duty to do no harm"	• Reliability and utility of genetic tests and identified variations • Potential immediate and future harm of sharing genetic information • Genetic testing without clinical utility or available treatment • Disclosure of incidental findings • Interpretation of disease risk based on genetic information
Justice	"treating people fairly; equitable distribution of risks and benefits."	• Access to genetic and genomic testing and treatments • Genetic treatment vs. personal quality enhancement • Use of whole genome sequencing (WGS) both inside and outside of research

Adapted from Dahnke, M., & Dreher, H. M. (2006). Defining ethics and applying the theories. In V. D. Lachman (Ed.), *Applied ethics in nursing* (3-13). New York: Springer.

wrong action)? Is truth always best? Will a wrong action produce a good outcome (or, will the right action produce a bad outcome)?" During the Intention step (Step 2), rights and responsibilities toward the parties in the decision process are considered. The APRN considers "Does this respect the rights of all stakeholders? How will this affect relationships? What are my responsibilities

to all the parties involved? Which action is consistent with the sort of person I want to be?" The bioethics approaches considered during this step are virtue based, rights based, and care based.

In Steps 3 and 4 of this decision model, the larger situational context is weighed and outcomes or consequences are anticipated. Context, Step 3, recognizes that ethical decisions do not occur in vacuum, but are affected by the decision setting, the participants involved, and the circumstances of the situation. Context is illustrated in questions such as the following: "What is the timing of the action? What rules or obligations should be considered? Who is available to be present? What are the relationships in this context? Are we in a clinic or an intensive care unit? Is the context of this interaction a research study, clinical practice, quality monitoring, or a mix?" In the final step, Consequences (Step 4), a consequentialist or utilitarian approach is considered, with an emphasis on the outcomes or end result of the decision. Questions include "Which decision will produce the most good and do the least harm (utilitarian approach, often combined with justice and autonomy)? Will a wrong action produce a good outcome? What might be some unintended consequences?" Using a simple decision model such as this helps to translate and apply theoretical ethical principles into clinical practice.

4.3. ETHICAL STANDARDS AND ETHICAL COMPETENCE IN NURSING

Nursing has a rich tradition of advocating for the protection of, and respect for, the inherent rights of the recipient of nursing services. As noted in the American Nurses Association (ANA) *Code of Ethics for Nurses with Interpretive Statements* (the Code) (2015) p. v.), that recipient may be "an individual, family, group community or population." The Code emphasizes nursing's commitment to ethical principles such as privacy, confidentiality, right to self-determination, and primacy of the patient's interests. The ethical principles in the Code are also reflected in *The ICN Code of Ethics for Nurses* (ICN, 2012), including the nurse's responsibility to "promote an environment in which the human rights, values, customs, and spiritual beliefs of the individual, family and community are respected" (p.2), as well as to give statements on providing "accurate, sufficient and timely information in a culturally appropriate manner." The ICN code supports nursing actions to meet the needs of vulnerable populations and advocates for social justice in health care resource allocation.

Ethical standards provide the framework for ethical practice; developing ethical competence

as a nurse requires knowledge of the approaches, some essential skills, and use of a decision-making model. The six skills required to demonstrate ethical competence include the following:

- Recognizing an issue and understanding its significance
- Being willing to do something about the identified ethical issue
- Using ethical reasoning and a decision-making model to generate options
- Making a decision to resolve the ethical issue
- Taking action
- Reviewing and evaluating the actions taken

Ethical reflection occurs throughout the process. Development of ethical competence for genetic and genomic clinical practice starts from a consideration of the reasons we have for understanding genetics and the related issues that emerge as genetic and genomic science is translated into practice.

4.4. GENETIC AND GENOMIC COMPETENCIES

In genetic and genomic nursing, ethical principles enumerated in the ANA and ICN Code of Ethics for Nurses are further codified in the *Essentials of Genetic and Genomic Nursing: Competencies, Curricula Guidelines, and Outcome Indicators* (Consensus Panel, 2009) (herein referred to as *Essentials* document). The 2009 *Essentials* document provides guidance for nursing competencies for the professional registered nurse in the assessment, application, and integration of genetic and genomic knowledge in clinical care, patient and family support, and the nurse's professional responsibilities. In 2012, the *Essential Genetic and Genomic Competencies for Nurses with Graduate Degrees* was published jointly by the ANA and the International Society of Nurses in Genetics (ISONG) (Greco, Tinley, & Seibert, 2012). The 2012 competencies are intended to complement existing nursing competencies while integrating genetics and genomics into all nursing roles. The competency statements build on the 2009 *Essentials* document and focus on additional and higher level competencies expected of nurses with graduate degrees. Some competencies are identified as uniquely relevant to APRNs in their role as primary and acute health care providers. The 38 competencies are organized under seven major categories: (1) risk assessment and interpretation; (2) genetic education, counseling, testing, and results interpretation; (3) clinical management; (4) ELSI; (5) professional role; (6) leadership; and (7) research. For APRNs in professional practice, patient care competencies focus on the trajectory of patient care, from risk assessment and interpretation to genetic education, counseling, testing, and results interpretation of genetic information, and through the ongoing clinical management of genetic conditions. Throughout all these activities, it is expected that the APRN will identify and recognize the ethical, legal, and social implications implicit in care of patients and families diagnosed with, or at risk for, genetic conditions. Additionally, ethical APRN practice dictates the application of ethical principles in the integration of genetic knowledge with patient and family values and beliefs, decision-making regarding genetic testing, and communication of genetic information. The role of the APRN in ethical genetic and genomic care is not limited to the direct care role with the patient and family. Leadership within nursing education and the nursing profession, interprofessional collaboration, involvement in public education and policy discourse, and ethical behavior in nursing research comprise arenas for nursing ethical practice.

Within *Essential Genetic and Genomic Competencies for Nurses with Graduate Degrees* (Greco *et al.*, 2012), four competencies with ELSI are articulated; three of the competencies are described here. The first ELSI competency states that nurses with graduate degrees in nursing should be prepared to *facilitate ethical decision-making* related to genetics genomics congruent with the *client's values and beliefs*. In order to facilitate decision-making congruent with the client's values and beliefs, the client's values and beliefs must first be identified. This is best accomplished by identifying the APRNs own values with the accompanying emotions and reflecting on those beliefs. It is essential to pay attention to the APRNs intuition as the right thing to do in the situation is considered. After acknowledging values, they should be set aside while listening carefully to the client. Facilitating ethical decision-making requires skill. After recognizing the issue, identifying the stakeholders,

collecting the facts, and listing options, a simple decision-making model should be used before acting.

Another ELSI competency is *Implement effective strategies to resolve ELSI issues* related to genetics/genomics. The range of ELSI issues associated with genetics and genomics is diverse and extensive and involves collaboration with patients, families, and the interprofessional team. Categories of situations that have ethical implications include (1) genetic testing decisions and effects on clients, family members, and communities; (2) appropriate use of genetic testing (e.g., when treatment is not available, testing of minors for adult onset disease, direct-to-consumer (DTC) testing, expectations of "normal"); (3) handling of genetic information (confidentiality, use of information by employers, governmental agencies, courts, and schools); (4) genetic and genomic technology in disease treatment (risks and benefits, uncertainties and rapid discovery; uses of gene therapy); and (5) equity in access and costs of genetic tests and treatments. Recognizing the issues will become easier the more often they are encountered or discussed. Effective strategies for resolving these issues are found in basic nursing skills like careful listening, thorough assessment, compassionate communication, cultural sensitivity, and decisive intervention. Pavlish *et al.* (2011) identified additional ethics-specific actions to use in complex clinical situations. Communicating openly in a timely fashion with the health care team, speaking up, developing trust, arranging family conferences, and initiating referrals are suggested nursing actions. Consultation with ethics professionals should be employed when consensus is not achieved among the stakeholders or there is not clarity among those responsible for making the decision regarding how an ethical dilemma should be resolved.

The last ELSI competency is to *apply ethical principles* when making decisions regarding management of genetic and genomic information identified through clinical or research technologies (Greco *et al.*, 2012). The ethical principles of respect for autonomy, veracity, beneficence, nonmaleficence, and fidelity should be applied when appropriate. Responsible communication of incidental findings is a specific example of a situation requiring careful management.

Genetic and genomic core competencies have been established for all health professionals (National Coalition for Health Professional Education in Genetics [NCHPEG], 2007). In addition to meeting these basic competencies, nurses with graduate degrees actively engage with patients and families in risk assessment, genetic risk interpretation, and management of conditions with a genetic component. Therefore, the enhanced responsibilities in advanced practice demand nurses with graduate degrees demonstrate the genetic and genomic competencies commensurate with their role. Genetic and genomic clinical application often places the APRN in a central role when ethical questions or situations present in the patient care arena.

Ethical principles may seem elusive or removed from the daily health care decisions that guide clinical practice. The rapid pace of 15-minute appointments, varied health care conditions and needs, productivity goals, and the pressure to meet multiple demands are not conducive to a scholarly discussion (or implementation) of ethics in health care. However, it is precisely when practitioners are faced with deadlines, workplace pressures, and new genetic information and technologies that understanding the ethical, social, and legal implications of communication and decision-making with patients and adherence to ethical principles related to genomic care are vitally important. The following vignettes will illustrate clinical situations with ethical implications for advanced practice nursing. They are not intended to be comprehensive of all ethical genomic situations in practice, but they will highlight application of core ethics principles in genetic and genomic health care. Vignettes will demonstrate concepts across the trajectory of the APRN-patient clinical encounter, from risk assessment and interpretation through the testing process (education, counseling, testing, and results interpretation) and clinical management. The role of the APRN in scenarios with ethical implications will also be explored.

4.5. RISK ASSESSMENT AND INTERPRETATION

4.5.1. Vignette 1

Marcia Clemens, RN, DNP, a Family Nurse

Practitioner, is taking a family history of Susan Williams, age 29. She notes that Ms. Williams' mother and two maternal aunts died of breast cancer in their mid-30s. Ms. Williams has two sisters in their mid-20s who are in good health; and Susan herself has had no health issues. In addition, Susan tells Dr. Clemens, "I look just like my dad and his sisters, so I guess I don't need to worry about breast cancer." Dr. Clemens is not familiar with the specifics of *BRCA* testing but knows that genetic testing for familial breast cancer is available. She decides that because the three sisters are in good health, and Susan does not seem concerned about breast cancer, as a practitioner, she doesn't need to further address Ms. Williams' potential genetic risk at this time but notes genetic testing should be considered/addressed/discussed at the next appointment.

What ethical principles should Dr. Clemens consider when she advises Susan regarding her family health history and potential individual risk?

4.5.1.1. Commentary

Dr. Clemens has a responsibility to Susan, her own professional development, and the ethical standards of the nursing profession. Consider the following principles and virtues:

- *Autonomy:* The patient's right to choose available testing should be recognized, as well as her right to decline testing that may be offered, even if the testing is advised by the practitioner.
- *Beneficence/nonmaleficence:* The premise of "do good" and "do no harm" is a cornerstone of ethics for health care providers. The APRN has a duty to promote education that will inform Susan about her potential risks. How might that duty extend to family members, such as Susan's siblings? At the same time, how might "harm" be defined by Susan and her family members?
- *Justice:* Genetic testing is becoming more common and costs for some tests are becoming within reach for more patients. Genetic testing is not universally covered by all third-party payers; in addition, not all patients have access to health care coverage. Should

genetic testing be available only to those with the financial means to pay for testing? What ethical considerations should be weighed when determining costs of genetic testing and promoting equity of care for patients across populations?

- *Integrity:* In this scenario, Dr. Clemens has limited knowledge of *BRCA* testing. As an APRN, Dr. Clemens has a professional and ethical responsibility to become competent regarding emerging knowledge and technologies, including both consulting with and providing information to her health care colleagues. Ethical practice dictates Dr. Clemens not avoid discussion on genetic risk or delay providing the highest standards of health care (and potentially cause patient harm). Ethical options include consulting with a genetics professional or making a genetic counseling referral. Becoming competent as an APRN will also provide Dr. Clemens the knowledge on risk assessment to dispel Susan's myth that she is not at risk because she looks like her father's side of the family.

4.5.2. Vignette 2

As an Acute Care Nurse Practitioner, you are caring for Robbie Hernandez, a 62-year-old Hispanic male with atrial fibrillation. Mr. Hernandez also has diabetes mellitus, Type II, and a history of transient ischemic attacks (TIAs). You plan to treat Mr. Hernandez with Coumadin for 6 to 8 weeks to decrease the potential for a cerebrovascular accident (CVA) prior to his cardiologist restoring a normal sinus rhythm through cardioversion. Mr. Hernandez states that he is "sensitive to medication" and that his father had a difficult time being regulated on Coumadin. You could order genetic tests that would provide information regarding the patient's pharmacogenomic profile for metabolizing Coumadin, but your patient's insurance will not cover genetic testing.

How do you interpret the role of genetics in the assessment and interpretation of risk for this patient? What are the ethical issues of treatment without the additional information genetic testing could provide? How does ethics apply on a systems level to the distribution of health care services and resources? How could you be proactive in anticipating similar cases?

4.5.2.1. Commentary

Clinical care often presents the APRN with "competing priorities" and having to make decisions based on less than complete information. Limitations on practice illustrate ethical considerations for the practitioner. Principles include the following:

- *Nonmaleficence:* Given that this patient identifies a family history of being "sensitive to medication," Coumadin dosing by "trial and error" increases the risk of potential harm, either from insufficient anticoagulation or from increased susceptibility to bleeding. How does the practitioner weigh the risks and ethical dilemma of care management with incomplete information?
- *Truth telling:* Honesty in the APRN-patient relationship creates an obligation to discuss testing benefits with Mr. Hernandez and any associated costs. Are there circumstances in which the practitioner should *not* disclose this information? What ethical responsibility does the practitioner have for advocating for resources to help defray the cost of obtaining genomic information that would affect treatment?
- *Justice:* The fair allocation of resources suggests that each receive according to need. Each society has finite resources to provide for the health care needs of its people, along with a growing health care demand. How do we define "need" and "fair allocation"? According to a utilitarian approach, one might argue that the greatest good for the greatest number should be the goal, but defining that goal is difficult. What is the "greatest good" and how do we measure success?

4.6. GENETIC EDUCATION, COUNSELING, TESTING, AND RESULTS INTERPRETATION

4.6.1. Vignette 1

You are a nurse midwife working in a Women's Health Clinic. As part of your routine care of pregnant women, you and your staff offer cystic fibrosis carrier testing (CFCT) in accordance with the American College of Obstetricians

(ACOG) guidelines. The practice is a busy one. The tests planned during pregnancy are commonly explained in the initial prenatal visit by the prenatal education nurse while the patient waits for her prenatal examination with you. When you see Cindy, 12 weeks pregnant, and ask if she has any questions, she says, "No, I just signed all the forms. I figure you wouldn't offer me tests if they weren't good for my baby."

As part of your office CFCT protocol, testing is done first on the mother, and if the mother is positive for carrier status, then testing is done on the father, so a final risk assessment for the pregnancy can be determined. Cindy, your patient in the scenario above, subsequently has test results that indicate she is a carrier of the most common CF mutation, delta 508. When you explain to Cindy her carrier testing results, she is very distressed, states her husband is not the father (he is not aware of this), and declines to identify the baby's father. Cindy is not aware of any family history of CF and refuses further testing, because she doesn't want her husband to know he is not the father. Her sister, Molly, who is newly pregnant, also receives care at your clinic. Molly has not yet decided whether to have CF carrier testing. Cindy refuses to share her CF carrier results with her family. What are the ethical implications and how can they best be addressed?

4.6.1.1. Commentary

Ethical dilemmas are common in the prenatal environment. Clinical practice involves consideration of not only the pregnant patient and the patient's partner, but also the developing fetus. Genomic conditions illustrate how health (and illness) are not individual issues, but have multigenerational family consequences and implications.

Central to ethical concerns for genetic testing in prenatal care include the following:

- *Informed consent:* Patients should be fully informed of the indications for any medical testing, including genetic testing, what the test results mean, and what kind of decisions may be indicated as a result of test information. Tests that appear to the patient to be "routine" may provide information the patient is unprepared and unwilling to receive. The results may limit autonomy or

cause emotional distress or harm. The ethical APRN will assess for genomic health care literacy and provide opportunities to promote and ensure a robust informed consent process prior to prenatal genetic testing. Counseling and support resources to explain risk and thoroughly explore options with the patient throughout the testing and decision-making process are indicated. How can these be ensured in the clinic setting? How may the practitioner's attitude about genetic testing bias the process? How can the practitioner best support that the patient's autonomy is maintained regarding prenatal testing and post-testing decisions?

- *Privacy and confidentiality:* Cindy has a right to expect that her medical information will be private and confidential. This is an ethical obligation for every health care provider. The Health Insurance Portability and Accountability Act (HIPAA) of 1996 also makes it unlawful for a health care provider to share confidential patient information. The risk of CF to Cindy's baby cannot be fully assessed without testing the baby's biological father. The potential risk of CF to Molly's baby will not be known without CF carrier testing; knowing Cindy's CFCT results may influence Molly's decision for testing. As you consider the ethical factors and potential consequences, contemplate how you would counsel Cindy regarding information-sharing within her family. How would you address conflicts between Cindy's decisions and your own ethical values? What are the options for resolving diverse perspectives of your office colleagues regarding how (and to whom) genomic information should be made available?

4.6.2. Vignette 2

There are two families who present to your clinic with questions about genetic testing. In Exam Room A, Mr. Sorensen is with his 19- and 21-year-old daughters. His wife died of breast cancer 4 years ago, and he requests *BRCA* testing for his daughters to "avoid losing my daughters like I lost my wife." The 19-year-old daughter avoids eye contact, provides one or two word answers to questions, and indicates she is willing to have *BRCA* testing. The 21-year-old daughter states she doesn't want to know if she has a *BRCA* mutation, because she doesn't want her boyfriend to know there might be something "wrong with her."

In Exam Room B, 16-year-old Darrell accompanies his mother, who has Huntington's disease (HD). Darrell has been the primary caregiver for his mother over the past four years; today he asks you about whether he can be tested for HD. From his research on the internet, Darrell knows that HD is an autosomal dominant condition and that he has a 50% chance of inheriting the genetic mutation for HD. He is starting to date teenage girls and explore post–high school education options. Darrell wants to know his genetic status so he can consider what that means regarding personal relationships, his career options, and life trajectory.

For the patients and families in these two scenarios, what are the ethical questions and principles to consider? Which "ways of being" would be most useful? As an APRN, what are your responsibilities in meeting these ethical challenges and what resources can be valuable to meet these ethical needs? Do you know what you would choose? How might that influence your response?

4.6.2.1. *Commentary*

Both of these scenarios involve *ownership of decisions and information*, with an emphasis on the rights of minor children below the age of 21. Pregnant women can make genetic testing decisions under the age of 18; in most cases, other genetic testing decisions are reserved to individuals 18 years of age or older. For young adults over 18, decisions can still reflect significant parental pressure, whereas for those under 18, they face limited autonomy in making these decisions. The decision-making capacity for teens to make these important choices has been debated, with the emphasis being on delaying decisions until maturity to prevent harm. As in some of the previous scenarios, preserving *autonomy* and *preventing harm* are key principles. The ethical APRN is an advocate for the patient in this case, the daughters in the first scenario and the 16-year-old in the second. How might that advocacy be demonstrated?

4.7. CLINICAL MANAGEMENT

4.7.1. Vignette 1

Abigail, age 22, comes to your clinic after receiving her *BRCA* positive results. Her 37 year-old mother died of breast cancer when Abigail was 12. She brings in an article outlining *BRCA*-positive care management decisions by celebrities and tearfully insists on a double mastectomy and oophorectomy "as soon as possible.". How do you support her decision-making? What ethical considerations are present?

4.7.1.1. *Commentary*

For *BRCA*-positive young women, choices regarding communication to family members or significant others, relationships, career, and childbearing, as well as care management decisions of surveillance versus a prophylactic mastectomy and/or oophorectomy, can be daunting. A decision-making model (Act, Intention, Context, and Consequences) can assist the APRN in proceeding in an ethical manner.

- *Act:* Consider the action—in this case, double mastectomy and oophorectomy surgery. Why would this be a correct (or an incorrect) action to take? Can an action be correct at one point in time, but not advised at another? What are the most current recommendations for management, and at what age should different management options be employed? Although surgery could produce a good outcome (reduce cancer risk), are there other adverse outcomes that should be considered?
- *Intention:* Who else should be involved in the management plan? Are there other "stakeholders" in Abigail's surgery decision? Although she has a right to autonomy, is she cognizant of the consequences of her decision? Has she considered how family or personal relationships may be affected?
- *Context:* Where is Abigail in her life trajectory? Does she have a life partner and children? Are there milestones, such as childbearing, that she wishes to experience prior to the surgery? What kind of family support does she have? With whom is Abigail discussing

these life decisions? What is the urgency of the decision in this case, does the decision need to be made immediately, or is there the option of a more reflective process? What is driving the urgency of her desire for surgery?

• *Consequences:* What is the ultimate result of making a decision about surgery now? What strategies would allow for reduced cancer risk while providing the most flexible options for the patient? Are there unintended negative consequences of a decision now that could be avoided?

Important life and care management decisions should be considered carefully and thoughtfully. Emphasis on having adequate patient support to promote an ethical and reflective process that protects the patient's autonomy, prevents harm, and enables informed decision-making should be emphasized.

4.7.2. Vignette 2

James, age 41, has a strong family history of early-onset Alzheimer's disease. Worried about his risk of developing dementia, he sent a buccal sample last month to an internet-based genetic testing company. Today, he presents to your office with a computer printout of genetic test results, which indicate he may be at increased risk for several chronic conditions, as well as allele variations of undetermined significance. James is despondent over the information he received and wants to know if he can do anything to "change his destiny." What ethical dilemmas are present in DTC testing? Have you had DTC genetic testing? Why or why not?

4.7.2.1. Commentary

DTC testing has increased patient access to personal information, enabling individuals to assume increasing responsibility for their own health and health care. However, in this rapidly changing and complex scientific field, there are significant ethical implications to DTC:

• *Informed consent:* Misleading claims or partial information by companies about the value of particular genetic tests may compromise the patient's ability to make informed

decisions regarding genetic testing, or the implications of the test results.

• *Truthfulness:* Ethical questions include the accuracy and quality assurance of the laboratory testing process and the interpretation of test results. Unknown implications of test results or unfounded claims of disease risk associated with test results compromise the truthfulness of the data available to consumers.

• *Susceptibility for harm:* With DTC testing, continuity of care with a qualified health care professional to assess risk, provide patient teaching, and interpret test results may be lacking. In addition, there are insufficient ongoing support services for genetic test interpretation and counseling for recognized risk. Results of undetermined significance may also be misunderstood and create potential for adverse patient responses to genomic information.

The ethical dilemma for the APRN involves how to facilitate patient choice, autonomy, and informed consent, while limiting patient harm and adverse consequences from genetic information available outside of the provider-patient interaction. Promoting a strong nurse-patient relationship and the opportunity for genetic education and counseling in the clinical encounter is recommended.

4.8. LEGAL AND SOCIAL IMPLICATIONS OF GENETIC AND GENOMIC INFORMATION

The use (and misuse) of genetic and genomic information has both legal and social implications. Knowledge of genetic variation effects on health risk and treatment response creates the potential for discrimination against individuals and identifiable populations. These consequences include the ability to obtain and maintain health care insurance coverage and employment.

Two landmark pieces of legislation are designed to protect Americans against the potential for discrimination based on their genetic information. The first is the Genetic Information Nondiscrimination Act (GINA), which was passed in 2008 (National Human Genome Research Institute [NHGRI], 2012). GINA (Title I) was designed to afford individual protection against having genetic information used to deny or limit health insurance, whereas Title II of GINA prohibits requesting, requiring, collecting, or using genetic information in employment decisions. Genetic information protected encompasses an individual's genetic tests (including research study data), genetic tests of family members up to and including fourth degree relatives, genetic tests done in pregnancy or as a result of reproductive technology, and the occurrence of a disease or disorder in family members (including family history). Although health insurance is protected under GINA, other types of insurance, such as disability, long-term care, and life insurance underwriting are not protected by its provisions. In some cases, state law offers greater protection than the federal GINA legislation (United States [U.S.] Department of Health and Human Services [HSS], 2009).

> The law was designed "to ease concerns about discrimination that might keep some people from getting genetic tests that could benefit their health, . . . or take part in research studies without fear that their DNA information might be used against them in health insurance or the workplace" (NHGRI, 2014).

The second legislative action of particular interest to nurses, the Health Insurance Portability and Accountability Act of 1996, addresses the protection of health information. HIPAA rules were designed to protect patient confidentiality and the security of patient data. Provisions of HIPAA rules state that patient permission or authorization is required for the use or disclosure of protected information not directly related to treatment, payment, or health operations. In 2002, the HHS clarified what is intended by the protection of certain health information through issuing a "Privacy Rule" (HHS, 2003a). The Privacy Rule aims to ensure an individual's health information is protected while still promoting the flow of important information needed to provide high quality health care. This balance "permits important uses of information, while protecting the privacy of people who seek care and healing" (HHS, 2003b). HIPAA and the Privacy Rule apply to health care providers, health information, and health plans. The Privacy Rule protects all "individually identifiable health information,"

including demographics and physical or mental health conditions, held or transmitted by a covered entity or its business associate (HHS, 2003a). GINA definitions were added in 2013 to the HIPAA Final Rule and became effective in September, 2013. The clarification of the HIPAA protections specifies that genetic information is health information and subject to the same privacy protections as other health information. In addition, genetic information cannot be disclosed or used by health insurance plans or health insurance issuers for underwriting purposes (HIPAA, 2013). In the practice setting, this requires careful attention to verbal communication, charts, and computer screens so that they cannot be read by others. Strict policies must be followed to protect patient information both *within* the practice setting and when transmitting patient information to outside agencies or other treatment facilities.

For society, how genetic variation is perceived within the larger context of societal diversity influences cultural attitudes and mores, individual and group behavior, and national policy decisions. As genetic discovery and application in health care become more commonplace, our choices as a society will determine whether we embrace differences or whether individuals or populations will face discrimination based on real or perceived genetic differences. Societal implications of genetic and genomic advances include decisions of what test development will be supported by public funding and the type of genetic testing covered by health insurance. Implications may include what pharmaceutical innovations will be supported by research and development funding, and whether drugs will be developed for patients with a "common" genetic variant, with fewer therapeutic options for patients with a rarer polymorphism. Will subpopulations identified with higher chronic disease risk be seen as "less desirable" or traits associated with success preferentially chosen through preimplantation testing? The issues with societal implications related to genetic discovery are complex and will need thoughtful and collaborative public discussion. As nurses, nurse leaders, and patient advocates, we have a moral and ethical responsibility to advocate for the health and well-being of all of our patients. Our efforts are enhanced through learning about and accessing resources available to our patients and families. Health advocacy organizations such as the Genetic Alliance (http://www.geneticalliance.org/) and disease specific organizations such as the March of Dimes (http://www.marchofdimes.com/) and the Cystic Fibrosis Foundation (http://www.cff.org/) work to inform patients, families, health professionals, and policymakers of issues related to genetics, genomics, and the societal implications of genomic discovery.

4.9. CONCLUSION

Genomic clinical applications based upon genetic science elicit ethical concerns not raised to the same extent by other biomedical technologies. In discussing the ethical and social implications of genetic and genomic technologies, the potential therapeutic benefits must be considered alongside any unintended harms associated with their use. For many genetic and genomic disorders, there are limited effective treatments; identification of genetic risk and prevention are of paramount importance. Economic costs associated with treatment and lost productivity are also considerations. The economic drivers and constraints of novel genetic and genomic technologies highlight the ethical importance of regulatory oversight that promotes innovation as well as protects population health and public safety.

New technologies offer opportunities for early identification, prevention, and treatment. High interest issues in the next decade include testing for Alzheimer's disease, pre-implantation genetic diagnosis, whole genome sequencing (WGS) in both research and clinical practice, and the implications of genetic discoveries for identifiable populations. Additional ethical conflicts are inherent in the blurring lines between research and therapy, protecting the freedom to choose or decline genetic testing, and navigating health management plans that include lifestyle change secondary to genetic findings. Genetic health literacy promotion in patients and families during the communication of genetic information has both educational and ethical challenges given the subtle differences in medical, technical, and personal perspectives. Nonclinical applications for recreational purposes or for enhancement are not discussed here though questions about them may be encountered in practice. Future policy will be developed in all these areas and it is incumbent

on APRNs to claim a place at the table during the formative discussions. This will demonstrate achievement of the last ELSI competence (p. 12), "*Inform health care and research policy related to ELSI issues in genetics/genomics.*"

Providing sound clinical guidance and assisting clients with multiple uncertainties requires ethical competence. This chapter is based on the belief that there are numerous ethical challenges posed by the clinical application of genetic technology. Maintaining an ethical perceptual "lens" when managing genetic information and providing genomic health care is essential in meeting the evolving and complex future health needs of our patients and families.

4.10. REFERENCES

Alexander, L., & Moore, M. (2012). Deontological ethics. In Edward N. Zalta (Ed.), *The Stanford encyclopedia of philosophy* (Winter 2012 Edition). Retrieved November 12, 2013, from http://plato.stanford.edu/archives/win2012/entries/ethics-deontological/

American Nurses Association. (2015) *Code of ethics for nurses with interpretive statements*. Silver Spring, MD: Author. Retrieved June 10, 2015 from http://www.nursingworld.org/MainMenuCategories/EthicsStandards/CodeofEthicsforNurses/Code-of-Ethics-For-Nurses.html

Beauchamp, T. L., & Childress, J. F. (2009). *Principles of biomedical ethics (6th ed.)*. New York: Oxford University Press.

Bok, S. (1999). *Lying: Moral choice in public and private life*. New York: Vantage Books.

Boylan, M. (2000). *Medical ethics*. Upper Saddle River, NJ: Prentice Hall.

Consensus Panel on Genetic/Genomic Nursing Competencies. (2009). *Essentials of genetic and genomic nursing: Competencies, curricula guidelines, and outcome indicators* (2nd. ed.). Silver spring, MD: American Nurses Association.

Cystic Fibrosis Foundation (2014). *Cystic Fibrosis Foundation-Home.* Retrieved March 25, 2014, from www.cff.org

Dahnke, M., & Dreher, H. M. (2006). Defining ethics and applying the theories. In V. D. Lachman (Ed.), *Applied ethics in nursing* (pp. 3–13). New York: Springer.

Fowler, M. D. (2010). Nursing's ethical tradition: The 1870s to the rise of bioethics. In A. J. Davis, M. D. Fowler, & M. A. Aroskar, *Ethical dilemmas & nursing practice* (5th. ed., p. 34). Boston: Pearson.

Genetic Alliance (2014). *Genetic Alliance home page.* Retrieved March 25, 2014, from http://www.geneticalliance.org/

Greco, K. E., Tinley, S., & Seibert, D. (2012). *Essential genetic and genomic competencies for nurses with graduate degrees*. Silver Spring, MD: American Nurses Association and International Society of Nurses in Genetics. Retrieved November 12, 2013, from http://www.genome.gov/Pages/Health/HealthCareProvidersInfo/Grad_Gen_Comp.pdf

Health Insurance Portability and Accountability Act (HIPAA). (2013). *HIPAA Final Rule: Genetic Information Nondiscrimination Act (GINA) Definitions*. Retrieved March 25, 2014, from http://www.hipaa.com/2013/02/hipaa-final-rule-genetic-information-nondiscrimination-act-gina-definitions/

International Council of Nurses. (2012). *The ICN Code of Ethics for Nurses*. Retrieved on November 12, 2013, from http://www.icn.ch/images/stories/documents/about/icncode_english.pdf

March of Dimes (2014). *March of Dimes: Working together for stronger, happier babies*. Retrieved March 25, 2014, from http://www.marchofdimes.com/

National Coalition for Health Professional Education in Genetics (NCHPEG). (2007). *Core competencies for all health professionals*. Retrieved February 2, 2014, from http://www.nchpeg.org/index.php?option=com_content&view=article&id=237&Itemid=84

The National Commission for the Protection of Human Subjects of Biomedical and Behavioral Research, DHEW. (1979). The Belmont Report: Ethical Principles and Guidelines for the Protection of Human Subjects of Research. Retrieved on November 12, 2013, from http://www.hhs.gov/ohrp/humansubjects/guidance/belmont.html

National Human Genome Research Institute (NHGRI). (2012). *Genetic Information Nondiscrimination Act of 2008*. Retrieved on March 25, 2014, from https://www.genome.gov/10002328

National Human Genome Research Institute (NHGRI). (2014). *Genetic Information Nondiscrimination Act (GINA) of 2008*. Retrieved on March 25, 2014, from https://www.genome.gov/24519851

Pavlish, C., Brown-Saltzman, K., Hersh, M., Shirk, M., & Rounkle, A. (2011). Nursing priorities, actions, and regrets for ethical situations in clinical practice. *Journal of Nursing Scholarship, 43*(4), 385–395.

Pellegrino, E. D., & Thomasma, D. C. (1993). *The virtues in medical practice*. New York: Oxford University Press.

Taylor, C. (1993). Nursing ethics: The role of caring. *Association of Women's Health, Obstetrics, and Neonatal Nurses' Clinical Issues in Perinatal and Women's Health Nursing, 4*(4), 552–560.

United States Department of Health and Human Services (HSS) (2003a). *Health information privacy: The privacy rule*. Retrieved March 25, 2014, from http://www.hhs.gov/ocr/privacy/hipaa/administrative/privacyrule/index.html

United States Department of Health and Human Services (HSS) (2003b). *Health information privacy: Summary of the HIPAA privacy rule*. Retrieved March 25, 2014, from http://www.hhs.gov/ocr/privacy/hipaa/understanding/summary/

United States Department of Health and Human Services (HHS) (2009). *"GINA": The Genetic Information Nondiscrimination Act of 2008: Information for researchers and health care professionals*. Retrieved March 25, 2014, from https://www.genome.gov/Pages/PolicyEthics/GeneticDiscrimination/GINAInfoDoc.pdf

Velasquez, M., Andre, C., Shanks, T., & Meyer, M. J. (1996). *Thinking ethically: A framework for moral decision making*. Retrieved November 12, 2013, from http://www.scu.edu/ethics/practicing/decision/thinking.html

Chapter 5

Essentials of Pharmacogenomics

JUNE ZHANG
YU LIU
JEFFERY FAN
BRADLEY T. ANDRESEN
YING HUANG

Objectives:

- Discuss pharmacogenomics including pharmacogenomic testing of common drugs used in cancer therapeutics:
  — 5-fluorouracil (5-FU)
  — Irinotecan
  — 6-mercaptopurine (6-MP)
- Discuss the pharmacogenomics of common drugs used for cardiovascular diseases
  — Warfarin
  — Clopidogrel
- Explain the pharmacogenomics of abacavir used to treat human immunodeficiency virus
- Describe future role of nursing in pharmacogenomics

5.1. INTRODUCTION TO PHARMACOGENOMICS

Drug efficacy and adverse drug reactions (ADRs) often vary widely among patients. For many commonly prescribed medications, only a subset of patients respond favorably, whereas others may either experience poor response or severe ADRs (Sadee, 2011). The goal of personalized/precision medicine is to increase the likelihood of choosing the appropriate drug at the optimal dose for the right patient by using information from a patient's health history, behavior, and environment, as well as the genetic makeup (Price, 2013; Ritchie, 2012). *Personalized medicine* is defined as "the use of an individual's genetic profile in guiding decision regarding prevention, diagnosis, and treatment of disease" (National Institutes of Health, National Human Genome Research Institute, 2015). A newer taxonomy is focused on the concept of *precision medicine* (National Academy of Science [NAS], 2011). In precision medicine, according to the NAS, the "ultimate end point is the selection of a subset of patients with a common biological basis of disease, who are most likely to benefit from a drug or other treatment" (NAS, 2011, p. 37). Precision medicine takes individual variability into account utilizing a molecular approach including proteomics, metabolomics, genomics, and other cellular assays for prevention, diagnosis, screening, and treatment (Collins & Varmus,

June Zhang, Sun Yat-sen University, School of Nursing, Guangzhou, China
Yu Liu, Peking University, School of Nursing, Beijing, China
Jeffery Fan, Bradley T. Andresen, and Ying Huang, Department of Pharmaceutical Sciences, College of Pharmacy, Western University of Health Sciences, Pomona, CA.
Correspondence should be sent to: Dr. Ying Huang, Western University of Health Sciences, College of Pharmacy, 309 E. Second Street, Pomona, CA 91766, Tel: 909-469-5220, Fax: 909-469-5600, Email: yhuang@westernu.edu.

2015). Whether the term precision or personalized medicine is used, nurses will play a very important role in achieving such goals towards management of care.

Pharmacogenetics/pharmacogenomics, a rapidly growing field, has become one of the most important aspects for personalized/precision medicine. This subject field is expected to revolutionize clinical practice in the near future even though most drugs are currently prescribed to patients using the "one size fits all" approach (Ritchie, 2012; Zdanowicz, 2010). This interdisciplinary field blends the important components from the disciplines of genetics, genomics, and pharmacology (Johnson, 2003). Although the terms of pharmacogenetics and pharmacogenomics are used interchangeably, there are some distinguishing features between the 2 concepts. *Pharmacogenetics* is defined as the study of 1 or a few numbers of genes involved in the response to a drug, whereas *pharmacogenomics* refers to the study of all genes in the entire genome. Because pharmacogenomics covers more broadly the genome-wide analysis of genetic determinants of drug efficacy and toxicity (American Association of Pharmaceutical Scientists, 2013), it is the preferred term. Therefore, throughout this chapter, the term *pharmacogenomics* will be used consistently.

Personalized/precision medicine is effective only if the subsets of the patient population can be identified for specific therapeutic options (Simon, 2011). To identify which patients are more or less likely to benefit from a specific treatment, or to experience ADRs, it is critical to develop 1 or a panel of *predictive biomarkers*, which are defined as biological measurements that can be used to predict the outcome of therapeutic interventions (Simon, 2011). According to the results of testing with these predictive biomarkers, the patients can be classified as "responders," "nonresponders," or "toxic responders." Although many nongenetic factors, such as age, sex, drug treatment, family history of disease, body mass index, and smoking status, have already been used in the predictive models, it has been recently shown that genetic factors can contribute to the drug response outcome up to 95% (Belle & Singh, 2008). Therefore, for the use of pharmacogenomics in personalized/precision medicine, predictive biomarkers are measured by pharmacogenomics testing in specific patients, whereby the information can be used to choose the optimal drug and/or dose for the patient. Personalized/precision medicine does not mean that each patient is treated differently, but that the patient population is stratified according to the pharmacogenomics testing results into responders, nonresponders, or toxic responders before the therapy. This allows pharmacogenomics guided drug selection for each group of patients (see Figure 5.1). There have been many examples for predictive biomarkers being used in clinical setting (see below), in particular, in the field of oncology, in which the nature of the disease has expedited the use of pharmacogenomics in development of such biomarkers (Simon, 2011). The important biomarkers that have shown value in clinical use are shown in Table 5.1.

Whether for the general concept of personalized/precision medicine or for the optimized use of specific drugs, the influence of pharmacogenomics will be far-reaching for all heath care professions, with the promise of improving therapeutic outcome. However, currently, the subject of pharmacogenomics has not been a major component covered in the curricula of nursing or other health professions (Moen & Lamba, 2012; Williams *et al.*, 2011). For example, in an early study by Edwards *et al.* (2006) to assess integration of genetics into curriculum by nurse practitioner (NP) faculty, the researchers found that 96% of the faculty reported no to minimal integration of pharmacogenetics into the curriculum; 68% of the faculty felt uncomfortable in teaching the topic; and 83% reported no pharmacogenetic training or education (Edwards *et al.*, 2006). In a similar study in 2010, only 11% of NP faculty surveyed reported they had either begun or integrated pharmacogenomics into their NP pharmacology course. To facilitate a better understanding of pharmacogenomic information, it is necessary to identify the essential components among the masses of genomic knowledge accumulated continuously in the biomedical literature. This chapter is intended to provide a foundation for clinical nurses, advanced practice registered nurses (APRNs), nurse leaders, nurse researchers, and nursing students or trainees, but not to offer a comprehensive reference. The foundations presented here will facilitate establishment of the genetic basis for some of the commonly observed variations in drug response and ADRs

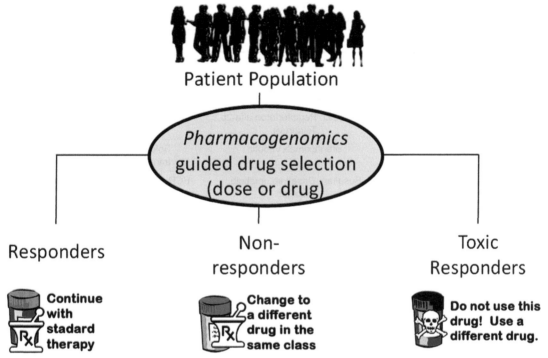

FIGURE 5.1. Pharmacogenomic information can be used by health care providers to identify responders, nonresponders, or toxic responders before the therapy leading to pharmacogenomics guided drug selection for each group of patients.

among patient populations. Because in Chapter 1 of the book, the authors have described the basic mechanisms of genomics, including gene structure, gene expression, and the variations in the genotype and phenotype of individuals. This chapter is focused on how genetic variation can explain an individual's response to drug therapy. The chapter begins with a discussion of the interactions between pharmacogenomics and how the body handles a drug (i.e., pharmacokinetics)

TABLE 5.1. *Pharmacogenomic Biomarkers in Drug Labels and Currently Available Testing.*

Pharmacogenomic Biomarkers	Drugs	Tests
Pharmacokinetic Biomarkers		
CYP2D6	Aripiprazole, Atomoxetine, Carvedilol, Cevimeline, Citalopram, Clomipramine, Clozapine, Codeine, etc.	AmpliChip® CYP450
CYP2C19	Carisoprodol,Citalopram, Clobazam, Clopidogrel, Diazepam, Rabeprazole	AccuType CP; AmpliChip® CYP450
CYP2C9	Celecoxib,Flurbiprofen, Warfarin	Warfarin Sensitivity
DPD	Capecitabine, Fluorouracil	DPD Enzyme Assay
TPMT	Azathioprine, Cisplatin, Mercaptopurine, Thioguanine	TPMT GenotypR or Prometheus TPMT Genetics
CYP1A2	Dexlansoprazole	P450-Glo
UTG1A1	Indacaterol, Irinotecan, Nilotinib	Invader UGT1A1 molecular assay
NAT1; NAT2	Isosorbide, Hydralazine, Rifampin, Isoniazid, Pyrazinamide	

(continued)

TABLE 5.1 (continued). Pharmacogenomic Biomarkers in Drug Labels and Currently Available Testing.

Pharmacogenomic Biomarkers	Drugs	Tests
Pharmacodynamic Biomarkers		
PML/RARα	Arsenic Trioxide, Tretinoin	PML/RARα t(15;17) Translocation Assay
LDL receptor	Atorvastatin	LDLR Test
IL28B	Boceprevir, Peginterferon alfa-2b, Telaprevir	Accutype IL28B Test
CD30	Brentuximab Vedotin	Soluble CD30, Fluorescent Immunoassay—ARUP Lab
Ph chromosome	Busulfan, Dasatinib, Imatinib, Nilotinib	BCR-ABL Quantitation; ABL Kinase Domain Sequencing
HLB-B*1502	Carbamazepine, Phenytoin	Carbamazepine Sensitivity Genotyping
EGFR	Cetuximab, Erlotinib, Gefitinib, Panitumumab	EGFR Mutation Test—Lab 21
KRAS	Cetuximab, Panitumumab	KRAS Mutation Test
G6PD	Chloroquine, Dapsone, Rasburicase	G6PD 2 Mutation—Arup Lab
Rh genotype	Clomiphene	Rh Genotyping
CD25	Denileukin Difititox	ONTAK Sensitivity
Factor V Leiden	Eltrombopag, Tamoxifen	Factor V Mutation Analysis
Antithrombin III deficiency	Eltrombopag	
HER2/NEU	Everolimus, Lapatinib, Pertuzumab, Trastuzumab	HercepTest™
ER&/PGR	Exemestane, Letrozole	
ER	Fulvestrant	
C-kit	Imatinib	
PDGFR	Imatinib	Myeloproliferative Disorders Panel
FIPL1-PDGFRα	Imatinib	
UCD	Sodium Phenylacetate, Sodium Benzoate, Sodium Phenylbutyrate	
Prothrombin mutations (F2)	Tamoxifen	Prothrombin (F2) G20210A Mutation—ARUP Lab
CFTR(G551D)	Ivacaftor	
Chromosome 5q	Lenalidomide	
CCR5	Maraviroc	
APOE2	Pravastatin	GenoType® ApoE
CD20 antigen	Tositumomab	B-Cell CD20 Expression—ARUP Lab
BRAF	Vemurafenib	cobas® 4800 BRAF V600 Mutation Test
VKORC1	Warfarin	Invader® Warfarin Sensitivity Molecular Assay

Data are derived from Table of Pharmacogenomic Biomarkers in Drug Labels at http://www.fda.gov/Drugs/ScienceResearch/ResearchAreas/Pharmacogenetics/ucm083378.htm and PharmGKB database at http://www.pharmgkb.org/

and how a drug affects the body (i.e., pharmacodynamics). The chapter also provides specific selected therapeutic areas as examples, such as oncology, cardiovascular, and infectious diseases applicable to the field of pharmacogenomics. Case studies are also presented as each pertains to a therapeutic agent and pharmacogenomics. Lastly, the chapter provides an overview of the future direction of pharmacogenomics in clinical application, in particular, how nurses can be involved in the use of pharmacogenomics information in personalized/precision medicines.

5.2. PHARMACOKINETICS (PK), PHARMACODYNAMICS (PD), AND PHARMACOGENOMICS

There has been a rapid growth in our understanding of how drug response can be influenced by genetic variations in a single gene or multiple genes. In the field of pharmacology, drug effects are often discussed from 2 perspectives: pharmacokinetics (PK) and pharmacodynamics (PD) (Johnson, 2003). PK describes the time course of the levels of a drug and its metabolites in plasma or different tissues and includes the processes of drug absorption, distribution, metabolism, and elimination (ADME). PD describes the pharmacologic effects of a drug on the body (either desired or undesired), involving binding of the drug to its targets and triggering drug response. Thus, PK can be viewed as describing how the body handles a given drug, whereas PD is what the drug does to the body. Of the nearly 20,000 to 25,000 genes encoded by the human genome, the most important genetic variations that need to be considered for personalized/precision medicine are those that affect the PK and/or the PD processes (Sadee, 2011). It has been well recognized that variations in either PK or PD can lead to variable drug efficacy or different risk of ADR (Johnson, 2003). Genetic variation is an important source for the variability in PK and PD.

The majority of the well-known pharmacogenomic biomarkers are involved in the PK or the PD process, including genes encoding for various drug metabolizing enzymes, drug transporters, and drug targets. The pharmaceutical industries and the United States (U.S.) Food and Drug Administration (FDA) have incorporated pharmacogenomics information of these biomarkers into guidance for drug development, labeling, and approval processes. The FDA has also published a list of FDA-approved drugs with pharmacogenomic information in their labels and corresponding biomarkers (U.S. FDA, 2015). According to the FDA,, "genomic information provided in drug labeling may include drug exposure and clinical response variability; risk for

ADR; genotype-specific dosing; mechanisms of drug action; and polymorphic drug target and disposition genes" (U.S. FDA, 2015, para 1). The commercially available pharmacogenomic tests for these validated, clinically useful biomarkers are listed in Table 5.1. The application of pharmacogenomics in health care is largely facilitated by the availability of these pharmacogenomic tests.

Among all the PK and PD related factors, the most important mechanisms by which genetic variation affect drug response is the modification of the activity of drug metabolizing enzymes. One well-known example is in the gene encoding for the drug metabolizing enzyme cytochrome P2D6 (CYP2D6). Different individuals may carry diverse forms of genetic variations for the *CYP2D6* gene, which lead to complete loss of function, partially reduced activity, or gaining excess enzymatic activity of CYP2D6. For drugs that are substrates of CYP2D6, individuals may have dramatically different levels of these drugs in the body (the PK aspect) as well as different therapeutic outcomes. Thus, the genotypes for the PK biomarkers (*CYP2D6* for this example) serve as an example that is used by health care providers to identify responders, nonresponders, or toxic responders, thereby optimizing drug and dose selection (Nair, 2010) (see Figure 5.1).

5.3. PHARMACOGENOMICS OF INDIVIDUAL DRUGS

5.3.1. Oncology Pharmacogenomics

5.3.1.1. 5-Fluorouracil (5-FU)

Specific Learning Objectives:

- Explain the inverse relationship between dihydropyrimidine dehydrogenase (DPD) activity and plasma concentrations of 5-FU.
- Discuss the availability of pharmacogenomic tests and their possible application in the selection and dosing of 5-FU.
- Explain the importance of pharmacogenomic tests for successful management of the dosing of the 5-FU.

Case Study—5-Fluorouracil (5-FU)

In 1985, a 27-year-old woman with breast cancer lapsed into a prolonged stuporous state after two cycles of 5-FU-containing chemotherapy and was found to have elevated concentrations of thymidine and uracil in her body fluids (Tuchman et al., 1985). Based on the pattern of these biochemical abnormalities in her family members and the known pathways of pyrimidine salvage, the investigators proposed that a heritable defect in the phase I metabolizing enzyme, dihydropyrimidine dehydrogenase (DPD), had led to the patient's severe 5-FU toxicity. This hypothesis was confirmed in a separate pedigree (Diasio, Beaver, & Carpenter, 1988) of an index patient with a similar course of treatment and neurotoxicity. She and multiple members of her family had reduced DPD activity, and the patient had undergone prolonged exposure to 5-FU after being re-challenged with a small dose. These two clinical case reports established that DPD is an important enzyme in the catabolism of 5-FU and that a heritable defect in enzyme function may lead to abnormal 5-FU metabolism and severe toxicity.

Clinical Pharmacogenomics of 5-FU

For several decades, 5-FU has served as an active agent against various types of solid tumors, particularly carcinomas of the breast and gastrointestinal tract, including oral, gastric, and colorectal tumors. Topically, fluorouracil acts against basal cell carcinomas and other malignant dermatologic entities. Various dosing schedules are used to administer fluorouracil (Baer & Williams, 1996; Saif, Chorma, Salamone, & Chu, 2009). High percentages (10% to 20%) of severe drug-related adverse events from 5-FU have been reported (Ciccolini, Gross, Dahan, Lacarelle, & Mercier, 2010; Sistonen, Smith, Fu, & Largiadèr, 2012). Some of the most common side effects or adverse events related to 5-FU are hematologic (e.g., leukopenia, anemia, neutropenic fever, and thrombocytopenia), gastrointestinal (e.g., mucositis, diarrhea, nausea, and vomiting), and neurotoxicities (Armstutz, Froehlich, & Largiadèr, 2011; Ciccolini et al., 2010; Kadoyama et al., 2012). These events can significantly impact outcomes regarding cure rates due to postponement or discontinuation of therapy (Ciccolini et al., 2010; Loganayagam et al., 2013). DPD deficiency has been shown to be a major predictor of severe 5-FU toxicity and to contribute to potentially lethal toxicities that may occur in patients who receive 5-FU at standard dosages (Ciccolini et al., 2010; Loganayagam et al., 2013). Estimates of 50% to 75% of 5-FU associated toxicities have been given attributed to DPD deficiency (Ciccolini et al., 2010)

DPD aids in the processing of thymine and uracil important gene structures, the basic building blocks of RNA and DNA. DPD is the key enzyme in the metabolic catabolism of 5-FU and 5-FU derivatives, such as capecitabine. The DPD activity was shown to be inversely related to the plasma concentrations of 5-FU in patients treated with continuous infusion of 5-FU (Harris, Song, Soong, & Diasio, 1990). The activity of DPD can be detected in a variety of tissues, although the liver is the main organ responsible for the catabolism of 5-FU (van Kuilenburg, van Lenthe, Blom, Mul, & Van Gennip, 1999). Because the activity of DPD in the liver correlated well with that in the peripheral blood mononuclear cells, the latter have been used as a surrogate to represent the total body DPD activity (Chazal et al., 1996).

Multiple efforts to validate the clinical value of testing DPD activity in the general patient population have had disappointing results. Laboratory assays of DPD activity in peripheral blood mononuclear cell had certain correlation with 5-FU clearance (Vokes et al., 1996) and the DPD activity in the liver (Chazal et al., 1996), where most 5-FU metabolism occurs. However, the peripheral blood enzyme assay has not been sufficiently associated with 5-FU clearance or severe toxicity to warrant routine use. Although the very first case of toxic death attributed to DPD deficiency in a patient treated with 5-FU was published more than 25 years ago (Tuchman et al., 1985), defining the best strategy to anticipate such dramatic outcomes is far from being settled in clinical oncology.

Patients with certain homozygous or certain compound heterozygous mutation in the dihydropyrimidine dehydrogenase gene (DPYD) are at increased risk for acute early-onset of toxicity as well as life-threatening or fatal adverse reactions by capecitabine due to reduced or absent activity of the enzyme (Claudle *et al.*, 2013; U. S. FDA, 2015b). Assessment of variants in the *DPYD* gene have been found in studies to be associated with 5-FU toxicity (Ciccolini *et al.*, 2010; Lee *et al.*, 2014; Loganayagam *et al.*, 2013; Rosmarin *et al.*, 2014; Sistonen *et al.*, 2012). Despite study findings, pretreatment screening for DPD status preferentially on a genotypic, a phenotypic, or a mixed basis, is still questioned today because of the frequency of variants among different patient populations (Armstutz *et al.*, 2011; Ciccolini *et al.*, 2010; van Kuilenburg, Ferdinandusse, & Wanders, 2013).

Due to countless reports demonstrating the relationships between DPD deficiency and severe toxicities with 5-FU/capecitabine, screening methods including genetic markers with high sensitivity and specificity for detecting DPD activity are warranted (Rosmarin *et al.*, 2014). Currently, routine screening for DPD status is not a common practice in most healthcare facilities despite the availability of genetic options at various testing services. At present, regulatory agencies both in the U.S. and in Europe have not established guidelines toward routine systematic pharmacogenetic testing with 5-FU despite clinical evidence for some screening as well as some studies showing improved outcomes (Ciccolini *et al.*, 2010). For individuals who are tested, the *Clinical Pharmacology and Therapeutics Implementation Consortium* (*CPIC*) guidelines for use of pharmacogenomics tests regarding "dosing" fluoropyrimidines (e.g., 5FU/capecitabine) recommends an alternative drug for patients who are homozygous for certain *DPYD* nonfunctional variants, because these patients are typically DPD deficient and at increased risk for severe or fatal drug toxicity. CPIC guidelines also includes consideration for a 50% reduction in starting dose of fluoropyrimidines for heterozygous patients (Claudle *et al.*, 2013; PharmGKB [Updated July 30, 2014])

Summary

Considering the ever-increasing number of patients who are likely to be treated with a fluoropyrimidine drug, 5-FU related severe toxicities will be a major concern in clinical oncology. Preventing severe toxicities with 5-FU would not only be cost effective, but would also affect the quality of life of the patient. Choosing a method

for identifying DPD-deficient patients at risk with fluoropyrimidine drugs remains an uneasy task. No method has stood out as a standard that would meet all the requirements (i.e., time and cost-effectiveness, availability, and relevance) of large-scale screening. However, whatever method is eventually chosen, evidence-based therapy is a better option than sticking with the blind administration of standardized dosages of 5-FU performed, regardless of the DPD status of patients with cancer.

5.3.1.2. Irinotecan (CPT-11)

Specific Learning Objectives:

- Explain the inverse relationship between UDP-glucuronosyltransferase 1A1 (*UGT1A1*) activity and SN-38 glucuronidation.
- Discuss the availability of pharmacogenetic tests and their possible role in the selection and dosing of irinotecan.
- Explain the importance of genotype tests to successfully guide the dosing of irinotecan.

Case Study—Irinotecan

A 49-year-old woman with metastatic colon cancer that progressed through two previous fluoropyrimidine based regimens was switched to oxaliplatin and irinotecan due to the fluoropyrimidine resistant tumors. During the fluoropyrimidine regimen, the patient presented with mild unconjugated hyperbilirubinemia that coincided with the fluoropyrimidine treatments. The initial tests with oxaliplatin and irinotecan were normal; however, after the first cycle of oxaliplatin and irinotecan, the patient presented with increased unconjugated bilirubin. Each of the 10 cycles of treatment resulted in a transient increase in bilirubin around days 5 to 7 that subsided to normal levels by days 12 to 13 with no change in liver enzymes. Yet, on the seventh day, after the first treatment cycle, the patient developed grade 4 diarrhea and neutropenia, which resolved when the bilirubin levels normalized. The patient experienced grade 4 neutropenia in all of the following cycles. She was the only one out of the 7 patients treated at this dose level to experience severe neutropenia. The patient was found to have decreased glucuronidated SN-38, the active metabolite of irinotecan. This symptom is usually described in patients with Gilbert's syndrome (Wasserman *et al.*, 1997), a condition characterized by periods of hyperbilirubinemia.

Clinical Pharmacogenomics of Irinotecan

As a chemotherapeutic agent, irinotecan is used extensively in the treatment for solid tumors, particularly colorectal cancer (Ma & McLeod, 2003), including the cases which are not responsive to fluorouracil therapy. Diarrhea is the most common adverse effect of irinotean and can be severe, causing hypovolemia in some cases. The diarrhea that occurs acutely (e.g., usually within 24 hours after dose administration) appears to involve a different mechanism from the diarrhea that occurs later (over 24 hours after dose administration). Nausea and vomiting are also common, but myelosuppression is often the dose-limiting adverse effect.

Irinotecan is a *prodrug* that is converted by carboxylesterase-2 to SN-38 (Hummerickhouse, Lohrback, Li, Boson, & Dolan, 2000), the active DNA topoisomerase I inhibitor that mediates the therapeutic and toxic effects of the drug. Most SN-38 is eliminated by glucuronidation, the enzymatic conjugation of glucuronic acid to form the more water-soluble metabolite SN-38 glucuronide (SN-38G). Patients with the highest SN-38: SN-38G ratios are at increased risk of one of the most common severe toxicities of irinotecan therapy: Grade 3–4 diarrhea (Gupta *et al.*, 1994).

Several groups contemporaneously identified alleles of UDP-glucuronosyltransferase 1A1 (*UGT1A1*) that cause a common benign familial condition of decreased bilirubin glucuronidation and increased serum bilirubin concentrations (Gilbert's syndrome). UGT1A1 mediated glucuronidation and irinotecan toxicity has been reported in cases of patients with Gilbert's syndrome (Lankisch *et al.*, 2008; Wasserman *et al.*, 1997) and was demonstrated by in vitro experiments proving that UGT1A1 is necessary and sufficient for SN-38 glucuronidation (Iyer *et al.*, 1998) and that SN-38 glucuronidation correlated inversely with the number of *UGT1A1*28* alleles

(Iyer *et al.*, 1998; Toffoli, Cecchin, Corona & Boiocchi, 2003). In general, *UGT1A1*28* is the most important allele for severe events such as neutropenia and/or diarrhea caused by SN-38, the active form of irinotecan (Hu, Yu, Pei, & Guo, 2010; Toffoli *et al.*, 2003). When compared with the wild-type alleles (*1/*1*), individuals homozygous with *28/*28 genotype have a significant 3.5-fold increase in the rate of severe Grade 3/4 neutropenia with the rate of severe neutropenia as high as 36% among homozygotes (Evaluation of Genomic Applications in Practice and Prevention [EGAPP], 2009). In 2005, the U. S. FDA approved the assay for *UGY1A1* genetic testing (U.S. FDA, 2005) and recommended that manufacturers of irinotecan amend the package insert of the drug to warn of the elevated risk of neutropenia for patients homozygous for *UGT1A1*28*. The warning recommended that these patients should receive a reduced starting dose of irinotecan by at least 1 level.

Adoption of *UGT1A1* testing for irinotecan dosing has been hampered for various reasons. The genotype-dependent actions for prescribing irinotecan are "standard dose" or "reduce dose," and it is not clear by how much the dose should be reduced. In addition, the association between genotype and hematologic toxicity seems to be influenced by the dose of irinotecan. Also, there is a lack of empirical evidence that dosing irinotecan on the basis of genotype improves the safety of irinotecan without compromising the efficacy of the therapy (Hoskins & McLeod, 2009). However, Inoue and colleagues (2013) showed that 1 or more genotypes of 3 *UGT1A* isozymes may be useful for predicting the adverse events caused by irinotecan-based chemotherapy (Inoue *et al.*, 2013). Thus, it might be possible to define subgroups with therapeutic consequences instead of withholding irinotecan from patients who may benefit from its considerate use. Currently, EGAPP found that the evidence is "insufficient to conclude whether *UGT1A1* genotyping should be used to determine *the best dose to prevent side effects* when treating patients with metastatic colon cancer" (EGAPP, 2009) of which irinotecan is a common treatment for the disease.

Summary

Irinotecan is one chemotherapeutic agent for

whom a patient's genetic information may help to guide clinical decision making. Individuals who are homozygous for the *UGT1A1*28* gene variant in particular are at a higher risk of clinical neutropenia and diarrhea when undergoing therapy with irinotecan. Determining *UGT1A* genetic information may play an important role in personalized/precision medicine regarding management and toxicity prevention. Irinotecan metabolism, however, is complex, and numerous genes besides *UGT1A1* have to be considered. Moreover, uncertainty remains regarding appropriate dosing of irinotecan based on genotype and whether modifying the dose decreases the risk for toxicity without compromising the efficacy of the therapy. Despite these issues, a strong argument for *UGT1A1* testing should be considered before the first dose of irinotecan in all patients, particularly given the high incidence of neutropenia in individuals homozygous for the gene variant.

5.3.1.3. 6-Mercaptopurine (6-MP)

Specific Learning Objectives:

- Explain the inverse relationship between thiopurine methyltransferase (TPMT) activity and concentrations of active thioguanine nucleotide (TGN) metabolites.
- Discuss the availability of pharmacogenetic tests and their possible role in the selection and dosing of 6-MP.
- Discuss the importance of genotype tests to successfully guide the dosing of the 6-MP.

Case study Mercaptopurine (6-mercaptopurine ([6-MP])

The case of a 6-year-old girl with acute lymphoblastic leukemia (ALL) demonstrated the potential benefit of thiopurine S-methyltransferase (TPMT) functional testing for adjusting the dosing of 6-MP (Evans, Horner, Chu, Kalwinsky, & Roberts, 1991). After receiving 6-MP, she developed myelosuppression and fever, requiring hospitalization and cessation of all agents in her treatment regimen. When her red blood

cell (RBC) thioguanine nucleotide (TGN) levels were measured to be 7 times the population median, she was restarted at full doses of the multiple agents in her potentially curative regimen, and reduction of the 6-MP dose to 6% of the standard dose enabled her to complete all remaining agents on schedule without further unanticipated adverse events.

Clinical Pharmacogenomics of Mercaptopurine

Mercaptopurine, the first of the thiopurine series found useful as an anticancer drug, is a prodrug; its principal active metabolites, thioguanine nucleotides (TGNs), preferentially kill rapidly growing cells by inhibiting DNA and RNA synthesis. As a cytotoxic agent, 6-MP is more widely used to treat various autoimmune disorders and prevent organ rejection. Mercaptopurine is used primarily in the treatment of childhood acute leukemia, and especially useful in maintaining remission of acute leukemia in children. The results have been less impressive in adults with acute leukemia, although remissions sometimes are obtained. Mercaptopurine is also used to induce remission in acute lymphoblastic leukemia (ALL) and chronic myelocytic leukemia (CML). Oral mercaptopurine is a daily component of maintenance therapy for the 2 to 3 years of childhood ALL treatment.

One of the most developed examples of clinical pharmacogenomics, in the context of therapeutics, involves the genetic polymorphism of thiopurine methyltransferase (TPMT). The *TPMT* gene is important in providing instructions for making the TPMT enzyme. TMPT is involved in the metabolism of thiopurine drugs such as 6-MP. This enzyme inactivates 6-MP through methylation, preventing production of TGNs that are responsible for drug efficacy; excessive formation, however, can lead to myelosuppression and gastrointestinal toxicity (Booth *et al.*, 2010; Knepper & McLeod, 2015; Relling *et al.*, 2011; Torkamani, Windle & Roth, 2013). Thus, TPMT enzyme "turns off" thiopurine drugs. With conventional doses of thiopurines, individuals who inherit 2 inactive *TPMT* alleles (homozygous deficient) universally experience severe myelosuppression; those who are heterozygous show moderate to severe myelosuppression and those who are homozygous for wild-type *TPMT* alleles have lower levels of TGN metabolites and consequently a lower risk of myelosuppression (Booth *et al.*, 2010; Relling *et al.*, 2010).

It is estimated that 86% to 97% of patients have the wild-type *TPMT* genotype, resulting in normal TPMT enzyme activity (Nguyen, Mendes, & Ma, 2011). There are numerous variant alleles of the *TMPT* gene, some that impact enzymatic activity. For example, approximately 90% of individuals of white race inherit high enzyme activity; 10%, intermediate activity (heterozygotes); and 0.3%, low or no activity (Ma & Lu, 2011; Maitland, Vasisht & Ratain, 2006). Family studies have shown that TPMT activity is inherited as an autosomal codominant trait. The clinical importance of this variation became evident when patients experiencing severe toxicity from thiopurine therapy were found to have low TPMT activity and high red blood cell (RBC) count TGN concentrations. Patients who inherit TPMT deficiency accumulate excessive cellular concentrations of TGN, predisposing them to hematopoietic toxicity, which has been fatal in some cases (Maitland *et al.*, 2006). Although the metabolism of mercaptopurine by TPMT is a major route of inactivation, the physiologic function of TPMT is uncertain (Thompson, 2010).

An important pharmacogenomic consideration in the use of purine analogs is that reduced dosing levels due to the presence of the *TPMP* variants does not reduce therapeutic efficacy, but greatly reduces toxicity associated with the use of purine analogs. Because TPMT activity and the measurement of RBC TGN levels are labor-intensive assays that are subject to laboratory-related variability, a molecular genetic test offers the potential for greater convenience and reproducibility. Multiple genetic variations of the *TPMP* gene have been identified. However, only 3 variants are present with sufficient prevalence to have a clinical impact. Three different variant alleles, referred to as *TPMT*2*, *TPMT*3A*, and *TPMT*3C*, account for 95% of all of the dysfunctional *TPMT* alleles detected and, importantly, there is high concordance between measured TPMT activity and the presence or absence of these polymorphisms (Maitland *et al.*, 2006). Therefore, genotyping tests have a high likelihood of being informative. Complementary phenotype laboratory tests can be helpful adjuncts to genotyping tests. Review of one of the largest documented cohorts of patients with acute toxicity from 6-MP therapy demonstrated that genotyping for common *TPMT* alleles could identify patients at risk for severe 6-MP toxicity and enable the integration of *TPMT* genotyping into the clinical management of 6-MP therapy (Evans *et al.*, 2001).

Variations among ethnic groups are extensive and may necessitate further characterization of additional *TPMT* variant for further therapeutic considerations among specific ethnic groups. The Product Information guide for 6-MP in the U. S. goes into considerable detail about the pharmacogenetic implications describing various DNA polymorphisms, as well as differences between ethnic groups. It also goes a step further to recommend that consideration is given to *TPMT* typing (phenotypic or genotypic) but does not make this mandatory, leaving it to individual health professionals to make this decision. The recent funding by the Australian Medical Benefits Scheme of *TPMT* DNA genetic testing is also noteworthy. This means that the *TPMT* DNA test has the tick of approval in terms of a formal evaluation of its clinical and economic utility, but it is left to the prescribing medical practitioner to decide whether to use pharmacogenetic monitoring and, if so, what to do with the DNA test results in terms of dose or regimen to use.

Summary

TPMT testing is recommended by different groups to predict the toxicity of thiopurine drugs in the treatment of individuals diagnosed with ALL. Patients with ALL who are homozygous for fully functional *TPMT* are at increased risk of detectable residual disease after standard-dose 6-MP consolidation treatment compared with heterozygous patients. Presumably, homozygous patients have higher TPMT activity and reduced tumor exposure to 6-MP compared with the population median; hence, *TPMT* genotyping might identify a patient subset that requires and can safely tolerate higher doses of 6-MP therapy. The tests could be used to screen for patients at risk of severe toxicity from 6-MP before the initiation of treatment or to help clinicians decide among management options when unexpected toxicity from the drug arises.

5.3.2. Pharmacogenomics for Cardiovascular Diseases

5.3.2.1. Warfarin

> **Specific Learning Objectives:**
>
> - Explain the contributes of *CYP2C9* and *VKORC1* genotypes to the variability in response to warfarin therapy.
> - Discuss the implication of the FDA labeling change regarding the impact of CYP2C9 and VKORC1 on the dose determination of warfarin.
> - Apply the FDA pharmacogenomics information on warfarin into nursing practice.

Case Studies

Genetic variants have shown to impact warfarin therapy. Two important cases have been reported by Khan and colleagues in 2003 to demonstrate the influence of genetic factors on warfarin sensitivity (Khan, Kamau, Daly, King, & Wynee, 2003). These two cases are presented below to denote the significance of pharmacogenomics in personalized/precision medicine.

Case #1—Warfarin

The initial case involved an 88-year-old woman who was symptomatic for a diagnosis of pulmonary embolism (PE). Laboratory data revealed a normal prothrombin time, and she received warfarin 10 mg daily for treatment of the PE. However her International Normalized Ratio (INR) (a measure typically used to monitor patients on warfarin or related oral anticoagulant therapy) peaked at 9.2 six days later after the initial treatment; treatment with vitamin K resulted in a below 2 level on day 11. She was later revealed to be homozygous for the *CYP 2C9*3* allele via genotyping (Khan *et al.*, 2003).

Case #2—Warfarin

In the second case, an 85-year-old woman diagnosed with an ileofemoral vein thrombosis was described. In this case, the patient's prothrombin time was initially normal, but after receiving warfarin treatment, her INR peaked at 13.2, returning to below 2 following two separate doses of intravenous vitamin K intravenously. Genotyping revealed that the patient was heterozygous for the *CYP 2C9*2* allele (Khan *et al.*, 2003).

Clinical Pharmacogenomics of Warfarin

Warfarin is a commonly used anticoagulant agent to prevent and treat thromboembolic diseases (e.g., deep vein thrombosis) or conditions that increases the risk for developing blood clots (e.g., atrial fibrillation; heart valve replacement). However, care must be given when administering the drug because of the difficulty in determining optimal dose as a result of its narrow therapeutic index, the increased risk for bleeding, and individual differences and variability in drug response (Li, Wang, Barone, & Malone, 2009). Warfarin is a racemic mixture of S and R enantiomers (types of molecules) with S-warfarin anticoagulant property greater than that of R-warfarin. (Akamine & Tsukasa, 2012; Li *et al.*, 2009). Cytochrome P450 enzyme specifically, CYP2C9 enzyme, is important in the metabolism of S-warfarin, converting the drug into inactive metabolites (Li *et al.*, 2009). The wild-type allele (*CYP 2C9*1*) is associated with normal enzymatic activity, particularly in individuals who are homozygous for the wild-type allele and who are considered extensive metabolizers (Dean, 2012; Scott, Khasawneh, Peter, Kornreich, & Desnick, 2010). There were 79 variants of the *CYP2C9* gene reported in 2013 (Leiden University Medical Center, 20042014). *CYP2C9* genetic polymorphisms have contributed to the variability in response of warfarin therapy (Schwarz & Stein, 2006; Wang, Wang, Huang, Su, & Zhou, 2009). Specifically, *CYP 2C9*2* and *CYP 2C9*3* are the 2 variant alleles considered to be significant risk factors for over-anticoagulation due to their reduced enzymatic activity and lower rate of warfarin clearance (Cavallari & Limdi, 2009; Dean, 2012 [updated 2013]; Rettie & Tai, 2006; Zhu *et al.*, 2007). For example, the *CYP 2C9*2* allele results in CYP2C9 proteins with approximately 70% activity, and much lower activity (20%) is found in the *CYP2C9*3* allele (Fisch, Perry, Stephens, Horenstein, & Shuldiner, 2013; Hill & Duncan, 2008). Because of the lower metabolism of S-warfarin from these 2 alleles (*2 or *3), there is a need for lower warfarin maintenance doses compared with patients who carry the wild-type allele (*1) (Dean, 2012).

Allele frequencies vary among ethnic groups. For example, the *CYP 2C9*2* allele is more common in Caucasians when compared to Asians and African Americans (Dean, 2012). Approximately 15% (95% confidence intervals [CI] 10.3–19.9%) of Caucasians are reported to have the *CYP 2C9*2* allele compared with lower rates among Asians (2.9% [95% CI 0.6–5.3%]) and African-Americans (2.8% [95% CI, 1.5–4.2%]) (Scott et al, 2010). In contrast, the *3 allele is a less common variant compared with the *2 allele, with less than 10% of the variant reported in all populations (Dean, 2012) and frequency rates of approximately 5% in Caucasians versus approximately 3.9% and 2.0%, respectively, among Asians and AfricanAmericans (Fisch *et al.*, 2013; Gage & Lesko, 2008; Hill & Duncan, 2008; Scott *et al.*, 2010). Therefore, the dose of warfarin needs to be adjusted to fit patients of different racial/ethnic groups.

VKORC1 is an important gene that encodes for vitamin K epoxide reductase complex 1 (*VKORC1*). The *VKORC1* gene is involved in the vitamin K cycle enzyme that controls the regeneration of reduced vitamin K (KH2), which is essential in the activation of clotting factors (Garcia & Reitsma, 2008; Johnson & Cavallari, 2013). This information is significant because warfarin works by inhibiting *VKORC1* complex (Johnson & Cavallari, 2013; Li *et al.*, 2009). There are numerous polymorphisms in *VKORC1*, and some influence warfarin management dosing. One important variant, *VKORC1 1639G>A* (G allele is replaced with A), has been reported to require lower warfarin doses compared with the wild-type allele (GG) (Chong & Buehler, 2013; Dean, 2012; Fisch *et al.* 2013). Published guidelines regarding *CYP2C9* and *VKORC1* genotyping and warfarin dosing are available from the Clinical Pharmacogenetics Implementation Consortium (CPIC) with an online supplement that includes information regarding other genes impacting warfarin dose requirements, examples of warfarin pharmacogenetic testing options, summary of rating systems used to grade the evidence, and other relative guidelines (Johnson *et al.*, 2011b). This supplement is available online at https:// www.pharmgkb.org/drug/PA451906.

Many factors have been associated with warfarin therapy, and individual variations occur regarding response to the drug. For example, age, body weight, diet, race/ethnicity, and male gender have all shown to affect warfarin therapy regarding variability in dose requirements (Absher, Moore, & Parker, 2002; Kamali *et al.*, 2004; Lane *et al.*, 2012; Mueller, Patel, Halawa, Dumitrascu, & Dawson, 2014). However, warfarin is initiated at a similar dose for all patients, typically 5 mg/day, with dose adjustment according to the INR. The problem with this trial-and-error dosing approach is that it often leads to over or under anticoagulation during the initial months of therapy, when the risk of bleeding is the greatest. In 1999, the genetic polymorphisms that influence the variability in warfarin dose requirements were first recognized. Since then, there has been a vast body of literature documenting the effects on warfarin dose of genetic variation in *CYP2C9*, the major drug metabolizing enzyme of S-warfarin, and vitamin K epoxide reductase (VKORC1), the protein target of warfarin (Johnson *et al.*, 2011a; Johnson *et al.*, 2011b).

A great number of studies suggested that bleeding risk during the first 1 to 3 months of warfarin therapy is up to 10-fold higher than subsequent monthly risk. Therefore, identification of the therapeutic dose for a given patient is needed. There are many warfarin pharmacogenetic algorithms developed that usually incorporate both genetic and clinical factors. One of the best validated algorithms is from the *International Warfarin Pharmacogenetics Consortium* (IWPC). This dosing algorithm is currently available online at http://pharmgkb.org/drug/PA451906.   Another algorithm available for warfarin dosing is that of *WarfarinDosing.org* (Washington University in St. Louis©), available online at http://www. warfaindosing.org and developed from a collaboration team of Gage and colleagues (Gage *et al.*, 2008; Gage & Lesko, 2008; Washington University in St. Louis©, 2015). This site provides estimates of therapeutic dosage for individuals warranting warfarin therapy based on clinical factors and *CYP2C9* and *VKORC1* genotypes if available (Washington University in St. Louis©, 2015). These 2 dosing algorithms using both genetic and nongenetic factors have shown to better predict warfarin dose when compared with the clinical algorithm (e.g., the usual 5 mg daily starting dose in estimating the stable warfarin dose) (Johnson *et al.*, 2011b).

To improve initial dosing estimates for anticoagulant therapy for individual patients, in 2007, the FDA approved prescribing information for Coumadin® regarding genetic information for individual patients and how it may influence response to drug therapy (U.S. FDA, 2007). In 2010, the FDA further revised the warfarin product label (U.S. FDA, 2010). Package inserts now contain information relating to pharmacogenomics, specifically *CYP2C9* and *VKORC1* polymorphisms including dosing recommendations with consideration of genotypes (Bristol-Myers Squibb, 2011). The FDA recommends health care professionals to consider the use of pharmacogenetic testing at the initiation of therapy to optimize warfarin use and reduce the risk of bleeding complications from the drug (U.S. FDA, 2007).

Summary

Warfarin is a widely prescribed anticoagulant with a very narrow therapeutic index. It is important to recognize that dosing can be improved by identifying individual genetic properties. Both *VKORC1* and *CYP 2C9* play an active role in the potential for predicting therapeutic warfarin doses. Warfarin pharmacogenomics aims to enhance our understanding of personalized/precision medicine by evaluating patient-specific determinants of warfarin response in order to improve dosing accuracy and reduce the risk for adverse effects with warfarin therapy.

5.3.2.2. Clopidogrel

Specific Learning Objectives:

- Describe the role of *CYP2C19* in the process of clopidogrel enzymatic metabolism.
- Discuss the relationship between *CYP2C19* and the clopidogrel efficacy among acute coronary syndrome (ACS) and postpercutaneous coronary intervention (PCI) patients.
- Explain the FDA label pertaining to *CYP2C19* genotype on clopidogrel efficacy.

Case Study—Clopidogrel

In a case report by Levy (2012), a 72-year-old man with vascular dementia resulting from recurrent strokes and small vessel cerebral ischemia is described. Clopidogrel (75 mg daily) was added to his daily aspirin for stroke prophylaxis 2 years ago. His dementia progressed and a cerebral magnet resonance imaging (MRI) showed additional infarcts and progression of small vessel ischemic changes. His wife had been assisting with his medications, and he did not believe he missed any doses. He used to take omeprazole, but that was stopped within a few months after the initiation of clopidogrel, and he is not currently taking any proton pump inhibitors (PPIs). He was started on fluoxetine for severe depression and anxiety about a year prior to starting clopidogrel, and the dose was gradually increased to 40 mg daily over the past few years. (Levy, 2012; website link http://www.internalmedicinenews.com/?id=495&tx_ttnews[tt_news]=94497&cHash=a2eb4eda66cb4914e6ccf1dc77aec3f8).

Significance of the Case

Pharmacogenomics play an important role in the management of clopidogrel. It is important to note the FDA warning to avoid the concomitant use of the proton pump inhibitors (PPIs), in particular, omeprazole or esomeprazole, with clopidogrel because of drug interactions. The use of esomeprazole or omeprazole may reduce the pharmacologic activity of clopidogrel by inhibiting CYP2C19 activity (U.S. FDA, 2013a; U. S. FDA, 2012). In addition, low efficacy of clopidogrel has been shown with the use of fluoxetine (Wang *et al.*, 2015). For this case, there are 2 possible explanations for the failure of clopidogrel in the patient. One is that the patient may have *CYP2C19* genetic variant(s), causing the poor metabolizer phenotype. The other is that fluoxetine is inhibiting CYP2C19 activity and mimicking the poor metabolizer phenotype (drug-drug interactions) (Levy, 2012). Genotyping for *CYP2C19* variants may aid in personalized/precision management of this individual.

Clinical Pharmacogenomics of Clopidogrel

Clopidogrel is an important medication

BOX WARNING FOR CLOPIDOGREL (Plavix®)

- Warn about reduced effectiveness in patients who are poor metabolizers of Plavix®. Poor metabolizers do not effectively convert Plavix to its active form in the body.

- Tests are available to identify genetic differences in CYP2C function.

- Consider use of other anti-platelet medications or alternative dosing strategies for Plavix in patients identified as poor metabolizers.

FIGURE 5.2. Example of information that should be included in the box warning of Clopidogrel (Plavix®) as part of prescribing information. (Taken from U.S. Food and Drug Administration Safety Announcement 03-12-2010 [last updated 12/23/2004]). Retrieved from www.fda.gov/drugs/drugsafety/PostmarketDrugSafetyInformationforPatientsandProviders/ucm203888.htm

commonly used in clinical practice. The drug inhibits platelet function and, with aspirin, plays a major role in preventing recurrent cardiovascular events in patients with an acute coronary syndrome (ACS) or those undergoing percutaneous coronary intervention (PCI) (Beitelshees, Voora, & Lewis, 2015; Collet et al., 2009; Johnson & Cavallari, 2013). Clopidogrel is a prodrug that needs to be converted to an active metabolite before it can achieve its antiplatelet effects (Johnson et al., 2012; Kazui et al., 2010). However, response variability and drug resistance are known to occur. Clopidogrel is mediated by various CYP enzymes, and genetic polymorphism in CYP2C19 contributes to variability in drug metabolism. The CYP2C19 enzyme has several common loss of function alleles (Strom et al., 2012), particularly CYP2C19*2 and CYP2C19*3 (Krishna, Diamond, & Saul, 2012; U. S. FDA. 2014). The wild-type CYP2C19*1 has fully functional metabolism of clopidogrel, whereas CYP2C19*2 and *3 alleles have no functional metabolism of the drug (Krishna et al., 2012; U.S. FDA, 2014). Poor metabolizers have 2 loss-of-function alleles, whereas intermediate metabolizers have 1 copy of a loss-of-function allele, resulting in decreased active metabolite levels and reduced antiplatelet effects (Krishna et al., 2012). There are other CYP2C19 gene variants besides the *2 and *3 alleles that may be associated with absent or reduced clopidogrel metabolism, but they occur less frequently than the *2 and *3 alleles (U.S. FDA, 2014).

Three important papers have highlighted the potential impact of CYP2C19 genotypes on ma-jor adverse cardiovascular events with clopidogrel therapy. These papers were published simultaneously in the New England Journal of Medicine (NEJM) and The Lancet in early 2009 (Collet et al., 2009; Mega et al., 2009; Simon et al., 2009). The CYP2C19*2 gene variant was shown to impact the prognosis of patients with myocardial infarction (MI) despite receiving clopidogrel treatment (Collet et al. 2009). Adverse events including death, MI, and coronary revascularization occurred more frequently among CYP2C19*2 gene carriers than noncarriers (Collet et al., 2009). Similar adverse cardiovascular events were found by Mega and colleagues (2009) among individuals with reduced function alleles in the CYP2C19 genes, particularly CYP2C19*2. Adverse cardiovascular events were also observedby Simon and colleagues (2009), who reported a higher rate of cardiovascular events in acute MI patients among those receiving clopidogrel and who had 2 CYP2C19 loss of function alleles, particularly *2, *3, *4, or *5 compared with those without these alleles. In another study, patients who took clopidogrel, who were found to be heterozygotes or homozygotes for CYP2C19 reduced function alleles, and who underwent PCI had a higher risk of major adverse cardiovascular events, including stent thrombosis (Mega et al., 2010). Currently, the FDA has added a black box warning as a safety announcement for Plavix® (clopidogrel) that includes information on the reduced effectiveness of the drug in patients who are poor metabolizers, as well as advise health care professionals regarding use of other antiplatelet medication or alternative dosing when using clopidogrel for those individuals who are poor metabolizers (U.S. FDA, 2014) (see Figure 5.1).

Summary

Understanding the PK and PD of clopidogrel is important in providing safe health care to patients regarding drug-to-drug interactions or based upon individual genetic variants that can impact adverse health events. Clopidogrel is metabolized to an active metabolite by CY2C19, and concomitant use of certain medications such as omeprazole may inhibit the activity of this enzyme, resulting in reduced antiplatelet activity. Genotyping for *CYP2C19* provides a means of personalized medicine, particularly for individuals with ACS who are post-PCI. Knowing this genotype can aid clinicians in finding appropriate measures regarding clinical management to optimize patient outcomes and to reduce risk of adverse cardiac events. For example, identifying individuals with a loss-of-function in *CYP2C19* may warrant alternative antiplatelet therapy (Scott *et al.*, 2013). Nurses should understand the pharmacogenetics of clopidogrel and how it is related to drug interactions, as well as how certain genetic variants can impact individuals diagnosed with ACS, especially post-PCI.

5.3.3. Pharmacogenomics for Infectious Diseases

5.3.3.1. Abacavir (Human Immunodeficiency Virus [HIV] Drug)

> **Specific Learning Objectives:**
>
> - Describe the relationship between *HLA-B*5701* and abacavir resulted hypersensitivity reaction (HSR) among HIV patients.
> - Explain the significance of *HLA-B*5701* genotype screening tests on preventing the side effects of abacavir.
> - Discuss the FDA label warrants on abacavir regarding the *HLA-B*5701* screening test before the treatment.
> - Apply the FDA suggestion on abacavir in nursing practice.

Case Study—Abacavir

This case report focuses on a 31-year-old white female of Northern European ancestry who is HIV-infected. Recent laboratory tests revealed an HIV plasma viral load of 20,000 copies per mL and a CD4+ T-lymphocyte count of 200, warranting therapy with abacavir; emtricitabine plus atazanavir; and trimethorprim/sulfamethoxazole (TMP-SMX) for prevention of opportunistic infection. There were no known allergies to medications. After 7 days, she returned to the clinic with a slight rash over the arms, trunk, and lower extremities but denied fever or other systematic complaints. The TMP-SMX was discontinued with some immediate resolution of symptoms; however, 2 weeks later, she returned with worsening symptoms, including fever, generalized maculopapular rash, nausea, vomiting, diarrhea, and generalized malaise.

Questions for Critical Thinking

- What is your judgment based on this case?
- Do you think the patient is experiencing an abacavir hypersensitivity reaction (HSR)? If it is, why does it happen? What will you do in this situation?

Clinical Pharmacogenomics

Abacavir is an example of how personalized/precision medicine can be used in clinical practice, particularly for pharmacogenomic testing in the prediction of ADRs. Abacavir is a guanosine reverse-transcriptase inhibitor and an important antiretroviral frequently used in combination with other antiretroviral agents as a treatment against infection due to the human immunodeficiency virus (HIV). The drug has been utilized by almost 1 million patients infected with HIV during the past decade (Phillips & Mallal, 2007). Although the medication is generally well tolerated, a hypersensitivity reaction (HSR) occurs in approximately 5% to 8% of individuals receiving abacavir, usually within (U.S. FDA, 2007) 6 weeks of starting the medication (Bannister *et al.*, 2008; Hetherington *et al.*, 2001; Hewitt, 2002; Ma *et al.*, 2011; Pucheril & Sharma, 2011; Stocchi *et al.*, 2012).

HSR is a potential life-threatening, multisystem reaction that may result in a host of symptoms. It is characterized by 2 or more clinical signs or symptoms, including fever, maculopapular rash, fatigue, malaise, myalgias, and arthralgias, as well as gastrointestinal, respiratory, neurologic, and/or musculoskeletal problems (Hetherington et al, 2001; Hewitt, 2002; Stocchi *et al.*, 2012; U.S. FDA, 2013b). Initially, the signs and symptoms of the reaction may be mild; however, continued abacavir use will result in progressively worsening symptoms. If any HSR is suspected or experienced by a patient on abacavir, the drug should be discontinued. Usually, the symptoms of HSR are resolved within 72 hours after discontinuation of the medication. Abacavir or abacavir-containing produce should not be restarted if discontinued due to HSR because it can result in a potentially life threatening reaction and even death (Hewitt *et al.*, 2002; Saag *et al.*, 2008; U.S. FDA, 2013b).

HSR due to abacavir is associated with the human leukocyte antigen (HLA) *B*5701* (*HLA-B*5701*) gene variant (Hetherington *et al.*, 2002; Mallal *et al.*, 2002). Race/ethnicity may play a significant role in the use of abacavir. Abacavir hypersensitivity appears to be higher among whites compared with individuals of African descent (Hewitt, 2002). This higher rate of hypersensitivity may be due to *HLA-B*5701* variation that differs among different racial/ethnic groups, being most common among people of Northern European descent and less so among people of African or Asian descent. Reported rates of HSR sensitivity to abacavir is approximately 5% to 8% for whites of Northern European ancestry compared with 1% to 3% among African-Americans (Coffey, 2008; Torkamani, Windle, & Roth, 2015). Furthermore, in Asian populations, the frequency of *HLA-B*5701* is very low and estimated at 1% (Torkamani *et al.*, 2015). Despite the racial/ethnic differences, the FDA recommends screening the *HLA-B*5701* allele for all patients prior to starting abacavir therapy and prior to reinitiating therapy with abacavir (U.S. FDA, 2008). This warning enables health care providers to reduce the risk of HSR when considering abacavir by pretherapy testing for the allele. The U.S. Department of Health and Human Service Panel on Antiretroviral Guidelines for Adults and Adolescents also recommends screening for the *HLA-B*5701* prior to abacavir initiation (Panel on Antiretroviral Guidelines for Adults & Children, 2011).

There are many available techniques used by laboratories to genotype *HLA-B*5701*, such as enzyme-linked immunosorbent assay (ELISA), flow cytometry, and sequence based genotyping (Stocchi *et al.*, 2012). A definitive immunologic diagnosis can be made by use of the abacavir skin patch test. It has been demonstrated that most patients with immunologically proven abacavir hypersensitivity carry the major histocompatibility allele *HLAB*5701* (Stocchi *et al.*, 2012). Mallal and colleagues (2002) performed a study in which patients that were to be started on abacavir were randomized to a pharmacogenetic screen for *HLA-B*5701* versus the standard clinical approach (Mallal *et al.*, 2002). Patients who carried this allele were treated with a non-abacavir–containing regimen. No patients in the *HLA-B*5701* screened arm developed immunologically proven abacavir hypersensitivity compared with 2.7% with the standard approach. Thus, the pharmacogenetic test had a 100% negative predictive value.

Summary

Abacavir-induced HSR among those with *HLA-B*5701* provides another example of how pharmacogenomics can be translated to personalized management (Cuo *et al.*, 2013). Screening for *HLA-B*5701* should be performed prior to initiation of abacavir therapy. Nurses should understand the pharmacogenetics of abacavir and how it is related to HSR among HIV patients treated with the drug.

5.4. OVERALL SUMMARY AND FUTURE OPPORTUNITIES FOR NURSES

In recent years, pharmacogenomic information has increased significantly, and different types of tests have developed to characterize genetic variations related to drug response. In this chapter, a brief discussion of the use of pharmacogenomics in selected oncology, cardiovascular, and anti-infective drugs is presented. Examples of each of these categories included the use of pharmacogenomics information in preventing HSR in individuals with HIV before prescribing abacavir, preventing adverse effects during chemotherapy with mercaptopurine, and use of genotyping for warfarin dosing. Knowing an individual's genetic profile has also been useful in determining the appropriate medication for treatment in some oncology conditions, such as that of women with an overproduction of HER2 protein in breast cancer and the use of trastuzumab. Pharmacogenomic information,therefore, has enabled health care providers to take a personalized approach towards patient care. By understanding pharmacogenomics, health care providers will be better able to select that agents work best for which patients.

Knowing one's genetic make-up has provided some promising approaches in improving outcomes in patient care; however, the availability of pharmacogenomic testing for comprehensive individualized personalized care is not yet available. With the rapid advances in technology, it is expected that other pharmacogenomics tests will be available; in particular, genome-wide approaches, such as whole-genome sequencing, have allowed health care providers to comprehensively assess genetic variations in almost all the human genes with known or unknown association with drug response. It has been anticipated that when the cost and turnaround time of sequencing the entire genome becomes low enough, it will become the method of choice for clinical pharmacogenomics tests. Based on pharmacogenomic information, patients can also be recommended to enroll in specific clinical trials where applicable (Roychowdhury *et al.*, 2011).

APRNs and those nurses working in clinical settings must review a patient's medication profile for suboptimal therapies, drug-drug interactions, and adverse drug reactions; as well as to assess patient adherence and compliance to therapy while sitting face to face with a patient. The ultimate goal is for nurses to individualize the therapy. Therefore, it is important for nurses to understand the concept of pharmacogenomics and also have access to patient-specific pharmacogenomic information. One of the most important aspects is the need to develop user friendly tools for pharmacogenomics data sharing among all health care providers. These tools should be developed by multi-disciplinary teams including both basic scientists and clinicians. The goal of these tools will be able to deal with large volumes of data generated from genomic tests. The National Institutes of Health (NIH), including the National Institute of Nursing Research, are currently providing funding opportunities for projects focusing on the development of a range

TABLE 5.2. Examples of Pharmacogenomic Websites.

Website	Purpose	Weblink (URL)
U. S. Food and Drug Administration (FDA)	Table of pharmacogenomic biomarkers Pharmacogenomics can play an important role in identifying responders and non-responders to medications, avoiding adverse events, and optimizing drug dose. Drug labeling may contain information on genomic biomarkers and can describe: • Drug exposure and clinical response variability • Risk for adverse events • Genotype-specific dosing • Mechanisms of drug action • Polymorphic drug target and disposition genes	http://www.fda.gov/drugs/scienceresearch/researchareas/pharmacogenetics/ucm083378.htm
	Pharmacogenomics and Its Role In Drug Safety (2008)	http://www.fda.gov/Drugs/DrugSafety/DrugSafetyNewsletter/ucm119991.htm
PharmGKB®	Resource that curates knowledge about the impact of genetic variation on drug response for clinicians and researchers.	https://www.pharmgkb.org/
National Institute of Health, National Institute of General Medical Sciences	The NIH Pharmacogenomics Research Network (PGRN): A network of scientists focused on understanding how a person's genes affect his or her response to medicines.	http://www.nigms.nih.gov/Research/SpecificAreas/PGRN/Pages/default.aspx
Pharmacogenomics Educational Program, University of California, San Diego©	Evidence-based curriculum, covering pharmacogenomics concepts and clinical applications	https://pharmacogenomics.ucsd.edu/

of computer-based tools, such as tools for automation in data collection, data processing and analysis, quality assessment, data integration and visualization, and clinical reporting systems (Calzone et al., 2013; National Institutes of Health, National Institute of General Medical Sciences, 2013). These funding opportunities have significant implications for nurse researchers and nurse administration particularly those working in informatics and genomics. This effort further supports the push for pharmacogenomics to become more commonplace in the clinic as well as inpatient settings and for all health care providers. A genomics reporter system also needs to be developed to convert the complex patterns of genotype of any individual into easy-to-use formats. Using the CYP2C9 enzyme as an example, based on the reports of a whole-genome sequencing assay, the entire health care team should be able to obtain information not only on the classification of poor or extensive metabolizers, but also sufficient levels of evidence to direct them toward a particular therapy. Table 5.2 provide examples of online pharmacogenomics resources to assist nurses in learning more about pharmacogenomics.

5.5. REFERENCES

Absher, R. K., Moore, M. E., & Parker, M. H. (2002). Patient-specific factors predictive of warfarin dosage requirements. *Annals of Pharmacotherapy, 36*(10), 1512–1517.

Akamine, Y., & Uno, T. (2012). Warfarin enantiomers pharmacokinetics by CYP2C19. In *Pharmacology, Gallelli, L* (Ed). InTech. Retrieved from http://www.iterchopen.com/books/pharmacology/the-effet-of-cyp2c19-genotypes-on-the- pharmacokinetics-of-warfarin-enantiomers

American Association of Pharmaceutical Scientists. (2013). Pharmacogenomics (PGx). Retrieved from http://www.aaps.org/Pharmacogenomics/

Amstutz, U., Froehlich, T. K., & Largiadèr, C. R. (2011). Dihydropyrimidine dehydrogenase gene as a major predictor of severe 5-fluorouracil toxicity. *Pharmacogenomics, 10*(6), 931–944.

Baer, C. L., & Williams, B. R. (1996). *Clinical pharmacology and nursing, 3rd ed.* Springhouse, PA: Springhouse Corporation.

Bannister, W. P., Friis-Møller, N., Mocroft, A., Viard, J. P., van Lunzen, J., Kirk, O., Gargalianos, P., . . . & EuroSIDA Study Group. (2008). Incidence of abacavir hypersensitivity reactions in euroSIDA. *Antiviral Therapy, 13*(5), 687–696.

Beitelshees, A. L., Voora, D., & Lewis, J. P. (2015). Personalized antiplatelet and anticoagulation therapy: Applications and significance of pharmacogenomics. *Pharmacogenomics and Personalized Medicine, 8*, 43–61.

Belle, D. J., & Singh, H. (2008). Genetic factors in drug metabolism. *American Family Physician. 77*, 11, 1553–1560.

Booth, R. A., Ansari, M. T., Tricco, A. C., Loit, E., Weeks, L., Doucette, S., . . . & Yazdi, F. (2010). Assessment of thiopurine methyltransferase activity in patients prescribed azathiopurine or other thiopurine-based drugs. *Evidence Report/Technology Assessment No. 196* (prepared by the University of Ottawa Evidence-based practice Center under Contract no. 290-2007-10059-I AHRQ Publication No. 11-E002). Rockville, MD: Agency for Healthcare Research and Quality. Retrieved from www.ahrq.gov/research/findings/evidence-based-reports/tpmt-evidence-report.pdf

Bristol-Myers Squibb (2011). Coumadin® (warfarin sodium) prescribing information. 293US-11PBS01503. Retrieved from packageinserts.bms.com/pi/pi_coumadin.pdf/

Calzone, K. A., Jenkins, J., Bakos, A. D., Cashion, A. K., Donaldson, N., Feero, W. G., . . . & Webb, J. A. (2013). A blueprint for genomic nursing science. *Journal of Nursing Scholarship, 45*(1), 1–9.

Cavallari, L. H., & Limdi, N. A. (2009). Warfarin pharmacogenomics. *Current Opinion in Molecular Therapeutics, 11*(3), 243–251.

Chazal, M., Etieen, M. C., Renee, N., Bourgeon, A., Richelme, H., & Milano, G. (1996). Link between dihydropyrimidine dehydrogenase activity in peripheral blood mononuclear cells and liver. *Clinical Cancer Research, 2*(3), 507–510.

Chong, K., & Buehler, B. (2013). Warfarin dosing and VKORC1/CYP2C9. *Medscape* (online) Retrieved from emedicine.medscape.com/article/1733331-overview

Ciccolini, J., Gross, E., Dahan, L., Lacarelle, B., & Mercier, C. (2010). Routine dihydropyrimidine dehydrogenase testing for anticipating 5-fluorouracil-related severe toxicities: Hype or hope? *Clinical Colorectal Cancer, 9*(4), 224–228.

Claudle, K. E., Thorn, C. F., Klein, T. E., Swen, J.J, McLeod, H. L., Diasio, R. B., & Schwab, M. (2013). Clinical Pharmacogentics Implementation Consortium Guidelines for dihydropyrimidine dehydrogenase genotype and fluoropyrimidine dosing. *Clinical Pharmacoloty & Therapeutics, 94*(6), 640–645.

Coffey, S. (2008). HLA-B*5701 screening for abacavir hypersensitivity. *USCF HIV InSite.* Retrieved from hivinsite.uscf.edu/insite?page-hmq-0805-04.

Collett, J. P., Hulot, J. S., Pena, A., Villard, E.., Esteve, J. B., Silvain, J., Payot, L., . . . Montalescot G. (2009). Cytochrome P450 2C19 polymorphism in young patients treated with clopidogrel after myocardial infarction: A cohort study. *Lancet, 373,* 9660, 309–317.

Collins, F. S., & Varmus, H. (2015). A new initiative on precision medicine. *New England Journal of Medicine, 372,* 793–795. Retrieved from www.nejm.org/doi/full/10.1056/NEJMp1500523.

Cuo, Y.L., Shi L.M., Hong, H. X., Su, Z. Q., Fuscoe, J., & Ning, B. T. (2013). Studies on abacavir-induced hypersensitivity reaction: a successful example of translation of pharmacogenetics to personalized medicine. *Science China-Life Sciences, 56*(2), 119–124. doi: 10.1007/s11527-013-4438-8.

Dean, L. (2012 March 8 [Updated 2013 March 18). Warfarin therapy and the genotypes *CYP2C9* and VKORC1. In: *Medical Genetics Summaries* [Internet]. Bethesda (MD): National Center for Biotechnology Information (US). Available from http://222.ncbi.nlm.nih.gov/books/NBK84174.

Diasio, R. B., Beavers, T. L. & Carpenter, J. T. (1988). Familial deficiency of dihydropyrimidine dehydrogenase: biochemical basis for familial pyrimidinemia and severe 5-fluorouracil-induced toxicity. *The Journal of Clinical Investigation, 81,* 1, 47– 51. Retrieved from http://www.ncbi.nlm.nih.gov/pmc/articles/PMC442471/

Edwards, Q., Maradiegue, A., Seibert, D., Macri, C., & Sitzer, L. (2006). Faculty members' perceptions of medical genetics and its integration into nurse practitioner curricula. *Journal of Nursing Education, 45*(3), 124–130.

Evaluation of Genomic Applications in Practice and Prevention (EGAPP) Working Group. (2009). Recommendations from the EGAPP Working Group: can UGT1A1 genotyping reduce morbidity and mortality in patients with metastatic colorectal cancer treated with irinotecan? *Genetics in Medicine, 11,* 1, 15–20.

Evans, W. E., Hon, Y. Y., Bogaars, L., Coutre, S., Holdsworth, M., Janco, R., . . . Relling, (2001). Preponderance of thiopurine S-methyltransferase deficiency and heterozygosity among patients intolerant to mercaptopurine or azathioprine. *Journal of Clinical Oncology, 19,* 8, 2293–2301.

Evans, W. E., Horner, M., chu, Y. Q., Kalwinsky, D. & Roberts, W.M. (1991). Altered mercaptopurine metabolism, toxic effects, and dosage requirement in a thiopurine methyltransferase-deficient child with acute lymphocytic leukemia. *The Journal of Pediatrics, 27,* 8, 432–437.

Fisch, A. S., Perry,C. G., Stephens, S. H., Horenstein, R. B. & Shuldner, A. R. (2013). *Pharmacogenomics of anti-platelet and anti-coagulation therapy. Current Cardiology Reports, 15*(7), 10.1007/211886-913-9371-3. doi: 10.1007/s11886-013-0381-3. Retrieved from www.ncbi.nlm.nig.gov/pmc/articles. PMC3809070/.

Gage, B. F., Eby, C., Johson, J.A. Deych, E., Rieder, M.J., Ridker, P.M., . . . McLeod, H.L. (2008) *Clinical Pharmacology and Therapeutics, 3,* 326–331.

Gage, B. F. & Lesko, L. J. (2008). Pharmacogenetics of warfarin: regulatory, scientific and clinical issues. *Journal of Thrombosis and Thrombolysis, 25,* 1, 45–51.

Garcia, A. A. & Reitsma, P.H. (2008). VKORC1 and the vitamin K cycle. *Vitamins and Hormones,78,* 23–33. doi: 10.1016/S00083-6729(07)00002-7.

Gupta, E., Lestingi, T. M., Mick, R., Ramirez, J., Vokes, E. E. & Ratain, M. J. (1994). Metabolic fate of irinotecan in humans: correlation of glucuronidation with diarrhea. *Clinical Research, 54,* 14, 3723–3725.

Harris, B. E., Song, R., Soong, S. J. & Diasio, R. B. (1990). Relationship between dihydropyrimidine dehydrogenase activity and plasma 5-fluorouracil levels with evidence for circadian variation of enzyme activity and plasma drug levels in cancer patients receiving 5-fluorouracil by protracted continuous infusion. *Cancer Research, 50,* 1, 197– 201.

Hetherington, S., Hughes, A. R., Mosteller, M., Shotino, D., Baker, K. L., Spreeen, W., Lai, E., . . . Roses, A. D. (2002). Genetic variations in HLA-B region and hypersensitivity reactions to abacavir. *Lancet, 359,* 9312, 1121–1122.

Hetherington, S., McGuirk, S., Powell, G., Cutrell, A., Naderer, O., Spreen, B., Lafon, S., Pearce, G. & Steel, H. (2001). Hypersensitivity reactions during therapy with nucleoside reverse transcriptase inhibitor abacavir. *Clinical Therapeutics, 23,* 10, 1603–1614.

Hewitt, R. G. (2002). Abacavir hypersensitivity reaction. *Clinical Infectious Diseases: An Official Publication of the Infectious Diseases Society of America, 34,* 8, 1137–1142.

Hill, C. E. & Duncan, A. (2008). Overview of pharmacogenetics in anticoagulation therapy. *Clinics in Laboratory medicine, 28,* 4, 513–524.

Hoskins, J. M. & McLeod, H. L. (2009) UGT1A and irinotecan toxicity: keeping it in the family. *Journal of Clinical Oncology, 27,* 15, 2419–2421.

Hu, Z.Y., Yu, Q., Pei, Q., & Guo, C. (2010). Dose-dependent association between UGT1A1*28 genotype and irinotecan-induced neutropenia: low doses also increase risk. *Clinical Cancer Research, 16*(15). doi: 10.1158/1078-0432.CCR-10-1122. Retrieved from Clincancerres.aacrjourals.org/content/16/15/3832.long.

Hughes, A. R., Mosteller, M., Bansal, A. T., Davies, K., Haneline, S. A., Lai, E. H., . . . Roses A. D., CNA30027 Study Team; CNA30032 Study Team. (2004). *Pharmacogenomics, 5,* 2, 203–211.

Hummerickhouse, R., Lohrback, K., Li, L., Bosron, W. F. & Dolan, M. E. (2000). Characterization of CPT-11 hydrolysis by human liver carboxylesterase isoforms hCE-a and hCE-2. *Cancer Research, 60,* 5, 1189–1192.

Inoue, K., Sonobe, M., Kawamura, Y., Etoh, T., Takagi, M., Matsumura, T., . . . Itoh, K. (2013) Polymorphisms of the UDP-glucuronosyl transferase 1A genes re associated with adverse events in cancer patients receiving irinotecan-based chemotherapy. *The Tohoku Journal of Experimental Medicine, 229*, 2, 107–114.

Iyer, L., King, C. D., Whitington, P. F., Green, M. D., Roy, S. K., Tephly, T. R., Coffman, B. L. & Ratain, M.J. (1998). Genetic predisposition to the metabolism of irinotecan (CPT-11). Role of uridine diphosphate glucuronosyltransferase isoform 1A1 in the glucuronidation of its active metabolite (SN-38) in human liver microsomes. *Journal of Clinical Investigation, 101*, 4, 847–854

Johnson, J. A. (2003). Pharmacogenetics: potential for individualized drug therapy through genetics. *Trends in Genetics, 19*, 11, 660–666.

Johnson , J.A., & Cavallari, L.H. (2013). Pharmacogenetics and cardiovascular disease-implications for personalized medicine. *Pharmacological Reviews, 65*, 987–1009.

Johnson, J. A., Cavallari, L. H., Beitelshees, A. L., Lewis, J. P., Shuldiner, A.R. & Roden, D.M. (2011a). Pharmacogenomics: application to the management of cardiovascular disease. *Clinical Pharmacology and Therapeutics, 90*, 4, 519–531.

Johnson, J. A., Gong, L., Whirl-Carrillo, M., Gage, B. F., Scott, S. A., Stein, C. M., . . . Altman, R. B. (2011b). Clinical Pharmacogenetics Implementation Consortium Guidelines for CYP2C9 and VKORC1 genotypes and warfarin dosing. *Clinical Pharmacology and Therapeutics, 90*, 4, 625–629.

Johnson, J. A., Roden, D. M., Kesjim K, H,m Ashley, E., Klein, T. E. & Shuldiner, A. R. (2012) Clopidogrel: a case for indication-specific pharmacogenetics. *Clinical Pharmacology and Therapeutics, 91*, 5, 774–776.

Kadoyama, K., Miki, I., Tamura, T., Brown, J. B., Sakaeda, T., & Okuno, Y. (2012). Adverse event profiles of 5-Fluorouracil and Capecitabine: data mining of the public version of the FDA adverse event reporting system, AERS, and reproducibility of clinical observations. *International Journal of Medical Sciences, 9*(1), 33–39. Retrieved from http://www.medsci.org/v09p0033.htm.

Kamali, F., Khan, T.I., King, B. P., Frearson, R., Kesteven, P., Wood, P., Daly, A. K. & Wynne, H. (2004). Contribution of age, body size and CYP2C9 genotype to anticoagulant response to warfarin. *Clinical Pharmacology and Therapeutics, 75*, 4, 204–212.

Kazui, M., Nishiya, Y., Ishizuka, T., Hagihara, K., Farid, N. A., Okazaki, O., Ikeda, T. & Kurihara, A. (2010). Identification of the human cytochrome P450 enzymes involved in the two oxidative steps in the bioactivation of clopidogrel to its pharmacologically active metabolite. *Drug Metabolism and Disposition, 38*, 1, 92–99.

Khan, T., Kamali, F., Daly, A., King, B. & Wynne, H. A. (2003). Warfarin sensitivity: be aware of genetic influence. *Age and Ageing, 32*, 2, 226–227.

Knepper, T. C. & McLeod, H. L. (2015). Heritage-spe-

cific mechanisms for cancer adverse reactions: one gene does not explain the world. *Journal of Clinical Oncology, 33*(11), 1230–1231.

Krishna, V., Diamond, G.A., & Kaul, S. (2012). *Circulation, 125*, 1288–1303.

Lankisch, T. O., Schulz, C., Zwingers, T., Erichsen, T.J., Manns, M.P, Heinemann, V., & Strassburg, C.P. (2008). Gilbert's syndrome and irinotecan toxicity: combination with UDP-glucoronosyltransferase 1A7 variants increases risks. *Cancer Epidemiology Biomarkers & Prevention, 17*. doi: 10.1158/1055-9965.EPI-07-2517. Retrieved from cebp.aacrjournals.org/content/17/3/695.long.

Lane, S., Al-Zubiedi, S., Hatch, E., Matthews, I., Jorgensen, A.L., Deloukas, P., . . . Pirmohamed, M. (2012). The population pharmacokinetics of R- and S0warfarin: effect of genetic and clinical factors. *British Journal of Clinical Pharmacoloty, 73*(1), 66–76. doi: 10.1111/j.1365-2125.2011.04051.x.

Lee, A.M., Shi, Q., Pavey, E., Alberts, S. R., Sargent, D.J., Sinicrope, F. A., . . . Diasio, R. B. (2014). DPYD variants as predictors of 5-fluorouracil toxicity in adjuvant colon cancer treatment (NCCTG N0147). *Journal of the National Cancer Institute, 106*(12). Retrieved from http://jnci.oxfordjournals.org/content/106/12/dju298.long.

Leiden University Medical Center (2004-2014). LOVD gene homepage. *Leiden Open Variation Data Base Mendelian Genetes, Cytochrome P450, family 2 subfamily C, polypeptide 9 (CYP2C9)*. Retrieved from https://grenada.lumc.nl/LOVD2/mendelian_genes/home.php?select_db=CYP2C9.

Levy, H.P. (2012). Clopidogrel pharmacogenetics in the clinic. *Internal Medicine News*. Retrieved from http://www.internalmedicinenews.com/?id=495&tx_ttnews[tt_news]=94497&cHash=a2eb4eda66cb4914e6ccf1dc77aec3f8.

Li, J., Wang, W., Barone, J., & Malone, B. (2009). Warfarin pharmacogenomics. *P & T, 34*(8). 422–427.

Loganayagam, A., Hernandez, A., Corrigan, A., Fairbanks, L., Lewis, C.M., Harper, P., . . . Marinaki, A.M. (2013). Pharmacogentic variants in the DPYD, TYMS, CDA and MTHFR genes are clinically significant predictors of fluorpyrimidine toxicity. *British Journal of Cancer, 108*(12), 2505–2515. Retrieved from http://www.ncbi.nlm.nih.gov/pmc/articles/PMC3694243/

Ma, Q. & Lu, A.Y.H. (2011). Pharmacogenetics, pharmacogenomics, and individualized medicine. *Pharmacological Reviews, 63*(2), 437–459.

Ma, M. K. & McLeod, H.L. (2003). Lessons learned from the irinotecan metabolic pathway. *Current Medicinal Chemistry, 10*, 1, 41–49.

Maitland, M. L., Vasisht, K. & Ratain, M.J. (2006). TPMT, UGT1A1 and DPYD: genotyping to ensure safer cancer therapy? *Trends in Pharmacology Science, 27*, 8, 432–437.

Mallal, S., Nolan, D., Witt, C., Masel, G., Martin, A.M., Moore, C., . . . Christiansen, F, T, (2002). Association between presence of HLA-B*5701, HLA-DR7, and HLA-DQ3 and hypersensitivity to HIV-1 reverse-transcriptase inhibitor abacavir. *Lancet, 359*, 9308, 727–732

Maradiegue, A.H., Edwards, Q. T., & Seibert, D. (2010). 5-years later: Have faculty integrated medical genetics into curriculum? *International Journal of Nursing Education Scholarship, 10*(1), 1–10.

Mega, J.L., Simon, T., Collet, J.P., Anderson, J.L., Antman, E.M., Bliden, K., . . . Sabatine, M.S. (2010). Reduced-funtion CYP2C19 genotype and risk of adverse clinical outcomes among patients treated with clopidogrel predominatly for PCI: a meta-analysis. *Journal of the American Medical Association (JAMA), 304*(16), 1821–1830.

Mega, J. L., Close, S. L., Wiviott, S. D., Shen, L., Hockett, R. D., Brandt, J. T., . . . Sabatine, M. S. (2009). Cytochrome p-450 polymorphisms and response to clopidogrel. *New England Journal of Medicine, 360*, 4, 354–362.

Moen, M. & Lamba, J. (2012). Assessment of healthcare students' views on pharmacogenomics at the University of Minnesota. *Pharmacogenomics, 13*, 13. 1537–1545.

Mueller, J.A., Patel, T., Halawa, A., Dumitrascu, A., & Dawson, N.L. (2014). Warfarin dosing and body mass index. *Annals of Pharmacotherapy, 48*(5), 584–588.

Nair, S. R. (2010). Personalized medicine: striding from genes to medicines. *Perspectives in Clinical Research, 1*, 4, 146–150. Retrieved from http://www.ncbi.nlm.nih.gov/pmc/articles/PMC3043364/

National Academy of Sciences, Committee on a Framework for Development a New Taxonomy of Disease; National Research Council. (2011). *Toward Precision Medicine: Building a Knowledge Network for Biomedical Research and a New Taxonomy of Disease.* Washington, D. C: The National Academies Press. Retrieved from http://www.nap.edu/catalog.php?record_id=13284.

National Institutes of Health, National Human Genome Research Institute. (2015). Personalized medicine. In *Talking Glossary of Genetic Terms.* Retrieved from http://www.genome.gov/glossary/ and ghr.nlm.nih.gov/glossary=personalizedmedicine.

National Institutes of Health, National Institute of General Medical Sciences. (2013). *What are pharmacogenomics and pharmacogenetics?* Retrieved from www.nigms.nih.gov/Research/FeaturedPrograms/PGRN/Background?pages/pgrn_faq.aspx.

Nguyen, C.M., Mendes, M.A.S., & Ma J.D. (2011). Thiopurine methyltransferase(TPMT) genotyping to predict myelosuppression risk. *PLOS Currents Evidence on Genomic Tests.* Retrieved from http://currents.plos.org/genomictests/article/thiopurine-methyltransferase-tpmt-xv5k9xg3o4yu-8/

Panel on Antiretroviral Guidelines for Adults and Adolescents. (2011). *Guidelines for the use of antiretroviral agents in HIV-1-infected adults and adoles-*

cents. Department of Health and Human Services, p.19. Retrieved from http://www.aids.info.nih.gov/ContentFiles/AdultandAdolescentGl.pdf.

PharmGKB (Last Update July 30, 2014). CPIC dosing guidelines for fluorouracil and DYPD. In *PharmGKB* [Online]. Retrieved from https://www.pharmgkb.org/guideline/PA166122686

Phillips, E. & Mallal, S. (2007). Drug hypersensitivity in HIV. *Current Opinion in Allergy and Clinical Immunology, 7*, 4, 324–330.

Price, D. K. (2013). *Pharmacogenomics and precision medicine: from laboratory to clinical practice.* Omics Group Conferences, 2nd International Conference on Translational Medicine (Abstract). Retrieved from http://www.omicsgroup.com/conferences/ACS/conference/pdfs/5555-Speaker-Pdf-T.pdf

Pucheril, D. & Sharma, S. (2011). The history and future of personalized medicine. *Manage Care* (Online). Retrieved from www.managedcaremag.com/content/history-and-future-personalized -medicine.

Relling, M. V., Gardner, E. E., Sandborn, W.J., Schmiegelow, K., Pui, C-H., Yee, S.W., . . . Klein, T. E. (2011). Clinical pharmacogenetics implementation Consortium Guidelines for thipurine methyltransferase genotype and thiopurine dosing. *Clinical Pharmacology Therapeutics, 89*(3), 387–391. doi: 10.1038/clpt.2010.320

Rettie, A. E. & Tai, G. (2006). The pharmocogenomics of warfarin: closing in on personalized medicine. *Molecular Interventions, 6*, 4, 223–227.

Ritchie, M. D. (2012). The success of pharmacogenomics in moving genetic association studies from bench to bedside: study design and implementation of precision medicine in the post-GWAS era. *Human Genetics, 131*, 10 1615-1626. doi: 10.1007/s00439-012-1221-z

Rosmarin, D., Palles, C., Church, D., Domingo, E., Jones, A., Johnstone, E., . . . Tolinson, I. (2014). Genetic markers of toxicity from capecitabine and other fluorouracil-based regimens: investigation in the QUASAR2 study, stematic review, and meta-analysis. *Journal of Clinical Oncology, 32*(10), 1030–1039.

Roychowdhury, S., Iyer, M. K., Robinson, D. R., Lonigro, R. J., Wu., Y. M., Cao, X., . . . Chinnaiyan, A. M. (2011). Personalized oncology through integrative high- throughput sequencing: a pilot study. *Science Translational Medicine, 3, 111, 11ra121. doi: 10.1126/scitranslmed.3003161.* Retrieved from http://www.ncbi.nlm.nih.gov/pmc/articles/PMC3476478/

Saag, M., Balu, R., Phillips, E., Brachman, P., Martorell, C., Burman, W., . . . Shaefer, High sensitivity of human leukocyte antigen-B*5701 as a marker for immunologically confirmed abacavir hypersensitivity in white and black patients. *Clinical Infectious Disease, 46*(7), 1111–1118.

Sadee, W. (2011). Pharmacogenomic biomarkers:

validation needed for both the molecular genetic mechanism and clinical effect. *Pharmacogenomics, 12*, 5, 675–680.

Saif, W.W., Chorma, A., Salamone, S.J. & Chu, E. (2009). Pharmacokinetically guided dose adjustment of 5-Fluorouracil: a rational approach to improving therapeutic outcomes. *JNCI Journal of the National Cancer Institute, 101*(22), 1543–1552. Retrieved from http://jnci.oxfordjournals.org/content/101/22/1543.full.

Schwarz, U. I. & Stein, C.M. (2006). Genetic determinants of dose and clinical outcomes in patients receiving oral anticoagulants. *Clinical Pharmacology and Therapeutics, 80*, 1, 7–12.

Scott, S. A., Khasawneh, R., Peter, I., Komreich, R. , & Desnick, R. (2010). Combined *CYP2C9, VKORC1* and *CYP4F2* frequencies among racial and ethnic groups. *Pharmacogenomics, 11*(6), 781–791. doi: 10.2217/pgs.10.49

Scott, S. A., Sangkuhl, K., Stein, C.M., Hulot, J-S., Mega, J. L., Roden, D.M., . . . Sabatine, M.S. (2013). Clinical Pharmacogenetics Implementation Consortium guidelines for CYP2C19 genotype and clopidogrel therapy: 2013 update. *Clinical Pharmacology & Therapeutics, 94*(3), 317–323.

Simon, R. (2011). Genomic biomarkers in predictive medicine: an interim analysis. *EMBO Molecular Medicine, 3*, 8, 429–435.

Simon, T., Verstuyft, C., Mary-Krause, M., Quteineh, L., Drouet, E., Meneveau, N., . . . Becquemont L: French Registry of Acute ST-Elevation and Non-ST-Elevation Myocardial Infarction (FAST-MI) Investigators. (2009). Genetic determinants of response to clopidogrel and cardiovascular events. *New England Journal of Medicine, 360*, 4, 363–375.

Sistonen, J., Smith, C., Fu, Y.K. & Largiadèr, C. R. (2014). A new DPYD genotyping assay for improving the safety of 5-fluorouracil therapy. *Clinica Chimica Acta, 414*, 109–111. doi: 10.106/j.cca.2012.08.015.

Stocchi, L., Cascella, R., Zampatti, S., Pirazzoli,A., Novelli, G. & Giardina, E. (2012). The pharmacogenomics HLA biomarker associated to adverse abacavir reactions: comparative analysis of different genotyping methods. *Current Genomics, 13*, 4, 314–320.

Strom, C.M., Goos, D., Crossley, B., Zhang, K., Buller-Burkle, A., Jarvis, M., . . . sun, W. (2011). Testing for variants in CYP2C19: population frequencies and testing experience in a clinical laboratory. *Genetics in Medicine, 14*(1), 95–100.

Thompson, T. A. (2010). Hematology/oncology pharmacogenomics. In Zdanowicz, M.M, *Concepts in Pharmacogenomics*, Chapter 8, p. 221 Bethesda, Maryland: American Society of Health-System Pharmacists.

Toffoli, G., Cecchin, E., Corona, G. & Boiocchi, M. (2003). Pharmacogenetics of irinotecan. *Current Medicinal Chemistry Anticancer Agents, 3*, 3, 225–237.

Torkamani, A., Windle, M.L. & Roth, K.S. (2015). Abacavir and HLA-B*5701. *Medscape.* Retrieved from emedicine.medscape.com/article/1969668-overivew.

Torkamani, A., Windle, M. L., & Roth, K. S. (2013). Azathioprine metabolism and TPMT. *Medscape.* Retrieved from emedicine.medscape.com/article/1829596

Tuchman, M., Stoeckeler, J. S., Kiang, D. T., O'Dea, R. F., Ramnaraine, M. L. & Mirkin,. B. L (1985) Familial pyrimidinemia and pyrimidinuria associated with severe fluorouracil toxicity. *New England Journal of Medicine, 313*, 4, 245–249.

U.S. Food & Drug Administration. (2015 [Last updated April 14, 2015]). *Table of Pharmacogenomics Biomarkers in Drug Labeling.* Retrieved from http://www.fda.gov/Drugs/ScienceResearch/ResearchAreas/Pharmacogenetics/ucm08337 8.htm

U.S. Food & Drug Administration. (2014, December 23). FDA drug safety communication: reduced effectiveness of Plavix (clopidogrel) in patients who are poor metabolizers of the drug. *Drugs—U.S. Food and Drug Administration.* Retrieved from www.fda.gov/Drugs/DrugSafety/PostmarketDrugSafetyInformationforPatientsandProviders/ucm203888.htm

U.S. Food & Drug Administration (2013a [December]). Plavix (clopidogrel bisulfate) tablet. *Safety—US. Food and Drug Administration.* Retrieved from www.fda.gov/Safety/MedWatch/SafetyInformation/ucm225843.htm.

U.S. Food & Drug Administration. (2013b [Last updated August 15, 2013]). *Information for Healthcare Professionals: Abacavir (marketed as Ziagen) and Abacavir-Containing Medications.* Retrieved from www.fda.gov/Drugs/DrugSafety/PostmarketDrugSafetyInformationforPatientsandProviders/ucm23937.htm

U.S. Food & Drug Administration. (2012). *Interactions between Esomeprazole/Omeprazole and Clopidogrel Label Change.* Retrieved from www.fda.gov/Safety/MedWatch/SafetyInformation/ucm327922.htm.

U.S. Food & Drug Administration. (2010, January). Coumadin (warfarin sodium) tablet and injection—Detailed View: Safety labeling changes approved by FDA Center for Drug Evaluation and Research (CDER). *U.S. Food & Drug Administration—Safety.* Retrieved from www.fda.gov/Safety/MedWatch/SafetyInformation/ucm201100.htm

U.S. Food & Drug Administration. (2008, July). Ziagen (abacavir sulfate) tablets and oral solution July 2008. *U.S. Food & Drug Administration—Safety.* Retrieved from www.fda.gov/Safety/MedWatch/SafetyInformation/Safety-RelatedDrugLabelingChanges/ucm121838.htm.

U.S. Food & Drug Administration. (2007, August 16). FDA approves updated warfarin (Coumadin)

prescribing information—new genetic information may help providers improve initial dosing estimates of the anticoagulant for individual patients. *News & Events, FDA News Release.* Retrieved from www.fda.gov/NewsEvents/Newsroom/PressAnnouncements/2007/ucm1008967.htm

U.S. Food & Drug Administration. (2005 [Last updated April 3, 2013]). FDA clears genetic test that advances personalized medicine. *FDA News Release (P05-53).* Retrieved from http://www.fda.gov/NewsEvents/Newsroom/PressAnnouncements/2005/ucm108475.htm

van Kuilenburg, A. B. P, Ferdinandusse, S., & Wanders, R. J. A. (2013). Screening for dihydropyrimidine dehydrogenase deficiency to prevent severe 5-fluorouracil and capecitabine-associated toxicity. *Ned Tijdschr Klin Chem Labgeneesk, 38,* 202–205. Retrieved from https://www.nvkc.nl/publicaties/documents/NedTijdschrKlinChemLabgeneesk201338202-205.pdf

van Kuilenburg, A. V., van Lenthe, H., Blom, M. J., Mul, E. P. & Van Gennip, A. H. (1999) Profound variation in dihydropyrimidine dehydrogenase activity in human blood cells: major implications for the detection of partly deficient patients. *British Journal of Cancer, 79,* 3, 620–626.

Vokes, E. E., Mick, R., Kies, M. S., Dolan, M. E., Malone, D., Athanasiadis, I., Haraf, D. J., . . . Ratain, M. J. (1996). Pharmacodynamics of fluorouracil-based induction chemotherapy in advanced head and neck cancer. *Journal of Clinical Oncology, 14,* 5, 1663–1671.

Wang, Z.Y., Chen, M., Zhu, L.L., Zeng, S., Xiang, M.X., & Zhou, Q. (2015). Pharmacokinetic drug interactions with clopidogrel: updated review and risk management in combination therapy. *Therapeutics and Clinical Risk Management, 11,* 449–467.

Wang, B., Wang, J., Huang, S.Q., Su, H.H. & Zhou, S. F. (2009). Genetic polymorphism of the human cytochrome P450 2C9 gene and its significance. *Current Drug Metabolism, 10*(7). 781–834.

Washington University in St. Louis ©. (2015). *Warfarin Dosing.* Retrieved from www.warfarindosing.org

Wasserman, E., Myara, A., Lokiec, F., Goldwasser, F., Trivin, F., Mahjoubi, M., Misset, J. L. & Cvitkovic, E. (1997). Severe CPT-11 toxicity in patients with Gilbert's syndrome: two Case reports. *Annals of Oncology, 8,* 10, 1049–1051

Williams, J. K., Prows, C. A., Conley, Y. P., Eggert, J., Kirk, M. & Nichols, F. (2011). Strategies to prepare faculty to integrate genomics into nursing education program. *Journal of Nursing Scholarship, 43,* 3, 231–238.

Zdanowicz, M. M. (2010). American Society of Health-System Pharmacists: concepts in pharmacogenomics. *American Journal of Pharmaceutical Education, 74,* 10, 195a Retrieved from http://www.ncbi.nlm.nih.gov/pmc/articles/PMC3058468/

Zhu, Y., Shennan, M., Reynolds, K. K., Johnson, N. A., Herrnberger, M. R. Valdes, R. Jr., & Linder, M. W. (2007). Estimation of warfarin maintenance dose based on VKORC1 (-1639 G > A) and CYP2C9 genotypes. *Clinical Chemistry, 53,* 7, 1199–1205.

Chapter 6

Preconceptual and Prenatal Genomics

MICHELLE MUNROE, DNP, COL, AN, CNM
DIANE SEIBERT, Ph.D, CRNP, FAANP, FAAN
DANA KNUTZEN, MS, CGC

Objectives:

- Describe the purpose of preconception care.
- Identify genetic conditions that should be identified prior to conception.
- Discuss specific genetic conditions that can affect male and female fertility.
- Identify the genetic concerns that should be discussed with families considering preimplantation diagnostic testing.
- Discuss maternal genetic conditions that may adversely impact pregnancy.
- Describe pregnancy complications associated with a genomic condition.
- Discuss prenatal screening.

6.1. INTRODUCTION

Many people fantasize about what their future children might look and act like long before a pregnancy occurs. Even when a child appears completely healthy at birth, new parents often need time to adjust to the reality of caring for a child who looks and behaves differently from what they had imagined. When a child is born with a genetic disorder or a physical defect, abandoning the fantasy of the "perfect child" often takes a long period of time and may be accompanied by a profound sense of loss. Healthcare providers can help parents begin to make this transition months before the actual delivery by making genomics a part of every provider-patient dialogue. This offers individuals an opportunity to think about and discuss their concerns, explore personal and familial risks, and consider their response to potential reproductive outcomes.

Rapid and often parallel scientific advances have pushed clinicians who work within the obstetric community to become and remain knowledgeable about genetics. This chapter provides an overview of some of the important genetic concepts that all nurses need to know when working with anyone of childbearing age.

6.2. ASSESSING RISK AND THE FAMILY HEALTH HISTORY (FHH)

One of the most important functions of genes is to pass the genetic code along to the next generation. Healthcare professionals working with individuals during this phase of life play an important role in assessing risk for expectant couples and their offspring. Although a family history is usually collected during a well woman visit and always re-examined early in prenatal care, most primary care clinicians do not construct a three-generation pedigree nor are many clinicians comfortable interpreting a family pedigree (Mathers *et al.*, 2010). In part, this has to do with the amount of time providers are given to see patients. In a recent study, over half of the primary care providers surveyed reported that a family health history (FHH) was important or very important. Yet, nearly 90% spent only 1 to 5 minutes collecting this information at the first visit, and over 33% never looked at or updated the FHH at subsequent visits (Fuller, Myers, Webb, Tabangin, & Prows, 2010). Many clinicians will also admit that their genetic knowledge is inadequate, making them unsure about what to do with the FHH information that they do obtain (Yoon,

Scheuner, Jorgensen, & Khoury, 2009). Still, the visual diagram of a three-generation FHH offers the opportunity to see patterns of familial disease that can't otherwise be appreciated.

Obtaining an accurate FHH to construct the three-generation pedigree is often a two-step process. The first step is getting accurate family health information. Many people are surprised when they realize how little they know about their family's health history. In prenatal settings, there are often additional challenges to collecting an accurate family health history. Pregnant young couples may not have been in a relationship for very long and many feel awkward or uncomfortable asking their parents or their partner's family for health information that may be perceived as "personal" or "private." Several electronic resources have been created to help families collect these important data. Some tools have been developed to gather information about specific inherited disorders such as cancer (My-Generations; http://www.northshore.org/genetics/mygenerations/), whereas others such as the Surgeon General's Family Health History tool (https://familyhistory.hhs.gov) gathers and displays information about a number of health conditions, including hypertension, cancer, diabetes, and heart disease. Encouraging families to complete an electronic tool may increase the amount of information obtained, decrease the stigma involved in "interviewing" family members, and provide important insights into an individual's risk. This may be particularly important in a prenatal setting, in which the main goals for collecting the FHH is to assess genetic risk for future generations and determine whether a couple might benefit from formal genetic counseling.

The public expects all nurses, regardless of educational preparation or specialty area, to use genetic and genomic information in daily practice. To help prepare nurses for this expectation, a baseline set of competencies was published in 2006 and revised in 2009 that outlines the core nursing competencies that all nurses should have achieved before entering practice (Calzone et al., 2011). Three years later, a second set of competencies was published, the *Essential Genetic and Genomic Competencies for Nurses With Graduate Degrees*, which establishes baseline genetic/genomic competencies for nurses prepared at the graduate level (Greco, Tinley, & Seibert, 2011).

Together, these two documents clearly articulate the expected practice competencies of any nurse working with a prenatal population.

Emerging genomic information is rapidly changing the way prenatal care is delivered. Prenatal education is evolving to include information about genetic testing. Practices are adopting new genetic screening guidelines and implementing them when applicable. Clinicians must understand that organizations do not always agree on which tests should be included on routine screening and should be prepared to discuss differences in reimbursement for genetic testing with patients (Bodurtha & Strauss, 2012). Genomic testing is applicable before, during, and after pregnancy, but the use of this information remains controversial.

6.3. PRECONCEPTION CARE

Nearly half of all pregnancies in the United States (U.S.) are unintended (Mosher, Jones, & Abma, 2012) and each year, 1 in 233 American newborns dies before turning one month old. Many of these infant deaths could be avoided if women and their partners consistently maintained a healthy lifestyle, avoided tobacco, and maintained normal body weight and blood pressure. Preconceptional counseling begins much earlier than many clinicians realize and truly is preventive healthcare at its best. Although many clinical encounters may not explicitly discuss pregnancy outcomes, preconception care is a subcontext to all preventive visits, and clinicians should begin these conversations with both boys and girls, beginning in early adolescence and continuing throughout the reproductive years (Oestergaard et al., 2011).

Scheduling a focused preconception counseling visit is particularly important for individuals who have known genetic conditions or family histories suggestive of an inherited genetic disorder. Until very recently, for example, women with inherited genetic conditions such as phenylketonuria (PKU) and cystic fibrosis (CF) did not live long enough to conceive, so few providers have had the experience of offering preconception counseling to high risk, but otherwise healthy individuals. To optimize prenatal outcomes, planning may need to begin years or even decades prior to conception, and specific recommendations regarding preconception care have been developed for some conditions such as sickle cell disease (SCD) and phenylketonuria (PKU) (Solomon, Jack, & Feero, 2008).

Several preconceptional care documents and guidelines have been published by a variety of healthcare professional organizations, including the American Congress of Obstetrics and Gynecologists, the American Academy of Family Physicians and the Centers for Disease Control and Prevention (CDC), and links to these documents are provided under the resources section at the end of this chapter. Every preconceptional counseling visit should include gathering a personal and family history; conducting a comprehensive physical examination; ordering appropriate laboratory tests; reviewing prescription, over-the-counter, and illicit medication use; determining whether a reproductive plan exists; providing nutrition counseling; assessing supplement use; evaluating weight and exercise habits; ensuring vaccinations are current; and addressing injury prevention (Lu, 2007). For couples with existing genetic conditions or family histories suggestive of a genetic condition, additional or more frequent visits may be necessary to ensure underlying disease is well controlled, pregnancy occurs at a time when maternal health is optimal, and unplanned pregnancy is avoided.

6.4. EPIGENETICS

Two epigenomic concepts are particularly important in perinatal/prenatal care: genomic imprinting and transgenerational epigenetics. Imprinting is the process in which the parent of origin becomes important, and to date over 50 imprinted human genes have been identified (Ishida & Moore, 2013). In contrast to the biallelic expression of most genes, in imprinted genes, normal function is dependent on the inheritance of one copy from each parent. If one parent contributes two copies or if one copy is missing, acquires a mutation, or is damaged by epigenetic changes, the affected individual may have developmental and/or, behavioral challenges and may be at higher for cancer (Soubry, Hoyo, Jirtle, & Murphy, 2014). Two of the most common disorders associated with imprinting errors are Angelman syndrome (AS) and Prader-Willi (PWS) syndrome. These very different syndromes are

caused by a disruption of methylation patterns on the long arm of chromosome 15. When no maternal copy of chromosome 15 is present or expressed, AS develops. Often misdiagnosed as cerebral palsy or autism, AS is characterized by severe intellectual and developmental disability, seizures, jerky movements (especially hand-flapping), and typically, a happy demeanor. Prader-Willi syndrome develops when the same stretch of chromosome 15 has alterations in paternal genes. Characteristic features of PWS include low muscle tone, short stature, incomplete sexual development, lack of eye coordination, learning disabilities, and an insatiable appetite that can lead to excessive eating and life-threatening obesity (Driscoll, Miller, Schwartz, & Cassidy, 1993).

Transgenerational epigenetics is the inheritance of characteristics that are not directed by DNA sequences. Broadly defined, transgenerational epigenetics can be inherited from parent to child or be created from developmental or social interactions (Jablonka & Raz, 2009). Examples of transgenerational inheritance are perhaps most clearly illustrated in the risk for development of diabetes in the offspring of adults exposed to famine. In a study of three generations of families living in Överkalix, Sweden, there were striking differences in the health outcomes of first- and second-generation family members depending on whether the father or mother had access to food during a relatively slow period of growth (ages 8 to 12 years) just prior to the onset of puberty. Offspring had reduced risk for cardiovascular death if fathers had limited access to food. The protective effect of paternal malnutrition also stretched into the next generation, with limited grand paternal nutrition being significantly associated with reduced risk for diabetic death in grandsons (Pembrey *et al.*, 2006). Dutch adults exposed to famine while in utero during World War II (1944 to 1945) had reduced methylation of *IGF2* genes and six decades later remained at increased risk for developing diabetes compared with their unexposed, same-sex siblings (Heijmans *et al.*, 2008). A recent publication described the developmental interactions between fetal and maternal genomes in brain development, which have been shown to have long-term effects on offspring behavior and cultural interactions (Keverne, 2013). Tremendous strides are being made in the area of epigenetics, but the domain is still in its infancy. Emerging evidence suggests, for example, that some epigenetic alterations caused by malnutrition may be modifiable if an affected neonate is identified and interventions such as dietary changes are instituted early in life (Godfrey, Lillycrop, Burdge, Gluckman, & Hanson, 2013).

6.5. SMOKING

The health of the father, long considered less important than maternal health, is now recognized as a risk factor for adverse prenatal outcomes. In recent studies, paternal age > 45 years has been associated with lower fertility and an increased risk for stillbirth, low birthweight, and preterm birth (Alio et al. 2012; Balasch & Gratacos, 2012). Irrespective of age, paternal smoking, and occupational exposures (particularly to lead and heavy metals) are known to degrade spermatogenesis, sperm mobility, and morphology, all of which are genetically driven. Other studies have shown that parental (maternal and paternal) smoking can alter embryos in unexpected and deleterious ways. Paternal smoking at the time of conception has been shown to alter the DNA contained in individual sperm, increasing the risk for childhood leukemia, which appears to be dependent upon the cytochrome P450 1A1 (*CYP1A1*) genotype of the fetus (Lee et al., 2009). Maternal smoking has been shown to damage male offspring through the exposure of fetal cells to polycyclic aromatic hydrocarbons. These toxins are postulated to induce apoptosis and decrease testicular weight, spermatogenesis, and ultimately sperm count in adulthood (Fukuda et al., 2011). Effects of smoking have typically been thought to be a maternal issue, but studies have shown that paternal smoking does have a negative impact on offspring. Fetal sex appears to be affected by paternal smoking at the time of conception (Fukuda et al., 2011). Although the exact mechanism is unknown, paternal smoking appears to delay or damage Y chromosomes and more X-bearing sperm ultimately reach the ovum, resulting in an increased number of female offspring among smoking men. Girls born to fathers who smoke are significantly ($P < 0.0001$) more likely to go through menopause earlier than girls born to fathers who do not smoke, even after controlling for maternal smoking, passive smoke exposure, and the woman herself smoking (Fukuda et al., 2011).

6.6. SEIZURE DISORDER

Seizure disorder is a central feature in more than 140 distinct genetic syndromes, such as tuberous sclerosis, neurofibromatosis, metabolic disorders, and mitochondrial diseases, but most people with recurrent seizures do not have a genetic syndrome. More than 20 genes are now recognized as playing a major role in susceptibility for developing epilepsy (Ottman et al., 2010). Much more work needs to be done in this area, but for now, the important "take away" message for nurses is to recognize that women with epilepsy, particularly those women using valproate for seizure control, are at significantly increased risk for adverse prenatal outcomes, particularly if the pregnancy is unplanned. Preconceptional counseling should begin early, utilizing a multidisciplinary approach, and reinforcement of the importance of using effective contraception until pregnancy can be planned is critical for these women and their babies.

6.7. NEURAL TUBE DEFECT (NTD)

Factors increasing the risk for having a child with a NTD include personal history of NTD, Hispanic descent, obesity, pregestational or gestational diabetes, female infants, hot tub or sauna use, and family history (child, sibling, niece, or nephew) of NTDs. Women with Type 1 Diabetes (T1DM) or taking medications such as valproic acid or carbamazepine are at increased risk for having an infant with NTD. The type of NTD may be associated with certain features; for example, maternal obesity is correlated with an increased risk for spina bifida, whereas anencephaly was more commonly seen in women of Hispanic ethnicity (Yang, Carmichael, Tinker, Shaw, & the National Birth Defects Prevention Study, 2012).

Folic acid supplementation has been recommended for nearly two decades to prevent NTD, because evidence from randomized trials in settings without nutritional fortification of food suggested that a multivitamin with folic acid reduces NTD risks. Observational studies further support this recommendation, reporting a reduction of NTDs when women took supplements with 0.4 mg (400 µg) of folic acid. Most women living in the U.S. do not eat enough fortified foods to provide optimal benefit without supplementation (Desposito *et al.*, 1999).

Mothers who had a prior pregnancy complicated by NTD may have a folic acid mutation interfering with folate metabolism or a mutation in a gene affecting DNA methylation. Valproic acid (VPA) in particular is a well-known risk factor for NTD, because it is a potent histone inhibitor. Folic acid supplementation reduces the risk for NTD when taken 3 months prior to conception and throughout the first few months of pregnancy, and research examining the role of other micronutrient supplementation, particularly vitamin B12 and zinc, in the development of NTD is ongoing (Wallingford, Niswander, Shaw, & Finnell, 2013).

6.8. GENETIC CONDITIONS AFFECTING FERTILITY

Although the numbers vary, approximately one-third of infertility can be attributable to male factors, one-third to female factors, and the final third is either unknown or both individuals have conditions adversely affecting fertility. Many genetic conditions can cause infertility, including chromosomal abnormalities, copy number variants, and single-gene disorders. Some genetic conditions impair ovulation or effect spermatogenesis or sperm function, and others disrupt normal embryo development. Conditions such as congenital adrenal hyperplasia (CAH), cryptorchidism, and Turner syndrome are often recognized at or shortly after birth; thus, a discussion of fertility may be part of the general discussion with parents at the time of formal diagnosis, and children often grow up knowing they may face fertility challenges in adulthood. Adults who first learn that they have a genetic diagnosis that impacts fertility often express shock, anger, and regret that they didn't know this information earlier, but reported being relieved that that there was an explanation for their infertility (Pastore, Morris, & Karns, 2008; Terzioglu, 2007).

Five of the more common genetic conditions with clearly described biologic mechanisms for infertility will be reviewed here, but this is by no means an exhaustive review, and nurses should appreciate that many adults with genetic disorders have reduced fecundity (the probability of achieving a live birth within a single menstrual cycle) (Berek & Novak, 2007). Reduced fecundity is not limited to major chromosomal anomalies or severe single gene disorders either. A large study comparing the fecundity of adults with major mental health disorders (schizophrenia, autism, bipolar disorder, depression, anorexia nervosa, or substance abuse) to that of their unaffected siblings and the general population found that with the exception of depression in women, adults affected with any of these disorders had significantly fewer children. Reduced fecundity was particularly pronounced in affected males, and the authors concluded that "strong selection exists against schizophrenia, autism, and anorexia nervosa and that these variants may be maintained by new mutations or an as-yet unknown mechanism." (Power *et al.*, 2013; p. 22). The CDC web site is a great starting point to learn more about genetics and infertility: http://www.cdc.gov/reproductivehealth/Infertility/PublicHealth.htm.

6.9. CONGENITAL ADRENAL HYPERPLASIA

Congenital adrenal hyperplasia (CAH) describes a group of related autosomal recessive disorders that all interfere somewhere along the complex biochemical pathways which culminate in the transformation of cholesterol into cortisol. Over 100 CAH mutations have been described, but 9 disease-causing mutations account for almost 95% of CAH cases. In all cases, however, low serum cortisol stimulates the pituitary gland to secrete high levels of adrenocorticotropic hormone (ACTH) in an attempt to stimulate the adrenal cortex to produce cortisol. Although unsuccessful at increasing cortisol levels, persistently high ACTH levels stimulate the adrenal gland to produce large amounts of androgens and mineralocorticoids, which may cause virilization and increase the risk for life-threatening salt wasting.

The most common form of CAH ia 21-hydroxylase deficiency (21-OHD). Infants with "classic" 21-OHD produce little to no cortisol and high ACTH levels causing virilization that begins in utero. Classic CAH can be divided into the simple virilizing form (androgen excess) and the more common salt-wasting (inadequate aldosterone production) form. Females with classic CAH may have been so masculinized in utero that they appear to be a normal male with undescended (nonpalpable) testes. More commonly, virilization is incomplete, causing ambiguous genitalia manifesting, as in varying degrees of clitoral enlargement and labioscrotal fusion or urogenital sinus. Affected girls usually have normal internal genitalia (fallopian tubes, ovaries, and uterus) and if appropriately treated, will have normal menarche; pregnancy is possible, although fertility may be reduced (Sit, Rothschild, & Wisner, 2006). Affected male infants may not be diagnosed unless they have a salt-wasting crisis in infancy or until late childhood, when they develop pseudoprecocious puberty.

Without treatment, androgen excess often manifests as precocious puberty, with voice deepening, cystic acne, accelerated growth, and shorter adult height as a result of early closure of epiphyseal plates. Even when appropriately treated, affected children are often shorter than predicted adult height. Approximately two-thirds of affected children develop hypertension within the first year of life. Untreated males have smaller than normal testes with progressive penile enlargement. Male fertility may be reduced because of androgenic suppression of the pituitary gland but is more commonly caused by testicular adrenal rest tumors (McCoy, Beal, Shipman, Payton, & Watson, 2006). Untreated females have persistent clitoral enlargement, male pattern baldness, hirsutism, and menstrual abnormalities (Nimkarn & New, 1993).

6.10. FRAGILE X SYNDROME

Fragile X syndrome (FXS) is the most common inherited causes of intellectual disability (ID) in males (Shapiro & Batshaw, 2011), but its effects are not limited strictly to males, nor does the mutation just affect cognition. Clinical manifestations are caused by a mutation on the long arm of the X chromosome in the *FMR1* gene. The *FMR1* gene produces a protein necessary for proper brain growth. A defect in the gene makes this person's body produce too little of the protein, or none at all. Over 99% of cases of FXS are caused by a trinucleotide repeat (i.e., CGG/CGG/CGG), which "hypermethylates" part of the gene, effectively sealing it shut and making it virtually impossible to copy the gene. The remaining cases of FXS (1%) are caused by point mutations, deletions, or duplications in the *FMR1* gene.

All individuals have several copies of the CGG triplet repeat in the *FMR1* gene, but symptoms vary based on the total number of repeats present. In general, the more CGG trinucleotide repeats an individual has inherited, the more symptomatic he/she will be. Males are usually more severely affected, because females have 2 X chromosomes, one of which usually produces normal protein. Males with FXS have greater than 200 repeats and demonstrate clinical features consistent with IDs/developmental delay, repetitive movements, hyperactive or impulsive behavior, hyperflexible joints, poor tone, macrocephaly, and large body size. Females with full mutations may be symptomatic (approximately 50% have ID), but manifestations are typically milder than in affected males. Individuals with 45 to 54 repeats are considered to be in the intermediate range and may either be asymptomatic or manifest only subtle behavioral problems. Premutation carriers (55 to 200 copies) typically have normal intellect and may be at increased risk for learning disabilities and social anxiety. More recently, premutation carriers have also been found to have other important clinical manifestations later in life. Both male and female premutation carriers are at increased risk for developing Fragile X-associated tremor/ataxia syndrome (FXTAS) after age 50 years, whereas females are also at increased (21%) risk for developing Fragile X premature ovarian insufficiency (FXPOI). Interestingly, adults with full mutations do not appear to develop FXTAS or FXPOI.

The impact of FXS on fertility varies by sex. Although Fragile X does not directly affect male fertility, research in other types of genetic ID has found that the more intellectually disabled a male is, the fewer children he fathers (Costain, Chow, Silversides, & Bassett, 2011). The greatest impact on female fertility is seen in female premutation carriers. Interestingly, those women with more than 55, but fewer than 80, repeats appear to be at highest risk for FXPOI (Pastore *et al.*, 2008). FXS is a prime example for why collecting a three-generation family health history in early adulthood is important in identifying potential inherited disorders. Identification of FXS features in family members (particularly brothers, fathers, and uncles) may stimulate early and ongoing conversations about fertility, pregnancy timing, and the risk for having a child with a full fragile X mutation.

6.11. TURNER SYNDROME

Approximately 1 in 2000 girls is diagnosed with Turner syndrome (TS). Roughly half are missing all of one X chromosome (45, X), approximately one quarter are mosaic for TS (i.e., 45, X/46, XX), and a final one-quarter have an X chromosome structural abnormality (Visser *et al.*, 2013). Because no Y chromosome is present, all affected individuals are female. Although TS is a rare disorder, the chromosomal anomaly is thought to occur in approximately 15% of all conceptions, nearly all (99%) of which end in miscarriage or stillbirth (Gravholt, Juul, Naeraa, & Hansen, 1996).

Several recent studies have explored challenges women with TS face across their lives. Repeatedly, studies have found that women with TS had significantly lower self-esteem, poorer body image, and lower social and appearance scores than women without TS (Wasserman & Asch, 2012). On average, women with TS live into their late 60s, but predicted life span is slightly shorter than normal, primarily because of an increased risk for cardiovascular and endocrine abnormalities (Freriks *et al.*, 2011). Affected women have normal intelligence, but many experience problems with nonverbal, social, and/or psychomotor skills. Many individuals with TS do well in school despite the associated learning disabilities that they may face.

Over 50% of women with TS have significant congenital heart defects, such as coarctation of aorta, elongation of the transverse aortic arch, bicuspid aortic valve, and progressive aortic root dilatation. The risk for aortic dissection in women with TS is therefore increased 100-fold (Mortensen *et al.*, 2011). Many affected women have low bone mineral density due to low estrogen levels and are at increased risk for osteopenia and osteoporosis. Metabolic and endocrine disorders such as subclinical hypothyroidism, glucose intolerance, dyslipidemia, and hypertension are more common in this population, as are congenital lymphedema, renal malformations, celiac disease, and hearing loss (Bakalov, Cheng, Zhou, & Bondy, 2009; Freriks *et al.*, 2011). Women with TS also have distinctive physical features, including webbed neck, broad chest with widely spaced nipples, and cubitus valgus. Despite some of the physical limitations, women with TS report that the things that distress them the most were infertility and sexual function, followed by short stature and then by the "general health" issues (Sutton *et al.*, 2005; Wasserman & Asch, 2012).

The average girl with TS reaches a final adult height of approximately 4 foot 7 inches, several inches below the predicted height of a woman born in the U.S. in the 21st century. The U.S. Food and Drug Administration (FDA) approved the use of growth hormone for girls with TS in 1996, and although expensive, it has been shown to increase adult height by about 2 inches. Estrogen has recently been added to the list of drugs that increases linear growth in girls with TS as well. Long shied away from by endocrinologists because estrogen suppresses linear growth when given (or produced) in high doses, recent studies have shown that in women with TS, low-dose estrogen in combination with growth hormone increases vertical height by an additional 2 cm, improves bone density, and accelerates sexual development (Ross *et al.*, 2011).

Most women with TS experience premature ovarian insufficiency caused by accelerated apoptosis in ovarian follicles that may begin as early as 18 weeks gestation. Some ovarian function may persist into early adolescence, and viable follicles have been found in the ovaries of 12 and 13 year old girls with TS, although the ovum quality is questionable (Visser *et al.*, 2013). Up to 15% of girls develop secondary sexual characteristics, but very few menstruate and most are infertile. Approximately 2% to 7% of girls with TS may have a spontaneous pregnancy, but most are mosaic for a normal cell line (46, XX). In those who do conceive, many women experience spontaneous miscarriages or fetal demise; nearly 20% of the babies have some congenital anomaly and female offspring are at increased risk for also having TS. Egg donation is an option but must be very carefully monitored, because these pregnancies are extremely high risk for both mother and baby. The French Study Group for Oocyte Donation study examined outcome data from 93 pregnant women with TS who had received oocytes between January 1991 and June 2009 and had advanced beyond 20 gestational weeks. Of the 93 pregnancies, only 37 (40%) ended with both a healthy baby and mother. A total of 37.8% were complicated by pregnancy-associated hypertensive disorders, including preeclampsia/eclampsia; 25% of the babies had intra-uterine growth restriction; and 40% delivered prematurely. Most significantly, 2 of the 93 mothers died from a ruptured aorta and one baby died after the mother developed eclampsia (Chevalier *et al.*, 2011). Every woman with TS contemplating pregnancy or who becomes pregnant should be evaluated by a cardiologist and must be counseled that she is at increased risk for aortic dissection and death (Carlson & Silberbach, 2007).

6.12. KLINEFELTER SYNDROME

Klinefelter syndrome (KS) (47, XXY) is the most common sex chromosome aneuploidy in males, with approximately 1 in every 660 males carrying at least one extra copy of the X chromosome, which can be inherited from either parent. Most affected men are asymptomatic, which makes KS very difficult to diagnose. It is estimated that only 25% of affected males receive a diagnosis, and most of them are diagnosed in their mid-30s, often when being worked up for infertility. KS is not benign, however, because affected men are at increased risk for developing a number of different disorders, including hypergonadotropic hypogonadism, low androgen levels, small genitals (testes and penis) and relatively more estrogen-like features. The classic KS phenotype is a male with low libido, low sperm count, scanty facial and body hair, narrow shoulders, wide hips, gynecomastia, decreased bone density, poor muscle tone, and low energy. Adults with KS are also at increased risk for developing T2DM and metabolic syndrome. Although most men with KS have normal IQs, many have mild cognitive impairments, such as language delay or learning disabilities, and benefit from speech therapy or special education (Groth, Skakkebaek, Host, Gravholt, & Bojesen, 2013). Although extremely rare, it is possible for

affected men to have more than 2 extra copies of the X chromosome (48, XXXY, 49, XXXXY), sex chromosome mosaicism (47, XXY/46, XX), and duplicate XY (48, XXYY).

6.13. CYSTIC FIBROSIS

CF is an autosomal recessive disorder caused by mutations in the *CFTR* gene on the long arm of chromosome 7. More than 1,300 CF mutations have been identified, categorized into one of 4 classes ranging from "mild" to "severe." Individuals who inherit two *CFTR* mutations may have "classic" CF (pulmonary diseases, poor growth/digestive disorders, pancreatic dysfunction/diabetes in late adolescence), "intermediate" symptoms (mild pulmonary dysfunction/chronic sinus infection), or may be completely asymptomatic, depending on the combination of mutations they have inherited. Individuals of Northern European Caucasian and Ashkenasi Jewish descent have a 1:29 carrier frequency and approximately 1:3,000 individuals are born with CF in these populations. Nearly all mutations carried by individuals in these populations can be identified on the pan ethnic "standard" CF panel, which screens for 23 mutations. Other ethnic groups may have equally high carrier frequencies, and screening panels may be supplemented with additional mutations to improve sensitivity for these groups. CF mutations are rare in some groups; thus genetic testing is not as sensitive or specific in these populations (Moskowitz, 2008).

Men and women with CF may experience reduced fertility or infertility. The *CFTR* gene plays an important role during embryogenesis. In normal male embryogenesis, the Wolffian duct forms and in the presence of androgens is transformed into structures linking the testis and prostate, including the vas deferens, epididymis, and seminal vesicles. In the absence of testosterone, the Wolffian duct regresses, and the mullerian ducts form the internal female genital structures (Hannema, Print, Charnock-Jones, Coleman, & Hughes, 2006). CFTR mutations impair the normal development of Wolffian ducts commonly disrupting male genital development, and occasionally female internal genital structures as well. Up to 90% of males with 2 *CFTR* mutations are missing the vas deferens, and 8% of severely affected females are reported to have congenital absence of the uterus and vagina (CAUV) (Ahmad, Ahmed, & Patrizio, 2013). Up to 50% of affected females ultimately conceive, but many women experience reduced fertility related to thickened cervical mucus that prevents sperm from penetrating the cervical os. Males with milder phenotypes, particularly the combination of deltaF508 and R117H mutations, may initially receive their CF diagnosis when they present with infertility and are found to have congenital bilateral absence of the vas deferens (CBAVD). CF should be at the top of the differential diagnosis list when a couple presents for an infertility evaluation, particularly if the male partner is diagnosed with azospermia and is ultimately found to have CBAVD (Ahmad *et al.*, 2013).

6.14. ASSISTED REPRODUCTIVE TECHNOLOGIES (ART)

Assisted reproductive technologies (ART) are relatively new; Louise Brown, the first "test tube" baby, was born on July 25, 1978. Although the majority of infants conceived using ART are healthy, emerging evidence suggests that ART may be associated with an increased risk of certain disorders, particularly epigenetic disorders such as Angelman syndrome and Beckwith-Wiedemann syndrome. It is unclear whether the ART procedures themselves, the cultures or culturing processes used to nourish the embryos in vitro, or invasive procedures such as intracytoplasmic sperm injection (ICSI) and cryopreservation are contributing to the increased risk for imprinting disorders (Bowdin, *et al.*, 2007).

Underlying maternal or paternal conditions associated with infertility may be causing the increased risk for epigenetic disorders, and ART may only be a surrogate marker. A recent evidence review culminating in a Canadian ART guideline found that infertile couples are at increased risk for adverse prenatal outcomes, such as multiple gestations, structural congenital abnormalities, chromosomal abnormalities, imprinting disorders, and childhood cancer compared with pregnancies of fertile couples. More research is needed to unravel the association between infertility, ART, and adverse obstetric and perinatal outcomes (Allen, Wilson, & Cheung, 2006).

6.15. PREIMPLANTATION DIAGNOSTIC TESTING (PGD)

Preimplantation genetic diagnosis (PGD) is a procedure used to screen embryos for genetic alterations during an IVF assisted pregnancy. The benefit of PGD is that only unaffected embryos are transferred to the uterus, providing an alternative to diagnostic procedures and/or termination in an already established pregnancy. PGD can decrease the risk for passing on a known, genetic abnormality and is currently offered for two major groups of disorders: single gene disorders such as Tay Sachs or CF and chromosomal disorders such as translocations, inversions, or deletions (Flinter, 2001). PGD is not without risks, however, because testing may not be conclusive; embryo damage may occur during the process of cell removal, and live birth rates are even lower than that of IVF pregnancies without PGD (Mastenbroek *et al.*, 2007).

6.16. MATERNAL GENETIC CONDITIONS THAT MAY ADVERSELY AFFECT PREGNANCY OUTCOMES

Medical advances have increased possibilities for women with genetic disorders to live longer with a better quality of life. Management of these disorders can be quite complicated and should be done with a multidisciplinary approach, utilizing the specialist needed to maximize the outcomes. Clinicians caring for pregnant women with genetic conditions should be aware that prenatal outcomes can be very poor for the mother, the baby, or both. Infants born to women with genetic disorders may be at increased risk for stillbirth, fetal growth restriction, and premature placental abruption. The best approach to decreasing morbidity and mortality outcomes is to maximize the person's health prior to conception. The best way to achieve this is for the couple to receive genetic counseling so they understand the maternal and fetal risks.

6.17. GESTATIONAL DIABETES

Gestational diabetes mellitus (GDM) is more common during pregnancies than either T1DM or T2DM. Women with GDM are at increased risk for polyhydramnios, preeclampsia, macrosomia, stillbirth, and operative delivery. Women diagnosed with GDM have an increased risk of developing T2DM later in life, a risk that appears to be paralleling the obesity epidemic. Several candidate genes are being studied to elucidate the steps in the process, culminating in the development of gestational diabetes, including genes associated with impaired b-cell function (*CD-KAL1, IGF2BP2, KCNQ1, KCNJ11, MTNR1B*), insulin resistance (*PPARG, TCF7L2*), and abnormal utilization of glucose (*GCK*) (Mao, Li, & Gao, 2012, Kwak, Jang, & Park, 2012). These genes are similar to those implicated in the development of T2DM, further supporting the correlation between GDM and T2DM. Early identification of women who have inherited GDM variants may lead to improved preventive and therapeutic interventions that can be tailored to match the genetic profiles of these women (Mao *et al.*, 2012). Because of the very strong relationship between environmental influences (poor nutrition, inactivity, behavioral patterns) and the development of diabetes, women should be counseled throughout the childbearing years to maintain a healthy lifestyle, including periodic blood glucose monitoring, to prevent or delay the development of GDM and potentially T2DM in older adulthood.

6.18. SICKLE CELL DISEASE

SCD is an autosomal recessive disorder described in 1910 by James Herrick. The disease manifests when an individual inherits 2 copies of a specific mutation in the *HBB* gene located on the short arm of chromosome 11. Most individuals with SCD live in or have ancestors who originated from Africa, South or Central America, the Caribbean islands, the Mediterranean, India, and Saudi Arabia, where malaria is endemic. Carrying one copy of an SCD mutation confers protection against malaria, but inheriting two SCD mutations results in the development of sickle cell disease. More information about SCD may be found in Chapter 12, Hematology. The incidence of SCD is lower in the U. S. but is still a significant problem, affecting 70,000 to 100,000 Americans, mainly those of African descent. More than 2 million Americans (1 in 12 AfricanAmericans) inherit one copy of the sickle cell mutation and are sickle cell carriers; these individuals are known as having the sickle cell trait (SCT).

Women with SCT are at increased risk for adverse health outcomes throughout life and in pregnancy. Pregnancy complications associated with SCT include an increased risk for fetal loss, low birth weight, preterm delivery and preeclampsia. One possible explanation is that hemoglobin sickling occurs during low oxygen states in people with SCT or SCD; because the placenta is a low-oxygen environment, sickling occurs in the intervillous spaces and decidual vessels. SCT carriers have also been shown to be at increased risk for amniotic infection and postpartum endometritis (Tsaras, Owusu-Ansah, Boateng, & Amoateng-Adjepong, 2009).

Women with SCD should be cared for by a perinatologist or co-managed by a perinatal specialist, because management of SCD during pregnancy is extremely complex and the pregnancy should be considered high risk.

6.19. CYSTIC FIBROSIS

The presence of maternal CF can contribute to poor fetal outcomes and cause deterioration in maternal wellbeing (Whitty, 2010). A pulmonologist specializing in CF is paramount to minimizing complications and improving pregnancy outcomes. Normal physiologic changes of pregnancy, such as pressure on the pulmonary or cardiovascular systems, can cause fetal and maternal morbidity and mortality, such as respiratory decompensation, pulmonary hypertension, and cardiac issues. The best indicator for a successful pregnancy outcome is the "Shwachman score: clinical status, nutritional status (percentage predicted weight for height), the extent of chest radiologic abnormalities (assessed by the Brasfield chest roentgenogram score), and the magnitude of pulmonary function impairment." (Whitty, 2010). Women with CF often struggle to attain/maintain a normal body weight. Prior to conceiving, however, they should be assisted in attaining a body weight that is as close as possible (approximately 90%) to ideal body weight.

Pregnancies complicated by maternal CF should be managed using a multidisciplinary approach that includes at least a dietitian, a maternal fetal medicine specialist/perinatologist, and a pulmonologist. Preconceptional counseling is critical, and the dialogue should begin years prior to conception.

6.20. MATERNAL PHENYLKETONURIA (PKU)

PKU is an autosomal recessive disorder that is more prevalent in Caucasian and East Asian populations (1:50 carrier frequency and 1:10,000 live births) in the U.S., but has much higher frequencies in Turkish (1/26 and 1:2600 live births) and Irish (1/33 and 1:4500 live births) communities (Mitchell, 2013).

Until newborn screening became widely available in the early 1960s and dietary restrictions prevented the severe cognitive impairment associated with untreated PKU, most adults with PKU did not reproduce. Metabolic control is necessary across the life span of affected individuals (National Institutes of Health Consensus Development Panel, 2001), particularly in women who may consider a pregnancy. Little has been published on the effects of elevated PKU levels on male fertility (Fisch, Matalon, Weisberg, & Michals, 1991), but more is known about the impact of maternal PKU on pregnancy. Maternal serum phenylalanine (Phe) levels must be controlled because too much Phe can cause fetal malformations and cognitive deficits, and too little Phe has been associated with intrauterine growth restriction, possibly as the result of decreased levels of essential amino acids (Teissier *et al.*, 2012). Even when Phe levels are tightly controlled, there is an increased risk for congenital anomaly (Rouse, 1997; Prick, 2012). "Safe" Phe blood levels vary slightly between references, but in general women should be counseled to maintain Phe levels between 120 and 360 micromoles/Liter (this range may also be reported as 2 to 6 mg/dL). In women with high serum Phe levels, it may take several weeks of careful dietary restriction to achieve these levels. The effectiveness of two other supplements, tetrahydrobiopterin (BH4) and phenylalanine ammonia lyase (PAL), are under investigation and may become standard of care in pregnancies complicated by PKU. BH4 is a co-factor in the biochemical pathway that breaks down PKU, increasing Phe tolerance and possibly allowing affected patients to eat a more diverse diet and maintain a more normal body weight (Trefz, 2005). PAL is the first step in the phenylpropanoid pathway, which ultimately degrades Phe to its harmless substrates transcinnamic acid and ammonia (Vernon, 2010).

Optimally, any couple in whom one (or both) are affected by PKU will be cared for by genetic specialists with experience treating adults living with PKU. Preconceptional counseling is critical for these couples, and the dialogue should begin years prior to conception.

6.21. PREGNANCY COMPLICATIONS WITH A GENOMIC ETIOLOGY

6.21.1. Preeclampsia

Preeclampsia can manifest at any time after 20 weeks gestation. Preeclampsia developing prior to 32 weeks is considered early onset and is associated with increased maternal and fetal morbidity and mortality compared with late onset preeclampsia (after 32 weeks). The condition is characterized by hypertension, proteinuria, edema, and if untreated, life-threatening seizures (eclampsia) may develop. Although the pathophysiology of preeclampsia has not yet been completely elucidated, it is theorized that the disorder may begin during implantation, because trophoblast cells remodel maternal blood vessels as they invade the uterine decidua (Sharkey & Macklon, 2013).

The term "eclampsia" was coined nearly 400 years ago (1619); the constellation of preeclampsia/eclampsia symptoms was described by Hippocrates centuries before that (Bell, 2010). The risks for developing preeclampsia increase when there is a positive family history, and recent studies have shown that early onset preeclampsia may be more linked to genetics and later onset disease more associated with environmental factors such as obesity (Trogstad, Magnus, & Stoltenberg, 2011).

Maternal, fetal, and paternal gene variations have all been associated with preeclampsia. Approximately 35% of the variance in susceptibility to preeclampsia has been attributable to maternal genes, 20% to fetal genes, and 13% to the combination of genes inherited from both parents. The contribution of paternal genes is debated; Boyd, Tahir, Wohlfahrt, and Melbye (2013) report only a weak link with late onset disease, but Dekker. Robillard, & Roberts (2011) point out that more research into paternal contribution to preeclampsia is needed, because several paternal factors have been linked to the disorder. The concept of the "dangerous" father was introduced over 30 years ago (Saftlas *et al.*, 2014). Cumulative exposure to paternal seminal fluid prior to conception and subsequent risk of preeclampsia. *Journal of reproductive immunology, 101*, 104–110. Dekker, 2002) highlighting paternal factors that increase risk for the development of preeclampsia. Risk factors include advanced paternal age (> 45 years), shorter sexual relationships, and first pregnancy with a new male partner via mechanisms such as seminal cytokine effects on maternal immunity, paternal HLA factors, and paternal SNPs, particularly those involved in regulating placentation (Dekker *et al.*, 2011). Although familial studies and candidate genes suggest an underlying genetic component to preeclampsia, the genetic causes remain unclear and genetic testing for this disorder is not implicated.

6.21.2. Peripartum Depression

Depression is the leading cause of disability in women, and approximately 1 in 7 women seek treatment for depression within two years of a pregnancy. Mood changes during the postpartum period are common, with 40% to 80% of women admitting to experiencing "postpartum blues," a mild, transient mood alteration during the first postpartum week (Buttner, O'Hara, & Watson, 2012). Postpartum psychosis, on the other end of the spectrum, is a psychotic episode that begins within two weeks of delivery and, although fortunately rare (approximately 0.1 to 0.5%), is an emergency requiring urgent evaluation, psychiatric referral, and often hospitalization (Sit, Rothschild, & Wisner, 2006). The Diagnostic and Statistical Manual of Mental Disorders, Fifth Edition (DSM-5), describes postpartum depression as "peripartum depression" (PPD), because up to 50% of women diagnosed with PPD experience depression prior to delivery (American Psychiatric Association, 2013). PPD manifests in up to 13% of postpartum women, but major risk factors include a history of depression, formula feeding, and cigarette smoking (McCoy *et al.*, 2006). Symptoms of PPD include sadness, fatigue, changes in sleeping and eating patterns, reduced libido, crying episodes, anxiety, and irritability (O'Hara & McCabe, 2013).

Given the high prevalence of postpartum blues

and significant hormonal changes that all women experience during the postpartum period, it is surprising that more women do not experience PPD. New research is beginning to shed light on genetic risk factors for PPD. In a recent study, researchers were able to correctly classify women as either "depressed" or "nondepressed" 84% of the time based on their gene expression profile and could predict clinical symptoms and depression severity using genetics as well (Segman *et al.*, 2010). Women with PPD also had reduced gene transcription during the immediate postpartum period and altered immune system activation in addition to other changes in cellular activity. One recent study showed an association between a mutation in the *HMCN1* gene on chromosome 1, which has four estrogen-binding sites, suggesting that the association between *HMCN1* and depression may involve the dramatic drop in estrogen levels after the placenta is delivered (O'Hara & McCabe, 2013). Pro-inflammatory cytokines, brain neuropeptides, and monoamines within the central nervous system have been linked to the diagnosis of depression (Corwin, Kohen, Jarrett, & Stafford, 2010).

6.21.3. Postpartum Hemorrhage

Postpartum hemorrhage (PPH) (blood loss >1000 mL) is a major cause of maternal morbidity worldwide and the most common cause of maternal death in the developed world. The incidence of postpartum hemorrhage severe enough to require transfusion and/or hysterectomy has doubled in the U.S. over the past decade, climbing from 1.9 in 1000 in 1999 to 4.2 in 1000 in 2008. Significant risk factors for PPH include advanced maternal age (≥ 35 years), multifetal pregnancy, uterine fibroids, preeclampsia, placental or uterine abnormalities (fibroids, uterine rupture, placenta previa, or placental abruption), and trauma during delivery (cervical laceration, forceps or vacuum application, and cesarean delivery), but none of these risks are new, nor do they explain the rapid increase in risk (Kramer *et al.*, 2013). Women with inherited bleeding disorders (hemophilia carriers), von Willebrand disease, and rare autosomal bleeding disorders (clotting factor deficiencies) are also at significantly increased risk for PPH, particularly during the first trimester and postpartum periods

(Shahbazi, Moghaddam-Banaem, Ekhtesari, & Ala, 2012). New data have found that the use of serotonin, non–serotonin reuptake inhibitors, and tricyclic antidepressants near the time of delivery increases the PPH risk nearly 1.5 times compared with women not using antidepressants (Palmsten *et al.*, 2013).

Genetics plays a role in nearly all these PPH risk factors, and work is being done to unravel the genes and biochemical pathways associated with many of these conditions. The goals will be to identify at-risk women prior to conception

and intervene early in life if possible to correct the condition. If that is not possible, enhanced screening could be offered during pregnancy; targeted intrapartum management could be initiated to prevent hemorrhage or optimally manage it if excessive bleeding does occur.

6.21.4. Prenatal Screening

The three goals of prenatal screening are as follows: (1) facilitate timely medical or surgical intervention before or after birth, (2) provide par-

TABLE 6.1. *Prenatal Genetic Genomic Resources.*

Resources
CAH
• Genetics Home Reference: http://ghr.nlm.nih.gov/condition/congenital-adrenal-hyperplasia-due-to-11-beta-hydroxylase-deficiency • GeneReviews: Nimkarn S., & New, M. I. 21-Hydroxylase-Deficient Congenital Adrenal Hyperplasia. 2002 Feb 26 [Updated 2010 Aug 24]. In: Pagon RA, Bird TD, Dolan CR, *et al.*, editors. GeneReviews™ [Internet]. Seattle (WA): University of Washington, Seattle; 1993-. Available from: http://www.ncbi.nlm.nih.gov/books/NBK1171/
Klinefelter Syndrome
• Groth, K.A., Skakkebæk, A., Høst, C., Højbjerg Gravholt, C., and Bojesen, A (2012). *Klinefelter Syndrome, A Clinical Update*, The Journal of Clinical Endocrinology & Metabolism. 98(1):20–30. • Genetics Home Reference: http://ghr.nlm.nih.gov/condition/klinefelter-syndrome • NIH Eunice Kennedy Shriver National Institute of Child Health and Human Development: http://www.nichd.nih.gov/health/topics/klinefelter/conditioninfo/Pages/symptoms.aspx
Cystic Fibrosis
• Seibert, D., & Fries, M. (2009). Screening and counseling for Cystic Fibrosis. In Monsen, R. B. (Ed.) *Genetics and Ethics In Health Care: New Questions in the Age of Genomic Health.* Silver Spring, MD: Nursesbooks.org • Schwarzer, J.U. & Schwarz, M. (2012). *Significance of CFTR gene mutations in patients with congenital aplasia of vas deferens with special regard to renal aplasia. Andrologia, 44*(5):305-7. • Cystic Fibrosis Foundation: http://www.cff.org/aboutCFFoundation/ • Ahmad A., Ahmed A., & Patrizio P., (2013). *Cystic Fibrosis and fertility,* Current Opinion in Obstetrics and Gynecology. http://www.ncbi.nlm.nih.gov/pubmed/23429570 • www.hopkinscf.org
Preconception
• ACOG Committee Opinion #313 (2005): The Importance of Preconception Care in the Continuum of Health Care (Flinter, 2001) • Family Physician: Recommendations for Preconception Care (Mastenbroek *et al.*, 2007)
Epigenetics
• Imprinting: http://www.ncbi.nlm.nih.gov/books/NBK5191/box/further_illus-95/?report=objectonly • Drugs and Lactation: http://toxnet.nlm.nih.gov/cgi-bin/sis/htmlgen?LACT
Sickle Cell Disease
• ACOG Practice Bulletin No. 78: Hemoglobinopathies in pregnancy • The Royal College of Obstetrics and Gynaecologists guideline entitled Green-top Guideline No. 61:Management of Sickle Cell Disease in Pregnancy (http://www.rcog.org.uk/files/rcog-corp/GTG61_26082011.pdf)
Gestational Diabetes
• http://joomla.isdpsg.org/
PKU
• http://newenglandconsortium.org/for-families/phenylketonuria-pku/maternal-pku-pregnancy/about-maternal-pku/

ents with information about the health of the fetus so they may make an informed decision about pregnancy management, and (3) offer parents an opportunity to prepare for a birth of a baby that may be stillborn, have a major health problem or disability, or require early intervention and/or a multidisciplinary team to optimize outcomes.

Prenatal screening began in the mid-1960s and was initially based completely on maternal age. Since that time, an ever-expanding list of screening tests has been developed, ranging from noninvasive (fundal height or fetal heart tone evaluation, serum screening, ultrasound) to invasive (amniocentesis and chorionic villus sampling [CVS]). Routine prenatal screening in some form or another is now offered to every pregnant woman receiving prenatal care in the U.S. The goal of prenatal screening initially was to identify pregnancies complicated by aneuploidy, such as Trisomy 13, 18, and 21. As prenatal screening has become more sensitive and specific, the scope of screening has expanded and screening for a number of fetal conditions, such as NTDs, sickle cell anemia, and CF are now routinely offered. Prenatal screening for other single gene disorders (Tay Sachs, thalassemia, and FXS) is possible but not currently recommended. As the number of screening options has increased, so has the cost, complexity, and educational requirements of both patients and providers.

In 2011, the prenatal screening landscape changed with the introduction of cell free fetal (cff) DNA testing. This noninvasive test evaluates fragments of fetal DNA floating freely in the maternal blood stream and can be collected as early as 10 weeks gestation. When screening for fetal aneuploidy, cff DNA is detected in maternal blood and measured to determine the number of chromosomal fragments from select chromosomes of interest (13, 18, 21, X, Y). If an unusually high level of a specific chromosome is identified, suggesting aneuploidy, additional testing (amniocentesis, CVS) may be done to confirm the diagnosis. In the U.S., cff DNA testing is offered only to high risk women, and it is important to counsel women that this test is not fully diagnostic, but is an advanced "screening test" that requires follow-up invasive testing to confirm the findings. More evidence is needed about the efficacy in low-risk populations, the suitability for use in twin gestations, IVF donor

pregnancies, etc. Disadvantages include the risk for a false-positive result requiring unnecessary invasive testing, increased parental stress with a positive result, and the lack of information about other genetic disorders.

6.21.5. Ethical Issues in Prenatal Genetics

Ethical issues abound in the prenatal period and can roughly be divided into categories based on when they emerge (prenatal, intrapartum, and postpartum). The ethical issues that involve genetics are largely centered in the prenatal period and primarily involve decisions about informed consent, choices related to prenatal testing, and diagnosis and treatment options/decisions. Torres and De Vries (2009) present a comprehensive overview of the major ethical issues to be considered during the perinatal period. Chapter 4 provides a more in depth look at ethical issues associated with genetic screening and testing.

6.22. REFERENCES

Ahmad, A., Ahmed, A., & Patrizio, P. (2013). *Cystic fibrosis and fertility. Curr Opin Obstet Gynecol.* doi: 10.1097/GCO.0b013e32835f1745

Alio, A. P., Salihu, H. M., McIntosh, C., August, E. M., Weldeselasse, H., Sanchez, E., & Mbah, A. K. (2012). The effect of paternal age on fetal birth outcomes. *American Journal of Men's Health, 6*(5), 427–435.

Allen, V. M., Wilson, R. D., & Cheung, A., Genetics Committee of the Society of Obstetricians and Gynaecologists of Canada (SOGC), & Reproductive Endocrinology Infertility Committee of the Society of Obstetricians and Gynaecologists of Canada. (2006). Pregnancy outcomes after assisted reproductive technology. [Practice Guideline Research Support, Non-U.S. Gov't]. *J Obstet Gynaecol Can, 28*(3), 220–250.

American Psychiatric Association, (2013). Diagnostic and Statistical Manual of Mental Disorders, Fifth Edition. Arlington, VA: American Psychiatric Publishing.

Bakalov, V. K., Cheng, C., Zhou, J., & Bondy, C. A. (2009). X-chromosome gene dosage and the risk of diabetes in Turner syndrome. [Research Support, N.I.H., Intramural]. *J Clin Endocrinol Metab, 94*(9), 3289–3296. doi: 10.1210/jc.2009-0384

Balasch, J., & Gratacos, E. (2012). Delayed childbearing: Effects on fertility and the outcome of pregnancy. [Review]. *Curr Opin Obstet Gynecol, 24*(3), 187–193. doi: 10.1097/GCO.0b013e3283517908

Balasch, K. A., Tromp, G., Romero, R., Olson, J. M.,

Lu, Q., Xu, Z., . . . & Kuivaniemi, H. (2007). Candidate-gene association study of mothers with preeclampsia, and their infants, analyzing 775 SNPs in 190 genes. [Research Support, N.I.H., Extramural Research Support, N.I.H., Intramural]. *Hum Hered, 63*(1), 1–16. doi: 10.1159/000097926

Bell, M. J. (2010). A historical overview of preeclampsia-eclampsia. [Historical Article Research Support, N.I.H., Extramural]. *J Obstet Gynecol Neonatal Nurs, 39*(5), 510–518. doi: 10.1111/j.1552-6909.2010.01172.x

Berek, J. S., & Novak, E. (2007). *Berek & Novak's gynecology* (14th ed.). Philadelphia: Lippincott Williams & Wilkins.

Bowdin, S., Allen, C., Kirby, G., Brueton, L., Afnan, M., Barratt, C., . . . & Reardon, W. (2007). A survey of assisted reproductive technology births and imprinting. *Human Reproduction, 22*(12) 3237–3240.

Boyd, H. A., Tahir, H., Wohlfahrt, J., & Melbye, M. (2013). Associations of personal and family preeclampsia history with the risk of early-, intermediate- and lateonset preeclampsia. *Am J Epidemiol, 178*(11):1611–1619.

Bodurtha, J, & Strauss, J. F. (2012). Genomics and Perinatal Care. *New England Journal of Medicine, 366*:64–73. doi: 10.1056/NEJMra1105043

Buttner, M. M., O'Hara, M. W., & Watson, D. (2012). The structure of women's mood in the early postpartum. [Validation Studies]. *Assessment, 19*(2), 247–256. doi: 10.1177/1073191111429388

Calzone, K. A., Jenkins, J., Prows, Calzone, K. A., Jenkins, J., Prows, C. A., & Masny, A. (2011). Establishing the outcome indicators for the essential nursing competencies and curricula guidelines for genetics and genomics. *J Prof Nurs, 27*(3), 179–191. doi: 10.1016/j.profnurs.2011.01.001

Carlson, M., & Silberbach, M. (2007). Dissection of the aorta in Turner syndrome: two cases and review of 85 cases in the literature. [Case Reports Review]. *J Med Genet, 44*(12), 745749. doi: 10.1136/jmg.2007.052019

Chevalier, N., Letur, H., Lelannou, D., Ohl, J., Cornet, D., Chalas-Boissonnas, C., . . . & French Study Group for Oocyte, D. (2011). Materno-fetal cardiovascular complications in Turner syndrome after oocyte donation: insufficient prepregnancy screening and pregnancy follow-up are associated with poor outcome. [Multicenter Study]. *J Clin Endocrinol Metab, 96*(2), E260-267. doi: 10.1210/jc.2010-0925

Corwin, E. J., Kohen, R., Jarrett, M., & Stafford, B. (2010). The heritability of postpartum depression. [Review]. *Biol Res Nurs, 12*(1), 73–83. doi: 10.1177/1099800410362112

Costain, G., Chow, E. W., Silversides, C. K., & Bassett, A. S. (2011). Sex differences in reproductive fitness contribute to preferential maternal transmission of 22q11.2 deletions. *Med Genet, 48*(12), 819-824. doi: 10.1136/jmedgenet-2011-100440

Dekker, G., Robillard, P. Y., & Roberts, C. (2011). The etiology of preeclampsia: The role of the father. [Review]. *J Reprod Immunol, 89*(2), 126–132. doi: 10.1016/j.jri.2010.12.010

Desposito, F., Cunniff, C., Frias, J.L., Panny, S.R., Trotter, T.L. & Wappner, R.S. (1999). Folic acid for the prevention of neural tube defects. *Pediatrics, 104* (2), 325–327.

Driscoll, D. J., Miller, J. L., Schwartz, S., & Cassidy, S. B. (1993). Prader-Willi syndrome. In R. A. Pagon, M. P. Adam, T. D. Bird, C. R. Dolan, C. T. Fong, & K. Stephens (Eds.), *GeneReviews*. Seattle (WA).

Fisch, R.O., Matalon, R., Weisberg, S., & Michals, K. (1991). Children of fathers with phenylketonuria: An international survey, *The Journal of Pediatrics, 118*(5), 739–741.

Flinter, F. A. (2001). Preimplantation genetic diagnosis. [Editorial]. *BMJ, 322*(7293), 1008–1009.

Freriks, K., Timmermans, J., Beerendonk, C. C., Verhaak, C. M., Netea-Maier, R. T., Otten, B. J., . . . & Timmers, H. J. (2011). Standardized multidisciplinary evaluation yields significant previously undiagnosed morbidity in adult women with Turner syndrome. [Research Support, Non-U.S. Gov't]. *J Clin Endocrinol Metab, 96*(9), E1517–1526. doi: 10.1210/jc.2011-0346

Fuller, M., Myers, M., Webb, T., Tabangin, M., & Prows, C. (2010). Primary care providers' responses to patient-generated family history. *J Genet Couns, 19*(1), 84–96. doi: 10.1007/s10897-009-9264-6

Fukuda, M., Fukuda, K., Shimizu, T., Nobunaga, M., Andersen, E.W., Byskov, A.G., & Andersen, C.Y. (2011). Paternal smoking habits affect the reproductive life span of daughters. *Fertility and Sterility, 95*(8), 2542–2544.

Godfrey, K. M., Lillycrop, K. A, Burdge, G. C., Gluckman, P. D. & Hanson, M. A. (2013). Non imprinted epigenetics in fetal and postnatal development and growth. *Nestle Nutrition Institute Workshop Series, 71*:57–63. doi: 10.1159/000342552. Retrieved from http://www.ncbi.nlm.nih.gov/pubmed/23502139.

Gravholt, C. H., Juul, S., Naeraa, R. W., & Hansen, J. (1996). Prenatal and postnatal prevalence of Turner's syndrome: A registry study. [Research Support, Non-U.S. Gov't]. *BMJ, 312*(7022), 16–21.

Greco, K. E., Tinley, S., & Seibert, D. (2011). Development of the essential genetic and genomic competencies for nurses with graduate degrees. [Review]. *Annu Rev Nurs Res, 29*, 173–190.

Groth, K. A., Skakkebaek, A., Host, C., Gravholt, C. H., & Bojesen, A. (2013). Clinical review: Klinefelter syndrome—A clinical update. [Research Support, Non-U.S. Gov't]. *J Clin Endocrinol Metab, 98*(1), 20–30. doi: 10.1210/jc.2012-2382.

Hannema, S. E., Print, C. G., Charnock-Jones, D. S., Coleman, N., & Hughes, I. A. (2006). Changes in gene expression during Wolffian duct development.

[Research Support, NonU.S. Gov't]. *Horm Res, 65*(4), 200–209. doi: 10.1159/000092408

Heijmans, B. T., Tobi, E. W., Stein, A. D., Putter, H., Blauw, G. J., Susser, E. S., . . . & Lumey, L. H. (2008). Persistent epigenetic differences associated with prenatal exposure to famine in humans. [Research Support, N.I.H., Extramural Research Support, Non-U.S. Gov't]. *Proc Natl Acad Sci USA, 105*(44), 17046–17049. doi: 10.1073/pnas.0806560105

Ishida, M., & Moore, G. E. (2013). The role of imprinted genes in humans. *Molecular Aspects of Medicine, 34*(4), 826–840. ISSN 0098-2997, http://dx.doi.org/10.1016/j.mam.2012.06.009.

Jablonka, E., & Raz, G. (2009). Transgenerational epigenetic inheritance: Prevalence, mechanisms, and implications for the study of heredity and evolution. *The Quarterly Review of Biology, 84*(2), 131–176. doi: 10.1086/598822

Keverne, E. B. (2013). Importance of the matriline for genomic imprinting, brain development and behaviour. [Review]. *Philos Trans R Soc Lond B Biol Sci, 368*(1609), 20110327. doi: 10.1098/rstb.2011.0327

Kramer, M. S., Berg, C., Abenhaim, H., Dahhou, M., Rouleau, J., Mehrabadi, A., & Joseph, K. S. (2013). Incidence, risk factors, and temporal trends in severe postpartum hemorrhage. *Am J Obstet Gynecol.* doi: 10.1016/j.ajog.2013.07.007

Kwak, S.H., Jang, H.C. & Park, K.S. (2012). Finding Genetic Risk Factors of Gestational Diabetes. *Genomics and Informatics, 10*(4):239–43.

Lee, K.M., Ward, M.H., Han, S., Ahn, H.S., Kang, H.J., Choi, H.S., Shin, H.Y., Seo, J.J., Choi, J.E., Ahn, Y.O., & Kang, D. (2009). Paternal smoking, genetic polymorphisms in CYP1A1 and childhood leukemia risk. *Leukemia Research. 33*(2): 250–258. doi:10.1016/j.leukres.2008.06.031.

Laivuori, H. (2007). Genetic aspects of preeclampsia. [Research Support, Non-U.S. Gov't Review]. *Front Biosci, 12*, 2372–2382.

Mao H, Li Q, Gao S. (2012). Meta-Analysis of the Relationship between Common Type 2 Diabetes Risk Gene Variants with Gestational Diabetes Mellitus. *PLoS ONE 7*(9): e45882. doi:10.1371/journal.pone.0045882

Mastenbroek, S., Twisk, M., van Echten-Arends, J., Sikkema-Raddatz, B., Korevaar, J. C., Verhoeve, H. R., . . . van der Veen, F. (2007). In vitro fertilization with preimplantation genetic screening. [Comparative Study Multicenter Study Randomized Controlled Trial Research Support, Non-U.S. Gov't]. *N Engl J Med, 357*(1), 9–17. doi: 10.1056/NEJMoa067744

Mathers, J., Greenfield, S., Metcalfe, A., Cole, T., Flanagan, S., & Wilson, S. (2010). Family history in primary care: understanding GPs' resistance to clinical genetics—qualitative study. [Multicenter Study Research Support, Non-U.S. Gov't]. *Br J Gen Pract, 60*(574), e221–230. doi: 10.3399/bjgp10X501868

McCoy, S. J., Beal, J. M., Shipman, S. B., Payton, M. E., & Watson, G. H. (2006). Risk factors for postpartum depression: a retrospective investigation at 4-weeks postnatal and a review of the literature. [Review]. *J Am Osteopath Assoc, 106*(4), 193–198.

Mitchell, J.J. (2013). Phenylalanine Hydroxylase Deficiency Synonym: PAH Deficiency. Includes: Hyperphenylalaninemia (HPA), Phenylketonuria (PKU), Variant PKU. *GeneReviews.* Seattle (WA).

Morison, I. M., Ramsay, J. P., & Spencer, H. G. (2005). A census of mammalian imprinting. [Comparative Study, Research Support, Non-U.S. Gov't., Review]. *Trends Genet, 21*(8), 457–465. doi: 10.1016/j.tig.2005.06.008

Mortensen, K. H., Hjerrild, B. E., Stochholm, K., Andersen, N. H., Sorensen, K. E., Lundorf, E., . . . Gravholt, C. H. (2011). Dilation of the ascending aorta in Turner syndrome—A prospective cardiovascular magnetic resonance study. [Research Support, Non-U.S. Gov't]. *J Cardiovasc Magn Reson, 13*, 24. doi: 10.1186/1532-429X-13-24.

Mosher, W.D., Jones, Jo and Abma, J.C. (2012). Intended and Unintended Births in the United States: 1982–2010. *National Health Statistics Reports. 55*, 1–28.

National Institutes of Health Consensus Development Panel. (2001). National Institutes of Health Consensus Development Conference Statement:Phenylketonuria: Screening and Management. *Pediatrics, 108*;972.

Nimkarn, S., & New, M. I. (1993). 21-Hydroxylase-Deficient Congenital Adrenal Hyperplasia. In R. A. Pagon, T. D. Bird, C. R. Dolan, K. Stephens & M. P. Adam (Eds.), *GeneReviews.* Seattle (WA).

O'Hara, M. W., & McCabe, J. E. (2013). Postpartum depression: current status and future directions. *Annu Rev Clin Psychol, 9*, 379–407. doi: 10.1146/annurev-clinpsy-050212-185612

Ottman, R., Hirose, S., Jain, S., Lerche, H., Lopes-Cendes, I., Noebels, J. L., . . . Scheffer, I. E. (2010). Genetic testing in the epilepsies—Report of the ILAE Genetics Commission. *Epilepsia, 51*(4), 655–670. doi: 10.1111/j.1528-1167.2009.02429.x

Palmsten, K., Hernandez-Diaz, S., Huybrechts, K. F., Williams, P. L., Michels, K. B., Achtyes, E. D., . . . Setoguchi, S. (2013). Use of antidepressants near delivery and risk of postpartum hemorrhage: cohort study of low income women in the United States. *BMJ, 347*, f4877. doi: 10.1136/bmj.f4877

Pastore, L. M., Morris, W. L., & Karns, L. B. (2008). Emotional reaction to fragile X premutation carrier tests among infertile women. [Research Support, Non-U.S. Gov't]. *J Genet Couns, 17*(1), 84–91. doi: 10.1007/s10897-007-9129-9

Pembrey, M. E., Bygren, L. O., Kaati, G., Edvinsson, S., Northstone, K., Sjostrom, M., . . . Team, A. S. (2006). Sex-specific, male-line transgenerational responses in humans. [Comparative Study Research Support, Non-U.S. Gov't]. *Eur J Hum Genet, 14*(2), 159–166. doi: 10.1038/sj.ejhg.5201538

Power, R. A., Kyaga, S., Uher, R., MacCabe, J. H., Langstrom, N., Landen, M., . . . Svensson, A. C. (2013). Fecundity of patients with schizophrenia, autism, bipolar disorder, depression, anorexia nervosa, or substance abuse vs their unaffected siblings. [Comparative Study Research Support, Non-U.S. Gov't]. *JAMA Psychiatry, 70*(1), 22–30. doi: 10.1001/jamapsychiatry.2013.268

Ross, J. L., Quigley, C. A., Cao, D., Feuillan, P., Kowal, K., Chipman, J. J., & Cutler, G. B., Jr. (2011). Growth hormone plus childhood low-dose estrogen in Turner's syndrome. [Randomized Controlled Trial, Research Support, N.I.H., Extramural Research Support, Non-U.S. Gov't]. *N Engl J Med, 364*(13), 1230–1242. doi: 10.1056/NEJMoa1005669

Saftlas, A. F., Rubenstein, L., Prater, K., Harland, K. K., Field, E., & Triche, E. W. (2014). Cumulative exposure to paternal seminal fluid prior to conception and subsequent risk of preeclampsia. *Journal of reproductive immunology, 101,* 104–110.

Segman, R H Goltser-Dubner, T Weiner, I Canetti, L Galili-Weisstub, E Milwidsky, A Pablov, V Friedman N and Hochner-Celnikier D (2010) Blood mononuclear cell gene expression signature of postpartum depression. *Molecular Psychiatry 15,* 93–100; doi:10.1038/mp.2009.65.

Shahbazi, S., Moghaddam-Banaem, L., Ekhtesari, F., & Ala, F. A. (2012). Impact of inherited bleeding disorders on pregnancy and postpartum hemorrhage. [Research Support, Non-U.S. Gov't]. *Blood Coagul Fibrinolysis, 23*(7), 603–607. doi: 10.1097/MBC.0b013e3283566af9

Shapiro, B., & Batshaw, M. (2011). *Intellectual disability* (19th ed.). Philadelphia, PA: Saunders Elsevier.

Sharkey, A. M., & Macklon, N. S. (2013). The science of implantation emerges blinking into the light. *Reproductive biomedicine online.*

Sit, D., Rothschild, A. J., & Wisner, K. L. (2006). A review of postpartum psychosis. [Research Support, Non-U.S. Gov't Review]. *J Womens Health (Larchmt), 15*(4), 352–368. doi: 10.1089/jwh.2006.15.352

Solomon, B. D., Jack, B. W., & Feero, W. G. (2008). The clinical content of preconception care: genetics and genomics. *American journal of obstetrics and gynecology, 199*(6), S340–S344.

Soubry, A., Hoyo, C., Jirtle, R. L., & Murphy, S. K. (2014). A paternal environmental legacy: evidence for epigenetic inheritance through the male germ line. *Bioessays, 36*(4), 359–371.

Sutton, E. J., McInerney-Leo, A., Bondy, C. A., Gollust, S. E., King, D., & Biesecker, B. (2005). Turner syndrome: four challenges across the lifespan. [Research Support, N.I.H., Intramural Research Sup-

port, Non-U.S. Gov't]. *Am J Med Genet A, 139A*(2), 57–66. doi: 10.1002/ajmg.a.30911

Terzioglu, F. (2007). Anxiety of infertile men who undergo genetic testing for assisted reproductive treatment. *J Psychosom Obstet Gynaecol, 28*(3), 147–153. doi: 10.1080/01674820701322095

Teissier, R., Nowak, E., Assoun, M., Mention, K., Cano, A., Fouilhoux, A., Feillet, F., Ogier, H., . . . & AFDPHE (Association Française pour le Dépistage et la Prévention des Handicaps de l'Enfant). (2012). Maternal phenylketonuria: Low phenylalaninemia might increase the risk of intra uterine growth retardation. *Journal of Inherited Metabolic Disease, 35*(6):993-9. doi: 10.1007/s10545-012-9491-0. Epub 2012 Jun 5.

Torres, J. M., & De Vries, R. G. (2009). Birthing ethics: what mothers, families, childbirth educators, nurses, and physicians should know about the ethics of childbirth. *J Perinat Educ, 18*(1), 12–24. doi: 10.1624/105812409X396192

Trogstad, L., Magnus, P., & Stoltenberg, C. (2011). Pre-eclampsia: risk factors and causal models. *Best practice & research Clinical obstetrics & gynaecology, 25*(3), 329–342.

Tsaras, G., Owusu-Ansah, A., Boateng, F. O. & Amoateng-Adjepong, Y. (2009). Complications associated with sickle cell trait: a brief narrative review. *The American journal of medicine, 122*(6), 507–512.

Visser, J. A., Hokken-Koelega, A. C., Zandwijken, G. R., Limacher, A., Ranke, M. B., & Fluck, C. E. (2013). Anti-Mullerian hormone levels in girls and adolescents with Turner syndrome are related to karyotype, pubertal development and growth hormone treatment. [Research Support, Non-U.S. Gov't]. *Hum Reprod, 28*(7), 1899–1907. doi: 10.1093/humrep/det089

Wallingford, J.B., Niswander, L.A., Shaw, G.M., & Finnell, R.H. (2013). The Continuing Challenge of Understanding, Preventing and Treating Neural Tube Defects. *Science, 339,* 1047–1053. Retrieved from DOI: 10.1126/science.1222002.

Wasserman, D., & Asch, A. (2012). Reproductive medicine and Turner syndrome: Ethical issues. [Review]. *Fertil Steril, 98*(4), 792–796. doi: 10.1016/j.fertnstert.2012.08.036

Whitty, J.E. (2010). *Cystic Fibrosis in Pregnancy. Clinical Obstetrics and Gynecology 53*(2):369–76.

Yang, W, Carmichael, S.L., Tinker, S.C. Shaw, G.M., and the National Birth Defects Prevention Study. (2012). Association between Weight Gain during Pregnancy and Neural Tube Defects and Gastroschisis in Offspring. *Birth Defects Research 94,* 1019–1025.

Yoon, P. W., Scheuner, M. T., Jorgensen, C., & Khoury, M. J. (2009). Developing Family Healthware, a family history screening tool to prevent common chronic diseases. *Prev Chronic Dis, 6*(1), A33.

Chapter 7

Newborn Screening

KAREN L. ZANNI, MSN, ARNP-BC, RN

Objectives:

- Discuss the history of newborn screening.
- Describe the consent process for newborn screening.
- Describe the process for obtaining, analyzing, and reporting newborn screening results.
- Identify three ethical, legal, and social (ELSI) issues often encountered in newborn screening.

7.1. INTRODUCTION

In 2013, newborn screening (NBS) celebrated its 50th anniversary as one of the largest and most successful public health initiatives in United States (U.S.) history. Every year, NBS saves more than 12,000 babies from death or a lifetime of intellectual or physical disability through its coordinated system of testing, follow-up, diagnosis, treatment, education, and evaluation (Centers for Disease Control and Prevention, 2013) (Watson, Mann, Lloyd-Puryear, Rinaldo, & Howell, 2006). NBS programs are mandatory, state-based public health programs that provide American newborns with presymptomatic testing and follow-up care for various congenital disorders, including genetic and metabolic conditions, hearing loss, human immunodeficiency virus (HIV), and hematologic and other genetic conditions. The goal of NBS programs is to identify treatable disorders early, preferably before the onset of symptoms; ensure timely diagnosis; and promptly initiate medical care for potentially life-threatening conditions (Kemper *et al.*, 2012).

The process of screening begins shortly after birth, with a heel-stick to draw enough blood to saturate a few circles on a "Guthrie card," which is a special filter paper containing the blood spot and identifying information, such as the mother's name, hospital of birth, baby's medical record number, doctor's name, and other clinical information. The specimen or dried blood spot is collected by a health-care provider during the first 24 to 48 hours of life. To ensure rapid analysis, the filter paper cards with the dried blood spots are sent overnight to a state designated NBS laboratory. When a test result falls outside the normal reference range, laboratory or follow-up personnel contact the birthing facility and the newborn's physician to make certain the child receives the proper diagnostic work-up and treatment. Some states offer point-of-care (POC) NBS (hearing screening, and pulse oximetry tests to detect congenital heart defects), which provides opportunities to expand universal NBS. Each state establishes its own protocols and standards, but generally the components (specimen collection, laboratory testing, follow-up, provider and public education, verification of diagnosis, treatment, and ongoing program evaluation) are similar (Lloyd-Puryear *et al.*, 2006).

7.2. HISTORY OF NEWBORN SCREENING

Dr. Robert Guthrie's test for phenylketonuria (PKU) came into use about 50 years ago. Since then, countless children have been saved from severe lifelong disability. NBS began in 1963 when Massachusetts and three other states began testing for PKU with Robert Guthrie's bacterial inhibition assay for the quantification of phenylalanine levels in dried blood spots (Dhondt, 2007; Guthrie & Susi, 1963; Maccready & Hussey, 1964). The Children's Health Bureau, which is part of the Health Resources and Services Administration (HRSA), funded Dr. Guthrie's early work focused on developing a PKU screening test and then sponsored cost-effectiveness studies for PKU screening. At the same time, advocates for children remained concerned that children with undetected PKU were at high risk for mental retardation (Alexander & van Dyck, 2006). The National Association for Retarded Citizens proposed model legislation for creation of public programs to address low detection rates and conducted an extensive grass-roots lobbying effort to support passage of mandatory PKU screening legislation (Alexander & van Dyck, 2006). Many state health departments supported the adoption of such legislation and other advocacy groups, such as the March of Dimes, mobilized volunteers to lobby for passage of legislation at the state level. The National Research Council of the National Academy of Sciences (NAS/NRC) established criteria for population-based screening systems in 1975. Screening criteria used to guide the selection of conditions included evidence of substantial public health benefit and acceptance; feasibility of screening for the selected disorders; satisfactory laboratory methods; appropriate laboratory facilities and quality control; resources for counseling, treatment, and follow-up; acceptable costs; effective education; and evaluation of program quality (National Research Council [U.S.] Committee for the Study of Inborn Errors of Metabolism., 1975). Advances in new technology helped state NBS programs expand, and many states began to offer screening for other conditions such as congenital hypothyroidism, congenital adrenal hyperplasia, sickle cell disease, and galactosemia.

NBS was and continues to be organized and administered at the state level; therefore, different states offer various numbers and types of NBS tests based on budgetary and political considerations as well as access to and willingness to finance expensive multiplex technologies, such as tandem mass spectrometry (MS/MS). In 2000, the American Academy of Pediatrics Newborn Screening Task Force released a report suggesting that greater uniformity among programs would benefit families, professionals, and public health agencies (AAP Newborn Screening Task Force, 2000; Lloyd-Puryear et al., 2006). The HRSA Maternal and Child Health Bureau then contracted with the American College of Medical Genetics (ACMG)

to develop a process to improve uniformity. The ACMG task force used data from the National Newborn Screening and Genetics Resource Center to help with its assessment, which culminated in the development of a recommended, uniform panel of conditions (U.S. Department of Health and Human Services, 2013; Watson et al., 2006). When considering what conditions to include on the panel, the task force took into consideration the: available scientific evidence, availability of a screening test, presence of an efficacious treatment, adequate understanding of the natural history of the condition, and whether the screening test results related to a clinically significant condition. Using these parameters, conditions were assigned as "core", "secondary target" or not appropriate for NBS. The ACMG task force recommended that state NBS programs mandate testing for core conditions and report secondary target conditions that could be identified during screening, including clinically significant conditions and the definitive identification of carrier status (Watson et al., 2006).

The U.S. Secretary of Health and Human Services (HHS) Advisory Committee on Heritable Disorders in Newborns and Children (SA-CHDNC) provides ongoing guidance to state NBS programs about which conditions should be included in screening (i.e., the "Recommended Uniform Screening Panel") (U.S. Department of Health and Human Services, 2013). The SA-CHDNC conducts evidence-reviews and nominates new conditions for inclusion on the panel. These recommendations are then reviewed by the HHS secretary, who either approves or rejects them. The new panel goes forward to state NBS programs, who then use these recommendations to develop individual state screening panels (Jackson, Crider, & Olney, 2010). Two conditions, severe combined immunodeficiency and congenital heart disease, were added to the Recommended Uniform Screening Panel in 2010, bringing the total number of recommended conditions to 31.

Many new technologic advances have emerged since the Guthrie bacterial inhibition assay was developed in the 1950s. With the development of MS/MS, which measures amino acid and acylcarnitine levels, alongside the plummeting cost of genetic testing, NBS programs rapidly expanded. In 1990, MS/MS was first used to simultaneously test for multiple analytes in dried blood spots and since then, the technology has become routine practice in NBS (Chace, Kalas, & Naylor, 2003). MS/MS technology is useful for NBS, because most of the molecules are small metabolites, which allows for simultaneous analysis of a wide variety of different analytes. MS/MS technology offers high-throughput with sufficient sensitivity and specificity at a low cost (Chace, Kalas, & Naylor, 2003). As MS/MS increased in use, NBS programs called on organizations such as the Centers for Disease Control and Prevention (CDC) to assist with quality assurance. As a result, the Newborn Screening Quality Assurance Program (NSQAP) was developed to assist state health departments and laboratories to maintain and enhance the quality of test results by providing proficiency testing, reference materials, consultation, and training (Prevention, 2013).

In the early 1990s, technologic advances enabled researchers to extract DNA and biochemical analytes from the dried blood spots on the NBS filter papers (McCabe, Huang, Seltzer, & Law, 1987). Until recently, these results were used primarily as confirmatory tests to rule in/out conditions identified using MS/MS. For example, if MS/MS results reveal elevated immune reactive trypsinogen levels, DNA from the dried blood sample was used to search for cystic fibrosis mutations on chromosome 7. DNA is now increasingly being used in parallel with MS/MS as part of the initial NBS evaluation in an effort to reduce the false positive rates, decrease follow-up costs, and eliminate parental anxiety associated with the evaluation of false positives. Although DNA analysis has a lower sample throughput, the additional test can either strongly support the presumption in the situation of a true positive result or invalidate the notion that the patient has the disorder. "Second-tier tests" improve sensitivity and specificity, increase speed of diagnosis and treatment, and reduce the number of false-positives that can add to cost related to follow-up (Bhardwaj *et al.*, 2003). DNA testing also facilitates differentiation between similar disorders, such as sickle cell anemia and sickle/beta thalassemia (Clarke & Higgins, 2000), and is commonly performed for hemoglobinopathies, galactosemia, cystic fibrosis, and medium-chain acyl-CoA dehydrogenase deficiency.

In 2008, the Wisconsin NBS program began

screening for severe combined immunodeficiency using a molecular assay as a primary screening test (Baker *et al.*, 2010). The Association for Public Health Laboratories (APHL) has been working in partnership with the CDC Newborn Screening and Molecular Biology Branch to address recent developments in molecular testing, which has led to the development of a data-sharing molecular resources web site for NBS programs, in which NBS laboratories can receive an assessment of their molecular capabilities (Association of Public Health Laboratories [APHL], 2013). Quality improvement for NBS laboratory tests, as well as for the NBS system as a whole, will continue to be a priority in the years to come.

7.3. NEW TECHNOLOGIES

New technologies have the potential to change the landscape of NBS. One practical solution to cost and specimen limitation problems is to develop assays that can be translated onto a miniature testing platform, such as a microfluidic chip, which uses smaller specimen volume at a reduced testing cost. Test platforms have become efficient with the lab-on-a-chip concept, enabling fluid dispensing, transport, mixing, incubation, detection, and disposal within a self-contained unit (Millington *et al.*, 2010). Digital microfluidics has several advantages, the most important being reconfigurability and scalability. These features offer a truly generic microfluidic platform, which has already been used to develop several assays, including immunologic, enzymatic, and DNA-based tests of the type currently used in NBS laboratories (Millington *et al.*, 2010). In the future, these high-throughput platforms may be used to do NBS analysis in the hospital's clinical laboratory rather than collecting and shipping dried blood specimens to a central laboratory and waiting days to weeks for results. NBS could occur in the birthing facility, and results would be readily available, thus decreasing the number of missed diagnoses as a result of untestable specimens or the inability to locate infants lost to follow-up. DNA sequencing technologies are becoming so advanced that next-generation sequencing may offer fast and affordable genome sequencing in the clinical laboratory, augmenting current NBS approaches. Further work is required to determine if DNA sequencing will be useful in the

NBS setting and whether the benefit of using this technology outweighs the cost.

New DNA sequencing technologies offer increasingly comprehensive identification of genetic conditions and susceptibilities. Tests based on these technologies are generating a different approach to screening that seeks to inform individuals about all of their genetic traits and susceptibilities for purposes that incorporate rapid diagnosis, family planning, expediting of research, and the traditional screening goals of improving disease prevention. In the future, entire human genomes may be sequenced at birth, allowing individuals to have the option of receiving information about later-onset diseases for which effective interventions may be available. In 2013, four research teams across the United States were awarded a total of $5 million under a new Genomic Sequencing and Newborn Screening Disorders program jointly funded by the Eunice Kennedy Shriver National Institute of Child Health and Human Development and the National Human Genome Research Institute. The four pilot programs will examine whether conducting whole genome or exome sequencing provides useful medical information beyond what is already delivered by current newborn screening. They will also examine the technical, clinical, and ethical aspects of genomics research in newborns and its potential to improve newborn healthcare (Eunice Kennedy Shriver National Institute of Child Health and Human Development, 2013). Using these tests to conduct population screening will most likely increase the counseling and diagnostic challenges already encountered in NBS programs, including false-positive and ambiguous test results, over diagnosis, and incidental findings. Whether DNA sequencing is desirable requires further empiric research and careful deliberation on the part of everyone involved, including researchers, clinicians, public health officials, health care payers, and especially those who will be the recipients of this novel screening approach.

7.4. ETHICAL, LEGAL, SOCIAL, AND PRACTICAL CONSIDERATIONS

Ethical, legal, and logistical considerations have always existed for NBS programs. Some of the most well-known recent issues, reviewed here, include informed consent; storage and use of residual dried blood spots; acquiring genomic information that is not currently actionable, but that may be indicate risk for future, unrelated disorders; and practical issues such as the cost of NBS.

7.4.1. Consent

Like other issues in NBS, consent policies and requirements vary depending on the state. Many state NBS programs have an "opt-out" policy mandating testing unless parents or guardians decline testing due to religious or other reasons. Not all states allow parents to opt-out, however; some groups oppose opt-out policies, contending that parents and guardians should be educated on NBS and provide written consent prior to testing (Dhanda & Reilly, 2003). Even the earliest NBS screening programs were built on the opt-out policy, under the ethical premise that the best interest of a child supersedes the family's decision-making rights. This is particularly important in NBS, because many of the conditions tested for have severe and rapid consequences if left undetected and untreated (Lewis, Goldenberg, Anderson, Rothwell, & Botkin, 2011). NBS programs continue to work with organizations such as the APHL and Genetic Alliance to educate and inform parents and providers about the benefits of NBS (APHL, 2013; Health Resources and Services Administration, 2013), and all screening programs have written guidelines in place to protect privacy and confidentiality throughout the process.

7.4.2. Residual Dried Blood Spots

After a newborn is screened, a small amount of dried blood remains on the filter paper card, which is often stored for later use in accordance with individual state statutes and/or policies. These residual dried blood spots serve many purposes, but it is important to note that parental consent for later use is often not obtained or required (Therrell, Johnson, & Williams, 2006; Therrell Jr. & Hannon, 2012; Therrell Jr. et al., 2011). A 2008–2009 survey of state laws found that 20 states address retention and/or residual NBS dried blood spot use; 13 states address the use of information related to dried blood spots;

and the remaining 17 states and the District of Columbia have no laws governing residual blood spots (APHL, 2013). Several states allow the residual dried blood spots to be used for public health and scientific research purposes, and many do not require parental notification of these additional uses. Justifying the use and storage of residual dried blood spots is a contentious issue for NBS programs and parents (APHL, 2013).

Residual dried blood spots are primarily used for quality assurance purposes and internal laboratory quality control. This includes confirmation of original results, method validation, and assay quality control, all required of clinical laboratories, but they have considerable additional value as well. They are essential for quality improvement and are critical when new screening tests are developed (Therrell et al., 2006). Dried blood spots provide invaluable data on the spectrum of genetic disorders in the general population. A NBS test cannot be introduced until pilot studies are done to determine disease severity, incidence, and genetic etiology in the general population and selected subpopulations, the performance characteristics of screening and diagnostic tests, and response to interventions. The only source of material available to carry out these pilot studies is the residual dried blood spot.

Some state programs permit controlled access to residual dried blood spots for reasons unrelated to NBS, including requests for additional screening and research or for public health or academic purposes (Lewis et al., 2011). The Coordinating Center of the Newborn Screening Translational Research Network (NBSTRN) facilitates research to improve the health outcomes of newborns with genetic or congenital disorders through an infrastructure that provides the research community access to NBS resources. Acknowledging the barriers researchers face when locating or acquiring residual dried blood spots, the NBSTRN developed the Virtual Repository of Dried Blood Spots (VRDBS), a secure web-based tool providing NBS program information from participating states. Through this repository, researchers can have access to deidentified information from over 2 million dried blood spots (Newborn Screening Translational Research Network [NBSTRN], 2013). The Michigan Department of Community Health launched the Michigan BioTrust for Health to improve preservation

and utility of residual NBS dried blood spots for biomedical research. The goals of the program are to make residual dried blood spots more useful for medical and public health research; specimens are currently being used to study exposures to toxic substances, birth defects, and chronic and genetic diseases (Duquette, Langbo, Bach, & Kleyn, 2012). The range of uses and diverse and nearly complete population coverage of residual dried blood spots make these samples irreplaceable.

Although the general public is largely supportive of the use of residual dried blood spots for quality assurance and biomedical research, in a recent study, parents of children with phenylketonuria and leukemia were more strongly supportive than the general public regarding the use of these samples for research. Despite this supportive attitude, these parents shared similar concerns regarding privacy protections (Nagaraj et al., 2014). Issues surrounding the use and storage of residual dried blood spots after completion of laboratory testing are not new. The first lawsuit (Bearder et al. v. State of Minnesota, 2011) (Knutson et al., 2011) came from families in Minnesota who alleged that storage and use of residual dried blood spots violated the states' Genetic Privacy Act (Hu, 2012), and the Minnesota Supreme Court ruled against the Minnesota Department of Health. Written consent is now required for long-term storage and use of residual dried blood specimens and test data in Minnesota. The following year, Minnesota passed legislation specifying timeline requirements by which blood specimens and test results must be destroyed. In Minnesota, unless specifically authorized by written consent, the Minnesota Department of Health routinely destroys residual dried blood specimens from babies born after the Bearder et al. v. State of Minnesota (2011) decision. If NBS results are negative, the specimens are destroyed after 71 days, and if the results are positive, the dried blood spots and all additional test results are destroyed after 24 months (Knutson et al., 2011).

The second lawsuit was filed against the Texas State Department of Health by families who claimed storage and use of NBS for undisclosed research purposes violated their constitutional protection from unlawful search and seizure (Texas Western District Court, 2009). The terms of the settlement required the state to destroy more than 5 million residual dried blood spots and led to changes in legislation that required a parental option to request the destruction of the specimens after completion of NBS. As a result of this case (*Higgins et al. v. Texas Department of State Health Services,* 2012) (Texas Western District Court, 2009), additional statutory changes became effective requiring parental consent for the use of residual dried blood spots for public health research outside the state public health agency and storage for more than two years (Caggana *et al.*, 2013).

Combining information from NBS programs with other health data could greatly improve the delivery of health care, although difficult issues of privacy, security, and technologic coordination still need to be resolved. NBS programs are taking a proactive approach to engaging the health community in an open, interactive dialogue on policy developments for residual dried blood spot storage, use, and destruction. Open and informed dialogue, along with education about the benefits of using residual dried blood spots to support NBS and public health, may help address some of the more difficult questions and controversies that exist (Therrell Jr. & Hannon, 2012). Greater transparency about dried blood spot use will help build trust and resolve the public's concern on the potential misuse of these specimens. There is evidence that these residual dried blood spots can be used anonymously, responsibly, and without a privacy risk to the infant or extended family. Given the potential to advance science and clinical care for newborns, their families, and society through the use of residual dried blood spots, continued efforts are important to protect this valuable resource.

7.4.3. Incidental Findings

NBS can reveal information about an infant that may be irrelevant to the infant's health, but may have important implications for families. NBS tests are sensitive enough to detect newborns who are carriers for recessive disorders, such as sickle cell disease or cystic fibrosis. Several conditions that are related to classic severe combined immunodeficiency disease (SCID), but that do not fit the formal description of the disease, may be identified through NBS but may

or may not be reported, depending upon the state in which the NBS testing was done (Routes *et al.*, 2009). Molecular testing can also reveal important information about paternity or about parental genetics, raising additional concerns and considerations.

State NBS programs are mandated to report only results associated with disorders on the approved panels, but when medical information is acquired incidentally and not disclosed, it may seem to families that valuable medical information is being deliberately withheld (Botkin et al., 2006). There is an urgent need for consensus recommendations that outline reporting and followup of carriers and for appropriate management of intermediate results and incidental findings.

7.5. IMPLICATIONS FOR EDUCATORS, RESEARCHERS, AND ADMINISTRATORS

NBS is a highly complex public health initiative that is managed at the state level and that involves a large number of stakeholders, including affected infants, children, and their families, practitioners, birthing facilities, treatment centers, schools, public health officials, legislators, and the general public. The goal of NBS is to rapidly identify infants with selected conditions and then initiate treatment, coordinate the efforts of stakeholders, and ensure that every affected infant receives the appropriate treatment and long-term follow-up irrespective of where he or she lives. Public interest groups continue to pressure state NBS programs to expand the list of approved conditions that may be reported on NBS panels, but adding a new condition to screening requires time and effort to develop confirmatory tests, create management protocols, and prepare educational materials for both parents and health care providers. NBS programs in all states are working to find solutions to these challenges as part of the mission to provide high-quality services. Nurses, nurse educators, and nurse researchers are well-positioned to inform and shape NBS care and services by ensuring that these programs are implemented safely and effectively and that the nursing work force is educated and prepared to engage in the important NBS dialogue and by developing research in the area of newborn screening.

7.6. REFERENCES

AAP Newborn Screening Task Force. (2000). Serving the family from birth to the medical home. Newborn screening: A blueprint for the future—A call for a national agenda on state newborn screening programs. *Pediatrics, 106*(2), 389–427.

Alexander, D., & van Dyck, P. C. (2006). A vision of the future of newborn screening. *Pediatrics, 117*(5 Pt 2), S350-354. doi: 10.1542/peds.2005-2633O

Association of Public Health Laboratories. (2013). Newborn screening molecular resources. Retrieved 3 November 2013, 2013, from http://www.aphl.org/aphlprograms/newborn-screening-and-genetics/molecular/pages/default.aspx

Baker, M. W., Laessig, R. H., Katcher, M. L., Routes, J. M., Grossman, W. J., Verbsky, J., . . . & Brokopp, C. D. (2010). Implementing routine testing for severe combined immunodeficiency within Wisconsin's newborn screening program. [Research Support, Non-U.S. Gov't Research Support, U.S. Gov't, P.H.S.]. *Public Health Rep, 125*(Suppl 2), 88–95.

Bearder et al. vs the State of Minnesota, A10-0101 C.F.R. (2011).

Beleno et al. v. Texas Department of State Health Services et al. 5:2009cv00188 C.F.R. (2009).

Bhardwaj, U., Zhang, Y. H., Jackson, D. S., Buchanan, G. R., Therrell, B. L., Jr., McCabe, L. L., & McCabe, E. R. (2003). DNA diagnosis confirms hemoglobin deletion in newborn screen follow-up. [Case Reports Research Support, Non-U.S. Gov't]. *J Pediatr, 142*(3), 346–348. doi: 10.1067/mpd.2003.117

Botkin, J. R., Clayton, E. W., Fost, N. C., Burke, W., Murray, T. H., Baily, M. A., . . . Ross, L. F. (2006). Newborn screening technology: Pproceed with caution. [Research Support, N.I.H., Extramural]. *Pediatrics, 117*(5), 1793–1799. doi: 10.1542/peds.2005-2547

Caggana, M., Jones, E. A., Shahied, S. I., Tanksley, S., Hermerath, C. A., & Lubin, I. M. (2013). Newborn screening: from Guthrie to whole genome sequencing. [Research Support, N.I.H., Extramural]. *Public Health Rep, 128*(Suppl 2), 14–19.

Centers for Disease Control and Prevention. (2013). Newborn screening: Saving lives for 50 years. *CDC Features.* Retrieved November 3, 2013, from http://www.cdc.gov/features/newbornscreening50years/

Chace, D. H., Kalas, T. A., & Naylor, E. W. (2003). Use of tandem mass spectrometry for multianalyte screening of dried blood specimens from newborns. [Review]. *Clin Chem, 49*(11), 1797–1817.

Clarke, G. M., & Higgins, T. N. (2000). Laboratory investigation of hemoglobinopathies and thalassemias: Review and update. [Review]. *Clin Chem, 46*(8 Pt 2), 1284–1290.

Dhanda, R. K., & Reilly, P. R. (2003). Legal and ethical issues of newborn screening. *Pediatr Ann, 32*(8), 540–546.

Dhondt, J. L. (2007). Neonatal screening: from the 'Guthrie age' to the 'genetic age'. [Historical Article]. *J Inherit Metab Dis, 30*(4), 418–422. doi: 10.1007/s10545-007-0624-9

Duquette, D., Langbo, C., Bach, J., & Kleyn, M. (2012). Michigan BioTrust for Health: public support for using residual dried blood spot samples for health research. *Public Health Genomics, 15*(3-4), 146–155. doi: 10.1159/000336565

Eunice Kennedy Shriver National Institute of Child Health and Human Development. (2013). Genomic Sequencing and Newborn Screening Disorders (U19) (Vol. 2013).

Guthrie, R., & Susi, A. (1963). A Simple Phenylalanine Method for Detecting Phenylketonuria in Large Populations of Newborn Infants. *Pediatrics, 32*, 338–343.

Health Resources and Services Administration. (2013). Baby's first test: how screening works Retrieved 3 November 2013, 2013, from http://www.babysfirsttest.org

Hu, S. (2012). Minnesota Supreme Court hears whether the Genetic Privacy Act protects newborn blood spot samples obtained under the state's newborn screening statutes—*Bearder v. State of Minnesota*. [Legal Cases]. *Am J Law Med, 38*(1), 225–227.

Jackson, J. M., Crider, K. S., & Olney, R. S. (2010). Population-based surveillance for rare congenital and inherited disorders: models and challenges. [Review]. *Adv Exp Med Biol, 686*, 133–150. doi: 10.1007/978-90-481-9485-8_9

Kemper, A. R., Kus, C. A., Ostrander, R. J., Comeau, A. M., Boyle, C. A., Dougherty, D., . . . Human Services Advisory, C. (2012). A framework for key considerations regarding point-of-care screening of newborns. [Research Support, Non-U.S. Gov't]. *Genet Med, 14*(12), 951–954. doi: 10.1038/gim.2012.89

Lewis, M. H., Goldenberg, A., Anderson, R., Rothwell, E., & Botkin, J. (2011). State laws regarding the retention and use of residual newborn screening blood samples. [Research Support, N.I.H., Extramural]. *Pediatrics, 127*(4), 703–712. doi: 10.1542/peds.2010-1468

Lloyd-Puryear, M. A., Tonniges, T., van Dyck, P. C., Mann, M. Y., Brin, A., Johnson, K., & McPherson, M. (2006). American Academy of Pediatrics Newborn Screening Task Force recommendations: how far have we come? *Pediatrics, 117*(5 Pt 2), S194-211. doi: 10.1542/peds.2005-2633B

Maccready, R. A., & Hussey, M. G. (1964). Newborn Phenylketonuria Detection Program in Massachusetts. *Am J Public Health Nations Health, 54*, 2075–2081.

McCabe, E. R., Huang, S. Z., Seltzer, W. K., & Law,

M. L. (1987). DNA microextraction from dried blood spots on filter paper blotters: potential applications to newborn screening. [Research Support, U.S. Gov't, Non-P.H.S. Research Support, U.S. Gov't, P.H.S.]. *Hum Genet, 75*(3), 213–216.

Millington, D. S., Sista, R., Eckhardt, A., Rouse, J., Bali, D., Goldberg, R., . . . Pamula, V. (2010). Digital microfluidics: a future technology in the newborn screening laboratory? [Research Support, N.I.H., Extramural Research Support, Non-U.S. Gov't]. *Semin Perinatol, 34*(2), 163–169. doi: 10.1053/j.semperi.2009.12.008

Nagaraj, C. B., Rothwell, E., Hart, K., Latimer, S., Schiffman, J. D., & Botkin, J. R. (2014). Attitudes of Parents of Children with Serious Health Conditions regarding Residual Bloodspot Use. *Public health genomics, 17*(3), 141–148.

National Research Council (U.S.). Committee for the Study of Inborn Errors of Metabolism. (1975). *Genetic screening: programs, principles, and research.* Washington: National Academy of Sciences.

Newborn Screening Translational Research Network. (2013). Virtual Repository of Dried Blood Spots (VRDBS) Retrieved 3 November 2013, 2013, from https://www.nbstrn.org/research-tools/virtual-repository-of-dried-blood-spots

Prevention, C. f. D. C. a. (2013). Newborn Screening Quality Assurance Program. *Laboratory Quality Assurance and Standardization Programs* Retrieved 3 November 2013, 2013, from http://www.cdc.gov/labstandards/nsqap.html

Routes, J. M., Grossman, W. J., Verbsky, J., Laessig, R. H., Hoffman, G. L., Brokopp, C. D., & Baker, M.

W. (2009). Statewide newborn screening for severe T-cell lymphopenia. [Research Support, Non-U.S. Gov't

Research Support, U.S. Gov't, P.H.S.]. *JAMA, 302*(22), 2465–2470. doi: 10.1001/jama.2009.1806

Therrell, B. L., Johnson, A., & Williams, D. (2006). Status of newborn screening programs in the United States. [Research Support, U.S. Gov't, P.H.S.]. *Pediatrics, 117*(5 Pt 2), S212–252. doi: 10.1542/peds.2005-2633C

Therrell, B. L., Jr., & Hannon, W. H. (2012). Newborn dried blood spot screening: residual specimen storage issues. [Comment]. *Pediatrics, 129*(2), 365–366. doi: 10.1542/peds.2011-3416

Therrell, B. L., Jr., Hannon, W. H., Bailey, D. B., Jr., Goldman, E. B., Monaco, J., Norgaard-Pedersen, B., . . . Howell, R. R. (2011). Committee report: Considerations and recommendations for national guidance regarding the retention and use of residual dried blood spot specimens after newborn screening. *Genet Med, 13*(7), 621–624. doi: 10.1097/GIM.0b013e3182147639

United States Department of Health and Human Services. (2013, 24 April 2013). Discretionary Advisory Committee on Heritable Disorders in Newborns and Children Retrieved 3 November 2013, 2013, from http://www.hrsa.gov/advisorycommittees/mchbadvisory/heritabledisorders/

Watson, M. S., Mann, M. Y., Lloyd-Puryear, M. A., Rinaldo, P., & Howell, R. R. (2006). Newborn screening: toward a uniform screening panel and system. [Guideline]. *Genet Med, 8, Suppl 1*, 1S–252S. doi: 10.1097/01.gim.0000223891.82390.ad

Chapter 8

Genetic Considerations in Childhood

HEATHER L. JOHNSON, DNP, FNP-BC, FAANP
JOANNA SPAHIS, RN, CNS, APNG
DALE H. LEA, RN, MPH, CGC

Objectives:

- List conditions that may cause dysmorphology.
- Discuss normal and abnormal human growth and development.
- Describe principles of screening in a pediatric population.
- Discuss key issues in helping adolescents transition to adult health care.

8.1. INTRODUCTION

From conception, human growth and development occurs in a predictable and orderly fashion, offering clinicians the opportunity to intervene if necessary. Many factors such as poor nutrition; acute and chronic illnesses; harmful physical, emotional, or social environments; and genetic makeup have been shown to interfere with normal growth and development. When alterations in developmental trajectory occur, a variety of different health care professionals may become engaged in a concerted effort to help optimize every child's cognitive and developmental function. Nurses are critical members of the health care team, because they work on the front line in health care and are often among the first to recognize alterations in development.

The incidence of chromosomal abnormalities in the population of live born infants is about 6 in 1000. In children with developmental delays, a causative genetic diagnosis can be found in as many as 14% using chromosome microarray technologies (Cooper *et al.*, 2011). With new and developing genetic technology, understanding of the impact of genetics on typical and atypical growth and development is expanding (Zitelli, McIntire, & Nowalk, 2012b). Although most children are screened for some genetic disorders at birth, the current state of genetic testing does not identify all children at risk for growth or developmental problems, so children are usually identified by clinicians working in nongenetics settings. This chapter describes the approach to the assessment of children with dysmorphic features or alterations in growth and development suggestive of a genetic syndrome and offer suggestions on how to support children and their families as these children transition into adulthood.

8.2. ASSESSMENT OF CHILDREN WITH ATYPICAL FEATURES, GROWTH, OR DEVELOPMENT

The RAPID approach, a useful acronym discussed in Chapter 2 to aid in the genetic/genomic risk assessment, can be used to evaluate children with atypical features, growth, or development. This *Risk Assessment* entails determining the *Probability* of risk by *Identifying* red flags or abnormalities through appropriate *Data* collection. Assessing a child with atypical features, growth, and/or development begins by collecting data, including a complete family pedigree that incorporates a minimum of three generations, the obstetrical and birth histories, and the infant/child's medical history. Data collection also includes a thorough physical examination with accurate somatic measurements and evaluation of any developmental delays or parental concerns. The history should cover the prenatal period, including maternal health and habits before and during pregnancy, parents' health and age at conception, ethnicity, consanguinity, teratogen exposure, amniotic fluid volumes, and fetal activity. The perinatal and postnatal history should encompass the child's gestational age at birth; birth weight, length, and head circumference; duration of hospitalization; perinatal/postnatal complications; family history; nutritional and social history; a complete review of systems; pattern of growth; and achievement of milestones. Hospital discharge summaries and any prenatal testing results such as ultrasound, amniocentesis, or chorionic villus sampling (CVS) may be needed for a complete picture.

8.3. DYSMORPHOLOGY

The physical examination is particularly important when assessing the health and wellbeing of infants, young children, and adolescents, because it provides information about a child's health, growth, and development, as well as features and/or abnormalities or malformations consistent with alterations in morphologic development, commonly referred to as *dysmorphology*. Dysmorphology focuses on children who have congenital malformations or unusual facial features that are often associated with other developmental delays, such as motor or cognition (Smithson & Winter, 2004). The data can then be used to guide the development of a differential diagnosis and direct further testing and evaluation (Gupta & Kabra, 2007). The presence of a single major structural abnormality is strongly indicative of a genetic irregularity (Zitelli *et al.*, 2012b), which almost always prompts a genetic referral. Evaluating a child with one minor finding is more challenging because the finding may be a normal variant, an isolated feature of a nonsyndromic condition, or the only syndromic feature a nongeneticist might recognize. Major and minor features associated with genetic syndromes are listed in Table 8.1.

Whenever a physical abnormality is present, particularly if the abnormality is commonly associated with a malformation syndrome or genetic disorder, a dysmorphology examination is particularly helpful and a referral to a dysmorphologist, a pediatric geneticist, or a developmental pediatrician should be considered (Reardon & Donnai, 2007). This specialized examination is conducted to identify unusual physical characteristics that, when considered together, may offer clues to the underlying cause of the condition.

During the dysmorphology examination, special attention is paid to the skin, face, skull, hands, feet, joints, skeleton, genitalia, and anus, and detailed measurements of the body such as the length of fingers, hand widths, distance between the eyes, etc., are often made (Gupta & Kabra, 2007; Reardon & Donnai, 2007). It may be important to examine parents and other family members to see if subtle atypical features are shared variations of normal, or whether the anomalies are consistent with a genetic syndrome. A careful, thorough history and examination done early in the discovery process can minimize unnecessary tests and significantly decrease the stress and cost of making a diagnosis (Zitelli *et al.*, 2012b).

Nurses need to understand the dysmorphology evaluation process and its purpose, because they are often the first to recognize physical or behavioral anomalies and identify the need for further evaluation (Skirton & Patch, 2002). Although nurse educators and nurse administrators often are not involved in direct patient care, they too should be familiar with the dysmorphology examination so they can facilitate system supports for education and oversight of children and families with genetic conditions. Advanced practice nurses must have adequate knowledge of genetics and genetic syndromes to determine whether a congenital abnormality is isolated or if there is a pattern to the anomalies suggestive of a genetic syndrome so that an appropriate referral for further evaluation can be made (Greco, Tinley, & Seibert, 2012).

8.4. COMMON GENETIC CONDITIONS

Approximately 3% to 4% of all babies are born with some type of birth defect, also known as a congenital anomaly (Centers for Disease Control and Prevention [CDC], 2013). The World Health Organization (WHO) defines these defects as "structural or functional anomalies, including metabolic disorders, which are present at the time of birth" (WHO, 2012, para. 4). Congenital abnormalities may be isolated or form a pattern, suggesting an underlying genetic condition or syndrome. Syndromes are recognizable conditions or abnormalities that are presumed to indi-

TABLE 8.1. Features of Genetic Syndromes.

Head	Musculoskeletal
Dysmorphic skull	Connective tissue abnormalities
Craniosynostosis	Hypermobile joints or joint laxity
Microcephaly	Ability to oppose thumb to volar forearm
Macrocephaly	Abnormal upper-to-lower segment ratio
Frontal bossing	Skeletal disproportion
Facial asymmetry	Arm span that exceeds height
Meningomyelocele[a]	Limb deformities
High forehead	Long bone fractures
Low set posterior hairline	Scoliosis
Vertical furrowing of central forehead	Kyphosis
Round face	Vertebral anomalies
Long face	Joint contractures
Flat facies	Frequent or sprains, dislocations, and subluxations
Midline defects	Early onset chronic musculoskeletal pain
Finely arched, heavy eyebrows	Long, thin extremities
	Cubitus valgus or turned-in elbows
	Small hands and feet
Eyes	**Hands**
Long eyelashes	Arachnodactyly
Ptosis	Polydactyly, extra digits[a]
Epicanthal folds of the eyes	Absent thumbs[a]
Upward or downward slanting palpebral fissures of the eyes	Ectrodactyly,[a] missing or deficient central digits of the hand
Hypertelorism or wide set eyes	Clinodactyly, bent or curved fifth fingers
"Almond shaped" eyes	Syndactyly (webbing)
Prominent eyes	Short fifth finger
Colobomas or other iris anomalies	Single transverse (simian) palmar creases
Strabismus	Bridged palmar crease, two transverse palmar creases that are connected
Nystagmus	
Keratoconus	
Vision defects or blindness	
Glaucoma	
Cataracts	
Retinal detachment	
Ocular lens subluxation, ectopia lentis	
Brushfield spots or spots on the periphery of the iris	
Ears	**Feet**
Preauricular pits or tags	Wide space between first and second toe
Deafness	Ectrodactyly:[a] missing or deficient central digits of the foot
Long, wide or protruding ears	Bilateral clubfoot, congenital talipes equinovarus[a]
Folded or dysplastic ears	Rocker-bottom feet
Creases in the earlobes	Pes planus
Microtia[a]	Toe walking
Low set ears	
Nose	**Stature, weight and growth**
Flat or broad nasal bridge	Short stature
High nasal bridge	Tall stature
Small nose	Obesity
Choanal atresia[a]	Failure to thrive
	Alterations in growth velocity

(continued)

TABLE 8.1 (continued). Features of Genetic Syndromes.

Lower face, mouth and neck	Skin, hair and nails
Malar or mandibular hypoplasia	Redundant skin folds
Short, long or flat philtrum of the upper lip	Fragile skin
Cleft lip[a]	Easy bruising
Cleft palate[a]	Impaired wound healing
Bifid uvula	Atrophic scarring
High, arched palate	Skin hyperextensibility
Small or large mouth	Striae, especially in unusual places
Delayed dental development	Sparse or patchy hair distribution
Single, central incisor	Hirsutism
Hypodontia	Sparse pubic or axillary hair in prepubescent/
Conical anterior teeth	pubescent
Macroglossia or protruding tongue	Rashes or eczema
Poor sucking or swallowing	Nail anomalies
Prominent jaw	"Velvety" skin
Micrognathia or small lower jaw	Hypopigmented, fair, sun-sensitive skin
Microretrognathia, small, mandible that is posteriorly	Hyperpigmentation
placed	Café-au-lait spots
Short or webbed neck	Freckling
	Neurofibromas
	Hemangiomas
	Telangiectasia
	Abnormal fat distribution, especially lower trunk, buttocks and proximal limbs

Chest and cardiovascular	Generalized and neurological
Congenital heart disease	Poor healing, impaired immunity
Coarctation of the aorta	Seizures
Aortic aneurysm	Ataxia
Vascular anomalies	Abnormal tone- hypertonia or hypotonia
Pectus excavatum or carinatum	Decreased Moro reflex
Shield chest with widely spaced nipples	Decreased deep tendon reflexes (DTRs)
Underdeveloped breasts	Poor motor coordination
Gynecomastia	

Genital anomalies	Mental health, developmental and cognitive
Micropenis	Cognitive impairment
Hypospadias[a]	Cat-like cry
Cryptorchidism	Speech delay
Inguinal or femoral hernias	Perseverative speech or behavior
Macroorchidism or enlarged testicles	Developmental delays, impairments or loss of
Fused labia with enlarged clitoris[a]	milestones
Amenorrhea	Learning disabilities
Sterility	Behavioral problems
Absence of secondary sex characteristics in	Mood disorders
adolescence	Emotional lability
	Extreme temper tantrums
	Extreme overeating
	Inappropriate paroxysms of laughter
	Schizoid tendencies
	Hand flapping
	Avoidance of socialization
	Rocking
	Short attention span with or without hyperactivity
	Persistent mouthing of objects

(continued)

TABLE 8.1 (continued). Features of Genetic Syndromes.

GI & abdominal anomalies
Omphalocele
Umbilical hernia
Duodenal atresia
Hirschsprung's disease
Imperforate anus[a]
Renal/ureteral anomalies or horseshoe kidney
Multiorgan defects
Gluten intolerance or Celiac disease

[a]Major structural anomalies which are significantly associated with genetic syndrome.
Sources: Cooke, Divall, & Radovick *et al.*, 2011; Pyeritz, 2012; Reardon & Donnai, 2007; Zitelli *et al.*, 2012b.
Note: Although this list is broad, it may not represent all possible features.

cate a particular disease or trait (Human Genome Project, 2012). Cleft palate, for example, can be an isolated malformation involving a single organ system, or may be a part of a more complex syndrome, such as Stickler Syndrome, which is characterized by a distinctive facial appearance, eye abnormalities, hearing loss, and joint problems or Treacher-Collins Syndrome, a condition that affects the development of bones and other tissues of the face (U.S. National Library of Medicine, 2012b, 2013). Down syndrome (DS), a chromosomal abnormality associated with intellectual disability (ID), a characteristic facial appearance and low muscle tone, is another example of a genetic condition in which individuals present with a characteristic pattern of congenital abnormalities (Davidson, 2008; U.S. National Library of Medicine, 2012a).

Several genetic syndromes associated with dysmorphic features can be diagnosed in newborns and young children, including Patau syndrome (Trisomy 13), cri du chat, velocardiofacial syndrome (VCFS), and neurofibromatosis 1. Trisomy 13 is a genetic disorder in which the infant has inherited three copies of chromosome 13 instead of the usual two copies. Clinical symptoms include cleft lip and palate, closely set eyes, scalp defects such as missing skin, extra fingers or toes, low set ears, a small head (microcephaly), and limb abnormalities. Many affected infants also have congenital heart defects and develop severe mental retardation (Aypar, Yildirim, Sert, Ciftci, & Odabas, 2011).

Cri du chat ("Cat's Cry" in French) is caused by a deletion in the short arm of chromosome 5.

As the name suggests, these infants often have a very distinctive, high-pitched cry that sounds like the cry of a cat. Most affected individuals have ID, delayed development, and a number of characteristic features including low birth weight, poor tone, a small head with a round face, and distinctive facial features including wide spaced eyes, low set ears, broad nasal bridge, and small jaw. Affected children may have a congenital heart defect, neurologic and renal abnormalities (Mainardi *et al.*, 2006).

Velocardiofacial syndrome (VCFS) is an autosomal dominant condition that occurs when a small piece of chromosome 22 is deleted near the middle of the 22nd chromosome (22q11.2 deletion). Clinical features vary widely, even within the same family. If a child is born with cleft palate or other palatal abnormalities, it may be diagnosed in infancy. But VCFS may go undiagnosed for years, even though nearly 75% of affected individuals are born with major cardiac defects, such as tetralogy of Fallot, interrupted aortic arch, ventricular septal defect, or truncus arteriosus. Nearly 90% of affected individuals have learning difficulties; over 75% have immune deficiency, increasing the likelihood of rheumatoid arthritis or Graves' disease; and approximately 30% have renal abnormalities. Other clinical features include seizures, skeletal abnormalities (scoliosis, craniosynostosis), growth hormone deficiency causing short stature, and significant feeding, voiding or gastrointestinal problems (e.g., swallowing problems, imperforate anus, or intestinal malrotation [McDonald-McGinn, Emanuel, & Zackai, 2013]). For more information on the cardiovascular implications of VCFS, please see Chapter 11.

Many genetic syndromes have characteristic skin findings as well. A child with more than 6 café-au-lait (CAL) patches on his or her skin, for example, should be closely examined for *neurofibromatosis 1* (NF1), also called von Recklinghausen disease. NF1 is an autosomal dominant disorder caused by a mutation in the large neurofibromin 1 gene located on the long arm of chromosome 17. Approximately one-half of all NF1 mutations arise spontaneously and many children have no other affected family members. As with all autosomal dominant disorders, however, once the mutation is present, the risk for passing that mutation on is 50%. Common clini-

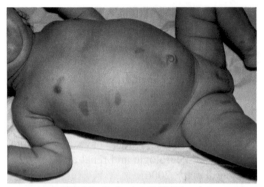

FIGURE 8.1. Café-au-lait (CAL) patches.

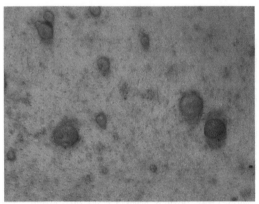

FIGURE 8.3. Plexiform neurofibromas.

cal features of NF1 include CAL patches (Figure 8.1), which appear between ages 1 and 5 years; axillary freckling; large head circumference; iris Lisch nodules (Figure 8.2); and learning disabilities. More serious manifestations, which typically emerge at/after adolescence, include plexiform neurofibromas (Figure 8.3), optic nerve and other central nervous system gliomas, malignant peripheral nerve sheath tumors, scoliosis, and vasculopathies. Because manifestations vary widely, even between family members, and new clinical findings emerge throughout life, all individuals with NF1 should receive annual physical and ophthalmologic examinations, regular developmental assessment screening, a genetics consultation, and other studies depending on clinical signs and symptoms. The value of routine head magnetic resonance image (MRI) screening is controversial, but any patient with central nervous system, skeletal, or cardiovascular findings should be managed by an appropriate specialist (Friedman, 2013).

Any time an abnormal physical feature or unusual developmental pattern is recognized in childhood, further discussion and evaluation of that individual and his or her family is required. Initial steps include communicating concerns to the family so that they understand the reason for further investigations, examining other family members, and possibly referral to a genetic specialist. One way to initiate these challenging conversations is to ask the parents if their child resembles another family member. This may offer the opening the parents need to express concerns about their child's appearance and development. The discussion can then focus on the reason for the careful, detailed history, physical examination, and evaluations of growth and development.

8.5. GROWTH

Evaluation of the child's growth is an important part of the genetic/genomic assessment. Growth is an objective, measurable increase in the physical size of the body. The American Academy of Pediatrics (AAP) developed guidelines for monitoring and screening to improve and promote child growth and development. *Bright Futures: Guidelines for Health Supervision of Infants, Children, and Adolescents* is a useful text by the AAP for health care providers that establishes the standards for assessing growth and development during well child or health supervision visits (Hagan, Shaw, & Duncan, 2008). Based on these recommendations, clinicians must accurately measure and plot growth at specific intervals. Height, weight, and head circumference are measured and compared to statistical norms for chil-

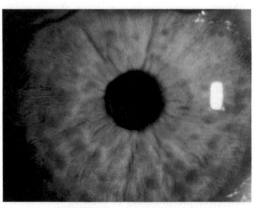

FIGURE 8.2. Iris Lisch nodules.

dren of a specific age and sex using growth charts from the CDC or the World Health Organization (WHO) (CDC, May 30, 2000; Grummer-Strawn, Reinold, Krebs, National Center for Chronic Disease Prevention and Health Promotion (U.S.), & CDC (U.S.), 2010) . The CDC and WHO growth charts can be found via the CDC web site at http://www.cdc.gov/growthcharts/ and http://www.cdc.gov/growthcharts/who_charts.htm.

A single weight or height measurement only provides a snapshot of growth. To evaluate patterns of growth, measurements must be accurately performed and plotted over time. The CDC recommends that all children's growth be measured and plotted using the appropriate CDC or WHO growth charts. Although most children's growth can be plotted on standard growth charts, special charts have been developed for several groups of children. Children born at low or very low birth weights have their own growth charts, most recently published in 2000 (CDC, May 30, 2000), as do children with genetic conditions associated with growth alterations, such as Trisomy 21 (DS), Prader-Willi syndrome, Williams syndrome, Cornelia DeLange syndrome (CdLS), Turner syndrome (TS), Rubinstein-Taybi syndrome, Marfan syndrome (MFS), and Achondroplasia (CdLS Foundation, 2010; Erkula, Jones, Sponseller, Dietz, & Pyeritz, 2002; Gawlik, Gawlik, Augustyn, Woska, & Malecka-Tendera, 2006; Hoover-Fong, McGready, Schulze, Barnes, & Scott, 2007; Martin, Smith, Cole, & Preece, 2007; Myrelid, Gustafsson, Ollars, & Anneren, 2002; Rosenbloom & Butler, 2012; Rubinstein-Taybi Society, n.d.). These population-specific growth charts have significant limitations, including small study sample sizes, but they assist clinicians in evaluating for co-morbid conditions, such as risk for congenital heart disease in children with DS (Van Gameren-Oosterom *et al.*, 2012). These growth charts should be used in combination with standard CDC or WHO growth charts, and the AAP recommends that all growth data be incorporated into electronic health records (EHR) where feasible (Rosenbloom *et al.*, 2010).

Measurement and determination of growth should be performed using age-appropriate, properly calibrated equipment at birth and at every clinic visit throughout childhood. The importance of collecting accurate data and plotting the data on the appropriate growth charts cannot be overstated. Although accurate measurements are not always easy to obtain because of age and cooperation of the child, growth patterns are key data points necessary for diagnosing and following children with genetic diseases.

The term "stature" describes the natural height of a human being in the upright position. Because stature and growth potential are based on the individual's genetic background, a child may be born smaller than expected for their genetic makeup and grow very quickly until they reach their genetically predetermined growth channel, called "catch-up growth." "Catch-down growth" is the opposite phenomenon, where a child's growth slows until they reach their growth channel. Catch-up and catch-down growth usually only occur within the first 18 to 24 months of life until genetically predetermined growth curves and velocities are reached. Children typically maintain this growth trajectory or curve until puberty (Cooke, Divall, & Radovick, 2011). Any deviance from this established normal growth channel should raise suspicion of pathology.

Alterations in normal growth patterns can provide important clues to the presence of a disorder and can easily be seen when accurate measurements are placed on the appropriate chart. When growth crosses major percentiles or lines on the growth chart in either direction, it is cause for concern. Children who fall off their weight curve earlier and more significantly than their height curve may have a nutritional or gastrointestinal cause for short stature, as demonstrated by curve A (Figure 8.4). Children who maintain the same weight but have slow height growth often have an endocrine cause for poor growth (curve B). Kids who track at the lower end of the curve for weight and height but are growing within the context of their familial genetic potential likely have familial short stature (curve C). Because errors in measurement and plotting on growth charts are common, the first step when evaluating a child who has crossed major percentiles is to re-measure and re-plot.

When a child's height falls 2 standard deviations (SD) below the normal range (< 3rd percentile), if growth velocity slows and crosses major percentiles, or if the child's height falls below the expected range based on a calculation of mid-parental height (Table 8.2), a work up for short

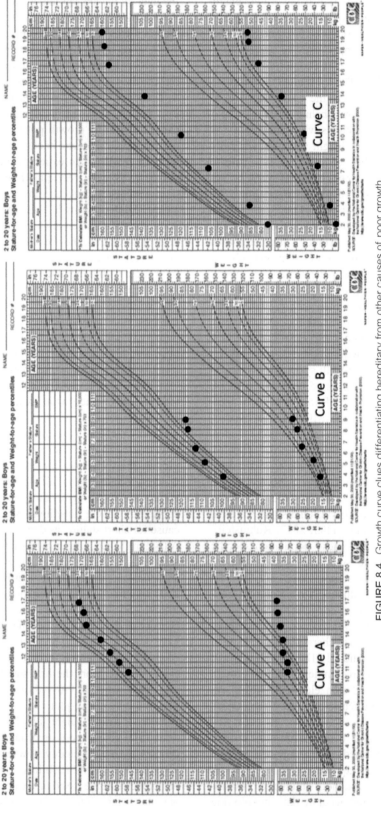

FIGURE 8.4. Growth curve clues differentiating hereditary from other causes of poor growth.

TABLE 8.2. *Calculating Mid-parental Height.*

Boys: $\dfrac{\text{(Mom's height in cm + 13 cm) + Dad's height in cm}}{2}$

Girls: $\dfrac{\text{(Dad's height in cm} - 13 \text{ cm)} + \text{Mom's height in cm}}{2}$

Example:

Father's height = 5′11″ = ~180 cm

Mother's height = 5′6½″ = ~169 cm

Boy child: $\dfrac{(169 \text{ cm} + 13 \text{ cm}) + 180 \text{ cm}}{2} = \dfrac{362}{2} = 181$ cm mid-parental height

Girl child: $\dfrac{(180 \text{ cm} - 13 \text{ cm}) + 169 \text{ cm}}{2} = \dfrac{336}{2} = 168$ cm mid-parental height

Note: Although mid–parental height is less reliable than growth charts, it is useful in putting the child's growth in context. The mid–parental height can be compared to the child's growth chart by following the child's current growth curve to the 20-year mark. If the height at the 20-year mark is within 5 cm of the mid–parental height, it is appropriate for the family (Nwosu & Lee, 2008).

stature or growth retardation should be initiated (Cooke *et al.*, 2011). Conversely, if a child's height is ≥ 2 SD above the mean for age and sex (> 97th percentile), crosses major percentiles, or is greater than expected based on calculation of mid–parental height, he or she should be evaluated for excess growth or tall stature (Cooke *et al.*, 2011). Most short or tall stature is caused by normal variants, but genetic conditions should be considered as potential causes in the differential diagnosis. Focused diagnostic tests for short and tall stature (Tables 8.3 and 8.4) used in conjunction with the algorithms presented in the upcoming pages aid in the evaluation of short and tall stature.

8.6. SHORT STATURE

When a child presents with short stature or abnormally slow growth, a comprehensive family

TABLE 8.3. *Recommended Diagnostic Testing for the Evaluation of Short Stature based upon Suspected Conditions.*

Diagnostic Tests	Suspected Condition
25-hydroxyvitamin D, 1,25 dihidroxyvitamin D, parathyroid hormone, Alkaline phosphatase, Bone age	Vitamin D deficiency
Celiac Ab panel, antiendomysial Ab, antigliadin Ab, tissue transglutaminase, possible endoscopy	Celiac disease
ESR, C-Reactive protein	Inflammatory conditions
Ferritin, iron, TIBC	Iron deficiency
Free thyroxine, TSH	Hypothyroidism
IGF-1, IGF binding protein 3, GH stimulation test	Growth hormone deficiency
Karyotype	Turner syndrome
MRI (if abrupt growth +/- neurological symptoms are present)	Craniopharyngioma
Sweat chloride test	Cystic fibrosis
Stool studies for ova & parasites, stool smear, prealbumin, travel history	Malnutrition secondary to intestinal parasite
Timed serum, salivary or urine cortisol tests, dexamethasone suppression test	Cushing disease

Ab = antibody, ESR = sedimentation rate, GH = growth hormone, IGF = insulin-like growth factor, MRI = magnetic resonance imaging, TIBC = total iron binding capacity, TSH = thyroid stimulating hormone

TABLE 8.4. Recommended Diagnostic Testing for the Evaluation of Tall Stature based upon Suspected Conditions.

Diagnostic Tests	Suspected Condition
17α-hydroxyprogesterone, HCG, DHEAS, estradiol, LH, FSH, testosterone, bone age	Precocious puberty
17α-hydroxyprogesterone, HCG, DHEAS, estradiol, LH, FSH, testosterone, bone age	Androgen or estrogen deficiency/estrogen resistance
Clinical criteria for diagnosis of Marfan syndrome, genetic consultation	Marfan syndrome
GH, IGF-1, IGF-binding protein 3	GH excess
Homocysteine, methionine	Homocysteinuria
Insulin, glucose	Beckwith-Wiedemann syndrome
Karyotype, LH, FSH, testosterone	Klinefelter syndrome
Karyotype	XYY

DHEAS = Dehydroepiandrosterone sulfate, FSH = follicle stimulating hormone, GH = growth hormone, IGF = insulin-like growth factor, HCG = human chorionic gonadotropin, LH = luteinizing hormone

pedigree, history, and physical should be conducted and a diagnostic evaluation performed. When a genetic condition known to cause short stature is suspected, growth patterns and the presence/absence of dysmorphic features become highly valuable pieces of data (Table 8.1 referred to earlier in this chapter), and algorithms (Figure 8.5) can help to narrow the field of possibilities. Approximately 50% to 70% of children referred for the evaluation of short stature have constitu-

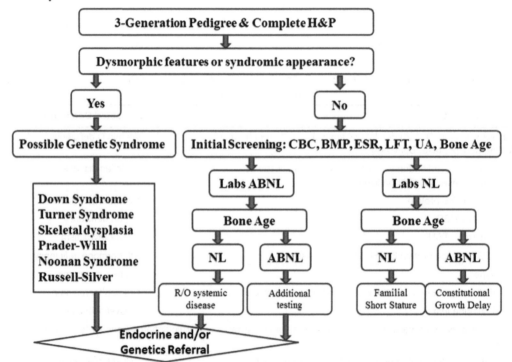

FIGURE 8.5. Systematic evaluation of children with short stature or growth deceleration. Abbreviations: CBC = Complete blood count, BMP = basic metabolic panel, ESR = erythrocyte sedimentation rate, LFT = liver function test, TSH = thyroid stimulating hormone, UA = urinalysis.

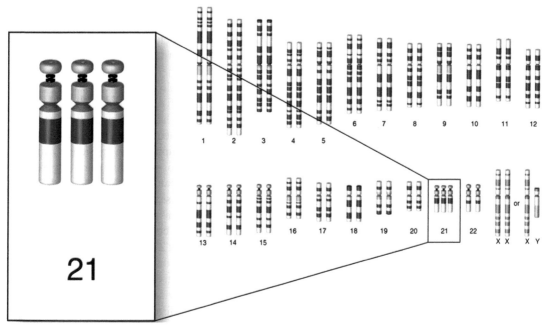

FIGURE 8.6. Down syndrome (Trisomy 21) karyotype. Obtained from: http://www.genome.gov/dmd/img.cfm?node=Photos/Graphics&id=85155. Date Taken: 06/12/2010, Credit Darryl Leja, NHGRI, H x W: 1875 x 1146. Rights Public.

tional growth delay (CGD) or familial short stature (Lam, Hau, & Lam, 2002; Papadimitriou *et al.*, 2012). Fewer than 19% are diagnosed with a pathologic chromosomal abnormalities, primarily TS, which is associated with having 45 chromosomes and only one X chromosome (XO) (Seaver & Irons, 2009). Other conditions associated with short stature include pulmonary, renal, gastrointestinal (GI), systemic disease, endocrinopathies, and other genetic syndromes (Table 8.5) (Seaver & Irons, 2009).

Laboratory tests can be very helpful when conducting an initial workup of a child with delayed growth, particularly in children who have no other features of a syndromic genetic condition. A complete blood count (CBC) may reveal anemia or blood dyscrasias associated with Fanconi anemia or Thalassemia (Kalb, Neveling, Nanda, Schindler, & Hoehn, 2006; Karimi, Haghpanah, Taher, & Cappellini, 2012). Abnormal liver or renal function tests or electrolyte disturbances may signify congenital adrenal hyperplasia or TS (Zitelli *et al.*, 2012b). An elevated erythrocyte sedimentation rate (ESR) may signal juvenile idiopathic arthritis or inflammatory bowel disease (IBD) (Cooke *et al.*, 2011). Altered thyroid stimulating hormone (TSH) and/or glucose levels are

associated with several endocrinopathies, including diabetes, Hashimoto's thyroiditis, or Grave's disease (Cooke *et al.*, 2011). Other focused diagnostic tests are outlined in Table 8.3 (Admou *et al.*, 2012).

Individuals with DS have inherited a full or partial extra copy of chromosome 21. This ge-

Sandal toe, flat nasal bridge, epicanthal folds, upslanting eyes, short webbed neck, small ears, bridge palmar crease

FIGURE 8.7. Phenotypic features of Down syndrome. Illustrated by Mark Weber, MS, RN.

netic syndrome is most commonly associated with short stature and, as is the case in many such syndromes, clinical features are usually evident at birth although some presentations may be so minor as to be missed. Approximately 1 in 700 live-born infants have DS—with manifestations ranging from mild to "classic" depending on the amount of extra genetic material the child has inherited (Figure 8.6) (Cooke *et al.*, 2011; Megarbane *et al.*, 2009). Most children with DS are short at birth and grow slowly throughout childhood and, as a result of delayed skeletal maturation and pubertal growth spurts; most adults with DS are usually shorter than predicted based on mid–parental height. The classic DS phenotype includes upslanting palpebral fissures, epicanthal folds, a flat nasal bridge, small ears, short or webbed neck, a bridged palmar crease, wide space between the first and second toes ("sandal toe"), mild to severe cognitive impairment, and short stature. Up to 50% of affected children have congenital heart and/or gastrointestinal

anomalies (Figure 8.7) (Megarbane *et al.*, 2009; Zitelli *et al.*, 2012b).

TS is also associated with short stature. About 1 in 2000 live-born infants has a complete or partial absence of one " chromosome (45, X) and is an obligate female (Figure 8.8) (Zhong & Layman, 2012; Zitelli *et al.*, 2012b). The classic phenotype of TS includes webbing of the neck, cubitus valgus (turned in elbows), shield-chest with widely-spaced nipples, low posterior hair line, and malformed or protruding ears (Figure 8.9). Other clinical features include a failure to develop secondary sex characteristics (breast buds, pubic hair, or menses), renal anomalies, bicuspid aortic valve, and coarctation of the aorta (Zhong & Layman, 2012; Zitelli *et al.*, 2012b). Girls with TS often have a distinctive neurodevelopmental profile with relatively strong verbal skills, but weak math and visual-spatial skills (e.g., a nonverbal learning disability) (Hong & Reiss, 2012; Zitelli *et al.*, 2012b). Because the clinical features of TS are often subtle, karyotyping should

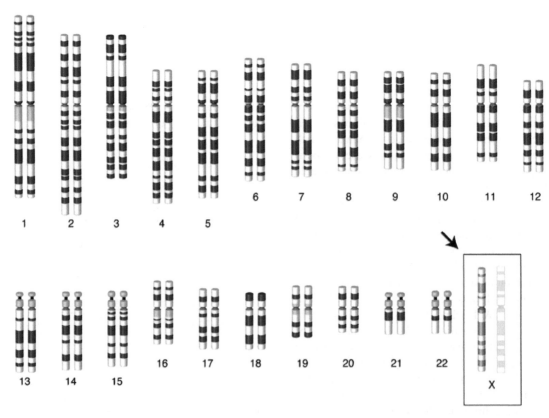

FIGURE 8.8. Turner Syndrome (45, X) karyotype. Obtained from: http://www.genome.gov/dmd/img.cfm?node=Photos/ Graphics&id=85205. Date Taken: 6/12/2010 Credit: Darryl Leja, NHGRI, HxW 1904 x 1610. Rights public.

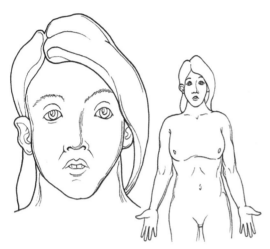

Webbed neck, protruding ears, cubitus valgus, shield chest, lack of secondary sex characteristics

FIGURE 8.9. Phenotypic features of Turner syndrome. Illustrated by Mark Weber, MS, RN.

be strongly considered whenever a young girl is being evaluated for short stature.

8.7. TALL STATURE

Theoretically, there should be as many children with heights > 2 SD above the mean (tall) as there are > 2 SD below the mean (short), but a chief compliant of "tall stature" is far less common than the complaint of short stature (Cooke *et al.*, 2011). Height, like many physical characteristics, tends to shift toward the mean. Therefore, children with unusually tall parents are usually shorter than their parents, just as children with shorter parents are often ultimately taller than their parents (Cooke *et al.*, 2011). The most common cause of tall stature is familial tall stature. However, tall stature can be an important sign of underlying pathology, so it is important to distinguish pathology from a normal variant with a thorough evaluation.

Children with familial tall stature are often within the normal height and weight ranges at birth with accelerated growth beginning in childhood. Children with growth disorders (e.g., Marfan, Sotos, or Beckwith-Wiedemann syndromes) are often > 90th percentile for height and weight at birth, and this pattern of accelerated growth persists throughout childhood (Douglas *et al.*, 2003; Moon & Davies, 2010; Pyeritz, 2012). Figure 8.10 contains an algorithm for the evaluation of tall stature. Table 8.6 presents the genetic anomaly and inheritance/mutation pattern for select syndromes associated with tall stature.

Marfan and Klinefelter Syndromes are among the leading pathologic causes of genetic tall stature. Marfan Syndrome (MFS) is an autosomal dominant connective tissue disorder (Pyeritz, 2012). Worldwide incidence of MFS is 1 in 5000. In addition to tall, slender stature, classic MFS features include hyperextensible joints, arachnodactyly (long, thin fingers), and kyphoscoliosis (Figure 8.11). In later childhood or adulthood, individuals may experience dislocation of the ocular lens (ectopia lentis) or dissecting aortic aneurysm (Cooke *et al.*, 2011). Other skeletal, ocular, cardiovascular, or pulmonary abnormalities may occur, including muscular and adipose hypoplasia, hernias, dural ectasia (widening of the dural sac surrounding the spinal cord), and renal and hepatic cysts. Table 8.7 contains a summary of the American College of Medical Genetics (ACMG) criteria for diagnosing MFS (Pyeritz, 2012). Because other conditions have presenting symptoms that are very similar to MFS, consultation with a geneticist is strongly recommended.

Klinefelter Syndrome (KS; 47, XXY) occurs in approximately 1 in 500 newborn males and is the most common sex chromosome variation (Figure 8.12) (Sabin, Werther, & Kiess, 2011; Zitelli *et al.*, 2012b). KS clinical features are of-

TABLE 8.5. Genetic/chromosomal Disorders that May Result in Short Stature and Mode of Inheritance.

Genetic Disorder	Genetic Anomaly	Inheritance
Down syndrome	Trisomy 21 (3 copies of chromosome 21)	Sporadic
Turner syndrome	45, X (missing copy of X chromosome)	Sporadic
Prader-Willi	gene 15q11-q13	Sporadic
Skeletal achondroplasia	*FGFR3*	Autosomal dominant

TABLE 8.6. Genetic/chromosomal Disorders that may Result in Tall Stature and Mode of Inheritance.

Genetic Disorder	Genetic Anomaly	Inheritance/Mutation Pattern
Marfan syndrome	FBN1	Autosomal dominant ~25% de novo mutations
Klinefelter syndrome	47, XXY	Sporadic
Sotos syndrome	NSD1	Intragenic
Beckwith-Wiedemann syndrome	Dysregulation of imprinted genes at 11p15.5	Sporadic Autosomal- preferential maternal transmission

ten very subtle, and only about 25% of affected males will receive a diagnosis during childhood. Most men with KS receive the diagnosis during an infertility work-up. The extra copy of the X chromosome causes a number of deleterious changes in the male reproductive tract. Although the mechanisms are not yet well understood, infertility in men with KS seems to be the result of a gradual hyalinization of seminiferous tubules during midpuberty, leading to an abnormally low (< 6 milliliters [mL])) testicular volume, loss of germ cells, and very low or absent sperm counts. Although hormone levels are normal in childhood, puberty is generally delayed. As puberty advances, the testes gradually lose volume, follicle-stimulating hormone (FSH) and leutinizing

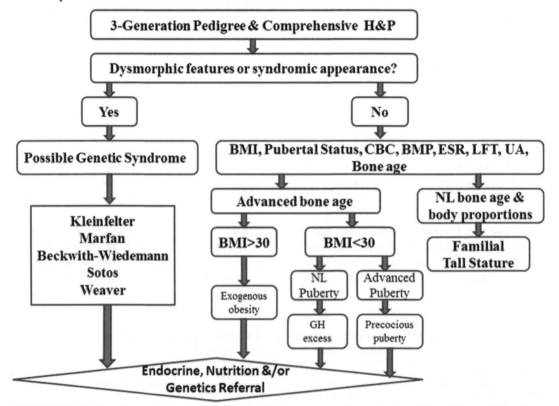

FIGURE 8.10. Systematic evaluation of children with tall stature or growth acceleration. Abbreviations: CBC = Complete blood count, BMI = body mass index, BMP = basic metabolic panel, ESR = erythrocyte sedimentation rate, GH = growth hormone, H&P = history and physical, LFT = liver function test, NL = normal, TSH = thyroid stimulating hormone, UA = urinalysis.

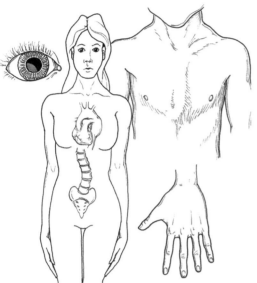

Dislocated ocular lens, tall slender stature, aortic aneurysm, scoliosis, pectus excavatum, arachnodactyly

FIGURE 8.11. Phenotypic features of Marfan syndrome. Source: Pyeritz, 2012 Illustrated by Mark Weber, MS, RN.

hormone (LH) levels rise, and testosterone levels fall. Physical virility in KS is widely variable (Figure 8.13). Sexual dysfunction, linked to low testosterone levels, is not uncommon, but fertility may still be possible because many men with KS may have small areas of focal spermatogenesis. In these men, surgical retrieval of sperm followed by intracytoplasmic sperm injection (ICSI) may be a viable pregnancy option for some couples (Groth, Skakkebaek, Host, Gravholt, & Bojesen, 2013; Sabin *et al.*, 2011; Zitelli *et al.*, 2012b). As with any genetic disorder causing infertility, referral to a genetic counselor or medical geneticist is strongly recommended for a thorough discussion of the risks and implications of potentially passing the genetic mutation on to the next generation. For more details regarding infertility and genetic counseling issues, see the "Prenatal" section in Chapter 5. Other features of KS include scoliosis, which commonly develops during adolescence, and although men with KS have an IQ that is about the same as the general population,

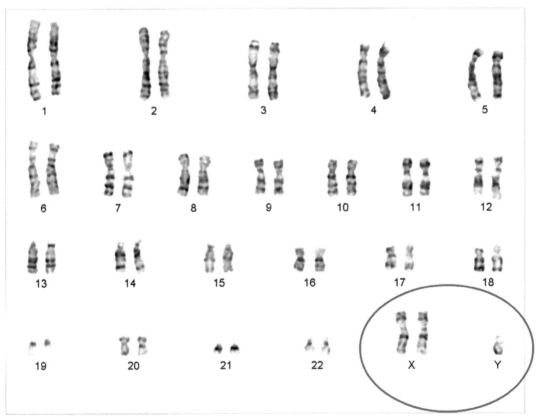

FIGURE 8.12. Karyotype of Klinefelter Syndrome (47, XXY). Obtained from: http://genewikiplus.org/wiki/File:Human_chromosomesXXY01.png.

TABLE 8.7. Diagnostic Criteria for Marfan Syndrome.

In the absence of a family history of MFS, diagnosis is made in one of the following situations:
1. A dilated aortic root (defined as greater than or equal to two standard deviations above the mean for age, sex, and body surface area, i.e., a Z-score of > +2)   AND   ectopia lentis
2. A dilated aortic root   AND   a clearly pathologic mutation in FBN1
3. A dilated aortic root   AND   multiple systemic features
4. Ectopia lentis   AND   mutation in FBN1 previously associated with aortic disease
If there is a positive family history of MFS, then diagnosis is made if any of the following conditions are present:
1. Ectopia lentis (dislocated ocular lens)
2. Multiple systemic features
3. A dilated aortic root

many have problems with language, problem solving, and planning (Sabin *et al.*, 2011; Zitelli *et al.*, 2012b). Boys with KS may also have social and behavioral disorders that warrant evalu-

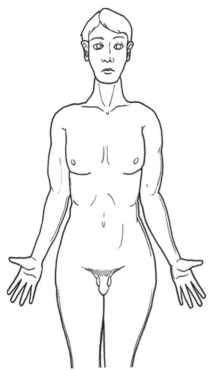

FIGURE 8.13. Phenotypic features of Klinefelter Syndrome (47, XXY). Illustrated by Mark Weber, MS, RN.

ation, psycho-educational testing and screening for learning disabilities, attention-deficit/hyperactivity disorder (AD/HD), and autism spectrum disorders (ASD) (Ross *et al.*, 2012).

8.8. ATYPICALLY DEVELOPING CHILDREN

8.8.1. Principles of Development

Although the terms "growth and development" are often used interchangeably, "growth" refers to highly visible changes (increases) in body size, whereas "development" refers to advances in four defined areas: gross motor skills, fine motor skills, language-cognition, and social-emotional domains (Table 8.8) (Zitelli, McIntire, & Nowalk, 2012a). Development occurs simultaneously with nerve myelination and proceeds in a cephalocaudal (head to toe) and centrifugal (starting from the center and proceeding outward) manner. Therefore, an infant is able to lift his head before pushing up on his wrists or walking. Development in the four domains occurs in a predictable sequence and is assessed through achievement of developmental milestones. Although there may be variation between children in the timing of milestone acquisition, with few exceptions, milestones are achieved sequentially (Hagan *et al.*, 2008).

TABLE 8.8. Developmental Domains and Realm of Acquisition.

Developmental Domain	Realm of Acquisition
Gross motor	Large muscle groups, coordination
Fine motor	Small muscle groups, generally of the hands, eye-hand coordination
Language-cognition	Thinking, memory, learning, language acquisition, development of meaningful symbolic communication and comprehension
Social-emotional	Emotional reactions and interaction with others

8.8.2. Developmental Surveillance and Screening

Inquiring about milestones and evaluating for developmental delays at every well-child visit is referred to as developmental surveillance (American Academy of Pediatrics, 2006). A thorough developmental assessment should be initiated if infants are not meeting their expected milestones, if there is developmental incongruence, or if a parent expresses concerns about their child's development. Several standardized, validated screening tools are available to evaluate developmental delay, including the Ages & Stages Questionnaire (ASQ), the Pediatric Evaluation of Developmental Status (PEDS), and the Child Development Inventories (CDI). All children should be screened with a standardized tool at the 9-, 18- and 24- or 30-month wellchild visits (American Academy of Pediatrics, 2006). An additional autism-specific screening tool, such as the Modified Checklist for Autism in Toddlers (M-CHAT), should be administered at 18 and 24 months (Table 8.9) (Johnson & Myers, 2007). Parental concerns about development, even if routine screening test results are normal, should be taken very seriously and warrant either referral for definitive developmental evaluation or early follow-up. Children who exhibit pre-peech deficits or unusual social interactions should also receive supplemental, comprehensive developmental assessment (Table 8.10) (Armstrong, 2008; Johnson & Myers, 2007; Matson, Fodstad, & Dempsey, 2009).

Historically, the approach to children with developmental delays, especially boys, was "watch-

TABLE 8.9. Recommended Pediatric Developmental and Autism Surveillance and Screening Schedule.

Activity	Frequency
Developmental surveillance	Every well-child or health supervision visit
Developmental screening	9, 18, and 24 or 30 months
Autism-specific screening	18 and 24 months

ful waiting" before referring for developmental evaluation, but this "wait-and-see" attitude is no longer acceptable. Recent research in the area of neuroplasticity has clearly demonstrated that significant improvements in outcomes are possible with early intervention (Reichow, Barton, Boyd, & Hume, 2012). Neuroplasticity refers to the brain's ability to adapt and form new neural networks in response to new environments and novel situations. For centuries, it was hypothesized that the brain was essentially static, and the neural network was fixed in infancy, remaining the same throughout life without the ability to manipulate IQ and/or cognition. Researchers are finding that the brain is highly pliable or "plastic," and although neural tissue is more pliable early in life, neuroplasticity is present throughout the lifespan (Hrvoj-Mihic, Bienvenu, Stefanacci, Muotri, & Semendeferi, 2013). Because of neuroplasticity, early intervention in children with developmental delays and/or ASD results in significant gains in

TABLE 8.10. Prespeech and Social Deficits Possibly Exhibited in Children with Autism Spectrum Disorder (ASD).

Lack of eye contact
Absence of appropriate social smile, laugh
Decrease or absence of pointing at objects of interest (proto-declarative pointing)
Delays in language milestones
Lack of response to own name
Decreased alternating, two-way interactions between parents and child (social/emotional reciprocity)
Poor recognition of mother's, father's, or caregiver's voice
Lack of appropriate warm, joyful expressions
Lack of spontaneous sharing of enjoyments, interests or achievements
Lack of enjoyment of expressions of affection

language, cognitive abilities, adaptive behavior, and social skills, as well as reduced anxiety and aggression (Dawson & Burner, 2011). The earlier the delay is recognized and intervention is begun, optimally before 18 to 30 months of age, the better the outcomes (Reichow *et al.*, 2012; Warren *et al.*, 2011). Intensive intervention using applied behavioral analysis (ABA) techniques is the only therapy shown to be effective in treating children with ID and ASD. Advancements in neurodevelopmental genetics are desperately needed to improve our understanding of biological mechanisms, which in turn offers hope for additional and more effective treatment options.

8.8.3. Neurodevelopmental Genetics

From the time of conception, the nervous system is continually generating and shaping new neural pathways and connections. Any condition that disrupts typical neural development is considered a neurodevelopmental disorder (NDD). NDD phenotypes vary widely between affected individuals and individuals may exhibit no dysmorphology. NDD symptoms commonly evolve over time and impact a number of different functional areas, including cognition, emotions, learning disabilities, language, memory and motor function. The *Diagnostic and Statistical Manuals of Mental Disorders, Fifth Edition* (*DSM-5*) provides evidence-based definitions of the NDDs and includes six neurodevelopmental categories: Intellectual Developmental Disorders, Communication Disorders, Autism Spectrum Disorder, AD/HD, Specific Learning Disorder, and Motor Disorder (American Psychiatric Association, 2013; Rutter, 2011). The *DSM-5* and the *International Statistical Classification of Diseases and Health Related Disorders* (*ICD*) *9* and *10* rely heavily on clustering of symptoms to establish a diagnosis (Rutter, 2011). The challenge for clinicians is that there is significant overlap in symptoms and a wide variability of expression between syndromes and genetic disorders. Categorizing NDDs by etiology or causal pathway is equally challenging. In many cases, the etiology and causal pathways are unknown or multifactorial, having only a common endpoint (Rutter, 2011). There is a great deal of variability in the expression and behavior of individuals who have autism or ID. At the same time, they may have features that cross over with symptoms of other neurocognitive disorders, making precise diagnosis very challenging.

8.8.4. Autism Spectrum Disorders, Intellectual Disabilities, and Genomics

Studies of anatomic and functional brain development have improved scientific understanding of typical and atypical development patterns and plasticity. Individuals with autism generally exhibit anatomic and functional brain differences. Very young children affected with autism demonstrate accelerated brain growth, transient cerebral enlargement, and excess neurons in the prefrontal cortex (Chow *et al.*, 2012; Courchesne *et al.*, 2007; Giedd & Rapoport, 2010). Although children with ID may have macrocephaly or microcephaly, most will have a normal head size so it is important to remember that overall size of the head and brain and number of neurons does not imply a functional or cognitive advantage or disadvantage. Imaging studies done in older autistic children and adults show premature cortical thinning, neuron loss, and absence of enlargement (Chow *et al.*, 2012; Courchesne *et al.*, 2007; Giedd & Rapoport, 2010).

Autistic brain differences are not solely anatomic. Functional and genetic differences are also found. Functional magnetic resonance imaging (fMRI) studies expose differences in the functional regions responsible for socialization, "communication" between functional brain regions, and problems modulating brain activity in response to changes in task (Philip *et al.*, 2012). Abnormalities have also been found in genetic pathways responsible for cell number, neurodevelopment, and cortical lateralization, suggesting that genetic dysregulation in early neurodevelopment is responsible for later behavioral and cognitive deficits (Chow *et al.*, 2012).

Many genes influence the development of ASD and ID. Some are associated with behavioral pathology, and others cause cognitive impairments, but no single gene has been identified that consistently or predictably causes either ASD or ID. In fact, fewer than 25% of ASD cases and 14% of ID or developmental delay cases can be traced to any specific gene (Table 8.11) (Cooper *et al.*, 2011; Devlin & Scherer, 2012; Voineagu, 2012). Some recent discoveries suggest that genes in-

TABLE 8.11. Genetic Architecture in Autism Spectrum Disorders.

Genetic Risk Factor	Percent Contribution	Genes/Syndromes Implicated
ASD-related syndromes	~10%	Fragile X, tuberous sclerosis, phenylketonuria, Rett, Timothy, Potocki-Lupski syndromes
Rare chromosomal anomalies	~5%	Maternal 15q11-q13 duplication, trisomy 21, 45X Turner syndrome, 47XYY, 47XXY
Rare copy number variants	~5%	1q21.1, 3q37-q38, dup7q11.23, 15q11–13dup,15q13.3, 15q24, 16pdel, 16pdup, 16p11.2, 16p13.11del, dup17p12, 17q12del, 22q11.2,
Rare penetrant genes	~5%	*PTCHD1/PTCHD1AS, NRXN1, SHANK1, SHANK2, SHANK3,NLGN3, NLGN4x, NRXN3,CNTNAP2, DPP6*
Single nucleotide polymorphisms	unknown	Chromosome 1, SNP rs1625579 Chromosome 2, SNP rs17662626§ Chromosome 18, SNP rs17512836
Multigenic, intellectual disability and neuropsychiatric disorder genes, genes in common pathways	unknown	Intragenic
Effects of environment on gene expression or protein function, DNA mutation from parental age	unknown	Sporadic Autosomal- preferential maternal transmission

Note. ASD = Autism Spectrum Disorder, del = deletion, dup=duplication SNP = single nucleotide polymorphism, PTCHD = patched homology domain, AS = antisense, NRXN = neurexin, SHANK = SH3 and multiple ankyrin repeat domains, NLGN = neuroligin, CNTNAP = contact in associated protein, DPP = dipeptidyl-peptidase, DNA = deoxyribonucleic acid.

volved with voltage-gated calcium-channel signaling, autoantibodies against neuronal progenitor cells (NPCs), and retinoic acid-related orphan receptor-alpha (RORA) nuclear hormone receptors may be important in regulating cognitive development and function, providing potential new targets for future treatments (Cross-Disorder Group of the Psychiatric Genomics Consortium, 2013; Mazur-Kolecka *et al.*, 2013; Sarachana & Hu, 2013). Novel approaches are being used to locate ASD genes by using genetic and gene expression data to build sophisticated algorithms, such as DAWN (Detecting Association With Networks) to identify ASD gene "hot spots" (Liu *et al.*, 2014). Although progress is being made in identifying the genes associated with ASD, these studies do not account for the effects of multigenic inheritance, genes in common pathways, inherited mutations associated with parental age or the effects of the environment, other nongenomic factors, etc. This is an important distinction, because it is known that the environment affects gene expression and genetic variations affect an individual's response to environmental stress (Mefford, Batshaw, & Hoffman, 2012).

Autism traits are fairly evenly distributed across the general population. Some experts suggest that ASD qualities and "quirks" represent genetic variants, such as single nucleotide polymorphisms (SNPs) or copy number variants (CNVs) and that autism may represent a more extreme manifestation in one or more of the autistic traits that are more commonly found in a population (Hoekstra, Bartels, Cath, & Boomsma, 2008; Ronald & Hoekstra, 2011). If so, then some ASD risk factors and traits may be inherited and heritable, whereas spontaneous, de novo mutations are highly heritable, but not inherited (Ronald & Hoekstra, 2011). There is significant evidence that suggests that ASD is a highly heritable disorder, with risk up to 25 times higher in siblings of probands with ASD (Devlin & Scherer, 2012; Voineagu, 2012). ASD studies conducted in twins show striking heritability; monozygotic twins have concordance rates ranging from 70–95%, whereas dizygotic twins have rates of 6–31% (Ronald & Hoekstra, 2011; Voineagu, 2012). Although twins have high concordance rates, other relatives also demonstrate features of autism. Autism traits are more common in relatives of ASD probands who do not have the disorder, suggesting that some ASD characteristics represent the influence of shared family quirks or idiosyncrasies (Ronald & Hoekstra, 2011).

Areas ripe for further study include why certain individuals develop autism and why others do not. There are significant sex differences. Females are much less likely to develop autism than males, and research consistently reveals that although females may have inherited or acquired an ASD mutation, they are relatively protected from the effects of these mutations. Some possible explanations are that the genes on the X chromosomes may protect her and/or that her sex hormone levels (particularly testosterone) may modulate the impact of the mutation, resulting in a milder phenotype (Werling & Geschwind, 2013). Functional MRIs demonstrate areas of significant similarity in neural signatures between brains of children with ASD and their unaffected siblings, but unaffected siblings display regions of compensation (Kaiser *et al.*, 2010). There are many questions that remain to be answered, including why some children develop compensatory neural "work-arounds," whereas others do not. Research is rapidly expanding in a number of areas, including epigenetics, exploring the impact of micro-deletions and -duplications and mitochondrial mutations (Dhillon, Hellings, & Butler, 2011, Mefford, *et al.*, 2012). Despite the tremendous gains made in understanding the brain differences and etiologies of ASD and ID, little progress has been made in the development of more effective treatment options. Currently, the only options for improving outcomes for individuals with ASD/ID include early and prolonged intervention using applied behavioral analysis techniques and exploiting the principles of neuroplasticity to improve social, language, and cognitive functioning.

8.8.5. Transition to Adult Health Care for Youth with Genetic Disorders

Health care transition is "the purposeful, planned, and timely transition from child and family-centered pediatric health care to patient-centered adult-oriented health care" (Blum *et al.*, 1993). Health care transition planning is a challenge for nurses caring for any adolescent patient, but when care transition planning involves youth with genetic disorders, it can be especially problematic. In the United States, 18% of all youth have a special health care need, representing about 80% of all the funds spent on health

care for children (White, McManus, McAllister, & Cooley, 2012). Health care transition planning involves providing the adolescent and his or her family with the information and tools they will need to become more independent in managing their own health care over time. Youth with genetic conditions often have varying levels of chronic physical, mental, and developmental disabilities that may prevent them from becoming completely independent. The goal with this population is to work toward an increasing level of independence based upon individual strengths and abilities. This section of the chapter provides a general overview of transition issues for youth with genetic disorders and special needs to help clinicians prepare these patients and their families with the skills they will need to achieve independence in making health care decisions as they approach adulthood.

8.8.6. Evolution of Transition Planning

In 2002, the American Academy of Pediatrics, American Academy of Family Physicians, and other physician groups released a document designed to give physicians providing care to youth with special health care needs the knowledge and skills to facilitate the transition from pediatric to adult health care (A consensus statement on health care transitions for young adults with special health care needs, 2002). The overall goal was to maximize independent functioning while providing medically and developmentally appropriate care and maintaining coordination of services between providers. Key first steps in promoting successful transition include the following: (1) Identify appropriate health care professionals to care for the adolescent with special needs; (2) Identify core knowledge and skills needed to provide transitional care; (3) Prepare and maintain portable and accessible medical records; (4) Create a written health care transition plan with the patient and family by age 14 years; (5) Use the same guidelines for care for all patients, recognizing that youth with special health care needs may require more resources and services; and (6) Ensure that young people with special health care needs receive adequate and affordable health insurance coverage.

Two national surveys of children with special health care needs were conducted in 2005 to

2006 and 2009 to 2010 following the implementation of these guidelines to assess whether youth with special health care needs were receiving the support and resources they needed to make an adequate transition (U.S. Department of Health and Human Services, 2008, 2012). Sadly, the surveys revealed that only about 40% received needed support and resources. Those least likely to receive needed transition support were adolescents from low income families, those from racial or ethnic minority groups, and those without an identified medical home.

In 2011, the physician groups that published the 2002 transition consensus statement published another report outlining a framework for transition support to help health care providers put transition plans into practice (Cooley & Sagerman, 2011). One of the major constructs of the second consensus statement is that adolescents should be allowed to "rehearse" the transition from pediatric care to adult models of care before the actual transition to an adult practice. Youth without cognitive impairments should be allowed to "rehearse" without the parents in the examination room, unless written permission is obtained explicitly stating that parents will remain in the examination room.

8.8.7. Special Considerations for Youth with Genetic Conditions

There are many issues to consider when planning care transitions for families of youth with genetic conditions. Genetic disorders such as DS, for example, affect multiple body systems, requiring complex medical and preventive management and often necessitating longer appointment times and a variety of different specialists. Adults with DS may need a general practitioner, a cardiologist, an ophthalmologist, an endocrinologist, and an ear, nose, and throat specialist. Cognitive capacity varies widely depending on the genetic disorder or syndrome and may impact the young adult's ability to comprehend the impact of the disease, medications, and other care needed to maintain health. Adults with phenylketonuria (PKU) may understand their disease and the need for a special diet and the rationale for following it, but youth with severe autism or certain chromosome anomalies may not have the mental ability, communication skills, or self-care skills needed

to manage complex medical regimens or even routine tasks of daily living. Youth with genetic conditions or syndromes that affect their cognitive functioning often need a formal guardian assigned before turning age 18. Nurses should address guardianship and encourage parents to complete the legal steps necessary to secure guardianship by the time the youth reaches age 18.

It may be emotionally difficult for youth with genetic conditions to part with their pediatric care providers and specialists, many of whom share close relationships with them. There may be few qualified adult providers with adequate knowledge of a particular genetic condition, particularly for rare conditions such as Gaucher disease or other metabolic conditions. Transfer of pediatric records to adult care providers may also be problematic, although recent installation of electronic medical records systems in many institutions/offices has been helpful. For this reason, the transition must be planned well in advance of the transfer to adult care. In some instances, adults with complex needs have remained with pediatric health care providers well after the traditional age of transition.

The financial burden of caring for a family member with complex medical needs is significant. The high cost of medications, mobility equipment, and therapies coupled with a lack of insurance or limited community resources causes hardship for many adolescents as they transition to adulthood and support for parents of children with disabilities may be far from optimal as well. Youth with disabilities may have difficulty finding gainful employment and may not be able to afford independent living. Group homes and supervised living options may be limited, especially in rural areas. These young adults may be partially or completely dependent on others to provide their medical, physical, and psychosocial care. Some require guardianship and advocacy for life. For individuals with cognitive disabilities, many facets of adult life will require assistance, including transportation to appointments and help with insurance, billing, and financial issues, and obtaining medication refills. Because of these complexities, consultation with an estate planner who specializes in special needs estate planning may be of significant benefit to families. Special needs estate planners can help families navigate the world of guardianship, special needs trusts, available housing and health care options, disability laws, benefits, and other special health care considerations for transition.

8.9. THE SIX CORE ELEMENTS OF HEALTH CARE TRANSITION

In order to help health care providers improve transition of care in their practices, a federally funded organization called the National Health Care Transition Center (NHCTC) has developed a model called the Six Core Elements of Health Care Transition (National Healthcare Transition Center, n.d.). These are separate but related guidelines for pediatric and adult health care settings (Table 8.12).

8.10. USING TRANSITION TOOLS AND CHECKLISTS

Although some advocate planning for transitions at the age of diagnosis, most agree that early adolescence (12 to 14 years of age) is a feasible time to begin transition planning. Early preparation allows more time for the youth to learn necessary skills for adulthood. Parents also benefit from this additional time as they consider issues such as finding adult health care providers, appropriate housing, and obtaining guardianship, if needed. Progress toward goals and skills may be documented and shared with adult providers.

Many transition tools and checklists are available to help nurses assess the strengths and

TABLE 8.12. Six Core Elements of Health Care Transition from the National Health Care Transition Center.

Pediatric Health Care Setting	Adult Health Care Setting
1. Transition Policy • Develop a practice health care transition policy and share with providers, staff, youth, and families • Educate all staff about HCT best practices *Sample Policies:* *Washington, DC Learning Collaborative* *Denver, CO Learning Collaborative* *Boston, MA Learning Collaborative*	**1. Young Adult Privacy and Consent Policy** • Develop a practice young adult privacy and consent policy; share with providers, staff, patients, families • Educate all staff about privacy and consent practices *Sample Policies:* *Washington, DC Learning Collaborative*
2. Transitioning Youth Registry • Identify transitioning youth (current/future) and enroll in a transition registry; monitor all preparation, planning and outcomes (e.g., coordination of care) *Sample Registries:* *Washington, DC Learning Collaborative* *Boston, MA Learning collaborative*	**2. Young Adult Patient Registry** • Identify/enroll young adults in a practice registry; indicate levels of complexity; monitor adaptation to young adult model of care; note health/wellness status *Sample Registries:* *Washington, DC Learning Collaborative*
3. Transition Preparation • Assess and track all readiness for adult health care with youth and families • Use the Transition Readiness Assessment (youth, family) to address gaps in preparation, knowledge, and skills *Sample Readiness Assessment:* *Washington DC Learning Collaborative—Youth* *Washington, DC Learning Collaborative—Parent* *Denver, CO Learning Collaborative—Youth/Parent* *Minnesota Learning Community—(EHR example)* *Wisconsin Learning Community—Youth* *Wisconsin Learning Community—Parent* *Boston Learning Collaborative—Youth/Parent—* *　English and Spanish*	**3. Transition Preparation** • Discuss young adult model of health care (see definition); explain how to use the primary care practice including all access options • Use/continue to use the Transition Readiness Assessment (youth, family) to address gaps in knowledge/skills

(continued)

TABLE 8.12 (continued). Six Core Elements of Health Care Transition from the National Health Care Transition Center.

Pediatric Health Care Setting	Adult Health Care Setting
4. Transition Planning • Address all health care transition needs/gaps setting goals together with youth and family • Use the: 　—Health Care Transition (HCT) Action Plans: Action Plan Example One / Example Two 　—Portable Medical Summary 　—Emergency Care Plan (if needed) • Name and notify adult primary care practice of youth's pending transfer of care date (one year out) and arrange for individualized introduction *Sample Medical Summaries:* *Washington, DC Learning Collaborative*	**4. Transition Preparation** • Discuss young adult model of health care (see definition); explain how to use the primary care practice including all access options • Use/continue to use the Transition Readiness Assessment (youth, family) to address gaps in knowledge/skills
5. Transition and Transfer of Care Transfer from pediatric to new adult care location: • Assure direct communication with adult Primary Care Provider (PCP) and team (email, phone, in person "handshake") • Use the tool—Transfer of Care Checklist (pediatric, young adult) • Send a "Transition Package" containing a transfer letter and items named above and in the Transfer of Care Checklist • Initiate or coordinate specialty transitions as appropriate • Transition to young adult model of care in same location: See Core Elements 3, 4, and 5 in the right-hand column *Sample Transfer letters:* *Washington, DC Learning Collaborative*	**5. Transition and Transfer of Care** Transfer from pediatric to new adult care location: • Review Transfer of Care Checklist (pediatric, young adult) sent in the "Transition Package" to prepare for initial visits • Talk with and receive communications from pediatric PCP/team (email, phone, in person "handshake") • Provide office visit/encounters for transitioning young adults and continue with transition preparation and planning as needed • Transition to young adult model of care in same location: • Clarify PCP and coordinator of care contacts for young adult patient; implement Core Elements 3 and 4 as indicated; assist on-going specialty care transfers
6. Transition Completion • Pediatric/team are a resource for each transferred patient and their adult PCP/team following care transfer. Pediatric PCP/team makes contact with adult PCP/team ~3 months posttransfer to ensure success and continuity of care • Transition/transfer is declared complete	**6. Transition Completion** • Consult with pediatric PCP/team as needed; each young adult is integrated using a young adult model of care; the adult practice declares successful and complete HCT • Continue forward with a young adult model of care and appropriate care planning for all patients

Used by permission, available at http://www.gottransition.org/6-core-Elements.

weaknesses of their adolescent patients as they go through the transition process. These may be general tools used to assess any youth with special health care needs, or a tool created specifically for youth with a particular genetic disorder. The tools are used at different points in time to determine a patient's skills and abilities and to help set future goals.

Checklists provide a consistent way to consider the special needs of youth with genetic conditions on their journey to adulthood. These checklists commonly cover a number of different categories assessing the adolescent's overall functional level. Table 8.13 contains some sample behaviors for gauging functional level. For many children with genetic conditions and developmental disabilities, developing competencies in all of these areas may take a lot of time and many attempts to master.

Driving a car is a privilege that many adoles-

TABLE 8.13. Sample Categories for Assessing Functional Level of Adolescents with Genetic Conditions.

1. Knowledge of genetic condition
2. Medication
   - Administration
   - Safety
   - Refill procedures
3. Equipment/skills required for healthy, independent living:
   - Making appointments
   - Coordinating transportation to/from appointments
   - Accessing insurance, Medicaid, Medicare, etc.
4. Knowledge of wellness behaviors:
   - Proper diet
   - Exercise
   - Sleep
   - Birth control
   - Menstrual cycles
5. Activities of Daily Living:
   - Setting an alarm clock
   - Brushing/flossing teeth
   - Choosing attire appropriate for work and weather conditions
   - Dressing oneself
   - Preparing a "grocery" list
   - Cooking/preparing meals
   - Feeding oneself
   - Managing menstrual cycles
   - Navigating transportation to/from work
   - Safety procedures for going out alone
   - How/when to dial 911 for emergencies
6. Managing personal affairs:
   - Making a budget, paying bills, saving money, managing personal finances
   - Guardianship
   - Citizenship
   - Voting
   - Religious observances
   - Sports/recreation

cents strive to achieve. Many tasks occur simultaneously when driving a car. Perhaps the most important skill required to drive is the ability to maintain focus and avoid becoming distracted. Although many adolescents can learn to drive during a relatively quick driver's education course, not everyone is able to learn this task quickly. One adolescent with DS who successfully learned to drive first started by driving a

battery operated "Barbie Car" as a young child. She progressed to driving a golf cart with her father sitting next to her. As she moved to driving a regular car, she started on uncrowded rural roads and parking lots, later advancing to more complicated driving situations. In this way, the task was broken down into small, manageable tasks in which she could be successful while gaining confidence and eventual mastery. The ability to drive is a major stepping stone to independence.

Although it is difficult to predict what level of independence an adolescent with a genetic condition can achieve, he or she should be provided with the skills to maximize their level of autonomy in the transition to adulthood. Tools and checklists help nurses address important issues to ensure consistency of care. Nurses and clinicians in all settings need to be familiar with transition issues so that they can help youth with special needs achieve the greatest possible independence.

8.11. SUMMARY

Growth and development are predictable and orderly, allowing for screening and detection of abnormalities. A number of factors can interfere with typical growth and development, including a number of genetic disorders. A thorough history and physical are essential when monitoring and evaluating a child with dysmorphic features or alterations in growth or development. Major or minor features of genetic syndromes, anomalies of growth, and atypical development should raise suspicion of a specific genetic condition. Although no single physical feature defines genetic syndromes affecting growth, classic phenotypes can help narrow down the diagnosis. Using a systematic approach to assessment provides additional diagnostic information and a specific, focused evaluation.

Children with altered development or whose parents are concerned about their development warrant a diagnostic developmental assessment and prompt, early intervention when indicated. The *DSM-5* delineates, defines, and categorizes the neurodevelopmental disorders. Genetics and brain mapping have led to significant gains in the understanding of ASD and other NDDs. The hope is that these findings will eventually lead to new and improved treatments or a cure for

TABLE 8.14. Online Pediatric Genetic/genomic Resources.

Resource Title	Brief Description	Link
Pediatric On call	Approach to a Dysmorphic Child	http://www.pediatriconcall.com/fordoctor/Conference_abstracts/NEUROGENETICSDEL/Dysmor.asp
GeneReviews	Illustrated Glossary	http://www.ncbi.nlm.nih.gov/books/NBK5191/#IX-D
National Human Genome Research Institute	Learning about velo-cardio-facial syndrome	http://www.genome.gov/25521139
National Institutes of Health, National Institute of Child Health & Development	What are the signs and symptoms of fragile X syndrome?	http://www.nichd.nih.gov/publications/pubs/fragileX/sub8.cfm)
National Institute of Neurological Disorders and Stroke	NIH, Neurofibromatosis Information Page	http://www.ninds.nih.gov/disorders/neurofibromatosis/neurofibromatosis.htm
National Library of Medicine, MedLine Plus	Trisomy 13	http://www.nlm.nih.gov/medlineplus/ency/article/001660.htm
The National Health Care Transition Center	Got Transition?	http://www.gottransition.org/home
National Center for Medical Home Implementation	Children and Youth with Special Health Care Needs.	http://www.medicalhomeinfo.org/how/care_delivery/cyshcn.aspx
Shriner's Hospital for Children, Lexington, KY	Journey to Adulthood: A Transition Travel Guide.	http://chfs.ky.gov/NR/rdonlyres/F55ED346-CEE9-42EF-A1C5-1B3C339C18D9/0/TransitionBookDecember122011Final100pages.pdf

these conditions. Until this is realized, clinicians are in a position to identify children with genetic conditions early and coordinate evaluations and interventions to improve outcomes. As the child matures, nurse clinicians are key to guiding the adolescent and young adult in their transition into adulthood and maximizing independence. Tools and checklists are available to assist in documenting the transition process and help to provide consistency of care over time.

A special thank you to Dr. Jill Emerick and Dr. Lowry Shropshire for their editorial review and comments.

8.12. REFERENCES

Admou, B., Essaadouni, L., Krati, K., Zaher, K., Sbi-hi, M., Chabaa, L., . . . & Alaoui-Yazidi, A. (2012). Atypical celiac disease: from recognizing to managing. *Gastroenterol Res Pract, 2012*, 637187. doi: 10.1155/2012/637187

American Academy of Pediatrics. (2006). Identifying infants and young children with developmental disorders in the medical home: an algorithm for developmental surveillance and screening. *Pediatrics, 118*(1), 405–420. doi: 118/1/405 [pii] 10.1542/peds.2006-1231

American Psychiatric Association. (2013). Neurodevelopmental disorders, *Diagnostic and statistical manual of mental disorders, Fifth Edition*. Arlington, VA: American Psychiatric Association.

Armstrong, C. (2008). AAP Releases Guidelines on identification of children with Autism Spectrum Disorders. *American Family Physician, 78*(11), 1301–1305.

Aypar, E., Yildirim, M. S., Sert, A., Ciftci, I., & Odabas, D. (2011). A girl with metopic synostosis and trisomy 13 mosaicism: case report and review of the literature. *Am J Med Genet A, 155A*(3), 638–641. doi: 10.1002/ajmg.a.33839

Blum, R. W., Garell, D., Hodgman, C. H., Jorissen, T. W., Okinow, N. A., Orr, D. P., & Slap, G. B. (1993). Transition from child-centered to adult health-care systems for adolescents with chronic conditions. A position paper of the Society for Adolescent Medicine. *Journal of Adolescent Health, 14*(7), 570–576. doi: 1054-139X(93)90143-D [pii]

CdLS Foundation. (2010). Treatment Protocols. Retrieved Oct 26, 2012, from http://www.cdlsusa.org/professional-education/treatment-protocols.htm

Centers for Disease Control and Prevention. (2013). Birth Defects: Data & Statistics in the United States.

Centers for Disease Control and Prevention. (May 30, 2000). CDC Growth Charts: United States. Retrieved Oct 5, 2012, from http://www.cdc.gov/growthcharts/clinical_charts.htm

Chow, M. L., Pramparo, T., Winn, M. E., Barnes, C. C., Li, H. R., Weiss, L., . . . & Courchesne, E. (2012). Age-dependent brain gene expression and copy number anomalies in autism suggest distinct pathological processes at young versus mature ages. *PLoS Genet, 8*(3), e1002592. doi: 10.1371/journal. pgen.1002592 PGENETICS-D-11-02067 [pii]

Consensus statement on health care transitions for young adults with special health care needs. (2002). *Pediatrics, 110*(6 Pt 2), 1304–1306.

Cooke, D. W., Divall, S. A., & Radovick, S. (2011). Normal and aberrant Growth. In S. Melmed, K. S. Polonsky, P. R. Larsen, & H. M. Kronenberg (Eds.), *Williams textbook of endocrinology* (12th ed.). Philadelphia, PA: Elsevier-Saunders.

Cooley, W. C., & Sagerman, P. J. (2011). Supporting the health care transition from adolescence to adulthood in the medical home. *Pediatrics, 128*(1), 182–200. doi: 10.1542/peds.2011-0969 peds.2011-0969 [pii]

Cooper, G. M., Coe, B. P., Girirajan, S., Rosenfeld, J. A., Vu, T. H., Baker, C., . . . & Eichler, E. E. (2011). A copy number variation morbidity map of developmental delay. *Nature Genetics, 43*(9), 838–846. doi: 10.1038/ng.909 ng.909 [pii]

Courchesne, E., Pierce, K., Schumann, C. M., Redcay, E., Buckwalter, J. A., Kennedy, D. P., & Morgan, J. (2007). Mapping early brain development in autism. *Neuron, 56*(2), 399–413. doi: S0896-6273(07)00777-5 [pii] 10.1016/j.neuron.2007.10.016

Cross-Disorder Group of the Psychiatric Genomics Consortium. (2013). Identification of risk loci with shared effects on five major psychiatric disorders: a genome-wide analysis. *Lancet*. doi: S0140-6736(12)62129-1 [pii] 10.1016/S0140-6736(12)62129-1

Davidson, M. A. (2008). Primary care for children and adolescents with Down syndrome. *Pediatric Clinics of North America, 55*(5), 1099–1111, xi. doi: 10.1016/j.pcl.2008.07.001 S0031-3955(08)00151-X [pii]

Dawson, G., & Burner, K. (2011). Behavioral interventions in children and adolescents with autism spectrum disorder: a review of recent findings. *Current Opinion in Pediatrics, 23*(6), 616–620. doi: 10.1097/MOP.0b013e32834cf082

Devlin, B., & Scherer, S. W. (2012). Genetic architecture in autism spectrum disorder. *Current Opinion in Genetics and Development, 22*(3), 229–237. doi: 10.1016/j.gde.2012.03.002 S0959-437X(12)00036-6 [pii]

Douglas, J., Hanks, S., Temple, I. K., Davies, S., Murray, A., Upadhyaya, M., . . . & Rahman, N. (2003). NSD1 mutations are the major cause of Sotos syndrome and occur in some cases of Weaver syndrome but are rare in other overgrowth phenotypes. *Am J Hum Genet, 72*(1), 132–143. doi: S0002-9297(07)60511-4 [pii]

Erkula, G., Jones, K. B., Sponseller, P. D., Dietz, H. C., & Pyeritz, R. E. (2002). Growth and maturation in Marfan syndrome. *American Journal of Medical Genetics, 109*(2), 100115. doi: 10.1002/ajmg.10312

Friedman, J. M. (2013). Neurofibromatosis 1. doi: NBK1109 [bookaccession]

Gawlik, A., Gawlik, T., Augustyn, M., Woska, W., & Malecka-Tendera, E. (2006). Validation of growth charts for girls with Turner syndrome. *International Journal of Clinical Practice, 60*(2), 150–155. doi: IJCP633 [pii] 10.1111/j.1742-1241.2005.00633.x

Giedd, J. N., & Rapoport, J. L. (2010). Structural MRI of pediatric brain development: what have we learned and where are we going? *Neuron, 67*(5), 728–734. doi: 10.1016/j.neuron.2010.08.040 S0896-6273(10)00683-5 [pii]

Greco, K.E., Tinley, S., & Seibert, D.C. (2012). *Essential Genetic and Genomic Competencies for Nurses with Graduate Degrees.* Silver Spring, MD: American Nurses Association and International Society of Nurses in Genetics.

Groth, K. A., Skakkebaek, A., Host, C., Gravholt, C. H., & Bojesen, A. (2013). Clinical review: Klinefelter syndrome—A clinical update. *J Clin Endocrinol Metab, 98*(1), 20–30. doi: 10.1210/jc.2012-2382 jc.2012-2382 [pii]

Grummer-Strawn, Laurence M., Reinold, Christopher M., Krebs, Nancy Funnemark, National Center for Chronic Disease Prevention and Health Promotion (U.S.), & Centers for Disease Control and Prevention (U.S.). (2010). *Use of World Health Organization and CDC growth charts for children aged 0–59 months in the United States.* Atlanta, GA: Dept. of Health and Human Services, Centers for Disease Control and Prevention.

Gupta, N., & Kabra, M. (2007). Approach to a dysmorphic child. *Pediatric Oncall (Supp 2), 4.* Retrieved from http://www.pediatriconcall.com/fordoctor/Conference_abstracts/NEUROGENETICSDEL/Dysmor.asp

Hagan, Joseph F., Shaw, Judith S., & Duncan, Paula M. (2008). *Bright futures: Guidelines for health supervision of infants, children, and adolescents* (3rd ed.). Elk Grove Village, IL: American Academy of Pediatrics.

Hoekstra, R. A., Bartels, M., Cath, D. C., & Boomsma, D. I. (2008). Factor structure, reliability and criterion validity of the Autism-Spectrum Quotient (AQ): a study in Dutch population and patient groups. *Journal of Autism and Developmental Disorders, 38*(8), 1555–1566. doi: 10.1007/s10803-008-0538-x

Hong, D. S., & Reiss, A. L. (2012). Cognition and behavior in Turner syndrome: a brief review. *Pediatr Endocrinol Rev, 9 Suppl 2*, 710–712.

Hoover-Fong, J. E., McGready, J., Schulze, K. J., Barnes, H., & Scott, C. I. (2007). Weight for age charts for children with achondroplasia. *Am J Med Genet A, 143A*(19), 2227–2235. doi: 10.1002/ajmg.a.31873

Hrvoj-Mihic, B., Bienvenu, T., Stefanacci, L., Muotri, A. R., & Semendeferi, K. (2013). Evolution, development, and plasticity of the human brain: from molecules to bones. *Front Hum Neurosci, 7*, 707. doi: 10.3389/fnhum.2013.00707

Human Genome Project. (2012). Human Genome Project Information Archive. from http://web.ornl.gov/sci/techresources/Human_Genome/glossary.shtml

Johnson, C. P., & Myers, S. M. (2007). Identification and evaluation of children with autism spectrum disorders. *Pediatrics, 120*(5), 1183–1215. doi: peds.2007-2361 [pii] 10.1542/peds.2007-2361

Kalb, R., Neveling, K., Nanda, I., Schindler, D., & Hoehn, H. (2006). Fanconi anemia: Causes and consequences of genetic instability. *Genome Dyn, 1*, 218–242. doi: 92510 [pii] 10.1159/000092510

Karimi, M., Haghpanah, S., Taher, A. T., & Cappellini, M. D. (2012). beta-Thalassemia: New therapeutic modalities, genetics, complications, and quality of life. *Anemia, 2012*, 902067. doi: 10.1155/2012/902067

Lam, W. F., Hau, W. L., & Lam, T. S. (2002). Evaluation of referrals for genetic investigation of short stature in Hong Kong. *Chinese Medical Journal, 115*(4), 607–611.

Liu, L., Lei, J., Sanders, S. J., Willsey, A. J., Kou, Y., Cicek, A. E., . . . & Roeder, K. (2014). DAWN: a framework to identify autism genes and subnetworks using gene expression and genetics. *Molecular autism, 5*(1), 22.

Mainardi, P. C., Pastore, G., Castronovo, C., Godi, M., Guala, A., Tamiazzo, S., . . . & Bricarelli, F. D. (2006). The natural history of Cri du Chat Syndrome. A report from the Italian Register. *Eur J Med Genet, 49*(5), 363–383. doi: S1769-7212(05)00294-6 [pii] 10.1016/j.ejmg.2005.12.004

Martin, N. D., Smith, W. R., Cole, T. J., & Preece, M. A. (2007). New height, weight and head circumference charts for British children with Williams syndrome. *Archives of Disease in Childhood, 92*(7), 598-601. doi: adc.2006.107946 [pii] 10.1136/adc.2006.107946

Matson, J. L., Fodstad, J. C., & Dempsey, T. (2009). What symptoms predict the diagnosis of autism or PDD-NOS in infants and toddlers with developmental delays using the Baby and Infant Screen for aUtIsm Traits. *Dev Neurorehabil, 12*(6), 381–388. doi: 10.3109/17518420903029501

Mazur-Kolecka, B., Cohen, I. L., Gonzalez, M., Jenkins, E. C., Kaczmarski, W., Brown, W. T., . . . & Frackowiak, J. (2013). Autoantibodies against neuronal progenitors in sera from children with autism. *Brain Dev*. doi: 10.1016/j.braindev.2013.04.015

McDonald-McGinn, D. M., Emanuel, B. S., & Zackai, E. H. (2013). 22q11.2 Deletion syndrome. doi: NBK1523 [bookaccession]

Mefford, H. C., Batshaw, M. L., & Hoffman, E. P. (2012). Genomics, intellectual disability, and autism. *New England Journal of Medicine, 366*(8), 733–743. doi: 10.1056/NEJMra1114194

Megarbane, A., Ravel, A., Mircher, C., Sturtz, F., Grat-

tau, Y., Rethore, M. O., . . . & Mobley, W. C. (2009). The 50th anniversary of the discovery of trisomy 21: the past, present, and future of research and treatment of Down syndrome. *Genet Med, 11*(9), 611–616. doi: 10.1097/GIM.0b013e3181b2e34c

Moon, RJ, & Davies, JH. (2010). Evaluation of tall stature. *Pediatrics and Child Health, 20*(1), 43–45.

Myrelid, A., Gustafsson, J., Ollars, B., & Anneren, G. (2002). Growth charts for Down's syndrome from birth to 18 years of age. *Archives of Disease in Childhood, 87*(2), 97–103.

National Healthcare Transition Center. (n.d.). Six Core Elements of Health Care Transition (HCT). Retrieved March 29, 2013, from http://www.gottransition.org/6-core-elements

Nwosu, B. U., & Lee, M. M. (2008). Evaluation of short and tall stature in children. *American Family Physician, 78*(5), 597–604.

Papadimitriou, A., Douros, K., Papadimitriou, D. T., Kleanthous, K., Karapanou, O., & Fretzayas, A. (2012). Characteristics of the short children referred to an academic paediatric endocrine clinic in Greece. *Journal of Paediatrics and Child Health, 48*(3), 263–267. doi: 10.1111/j.1440-1754.2011.02256.x

Philip, R. C., Dauvermann, M. R., Whalley, H. C., Baynham, K., Lawrie, S. M., & Stanfield, A. C. (2012). A systematic review and meta-analysis of the fMRI investigation of autism spectrum disorders. *Neuroscience and Biobehavioral Reviews, 36*(2), 901–942. doi: 10.1016/j.neubiorev.2011.10.008 S0149-7634(11)00201-6 [pii]

Pyeritz, R. E. (2012). Evaluation of the adolescent or adult with some features of Marfan syndrome. *Genet Med, 14*(1), 171–177. doi: 10.1038/gim.2011.48 gim201148 [pii]

Reardon, W., & Donnai, D. (2007). Dysmorphology demystified. *Archives of Disease in Childhood. Fetal and Neonatal Edition, 92*(3), F225-229. doi: 92/3/F225 [pii] 10.1136/adc.2006.110619

Reichow, B., Barton, E. E., Boyd, B. A., & Hume, K. (2012). Early intensive behavioral intervention (EIBI) for young children with autism spectrum disorders (ASD). *Cochrane Database Syst Rev, 10*, CD009260. doi: 10.1002/14651858.CD009260.pub2

Ronald, A., & Hoekstra, R. A. (2011). Autism spectrum disorders and autistic traits: A decade of new twin studies. *Am J Med Genet B Neuropsychiatr Genet, 156B*(3), 255–274. doi: 10.1002/ajmg.b.31159

Rosenbloom, S. T., & Butler, M. G. (2012). Development and implementation of electronic growth charts for infants with Prader-Willi syndrome. *Am J Med Genet A, 158A*(11), 2743–2749. doi: 10.1002/ajmg.a.35581

Rosenbloom, S. T., McGregor, T. L., Chen, Q., An, A. Q., Hsu, S., & Dupont, W. D. (2010). Specialized pediatric growth charts for electronic health record systems: The example of Down syndrome. *AMIA Annu Symp Proc, 2010*, 687–691.

Ross, J. L., Roeltgen, D. P., Kushner, H., Zinn, A. R., Reiss, A., Bardsley, M. Z., . . . & Tartaglia, N. (2012). Behavioral and social phenotypes in boys with 47,XYY syndrome or 47,XXY Klinefelter syndrome. *Pediatrics, 129*(4), 769–778. doi: peds.2011-0719 [pii] 10.1542/peds.2011–0719

Rubinstein-Taybi Society. (n.d.). Height and weight charts for children with RTS. Retrieved Oct 26, 2012, from http://www.rubinstein-taybi.org/medical.html

Rutter, M. (2011). Research review: Child psychiatric diagnosis and classification: concepts, findings, challenges and potential. *Journal of Child Psychology and Psychiatry and Allied Disciplines, 52*(6), 647–660. doi: 10.1111/j.1469-7610.2011.02367.x

Sabin, M. A., Werther, G. A., & Kiess, W. (2011). Genetics of obesity and overgrowth syndromes. *Best Pract Res Clin Endocrinol Metab, 25*(1), 207–220. doi: S1521-690X(10)00125-9 [pii] 10.1016/j.beem.2010.09.010

Sarachana, T., & Hu, V. W. (2013). Genome-wide identification of transcriptional targets of RORA reveals direct regulation of multiple genes associated with autism spectrum disorder. *Mol Autism, 4*(1), 14. doi: 10.1186/2040-2392-4-14

Seaver, L. H., & Irons, M. (2009). ACMG practice guideline: genetic evaluation of short stature. *Genet Med, 11*(6), 465–470. doi: 10.1097/GIM.0b013e3181a7e8f8

Skirton, H., & Patch, C. . (2002). *Genetics for healthcare professionals: A lifestyle approach.* Oxford, U.K: BIOS.Scientific Publishers Limited.

Smithson, S. F., & Winter, R. M. (2004). Diagnosis in dysmorphology: clues from the skin. *Br J Dermatol, 151*(5), 953–960. doi: 10.1111/j.1365-2133.2004.06266.x

U.S. Department of Health and Human Services, Health Resources and Services Administration, Maternal and Child Health Bureau. (2008). The national survey of children with special health care needs chartbook 2005–2006. Retrieved March 29, 2013, from http://mchb.hrsa.gov/cshcn05/

U.S. Department of Health and Human Services, Health Resources and Services Administration, Maternal and Child Health Bureau. (2012). Findings from the 2009-2010 national survey of children with special health care needs. Retrieved March 29, 2013, from http://mchb.hrsa.gov/researchdata/mchirc/dataspeak/pastevent/january2012/index.html

United States National Library of Medicine. (2012a). Down Syndrome. Retrieved Nov. 12, 2013, from http://ghr.nlm.nih.gov/condition/down-syndrome

United States National Library of Medicine. (2012b). Treacher Collins Syndrome. Retrieved Nov. 12, 2013, from http://ghr.nlm.nih.gov/condition/treacher-collins-syndrome

United States National Library of Medicine. (2013). Stickler Syndrome.Retrieved Nov. 12, 2013, from http://ghr.nlm.nih.gov/condition/stickler-syndrome

Van Gameren-Oosterom, H. B., Van Dommelen, P., Oudesluys-Murphy, A. M., Buitendijk, S. E., Van Buuren, S., & Van Wouwe, J. P. (2012). Healthy growth in children with Down syndrome. *PLoS One, 7*(2), e31079. doi: 10.1371/journal.pone.0031079 PONE-D-11-18958 [pii]

Voineagu, I. (2012). Gene expression studies in autism: moving from the genome to the transcriptome and beyond. *Neurobiology of Disease, 45*(1), 69–75. doi: S0969-9961(11)00253-1 [pii] 10.1016/j.nbd.2011.07.017

Warren, Z., McPheeters, M. L., Sathe, N., Foss-Feig, J. H., Glasser, A., & Veenstra-Vanderweele, J. (2011). A systematic review of early intensive intervention for autism spectrum disorders. *Pediatrics, 127*(5), e1303–1311. doi: peds.2011-0426 [pii] 10.1542/peds.2011-0426

Werling, D. M., & Geschwind, D. H. (2013). Sex differences in autism spectrum disorders. *Current Opinion in Neurology, 26*(2), 146–153. doi: 10.1097/WCO.0b013e32835ee548

White, P. H., McManus, M. A., McAllister, J. W., & Cooley, W. C. (2012). A primary care quality improvement approach to health care transition. *Pediatric Annals, 41*(5), e1-7. doi: 10.3928/00904481-20120426-07

World Health Organization. (2012). Congenital anomalies fact sheet. Retrieved April 20, 2013, from http://www.who.int/mediacentre/factsheets/fs370/en/

Zhong, Q., & Layman, L. C. (2012). Genetic considerations in the patient with Turner syndrome-45,X with or without mosaicism. *Fertility and Sterility, 98*(4), 775–779. doi: 10.1016/j.fertnstert.2012.08.021 S0015-0282(12)02073-0 [pii]

Zitelli, BJ, McIntire, SC, & Nowalk, AJ. (2012a). Developmental-behavioral pediatrics. *Atlas of pediatric physical diagnosis* (6th ed., pp. 79–109). Philadelphia, PA: Saunders.

Zitelli, BJ, McIntire, SC, & Nowalk, AJ. (2012b). Genetic Disorders and Dysmorphic Conditions. *Atlas of pediatric physical diagnosis* (6th ed., pp. 1–44). Philadelphia, PA: Saunders.

Chapter 9

Aging and Genomics: Perspectives for the Graduate Level Nurse

DEBRA L. SCHUTTE, Ph.D RN

Objectives:

- Discuss the genomics of aging and its significance for health care practice.
- Review the current scientific trends related to the aging process.
- Explain the epidemiology of aging and its impact on disease development.
- Present the role of the advance practice nurse in the care of an aging population.

9.1. INTRODUCTION

The rise of the average age of the population will place an increasing demand upon our health care system and providers to meet the health promotion needs of the well elderly and to diagnose, treat, and support individuals experiencing age-related health conditions. The current worldwide population of persons over age 65 years is 524 million (National Institute on Aging [NIA], 2011); this number is estimated to reach 1.5 billion persons (or 16% of the world population) by the year 2050. While older adults live longer, the impact of age-related health conditions such as cancer, dementia (neurocognitive disorder), and cardiovascular disease is destined to increase. These demographic trends and age-associated sequelae provide a growing impetus to understand the etiology of aging in order to best promote healthy aging. Nurses with graduate degrees, whether specialized in gerontology or not, will increasingly play key roles in generating, monitoring, critiquing, and translating evidence related to aging into practice in order to best meet the needs of older adults worldwide. The purpose of this chapter is to (1) review the epidemiology of aging and its impact on health, (2) overview current trends related to the genomic etiology of aging, and (3) present perspectives on the impact of aging and aging etiology into the competencies and role of the graduate level nurse.

9.1.1. The Aging of the Population Worldwide

Two aspects of aging epidemiology are relevant to contemporary discussion about aging and health. These two factors include overall trends in global demographics and the consequent impact of these changing demographics on health and disease.

9.1.2. Trends in Aging Demographics

Several trends are impacting the relative proportion of young and old across the world. In the past, young children have typically outnumbered older adults. However, with a decrease in fertility rates and an increase in life expectancy, the population over age 65 years is projected to outnumber children under the age of five within the next 5 years (NIA, 2011). In addition, the total number of older adults is expected to increase dramatically. Specifically, although persons over age 65 years comprised 8% of the population in 2010, they are anticipated to comprise 16% of

Debra L. Schutte, Ph.D RN, Associate Professor, Room 138, Cohn Building, College of Nursing, Wayne State University, Detroit, MI 48202, E-mail: debra.schutte@wayne.edu, Tel: 313-577-4481

the population in 2050. During this same time frame, persons over age 85 years will expand in number by 35% (NIA, 2011).

9.1.3. Impact of Aging on Health and Disease

Although it is not completely clear whether actually living longer means "living longer and healthier," changing demographics have an impact on health and disease. First, there has been a shift in leading causes of death from communicable diseases to chronic and degenerative diseases. The leading causes of death continue to be cancer, heart disease, and diabetes. However, some age-related conditions, such as dementia, are now among the top ten leading causes of death (Tejada-Vera, 2013). With the aging population, the prevalence of common age-related conditions will increase in prevalence as well. For example, the prevalence of dementia, labeled as neurocognitive disorder in the *Diagnostic and Statistical Manual of Mental Disorders, Fifth Edition* (DSM-5) (American Psychiatric Association, 2013), is anticipated to increase dramatically from approximately 35 million people worldwide in 2010 to 115 million people in 2050 (Alzheimer's Association, 2013). This trend alone will have a striking impact on formal and informal caregivers who will be called upon to meet the needs of older adults with cognitive impairment and subsequent functional and behavioral sequelae whether in home or institutional settings.

9.2. THE ETIOLOGY OF AGING

The changing landscape of aging and the health of older adults continues to be the impetus for major research efforts to understand the biologic basis of aging. The longterm goals of this research are to identify targets for interventions to mitigate the course and sequelae of aging and associated health problems.

9.2.1. Overview of Aging

Aging is defined as all changes that occur over the course of the life of an organism and include changes at the cellular, tissue, organ, system, and organism level. Certainly, aging is a complex physiologic process influenced by interacting biologic pathways that further interact with environmental exposures, lifestyle, and chance events. Several operational definitions of aging have been used in research to examine the etiology of aging, including lifespan (age at death), health span (period of life when one is free of chronic illness or significant functional deficit), healthy aging (combination of old age and health), longevity (long duration of life, usually specified as attaining or exceeding a specified age), and exceptional longevity (defined as attaining or exceeding a specified age, often considered to be centenarians).

9.2.2. Genomics and Aging

The heritability of aging, or proportion of variability in aging that can be attributed to genes, is estimated at 25% (Hjelmborg *et al.*, 2006), validating the contributions of other factors (such as environment and chance) to the aging phenotype. Nonetheless, varied genomic approaches are being used to explore the genomic basis of aging, including using animal models of aging, examining genes associated with age-related health conditions, and examining genes associated with extreme aging phenotypes.

9.2.2.1. Animals as Model Systems for Aging

Animal systems, such as the roundworm (*Caenorhabditis elegans*), fruitfly (*Drosophila melanogaster*), mouse (*Mus musculus*), and rhesus monkey (*Rhesus macaque*) have proven effective models of human aging. The advantage of these models are the comparatively shorter lifespans in which to evaluate the effects of particular genes (e.g., manipulating a gene) or particular interventions (e.g., calorie restriction) on lifespan. As a result of research in animal models, numerous genes and biologic pathways have been implicated to affect life span, such as variations in the *AKT* and *FOXO3A* genes within the insulin/IGF-signaling pathway (Kenyon, 2010). To date, the environmental intervention of caloric restriction has been consistently shown to lengthen lifespan across several, but not all, species (NIA, 2011; Roberts & Speakman, 2013). The challenge subsequent to the identification of genes and biologic pathways in animal models is the validation of these genes and pathways in humans.

9.2.2.2. Age-related Health Conditions

One approach to understanding the biology of aging in humans is by examining the genes involved in common age-related diseases or health phenomena, such as Alzheimer's disease and frailty.

Alzheimer's Disease

Alzheimer's disease (AD) is a very common, age-related neurodegenerative condition that is the most common cause of irreversible dementia. The clinical manifestations of AD include a loss of cognitive ability from a previously attained level (or dementia), beginning with deficits in short-term memory and progressing to deficits in more complex cognitive processing. AD is also characterized by increasing dependence in managing one's instrumental activities of daily living (such as preparing meals, shopping, managing finances, and driving), as well as basic activities of daily living (such as eating, bathing, grooming, and toileting). Behavioral symptoms are another prevalent and particularly troubling manifestation of AD that include symptoms in the domains of mood, agitation, aggression (verbal and physical), psychosis (hallucinations and delusions), and lack of behavioral controls.

Significant progress has been made in explicating the genetic basis of AD over the last 25 years, in particular. To date, mutations in three genes are known to cause AD in a small subset of families exhibiting early ages at onset (prior to age 60) and autosomal dominant patterns of inheritance. Mutations in the amyloid precursor protein (*APP*) gene (Goate *et al.*, 1991; St. George-Hyslop *et al.*, 1987), presenilin 1 (*PSEN1*) gene (Mullan *et al.*, 1992; Schellenberg *et al.*, 1992), and presenilin 2 (*PSEN2*) gene (Levy-Lahad *et al.*, 1992) influence amyloid processing pathways, thus contributing to the production and deposition of beta amyloid protein in the brain (i.e., amyloid plaques). Mutations in these genes are inherited in an autosomal dominant pattern, meaning that each offspring of a person carrying one of these mutations has a 50% chance of inheriting the causative mutation. Genetic testing for mutations in these three genes is available for high-risk families, using protocols modeled after predictive and presymptomatic genetic testing for

persons with Huntington disease and ideally beginning with testing for a specific mutation in an affected individual (Goldman *et al.*, 2011). Predictive genetic testing in AD is recommended to be provided along with pretesting and post-testing genetic counseling to ensure that individuals are informed of the potential risks and benefits of testing. For example, potential benefits of predictive testing include clarification of one's chances of developing disease (decreasing uncertainty), clarification of risk for one's children, and the ability to make life and health care decisions accordingly. Potential risks of predictive genetic testing include psychological sequelae, such as anxiety, depressive symptoms, or survival guilt.

In addition to the causative mutations described above. The apolipoprotein E (*APOE*) gene plays a strong susceptibility role in the more common late onset AD. In the case of *APOE*, the ε4 allelic variant both increases risk and decreases ages at onset of AD in a dose-dependent manner (Pericak-Vance *et al.*, 1991). Although research is ongoing to examine the short- and long-term effects of genetic susceptibility testing for *APOE* status (i.e., revealing APOE status and disclosing risk of developing AD) (Green *et al.*, 2009), genetic testing is not currently recommended in clinical practice because of continued uncertainty about the clinical utility of this information (Goldman *et al.*, 2011).

Although AD is the most common cause of irreversible dementia, other health problems can cause dementia as well. The second most common cause of irreversible dementia is vascular dementia, resulting from a loss of neurons due to chronically reduced blood supply to the brain. No direct genetic causes of vascular dementia have been identified to date, although research is ongoing to identify potential susceptibility genes (Dwyer, Skrobot, Dwyer, Munafo, & Kehoe, 2013). A rare type of dementia that does have known genetic causes is frontotemporal dementia (FTD). FTDs (including Pick's disease) are progressive dementias characterized by neuropathologic changes (e.g., inclusions of proteins such as tau, TDP-43, and fused in sarcoma [FUS]) in the frontal and temporal lobes of the brain. Clinical features of frontotemporal disease vary by subtype, but include symptoms such as amnesia, aphasia, and losses of socially appropriate behavior and inhibitions. Mutations in several genes are associated with FTD, exhibiting autosomal dominant patterns of inheritance. Clinical genetic testing is available for FTD (Paulos & Massano, 2013).

Frailty

Another aging-related, high impact, health phenomena of relevance to both aging research and nursing practice is frailty. Numerous and variable conceptual definitions of frailty have been offered with little consensus (Gobbens, Luijkx, Wijnen-Sponselee, & Schols, 2010; Rodriguez-Manas et al., 2012; Theou, Brothers, Mitnitski, & Rockwood, 2013). Nonetheless, one widely used conceptual definition of frailty by Fried and colleagues (2004) defines frailty as a state of high vulnerability or an "aggregate expression of risk resulting from age- or disease-associated physiologic accumulation of subthreshold decrements affecting multiple physiologic systems (pg. 256)." Common operational definitions of frailty include indicators within the domains of nutritional status, energy, physical activity, mobility, and strength (Rodriguez-Manas et al., 2012) with frailty characterized as weakness, poor endurance, weight loss, low physical activity, and slow gait speed (Fried et al., 2001). Prevalence estimates of frailty vary, likely due to varied operational definitions. For example, Van Iersel and Rikkert (2006) found prevalence estimates ranging from 33% to 88% in the same sample of older adults depending upon the measure of frailty (Van Iersel & Rikkert, 2006). In addition, frailty places older adults at risk for falls, cognitive impairment, disability, hospitalization, institutionalization, and death (Rockwood et al., 2004). Despite the challenges in defining the syndrome, and given its strong association with aging, frailty has become a recent target of genomics research in an attempt to understand the biologic mechanisms underlying aging and to identify those who may be at a greater risk for frailty. For example, Almeida and colleagues (2012) identified a relationship between two DNA variants within the C-reactive protein (CRP), pentraxin-related gene and frailty in community-dwelling older men controlling for depression (Almeida et al., 2012). The *CRP* gene encodes for the CRP, an inflammatory marker involved in responses to physiologic stressors. Ho

and colleagues (2011) examined a set of DNA variants within 134 candidate genes representing points of interaction between skeletal muscle and inflammatory pathways in relationship to frailty in community-dwelling women. In this case, no associations achieved statistical significance when controlling for multiple comparisons. However, the strongest associations (prior to correcting for multiple comparisons) involved genes within the apoptosis and transcription regulation pathways rather than genes specific to inflammatory or skeletal muscle pathways (Ho et al., 2011). Additional research is needed to clarify the conceptual and operational definitions of frailty as a syndrome and then to validate and expand these early genetic association findings.

9.2.2.3. Extreme Aging Phenotypes

In addition to studying age-related health conditions such as AD and frailty, aging research has also focused on examining extreme variations in aging, including premature aging and exceptional longevity phenotypes. One rationale for this research is the hypothesis that the etiology or biologic pathways contributing to these extreme aging phenotypes will also be contributing to the normal aging process.

Premature Aging

Hutchinson-Gilford progeria syndrome (HGPS) is an extremely rare, segmental progeroid syndrome that affects 1 in 4 to 8 million live-births (Gordon, Brown, & Collins, 2011). The clinical phenotype of HGPS is very early childhood onset of features consistent with accelerated aging, such as a characteristic aged facies, early hair loss, loss of subcutaneous fat, as well as bone and cartilage changes (Gordon et al., 2011) HGPS is an autosomal dominant disorder that is almost always caused by a specific, de novo mutation in the lamin A/C (*LMNA*) gene (Eriksson et al., 2003). Werner syndrome is another progeroid disorder that results in clinical symptoms consistent with premature aging. In contrast to HGPS, the onset of Werner syndrome typically occurs in the early teen years and includes features of accelerated aging along with an increased incidence of cancer. Werner syndrome is an autosomal recessive disorder resulting from mutations in the *WRN* gene, where more than 70 disease-causing mutations have been identified (Oshima, Martin, & Hisama, 2012). The subsequent characterization of the function of these genes suggest several possible biological pathways for the aging process, including defective DNA repair, altered cell proliferation and senescence, and altered stem cell proliferation (Burtner & Kennedy, 2010).

Extreme Longevity

In contrast to premature aging, other researchers are studying the genetics of very long-lived individuals as a path to understanding the aging process. The definition of extreme longevity may differ between studies, but often involves persons ages 100 years or older (centenarians). Both candidate gene (hypothesis-driven) and genome-wide (hypothesis free) approaches to genetic association studies have been conducted in persons with extreme longevity and are currently cataloged in the LongevityMap (Budovskey *et al.*, 2013). Associations between DNA variants within the *APOE* and *FOXO3A* genes and longevity have been identified and replicated using candidate gene approaches. However, to date, DNA variations around the *APOE* gene are the only associations to reach genome-wide significance. (See Brooks-Wilson, 2013 for a comprehensive review of the genetics of longevity.) A remarkable observation from genetic research indicates that long-lived persons do not necessarily lack risk alleles for common complex diseases (Brooks-Wilson, 2013; NIA, 2011), suggesting that other mechanisms may ameliorate or shield the effects of these putative risk alleles.

9.2.3. Summary

Together, these varied approaches to genetics research, along with other lines of inquiry, have improved our understanding of the biology of aging and implicated several important physiologic pathways and processes. For example, there is a growing body of evidence suggesting epigenetics (i.e., heritable chemical modifications of DNA that influence gene expression), such as DNA methylation and histone modification, are associated with aging and age-related phenotypes (Ben-Avraham, Muzumbdar, & Atzmon,

2012). Mitochondria and oxidative stress are also strongly implicated in aging. Specifically, mitochondria, the cellular organelle responsible for energy production, plays an important role in oxidative phosphorylation and cell metabolism. Research to examine the association between mitochondrial genome variants (haplogroups) and life span are one strategy used to examine the role of mitochondria in aging (Santoro *et al.*, 2006), across many different populations with sometimes equivocal findings (Yang *et al.*, 2012; Courtenay *et al.*, 2012; Pinos *et al.*, 2012). The byproducts of cellular energy processes are also implicated in aging. Specifically, reactive oxygen species (i.e., chemically reactive molecules containing oxygen, such as oxygen ions and peroxides) are normal byproducts of energy metabolism in the mitochondria. An accumulation of reactive oxygen species, or oxidative stress, can then lead to age-dependent declines in biological function (Hwang, Jeong, & Lee, 2012). Oxidative stress (e.g., too many reactive oxygen species) and other processes (e.g., UV light and radiation) can cause DNA damage, pointing to the importance of DNA repair mechanisms in aging (Lombard *et al.*, 2005). Oxidative stress also has pro-inflammatory effects, which are further implicated in the aging process (Chung *et al.*, 2009). Finally, telomeres are important in cellular aging and their role in human aging remains an important area of inquiry. Telomeres are noncoding repetitive nucleotides that cap nuclear DNA at the ends of chromosomes. Telomeres shorten with each progressive cell replication until reaching a critical length, at which point the cell exits the cell cycle and senesces, or grows old. Research is ongoing to investigate the relationship between telomere length as a potential marker of aging in humans (Sanders & Newman, 2013). Overall, these research efforts illustrate the extraordinary complexity of the biology of aging and the influence of aging on physiologic processes across species. Although additional research is indicated across all aspects of aging research, implications for health care warrant consideration nonetheless.

9.3. AGING, GENOMICS, AND THE GRADUATE LEVEL NURSE

The emerging knowledge related to genetics

and aging presents exciting opportunities and challenges for graduate level nurses. As clinical experts and leaders, advanced practice nurses (APRNs) practice at the interface of knowledge discovery and translation. Nurse administrators play essential roles in building the structure and processes to support progressive, evidence-based care. Nurse scientists now possess genomics research tools and information to expand the production of knowledge. General acumen related to clinical and research genetics falls within the scope of practice of all nurses. And research evidence originating from the study of aging may have implications for clinical practice, whether one is specializing in gerontology or not. Therefore, it is critical that all graduate level nurses seize the opportunity to learn and lead in the area of genomics and our aging population.

9.3.1. Aging, Genomics, and the Advanced Practice Nurse

By virtue of their clinical specialization, experience, and leadership capacity, APRNs are in key positions to facilitate best practices relevant to genomics and age-related health care problems, whether practicing in a primary care or clinical nurse specialist role. In fact, a set of essential genetics and genomics competencies for nurses with graduate degrees was established in 2011 to help guide the practice of APRNs (Greco, Tinley, & Seibert, 2012). These essential competencies are categorized into several domains, which align with the seven role competencies of advanced practice nursing practice proposed by Hamric, Spross, and Hanson (2008), including direct clinical practice, expert coaching and guidance, consultation, collaboration, research, leadership, and ethical decision making. Opportunities exist to impact care related to genetics and aging within each of these role domains (see Table 9.1 for a summary).

9.3.1.1.   Direct Clinical Practice

First and foremost, APRNs are expert clinicians and provide direct care to clients, whether in a primary care, acute care, or long-term care setting. Their comprehensive assessment skills must now include systematically collecting genetic information, through a family history as-sessment. Collecting a three-generation family history, constructing a pedigree from that information, and analyzing that pedigree for patterns (such as clustering of health problems within families, or evidence of Mendelian patterns of inheritance) provides one mechanism for identifying individuals who may be experiencing or at risk for experiencing a genetic condition. In the case of AD, a family or geriatric nurse practitioner might conduct a family history assessment that is focused on the presence of dementia of all maternal and paternal relatives across at least three generations. Collecting age at symptom onset in persons with dementia will be important to help differentiate between early and late onset disease. If family history data suggests that genes may be playing a role in the etiology of AD in their family, then the APRN can review his or her findings with the family and offer a referral to specialty genetics services. APRNs, particularly in primary care settings, will also have growing opportunities to assist families in the interpretation of genetic testing results. Families may need information reinforced or have ongoing questions about the meaning of a particular genetic testing result and its implications for one's own health or the health of other family members. For more information on collecting a family history and conducting a risk assessment, see Chapter 2. In addition, APRNs will need to assess their client's coping skills and monitor for any untoward outcomes (such as depressive symptoms or anxiety).

Because not all current advances in genomics research and aging have immediate clinical application (e.g., genetic testing or genotype-driven interventions), another important practice skill for the APRN is maintaining access to resources designed to help clinicians keep abreast of genetic advances and current best practices. Several online resources are available to nurses and other providers (See Table 9.2). Some of these resources cover many phenotypes (e.g., Online Mendelian Inheritance in Man [OMIM], GeneTests, and GeneReviews) (OMIM, 9/30/2013). Other resources are a compilation of information about a single phenotype (e.g., Alzgene, LongevityMap).

9.3.1.2. Expert Coaching and Guidance, Consultation, and Collaboration

The three APRN competencies of expert

TABLE 9.1. Alignment of APN Competencies, Essential Genetic and Genomic Competencies, and Selected Professional Activities.

APRN Competencies (Hamric, Spross, & Hanson, 2008)	Essential Genetic and Genomic Competencies for Nurses with Graduate Degrees (Greco, Tinley, & Seibert, 2011)	Example Application of Genomic Competencies Related to the Genetics of Aging
Direct clinical practice	• Risk Assessment and Interpretation • Genetic Education, Counseling, Testing, and Results Interpretation • Clinical Management	• Collect and interpret family history data (pedigree) for persons at risk for common age-related health problems (e.g., Alzheimer's disease, age-related macular degeneration). • Provide patient teaching regarding genetics of common age-related conditions, such as AD (e.g., characteristics of autosomal dominant inheritance; risks to first-degree relatives). • Refer clients who may benefit from predictive genetic testing for specialty genetics services.
Expert coaching and guidance Consultation Collaboration	• Professional Role	• Coach other providers in the identification, referral, and support of clients experiencing or at risk for experiencing genetic conditions (such as early-onset AD). • Coordinate and/or provide CEU offerings related to 1) basic genomics concepts and principles and 2) the genetics of aging and common age-related conditions. • Lead journal clubs that focus on advances in aging and genetics. • Build relationships with specialty genetics providers to facilitate referrals and follow-up and mutual exchange of expertise.
Research	• Research	• Participate on research teams examining the role of genes in age-related conditions or in testing genotype-tailored or targeted interventions. • Lead research utilization projects (e.g., integration of family history assessments into patient intake or admission protocols).
Leadership (clinical, professional, and systems)	• Leadership	• Participate on interdisciplinary teams focused on coordination of care between primary care settings/inpatient settings/long-term care settings and specialty genetics providers. • Participate on interdisciplinary committees to integrate pedigree data into electronic medical records.
Ethical decision making	• Ethical, Legal, and Social Implications	• Advocate for genetics expertise and gerontology expertise on your institution's ethics committee.

coaching, consultation, and collaboration highlight the interactions and relationships APRNs foster with other care providers in their practice or institution. Expert coaching and guidance may include coaching and mentoring staff nurse providers in family health history assessment skills and interpretation of pedigrees. APRNs may be consulted for assistance with difficult cases (e.g., difficulties in collecting or interpreting genetic assessment information). The expert coaching role may also include coordinating or providing continuing education opportunities within one's organization. These offerings could include a review of basic genetics concepts and principles, advancing to the role of genetics in common age-related conditions, such as AD, and their clinical implications. Another mechanism for identifying, critiquing, and sharing new evidence within

TABLE 9.2. Selected Clinical Genetics Resources.

Name	URL	Description
Gene Tests	http://www.genetests.org/	GeneTests is a medical genetics information resource developed for health care providers and researchers. The database includes an international laboratory directory and an international clinic directory.
Gene Reviews	http://www.ncbi.nlm.nih.gov/books/ NBK1116/	"GeneReviews are expert-authored, peer-reviewed disease descriptions presented in a standardized format and focused on clinically relevant and medically actionable information on the diagnosis, management, and genetic counseling of patients and families with specific inherited conditions."
Online Mendelian Inheritance in Man (OMIM)	http://www.ncbi.nlm.nih.gov/omim/	"Online Mendelian Inheritance in Man (OMIM®) is a continuously updated catalog of human genes and genetic disorders and traits, with particular focus on the molecular relationship between genetic variation and phenotypic expression."
Alzgene	http://www.alzgene.org/	The AlzGene database provides a comprehensive field synopsis of genetic association studies performed in Alzheimer's disease, including metaanalyses for all eligible polymorphisms with sufficient data.
LongevityMap	http://genomics.senescence.info/ longevity/	The LongevityMap is a database of human genetic variants associated with longevity.

an organization is a journal club. APRNs working within acute or long-term care settings could lead journal clubs as a mechanism to critique and share current advances in genetics and aging as part of their expert coaching and guidance role. An especially important activity that exemplifies the professional role of collaboration includes building relationships with specialty genetics providers if this has not previously been a priority in one's institution or practice setting. Historically, clinical genetics services have been associated with the care of children and young families. Today, however, these provider connections are important, even in settings focused on the care of adults and older adults, and present opportunities for mutual sharing of expertise. For example, your setting may not be expert in specialty genetics interventions. However, a genetic specialty clinic may have relatively little expertise in the care of persons with dementia. As the genomic technology and utility continues to expand, interprofessional practice will become more crucial for patient care.

9.3.1.3. Research

APRNs can contribute to new knowledge related to the genomics of aging or the eventual testing of related interventions by participating on interdisciplinary research teams, assisting with recruitment, and data collection. Perhaps most importantly, though, APRNs can design and lead quality improvement or evidence-based practice change efforts as new best practices emerge related to genotype-driven diagnostic, prognostic, or treatment options. In the context of genomics and aging, an example project may be the implementation of a paper or electronic family health history tool within a unit or across an organization. A quality improvement initiative might involve setting referral criteria and establishing the referral and follow-up processes with area specialty genetics providers in order to increase access to care with particular emphasis on adult care units.

9.3.1.4. Leadership

In some respects, leadership skills are needed in order to enact all of the proposed competencies of the APRN role in relationship to genomics. However, an APRN may take on a specific leadership role in order to champion genomics and the care of older adults by bringing expertise to key committees or health policy-making venues, both internal and external to the organization.

9.3.1.5. Ethical Decision-making

Finally, APRNs can use their leadership skills to ensure that ethical decision-making is applied to the implementation of genomics-based health care for adults and older adults. For example, how are the principles of autonomy, beneficence, privacy, and confidentiality considered in the design and implementation of new policies and procedures for genetics and genomics-based health care? Is there sufficient expertise on the institution's ethics committee related to genetics and to the intersection of genetics and the care of older adults? These are the types of questions that APRNs might ask in assessing the resources, needs, and capacity of their practice setting related to providing genomics-based health care services.

9.3.2. Aging, Genomics, and the Nurse Administrator

Graduate prepared nurses in administrative positions within health care organizations hold several responsibilities that are relevant to the integration of genomics-based best practices. Aside from facilitating an overall culture of inquiry, nurse administrators can develop structures and processes to ensure that new genomics information triggers evidence-based practice and quality improvement efforts. In particular, mechanisms will be needed to scan the horizon (e.g., scientific literature, standards from professional organizations, or accrediting bodies) for genomics-based diagnostic or treatment strategies that may be relevant to older adults or other populations of interest within an institution. Nurse administrators can also ensure the integration of basic genomics principles and concepts into nursing orientation or annual skills fairs.

9.3.3. Aging, Genomics, and the Nurse Educator and Scientist

Nurse scientists have an overall responsibility to embrace new genomics tools and information in the conduct of research. In the context of aging and genomics, nurse scientists are examining the influence of genetic factors in the symptoms associated with AD (Schutte, Maas, & Buckwalter, 2003; Schutte, Reed, DeCrane, & Ersig, 2011),

as well as other health problems (Dunn *et al.*, 2013; Jun, Kohen, Cain, Jarrett, & Heitkemper, 2012). The goal of these research avenues is to contribute to the identification of biological pathways that may be targets for pharmacologic or nonpharmacologic therapies. Genomics also has the potential to provide a means of targeting or tailoring interventions based upon risk profiles that may include genomics information. Pharmacogenomics is one example of tailoring interventions based upon genetic information that holds promise for improving interventions for persons with age-related health problems, such as AD (Noetzli & Eap, 2013).

Finally, nurse educators are also responsible for generating an innovative curriculum to prepare nurses who are competent to practice in a health care system influenced by genomics technologies and information. Curricular content for graduate programs can be guided by *The Essentials of Master's Education in Nursing (AACN, 2011)* and the *Essentials of Genetic and Genomic Nursing Competencies, Curricula Guidelines, and Outcome Indicators* (Consensus Panel, 2009). Strategies are proposed to assist faculty in assessing the genetics literacy of students and faculty in order to target curricular changes (Daack-Hirsch, Dreissnack, Perkhounkova, Furukawa, & Ramirez, 2012). And finally, numerous instructional strategies are reported towards the goal of integration of genomics into undergraduate and graduate curricula (Garcia, Greco, & Loescher, 2011).

9.4. SUMMARY

A rapidly aging global population with a subsequent increased prevalence in age-related health problems will place increasing demands upon the health care system worldwide, including clinical experts and leaders such as APRNs and other graduate level nurses. Genomics research to explicate the etiology of aging and age-related health problems has already yielded opportunities for families with early-onset AD, for example, to clarify their risk for disease through genetic testing. These types of clinically valid genotype-based interventions will only continue to increase in number and scope. Consequently, APRNs, nurse administrators, nurse educators, and nurse scientists will be increasingly called upon to lead the discipline in the integration of genomics-based best practices for the care of adults and older adults.

9.5. REFERENCES

Almeida, O. P., Norman, P. E., van Bockxmeer, F. M., Hankey, G. J., & Flicker, L. (2012). *CRP* 1846G>A polymorphism increases risk of frailty, *Maturitas, 71*, 261–266.

Alzheimer's Association (2013). Alzheimer's disease facts and figures. *Alzheimer's & Dementia: The Journal of the Alzheimer's Association, 9*(2), 208–245.

American Association of College of Nursing. (2011). *The essentials of master's education in nursing.* Washington, DC: Author.

American Psychiatric Association. (2013, epub ahead of print). *Diagnostic and statistical manual of mental disorders, fifth edition.* http://dx.doi.org/10.1176/appi.books.9780890425596.910646

Ben-Avraham, D., Muzumdar, R. H., & Atzmon, G. (2012). Epigenetic genome-wide association methylation in aging and longevity. *Epigenomics, 4*(5), 503–509.

Brooks-Wilson, A. R. (2013, epub ahead of print). Genetics of health aging and longevity. *Human Genetics.* http://link.springer.com/article/10.1007/s00439-013-1342-z

Budovskey, A., Craig, T., Wang, J., Tacutu, R., Csordas, A., Lourenco, J., . . . & de Magalhaes, J.P. (2013). LongevityMap: A database of human genetic variants associated with longevity. *Trends in Genetics, 29*(10), 559–560.

Burtner, C.R., & Kennedy, B.K. (2010). Progeria syndromes and ageing: What is the connection? *Nature Reviews. Molecular Cell Biology, 11*(8), 567–578.

Chung, H.Y., Cesari, M., Anton, S., Marzetti, E., Giovannini, S. Seo, A. Y., . . . & Leeuwenburgh, C. (2009). Molecular inflammation: Underpinnings of aging and age-related diseases. *Aging Research Reviews, 8*(1), 18–30.

Consensus Panel on Genetic/Genomic Nursing Competencies. (2009). *Essentials of genetic and genomic nursing competencies, curricula guidelines, and outcome indicators* (2nd ed). Silver Spring, MD: American Nurses Association.

Courtenay, M. D., Gilbert, J. R., Jiang, L., Cummings, A. C., Gallins, P.J., Caywood, L., . . . & Scott, W. K. (2012). Mitochondrial haplogroup X is associated with successful aging in the Amish. *Human Genetics, 131*(2), 201–208.

Daack-Hirsch S., Driessnack, M., Perkhounkova, Y., Furukawa, R., & Ramirez. (2012). A practical first step to integrating genetics into the curriculum. *Journal of Nursing Education, 51*(5), 294–298.

Dunn, B., Aouizerat, B. E., Langford, D. J., Cooper B. A., Dhruva, A., Cataldo, J. K. . . . & Miaskowski, C. (2012). Cytokine gene variation is associated with depressive symptom trajectories in oncology patients and family caregivers. *European Journal of Oncology Nursing, 17*(3), 346–353.

Dwyer, R., Skrobot, O. A., Dwyer, J., Munafo, M., & Kehoe, P. G. (2013). Using Alzgene-like approaches to investigate susceptibility genes for vascular cognitive impairment. *Journal of Alzheimer Disease, 34*(1), 145–154.

Eriksson, M., Brown, W. T., Gordon, L. B., Glynn, M. W., Singer, J., Scott, L., . . . & Collins, F. S. (2003). Recurrent de novo point mutations in *lamin A* cause Hutchinson-Gilford progeria syndrome. *Nature 423*, 293–298.

Fried, L. P., Tangen, C. M., Walston, J., Newman, A. B., Hirsch, C., Gottdiener, J., . . . & Cardiovascular Health Study Collaborative Research Group. (2001). Frailty in older adults: evidence for a phenotype. *Journal of Gerontolology Medical Sciences, 56A*, M146–M156.

Garcia, S. P., Greco, K. E., & Loescher, L. J. (2011). Teaching strategies to incorporate genomics education into academic nursing curricula. *Journal of Nursing Education, 50*(11), 612–619.

Goate, A., Chartier-Harlin, M. C., Mullan, M., Brown, J., Crawford, F., Fidani, L., . . . & Hardy, J. (1991). Segregation of a missense mutation in the amyloid precursor protein gene with familial Alzheimer's disease. *Nature, 349*(6311), 704–706.

Gobbens, R. J., Luijkx, K. G., Wijnen-Sponselee, M. T., & Schols, J. M. (2010). Toward a conceptual definition of frail community dwelling older people. *Nursing Outlook, 58*(2), 76–86.

Goldman, J. S., Hahn, S. E., Catania, J. W., LaRusse-Eckert, S., Butson, M. B., Rumbaugh, M., . . . & Bird, T. (2011). Genetic counseling and testing for Alzheimer disease: Joint practice guidelines of the American College of Medical Genetics and the National Society of Genetic Counselors. *Genetics in Medicine, 13*(6), 597–605.

Gordon, L. B., Brown, W. T., & Collins, F. S. (2003, Dec 12 [Updated 2011 Jan 6]). HutchinsonGilford Progeria syndrome. In R.A. Pagon, M.P. Adam, & T.D. Bird (Eds). GeneReviews™ [Internet]. Seattle (WA): University of Washington, Seattle; 1993–2013. Available from: http://www.ncbi.nlm.nih.gov/books/NBK1121/

Greco, K. E., Tinley, S., & Seibert, D. (2012). *Essential Genetic and Genomic Competencies for Nurses with Graduate Degrees.* Silver Spring, MD: American Nurses Association and International Society of Nurses in Genetics.

Green, R. C., Roberts, J. S., Cupples, L. A., Relkin, N. R., Whitehouse, P.J ., Brown, T., . . . & Farrer, L. A. (2009). A randomized trial of APOE genotype disclosure for risk of Alzheimer's disease: the REVEAL Study. *New England Journal of Medicine, 361*, 245–254.

Hamric, A. B., Spross, J. A., & Hanson, C. M. (2008).

Advanced nursing practice: An integrative approach (4th Ed). St. Louis: Saunders Elsevier.

Hjelmborg, J., Iachine, I., Skytthe, A., Vaupel, J. W., McGue, M. Koskenvo, M., . . . & Christensen, K. (2006). Genetic influence on human lifespan and longevity. *Human Genetics, 119*, 312–321.

Ho, Y-Y., Matteini, A. M., Beamer, B., Fried, L., Xue, Q., Arking, D.E., . . . & Walston, J. (2011). Exploring biologically relevant pathways in frailty. *Journal of Gerontology: Medical Sciences, 66A*(9), 975–979.

Hwang, A. B., Jeong, D-U., & Lee, S-J. (2012). Mitochondria and organismal longevity, *Current Genomics, 13*, 519–532.

Jun, S. E., Kohen, R., Cain, K. C., Jarrett, M. E., & Heitkemper, M. M. (2014). TPH gene polymorphisms are associated with disease perception and quality of life in women with irritable bowel syndrome. *Biological Research for Nursing, 16*(1), 95–104.

Kenyon, C.J. (2010). The genetics of ageing. *Nature, 464*, 504–512.

Levy-Lahad E., Wasco, W., Poorkaj, P., Oshima, J., Pettingell, W., Yu, C., . . . & Wang, K. (1995). Candidate gene for the chromosome 1 familial Alzheimer's disease locus. *Science, 269*(5226), 973–7.

Lombard, D. B., Chua, K. F., Mostoslavsky, R., Franco, S., Fostissa, M., & Alt, F. W. (2005). DNA repair, genome stability, and aging. *Cell, 120*, 497–512.

Mullan, M, Houlden, H., Windelsprecht, M., Fidani, L., Lombardi, C., Diaz, P., . . . & Crawford, F. (1992). A locus for familial early-onset Alzheimer's disease on the long arm of chromosome 14, proximal to the alpha 1-antichymotrypsin gene. *Nature Genetics, 2*(4), 340–342.

National Institute on Aging (2011). *Biology of Aging: Research Today for a Healthier Tomorrow*. National Institute on Aging.

Noetzli, M. & Eap, C. B. (2013). Pharmacodynamic, pharmacokinetic and pharmacogenetic aspects of drugs used in the treatment of Alzheimer's Disease, *Clinical Pharmacokinetics, 52*(4), 225–241.

Online Mendelian Inheritance in Man, OMIM®. McKusick-Nathans Institute of Genetic Medicine, Johns Hopkins University (Baltimore, MD), (9/19/2013). World Wide Web URL: http://omim.org/

Oshima, J., Martin, G. M., & Hisama, F. M. (2002 Dec 2 [Updated 2012 Dec 13]). Werner Syndrome. In R.A. Pagon, M.P. Adam, & T.D. Bird (Eds). *GeneReviews™* [Internet]. Seattle (WA): University of Washington, Seattle; 1993–2013. Available from: http://www.ncbi.nlm.nih.gov/books/NBK1514/

Pinos, T., Nogales-Gadea, G., Ruiz, J. R., Rodriguez-Romo, G., Santiago-Dorrego, C., Fiuza-Luces, C., . . . & Lucia, A. (2012). Are mitochondrial haplogroups associated with extreme longevity? A study on a Spanish cohort. *Age, 34*(1), 227–233.

Roberts, S. B., & Speakman, J. (2013). Update on human calorie restriction research. *Advances in Nutrition, 4*(5), 563–564.

Paulos, J. P., & Massano, J. (2013). Clinical, genetic, and neuropathological features of frontotemporal dementia: an update and guide. *Acta Medica Portuguesa, 26*(4), 392–401.

Pericak-Vance, M. A., Bebout, J. L., Gaskell, P. C. Jr., Yamaoka, L. H., Hung, W. Y., Alberts, M.J., . . . & Roses, A.D. (1991). Linkage studies in familial Alzheimer disease: evidence for chromosome 19 linkage. *American Journal of Human Genetics, 48*(6), 1034–1050.

Rockwood, K., Howlett, S. E., MacKnight, C., Beattie, B. L., Bergman, H., Hebert, R., . . . & McDowell, I. (2004). Prevalence, attributes, and outcomes of fitness and frailty in community-dwelling older adults: report from the Canadian study of health and aging. *Journal of Gerontology A: Biological Sciences Medical Sciences, 59*, 1310–317.

Sanders, J. L., & Newman, A. B. (2013). Telomere length in epidemiology: biomarker of aging, agerelated disease, both or neither? *Epidemiologic Reviews, 35*, 112–131.

Santoro, A., Salvioli, S., Raule, N., Capri, M., Sevini, F., Valensin, S., . . . & Franceschi, C. (2006). Mitochondrial DNA involvement in human longevity. *Biochimica et Biophysica Acta, 1757*(9-10), 1388–1399.

Schellenberg, G. D., Bird, T. D., Wijsman, E. M., Orr, H. T., Anderson, L., Nemens, E., . . . & Martin, G. M. (1992). Genetic linkage evidence for a familial Alzheimer's disease locus on chromosome 14. *Science, 258*(5082), 668–671.

Schutte, D. L., Maas, M., & Buckwalter, K. C. (2003). A LRPAP1 intronic insertion/deletion polymorphism and phenotypic variability in Alzheimer Disease. *Research and Theory for Nursing Practice: An International Journal, 17*(4), 301–319.

Schutte, D. L., Reed, D. A., DeCrane, S., & Ersig, A. L. (2011). Saitohin and APOE polymorphisms influence cognition and function in persons with advanced Alzheimer Disease. *Dementia and Geriatric Cognitive Disorders, 32*:94–102 [doi: 10.1159/000329542].

St. George-Hyslop, P. H., Tanzi, R. E., Polinsky, R. J., Haines, J. L., Nee, L., & Watkins, P. C. (1987). The genetic defect causing familial Alzheimer's disease maps on chromosome 21. *Science, 235*(4791), 885–890.

Tejada-Vera, B. (March, 2013). Mortality from Alzheimer's disease in the United States: Data for 2000–2010. *National Center for Health Statistics Data Brief*, No. 116.

Theou, O., Brothers, T., Mitnitski, A., & Rockwood, K. (2013). Operationalization of frailty using eight commonly used scales and comparison of their ability to predict all-cause mortality. *Journal of the American Geriatrics Society, 61*(9), 1537–1551.

Van Iersel, M. B., & Rikkert, M. G. (2006). Frailty

criteria give heterogeneous results when applied in clinical practice. *Journal of the American Geriatrics Society, 54*, 728–729.

Yang, X., Wang, X., Yao, H., Deng, J., Jiang, Q., Guo, Y., . . . & Jiang, H. (2012). Mitochondrial DN polymorphisms are associated with the longevity in the Guangxi Bama population of China. *Molecular Biology Reports, 39*(9), 9123–9231.

Chapter 10

Respiratory Disorders

RAN HE, Ph.D, AGN-BC
JULIA EGGERT, Ph.D, AGN-BC, AOCN®

Objectives:

- Discuss the genetics of the most common respiratory disorders associated with single-gene changes.
- Describe the gene/environment interactions that processes by which common complex respiratory conditions develop.
- Identify the unique ethical issues often encountered in patients with genomic respiratory diseases.

10.1. INTRODUCTION

Lung diseases affect people of all ages and are a significant cause of morbidity and mortality worldwide, and there are many different kinds of respiratory disorders, many of which are actively being explored by genetic researchers. As in many other types of disorders, better understanding of the genetic and biochemical processes involved in development of disease often lead to new prevention and diagnostic approaches and novel therapy. Although early and significant advances have been made in understanding the biology of single-gene disorders such as cystic fibrosis and alpha 1-antitrypsin deficiency, more recent work has identified some of the genes associated with complex respiratory disorders, such as asthma and lung cancer. This chapter discusses some of the recent genomic discoveries that are changing understanding and treatment of respiratory disease.

10.2. SINGLE-GENE DISORDERS

10.2.1. Alpha 1-Antitrypsin Deficiency

Chronic obstructive pulmonary disease (COPD) is a collection of diseases characterized by airflow obstruction caused by the destruction of pulmonary alveoli, which are gradually transformed from bunches of small, grape-like spheres into large, irregular, air-filled sacs. As the disease progresses, affected individuals experience increasingly distressful symptoms including shortness of breath, persistent cough, and wheezing, and are at increased risk for developing lung cancer (Fry, Hamling, & Lee, 2012; Mason, Broaddus, Martin, King Jr., & Schraufnagel, 2010). Risk factors for emphysema, one of the more common forms of COPD, include age, smoking or exposure to secondhand smoke, exposure to occupational fumes or dust, or pollutants and the inheritance of *SERPINA1* deficiency alleles (Sharafkhaneh, Hanania, & Kim, 2008).

Alpha 1-antitrypsin (AAT) is a proteinase inhibitor (Pi), an enzyme produced and secreted in the liver that then travels in the bloodstream to the lungs, where it functions primarily to protect the lungs from damage caused by a protease enzyme called neutrophil elastase (NE). NE plays an important role in protecting the body from infection and inflammation, by helping to clear the lungs of damaged cells after an infection, and it may also play other roles in fighting pulmo-

---

Ran He, Ph.D, Adjunct Faculty, School of Health Sciences, Kaplan University
Julia Eggert, Ph.D, GNP-BC, AOCN®, Clemson University, Healthcare Genetics doctoral program,
School of Nursing, Clemson, SC 29634, E-mail: jaegger@clemson.edu, Tel: 864-640-1869 Fax: 864-656-5488

nary infection and inflammation. AAT breaks down NE and other neutrophil proteases, like protease-3 and cathepsin-G, and counteracts the cytotoxic effects of neutrophil defensins, helping to protect the lungs from prolonged exposure to caustic agents. AAT also appears to play other important roles, including facilitating issue repair and regulating pulmonary T-cell and natural killer cells (Siri, Farah, & Hogarth, 2012).

AAT deficiency (AATD) mutations are some of the most common genetic disorders among Northern European Caucasians, with a prevalence even higher than cystic fibrosis in that community (Siri *et al.*, 2012; de Serres, 2002). AAT, the only gene known to cause emphysema, is nested within a cluster of genes known as the *SERPIN* (serine or cysteine) family. AAT, or *SERPINA1*, is located on the long arm of chromosome 14 (14q3131.3) and contains four coding and three noncoding exons (DeMeo & Silverman, 2004). More than 120 different AAT alleles have been identified, the most common of which are classified by the symbols "M" (normal function), "S" (moderate deficiency), "Z" (severe deficiency), and "N" (null, or total absence of serum AAT).

The Z allele (Glu342Lys), the most common mutation (90% of affected individuals), is found primarily in individuals of southern Scandinavian and northwestern European descent, whereas the S allele (Glu264Val) is more prevalent in southern Europe. AAT mutations are relatively rare in individuals of Asian, African, and Middle Eastern descent (Kelly, Greene, Carroll, McElvaney, & O'Neill, 2010).

When AAT levels are low, NE accumulates, damaging pulmonary structures and causing the progressive obstruction and lung function loss characteristic of emphysema. The Z allele is particularly deleterious, because in addition to severely deficient AAT levels, the allele forms polymers that actively recruit neutrophils, accelerating lung tissue damage (Siri *et al.*, 2012). A relatively unusual feature of AATD is that alternative spellings are equally dominant (codominant), so individuals who inherit two different AAT alleles (heterozygotes) can express widely varying phenotypes, depending on the inherited combination of alleles (Siri *et al.*, 2012). In addition to pulmonary disease, individuals with severe AAT deficiency mutations may develop

TABLE 10.1. Example of Online Resources Useful in Understanding Genetic/genomic Respiratory Conditions.

Organization	Description	URI
Cystic Fibrosis	Genetic Home References	http://ghr.nlm.nih.gov/condition/cystic-fibrosis
Cystic Fibrosis Genetics	CF Foundation	http://ghr.nlm.nih.gov/condition/cystic-fibrosis
Emphysema Genetics Alpha-1 Antitrypsin Deficiency	The University of Utah	http://learn.genetics.utah.edu/content/disorders/whataregd/a1ad
American Lung Association		http://www.lung.org/lung-disease/tuberculosis/?gclid=CIq9iKqawLwCFeJF7AodVWEAbg
Asthma Genetics	The University of Utah	http://learn.genetics.utah.edu/content/health/history/asthma/
Asthma	CDC	http://www.cdc.gov/asthma/
American Lung Association	Lung Cancer	http://www.lung.org/lung-disease/tuberculosis/?gclid=CIq9iKqawLwCFeJF7AodVWEAbg
Lung Cancer	National Cancer Institute	http://www.cancer.gov/cancertopics/types/lung
My Cancer Genome		http://www.mycancergenome.org/content/disease/lung-cancer/ros1/67
Non-Small Cell Lung Cancer	NCCN Guidelines	http://www.nccn.org/professionals/physician_gls/pdf/nscl.pdf
Small Cell Lung Cancer		http://www.nccn.org/professionals/physician_gls/pdf/nscl.pdf
U.S. Equal Employment Opportunity Commission	Genetic information nondiscrimination act of 2008	http://www.eeoc.gov/laws/statutes/gina.cfm

TABLE 10.2. Clinical Effect of Alpha 1-Antitrypsin (AAT) by Genotype and Serum AAT Levels.

Genotype	Serum AAT Levels	Clinical Effect
Pi-MM	20–53 µmol/L	Normal
Pi-MS	20–48 µmol/L	Usually no clinical manifestations
Pi-SS	15–33 µmol/L	Usually no or only mild clinical manifestations
Pi-SZ	8–19 µmol/L	Increased risk of lung but not liver disease
Pi-MZ	12–35 µmol/L	Slightly increased risk of lung and liver disease
Pi-ZZ	2.5–7 µmol/L	High prevalence of severe disease
Pi-N/-	< 2.5 µmol/L	High prevalence of severe disease
Pi-N/N	None	High prevalence of severe disease

Adapted from Stoller, Lacbawan, & Aboussouan, 2006.

childhood- (jaundice, cirrhosis) or adult-onset (cirrhosis, fibrosis) liver disease; hepatocellular carcinoma, and other liver disorders. AAT mutations have also been associated with kidney disease and rheumatoid arthritis (Schlade-Bartusiak & Cox, 2008).

Even in individuals at theoretically high risk for developing severe emphysema or liver disease (i.e., Pi Z/Z), disease manifestations and COPD progression are highly variable, which suggests that other genes and environmental influences play a role in disease expression (Kelly *et al.*, 2010).

Chronic exposure to inflammatory stimuli, such as tobacco smoke or occupational fumes, frequent infections such as chronic bronchitis and pneumonia, and other lung disorders such as asthma all increase NE activity and accelerate lung damage in individuals with AAT deficiency (Kelly *et al.*, 2010). Prevention strategies include not smoking, avoiding secondhand smoke, and wearing a mask when exposed to chemical fumes or dust (Mason *et al.*, 2010).

Standard therapy for anyone with emphysema includes avoiding lung irritants, bronchodilators, steroids, oxygen therapy, rehabilitation, and lung volume reduction surgery in severe cases. AAT augmentation is an active area of research specifically addressing the special needs of individuals with AATD. Four AAT augmentation therapies have been developed and are actively being researched: (1) intravenous human plasma-derived augmentation therapy, (2) AAT inhalation therapy, (3) recombinant therapy, and (4) synthetic elastase inhibition therapy. Additional therapies under investigation include gene therapy by in-

jecting adeno-associated virus carrying the human *SERPINA1* gene, inhibiting intrahepatic polymerization of AAT, promoting hepatic secretion of AAT, inhibiting of neutrophil elastase by small molecule inhibitors, and prolonging the serum half-life of AAT (Stoller & Aboussouan, 2012; Brantly *et al.*, 2009).

Most cases of emphysema appear to be caused by a complex interplay of genetic susceptibility and environmental exposures, posing significant challenges to identifying specific genes associated with the disease (Wan & Silverman, 2009). Table 10.2 lists some of the genes other than AAT that may increase an individual's risk for developing emphysema.

Most of these candidate genes and alleles have been selected either because they play a role in regulating an important biochemical pathway (pathophysiologic hypothesis) or because they were identified through linkage or genome wide association studies.

10.2.2. Cystic Fibrosis

Cystic fibrosis is an autosomal recessive single-gene disorder that causes severe pulmonary and digestive system dysfunction (Knowles & Drumm, 2012). CF mutations are prevalent in white people of Northern European ancestry, less common in Hispanics, African-Americans, and Native Americans, and rare in Asians and Middle Easterners (Mogayzel & Flume, 2011). Approximately 1 in 25 Northern European Caucasians are "CF carriers," because they have one copy of a CF mutation, but are asymptomatic because one functioning gene produces enough normal protein to ensure normal lung and digestive function. About 30,000 Americans and 70,000 individuals worldwide do not produce normal protein levels, because they are born with 2 CF mutations (Mogayzel & Flume, 2011). These individuals often manifest with symptoms such as persistent cough, frequent lung infection, wheezing, shortness of breath, salty tasting skin, diarrhea, malnutrition, poor growth, weight loss, male infertility, and CF-related diabetes (CFRD) (NIH, 2012).

CF is caused by mutations in the CF transmembrane conductance regulator (*CFTR*) gene, a very large gene that encodes for a 1480-amino acid protein and that functions as a cyclic adenosine monophosphate–mediated (cAMPmediated) chloride channel (Cutting, 2010). Chloride channels transport negatively charged chloride ions across cell membranes, which osmotically pull water with them, regulating cell and tissue water levels and producing thin, freely flowing mucus, sweat, saliva, tears, and digestive enzymes that lubricate and protect organs and tissues such as the kidney, pancreas, intestine, heart, vas deferens, sweat ducts, and lungs (NIH, 2012; Guggino & Stanton, 2006). When chloride channels are not produced, or do not function correctly, water does not get across the membrane and secretions become thick and sticky, blocking block tubes, ducts, and passageways, especially in the lungs and pancreas (Rogan, Stolta, & Hornick, 2011). *CFTR* also regulates other important channels, including epithelial sodium channels (ENaC), potassium channels, and aquaporin water channels and plays a key role in the regulation of ATP-release mechanisms, anion exchangers, and sodium-bicarbonate transporters (Guggino & Stanton, 2006).

More than 1940 mutations have been identified (Cystic Fibrosis Gene Analysis Consortium, 2011) (Figure 10.1 and Figure 10.2), but the most common and one of the most severe CFTR mutations in the U.S. (70% of cases) is the *F508del* mutation, caused by a deletion of phenylalanine at position 508. *F508del* mutations cause misshapen (incorrectly folded) proteins to remain in the endoplasmic reticulum and degrade prematurely (Guggino & Stanton, 2006), effectively eliminating chloride channels and causing severe symptoms. *CFTR* mutations range from mild to severe, ranging from no *CFTR* expression at all,

unstable, truncated *CFTR* transcripts producing reduced chloride secretion or transfer of chloride across membranes, to a reduced amount of functional protein (Gibson, Burns, & Ramsey, 2003). The phenotype can vary widely depending on the type(s) of *CFTR* mutations an individual has inherited; people who inherit two severe mutations (such as *F508del*) may develop severe pulmonary and pancreatic exocrine insufficiency, whereas people who can still produce protein with at least some residual function may have relatively mild pulmonary and pancreatic symptoms (Knowles & Drumm, 2012). People who inherit one mild and one severe *CFTR* mutation (compound heterozygote) may be asymptomatic, may present with very mild symptoms such as sinusitis, or may be unaware they have CF until they learn they have CF during an infertility workup (Sosnay *et al.*, 2013).

Environmental factors and non-*CFTR* genetic variations of CF patients contribute to the various clinical CF phenotypes (Figure 10.3) (Knowles & Drumm, 2012). Environmental factors include secondhand smoke exposure, socioeconomic status, health care access, and air pollution (Collaco, Blackman, McGready, Naughton, & Cutting, 2010). Tumor growth factor-beta (TGF-β) has been associated with a worse pulmonary outcome in CF patients (Drumm *et al.*, 2005) as do genetic variants associated with reduced levels of mannose-binding lectin 2 (MBL2) (Dorfman *et al.*, 2008). Other modifier genes are listed in Table 10.3 (Davies, Alton, & Griesenbach, 2005).

Most people with CF attend school and work and have a better quality of life than in previous decades. Because of recent improvements in screening, treatments, and management of CF, patients with this disorder are living longer and

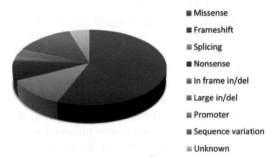

FIGURE 10.1. Distribution of *CFTR* gene mutations by type. Adapted from Cystic Fibrosis Gene Analysis Consortium, 2011.

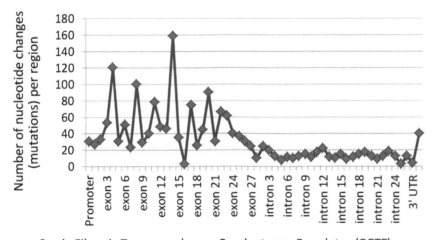

Cystic Fibrosis Transmembrane Conductance Regulator (*CFTR*) gene regions

FIGURE 10.2. Distribution of *CFTR* gene mutations by region. Adapted from Cystic Fibrosis Gene Analysis Consortium, 2011.

healthier lives (Cohen-Cymberknoh, Shoseyov, & Kerem, 2011). Although CF is not yet preventable, screening of at-risk individuals is widespread. At-risk individuals (Northern European Caucasians, Ashkenasi Jewish Ancestry, family history of CF) are offered screening in preconceptional and prenatal settings, and every state includes CF screening as part of the newborn screening tests to identify affected infants prior to the onset of symptoms (http://genes-r-us.uth-scsa.edu/sites/genes-r-us/files/nbsdisorders.pdf) (University of Maryland Medical Center, 2012).

All children with CF should be provided with nutrition and dietary counseling and closely monitored for growth and nutritional status. Individuals with pancreatic insufficiency should be offered early pancreatic enzyme replacement and vitamin supplementation to maintain weight and improve growth (Haupt, Kwasny, Schechter, & McColley, 2014). Treatment has historically been focused on supporting nutritional status and preventing and treating infection, but important strides have recently been made in correcting the underlying gene defect (Boyle & De Boeck, 2013).

TABLE 10.3. Emphysema Candidate Genes and Alleles.

Genes	Abbreviations	Higher Risk Alleles or SNPs
Matrix metalloproteinase 9	MMP9	T allele
Microsomal expoxide hydrolase	EPHX1	C allele
Heme oxygenase 1	HMOX1	L allele
Glutathione S-transferase P1	GST P1	A allele
Vitamin D binding protein	GC	IF allele
Beta$_2$-Adrenergic receptor	ADRB2	G allele (airway diameter)
TNF-alpha	TNF	A allele
Transforming growth factor-beta 1	TGFB1	Haplotype block of eight SNPs
Transforming growth factor-beta receptor-3	TGFBR3	SNPs (rs2296621 & rs2291477)
Bicaudal D homolog 1	BICD1	SNP (rs10844154)
Metallopeptidase inhibitor 2	TIMP2	SNP (rs2277698)
Serpin peptidase inhibitor, Clade E	SERPINE 2	SNPs (rs729631 & rs975278)
G protein-coupled receptor, family C, group 5, member A	GPRC5A	SNP (rs850937)
Latent transforming growth factor beta binding protein 4	LTBP4	SNP (rs947894)

Adapted from DeMeo *et al.*, 2007; Hersh *et al.*, 2009; Kong *et al.*, 2011.

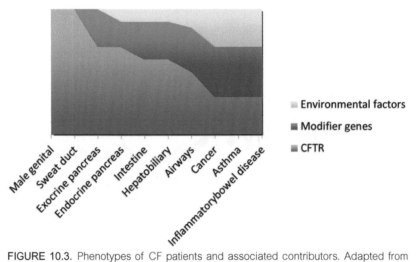

FIGURE 10.3. Phenotypes of CF patients and associated contributors. Adapted from Knowles & Drumm, 2012.

10.2.3. Primary Ciliary Dyskinesia

Primary ciliary dyskinesia (PCD) is a rare (prevalence 1/2,000 to 1/40,000 in the U.S.) autosomal recessive disorder that alters the structure and function of cilia, most notably the cilia in the respiratory tract (Boon, Jorissen, Proesmans & De Boeck, 2013). Affected individuals cannot effectively clear mucus from their respiratory tract, so bacteria accumulate, causing chronic otitis, sinusitis, and pulmonary infections. Over 75% of affected neonates develop pneumonia and transient tachypnea that often requires prolonged supplemental oxygen, and childhood bronchiectasis often persists into adulthood. Many individuals develop chronic sinus infection, and severe recurrent ear infections, and up to 50% of affected boys are infertile because of abnormalities in sperm motility (Boon *et al.*, 2013).

In addition to the pulmonary manifestations, genes involved in cilia regulation are now known to play important roles in the development of "laterality" during embryogenesis. Up to 50% of affected individuals have asymptomatic situs inversus totalis, in which virtually all internal organs are transposed: the heart is on the right side of the thorax (dextrocardia); the liver and gallbladder are on the left, and the stomach and spleen are on the right side of the abdomen; the right lung is bilobed and the left lung is trilobed; and the intestines, blood vessels, and nerves are reversed (Sutherland & Ware, 2009). Up to 6% of infants with PCD are born with more significant

and complex congenital anomalies known as heterotaxy, which is characterized by major congenital cardiac defects and other structural anomalies involving organs that develop as "pairs," such as the kidney and lung, and abnormal positioning of the stomach, intestines, liver, and lungs (Zariwala, Knowles, & Leigh, 2013).

Mutations associated with autosomal recessive PCD have been linked to 17 genes distributed across 11 chromosomes, all of which in some way influence the function or structure of proteins that form structural components of cilia or contribute to the force responsible for movement of ciliary bodies (Zariwala *et al.*, 2013). It is important to realize that much remains to be learned about the genetics of PCD, because more than 30% of individuals with PCD do not have a known mutation. Individuals suspect for the disorder should be counseled and tested by clinicians with expertise in the disorder.

10.3. COMPLEX DISORDERS

10.3.1. Infectious Disease

Individuals living during the mid-1800s had a life expectancy of less than 30 years, often because they died of fever during childhood. Infectious diseases were commonly believed to be caused by intrinsic factors, such as lethargy, fear, or sadness, because only a proportion of at-risk individuals developed particular diseases (Riley, 2005; Chapman & Hill, 2012). The association between family history and susceptibility to developing particular respiratory disorders was also recognized, because cases of tuberculosis tended to cluster within households, reinforcing the belief that tuberculosis was inherited (Chapman & Hill, 2012). At the dawn of the 20th Century, as germ theory began to emerge and tuberculosis was found to be caused by *Mycobacterium tuberculosis*, attention shifted away from individual factors (e.g., heredity) to the pathogen, and at least some diseases, notably infectious diseases, were now thought to have an extrinsic cause (Casanova & Abel, 2013). In 1931, Sir Archibald Edward Garrod, an English physician and a pioneer in the field of inborn errors of metabolism, attempted to refocus attention on the individual, proposing that individuals could be genetically predisposed to acquiring particular diseases (Garrod, 1931).

A current theory that inherited genetic predisposition may increase the risk for developing infectious diseases is gaining empiric support. Recent twin studies have found that genetic factors play a role in increasing susceptibility to acquiring tuberculosis, leprosy, poliomyelitis, and hepatitis B, and a study of adopted children found that a child was at significantly greater risk for dying from infection if his or her biological parent had also died prematurely from an infectious disease (Chapman & Hill, 2012).

A theoretical model that ascribes hereditary susceptibility to infection is based on the hypothesis that children who develop life-threatening primary infections may have inherited a single-gene predisposition to that particular infection (Table 10.5), whereas adults who develop a secondary infection or experience a reactivation of an earlier infection are likely to have a much more complex gene/environment explanation for the development of disease (Alcaïs *et al.*, 2010). This complex interaction of genes and environment creates disorders that are difficult to diagnose and treat, let alone determine how to prevent symptoms or exacerbation of the illness.

10.3.2. Neonatal Respiratory Distress Syndrome

Neonatal respiratory distress syndrome (RDS) is a complex disorder that develops when pulmonary surfactant levels are low in newborn lungs (Speer, 2011). Surfactant is a complex mixture of lipids, proteins, and glycoproteins produced, assembled, transported, secreted, and recycled by Type II pneumocytes. Surfactant is a slippery liquid that reduces surface tension inside the alveoli, preventing them from collapsing at the end of exhalation, which reduces the effort required to re-inflate them during inhalation. Full-term infants usually produce adequate surfactant, but preterm infants are at high risk for RDS because adequate surfactant production does not begin until late in pregnancy. Type II pneumocytes appear at approximately 24 weeks gestation but do not produce adequate surfactant levels until approximately 35 weeks gestation (Nkadi, Merritt, & Pillers, 2009).

Symptoms of RDS include apnea, cyanosis, grunting, inspiratory stridor, intercostal or subcostal retractions, nasal flaring, poor feeding, tachypnea, and a diffuse "ground glass" appearance on chest radiographs (Nkadi, Merritt, & Pillers, 2009). Antenatal corticosteroids and surfactant replacement have been shown to improve morbidity and mortality in preterm infants with RDS, non-Hispanic white infants had better outcomes than black or Hispanic infants independent of gestational age, weight, and other sociodemographic factors (Frisbie, Song, Powers, & Street, 2004; Kavvadia, Greenough, Dimitriou, & Hooper, 1998). More recent studies examining these findings have found that these outcome differences are most likely not attributable to biological differences, but to health care disparities. Data from a study examining birth certificate data from 19 states revealed that in 2006, white infants born at 28 weeks were 1.4 times more likely to receive surfactant than black infants and nearly twice as likely to be treated with surfactant then Hispanic infants. The disparity was even greater for infants born slightly older (28 to 31 weeks), with white infants receiving surfactant 1.8 times and 2.6 times more often compared to black and Hispanic infants at similar gestational ages. Antenatal steroids have been shown to significantly reduce mortality and morbidity, so disparities associated with maternal access to care also contribute to the ethnic divide (Rowley & Hogan, 2012).

Several maternal and fetal candidate genes and gene pathways have been independently associated with an increased risk for neonatal RDS.

Haas, *et al.* (2012) examined the association between maternal and fetal genetic polymorphisms in drug metabolism (specifically *CYP3A5*) and betamethasone (BMZ) pathways on neonatal RDS. A total of 109 mothers delivered 117 infants at a mean gestational age of 32.2 weeks, and 49% of the infants went on to develop neonatal RDS. An increased risk for neonatal RDS was associated with SNPs in maternal *CYP3A5* and glucocorticoid receptor pathway, and with SNPs in fetal adenylate cyclase 9 gene (*ADCY9*) and *CYP3A7* pathways (Haas *et al.*, 2012). A secondary analysis of the Haas data revealed several additional maternal and fetal SNPs in *IPO13*, a member of the importin-beta family of genes that encode for nuclear transport proteins. Mutations in fetal *IPO13* genes appear to be associated with the development of neonatal RDS despite antenatal corticosteroid treatment (Haas *et al.*, 2013). Prior to this study, mutations in the importin-beta family had only been associated with rabies and endometrial carcinoma. Genomic studies are increasingly valuable, because they open up new areas of research, improving disease understanding, and ultimately improving health outcomes.

10.3.3. Asthma

Asthma is a chronic inflammatory disease of the small airways of the respiratory system characterized by airway narrowing. Symptoms include wheezing, breathlessness, chest tightness, and coughing at night or early in the morning (Zahran, Bailey, & Garbe, 2011). Asthma is a complex disease that clusters in families, suggesting that genetics plays an important role in the predisposition and/or development of the disease. A number of different biochemical pathways, such as IgE, eosinophil levels, and bronchial hyperactivity, are associated with asthma development, so single-gene changes do not adequately explain heritability and susceptibility to asthma. It is thought that epigenetic factors, discussed in Chapter 1; environmental exposures; and developmental influences all play important roles in the development of disease, particularly because disease prevalence has increased over the past 30 years in both developed and developing countries (Durham, Wiegman, & Adcock, 2011, Vercelli, 2008). Known environmental triggers include air pollutants, respiratory viruses, tobacco smoke, airborne allergens, and endotoxins (Mukherjee & Zhang, 2011), and emerging evidence suggesting that dietary fiber can reduce allergic responses in the lung, decreasing asthma risk (Huffnagle, 2014). Allergen exposure increases the risk for developing allergic asthma, and exposure in infancy and early childhood in particular is associated with persistent symptoms. Clinical manifestations vary depending on the type of allergen (mold, pollen, dust) and the route of exposure (food vs. inhalant). Food allergies with skin and gastrointestinal manifestations are more common in young children, and with advancing age, inhaled allergens become more problematic (Rosenkranz, Rosenkranz, & Neessen, 2012).

Although many infants and young children have at least one wheezing episode during the first three years of life, children who experience recurrent wheezing, atopic dermatitis, or severe asthma symptoms are at increased risk for developing persistent asthma. Even in children with persistent asthma, however, symptoms often subside with age; by age 6, only 30% of children continue to wheeze (Castro-Rodriguez, 2011).

Asthma has long been recognized as having a genetic basis, because affected individuals tend to cluster in families, and there are marked sex and age differences. Asthma is more commonly diagnosed in boys than girls during the first decade of life and girls are diagnosed more often than boys after puberty (Rosenkranz *et al.*, 2012). Early twin studies found that asthma concordance was 4 times greater in monozygotic twins than it was in dizygotic twins (19% vs. 4.8%) (Edfors-Lubs, 1971). Genetics alone does not adequately explain asthma incidence and prevalence, however, because many children with asthma have no family history, and children who have family members with asthma do not always develop the disease (Rosenkranz *et al.*, 2012). Recent studies have shown that during the first year of life most of the variance in asthma prevalence is attributable to environmental exposures, but by age 3, genetic effects, rather than environmental, were more strongly associated with asthma than the environment (Bunyavanich, *et al.* 2013).

Locating the genes associated with asthma has been a challenge, because the disease is complex, involving interactions between many genes and different environmental triggers. Before massive parallel sequencing became commercially available in 2005, linkage analysis and gene association studies identified several genes thought to be associated with asthma, most of which regulated genes involved in regulating immunity or allergic inflammation. Advances in gene sequencing technology now make it possible to sequence billions of gene bases in a single analysis. Since this technology became available, large population based studies known as Genome Wide Association Studies (GWASs) have examined the genomes of thousands of patients looking for genetic spelling differences between individuals with and without asthma. The first GWAS to report an association between a previously unknown gene and asthma was published in 2007 (Moffatt *et al.*, 2007) and, since then, several other large GWAS studies have identified previously unknown genes and biological pathways associated with the development of asthma (Perin & Potočnik, 2014).

Identifying candidate asthma genes is further complicated, because genes appear to assort by phenotype; *CD14* is associated with adult but not childhood asthma and *CCR5* does not appear to play a major role in the development of asthma in people with atopic asthma, but has been associated with disease in people with nonatopic asthma. GWASs are also helping to identify genes associated with asthma severity and progression (Perin & Potočnik, 2014). In general, candidate genes can be categorized into four broad functional groups: (1) genes associated with innate immunity and immunoregulation, (2) genes associated with T helper 2– (Th2–) cell differentiation and effector functions, (3) genes associated with epithelial biology and mucosal immunity, and (4) genes associated with lung function, airway remodeling, and disease severity (see Table 10.4) (Vercelli, 2008; March, Sleiman, & Hakonarson, 2013).

10.3.3.1. Genes Associated with Immunity and Inflammation

A large GWAS published in 2007 identified a previously unknown gene on the long arm of chromosome 17 (17q21) that encodes for transmembrane proteins in the endoplasmic reticulum. They found that *ORMDL3* was strongly and reproducibly associated with childhood onset asthma (Moffatt *et al.*, 2007). The gene appears

TABLE 10.4. Modifier Genes in Cystic Fibrosis (CF) Phenotypes.

Classification of Modifier Genes	Product of Modifier Genes
Antiproteases	Alpha 1-antitrypsin (α-1-AT)
Inflammation	HLA region, TNF-α
Nitric oxide synthesis	NOS-1, NOS-3
Growth factors	TGF-β
Innate immunity	MBL-2
Airway responsiveness	β-AR

Adapted from Davies, Alton, & Griesenbach, 2005.

to play a role in regulating calcium levels and mediating cellular stress, which may partially explain its role in regulating inflammation (Cantero-Recasens *et al.*, 2010).

10.3.3.2. Genes Associated with T helper 2-Cell Differentiation and Effector Functions

Inflammation plays a central role in the development of asthma (Jafer, Mahmood, Fatah, & Jasim, 2007), and many genes have been associated with allergic asthma. Immune-mediated asthma is triggered when allergens and viruses prompt naïve CD4+ T cells to transform into T helper (Th) cells, often Th2 cells, that in turn secrete interleukin (IL)-4, IL-5, IL-9 and IL-13 cytokines. These inflammatory cytokines are responsible for many of the pathophysiologic features of asthma, including airway inflammation, mucus secretion, and airway hyperresponsiveness (Georas, Guo, De Fanis, & Casolaro, 2005). A number of different inflammatory profiles have been developed based on eosinophil levels, mucin composition, development of subepithelial fibrosis, and tissue response to corticosteroids (Choy *et al.*, 2011) In adults with mild to moderate asthma, Th2 expression was strongly correlated with both eosinophilia and allergy and involved a complex interplay between 79 genes regulating cytokines, chemokines, and growth factors and other inflammatory mediators (Choy *et al.* 2011).

10.3.3.3. Genes Associated with Epithelial Biology and Mucosal Immunity

Epithelial cells in the upper airway form the

body's 1st line of defense against allergens, as the allergen triggers receptors that stimulate recruitment and activation of immune cells (Eisele & Anderson, 2011). GWAS studies have located several genes (*L18R1, IL33, SMAD3, ORMDL3, HLA-DQ*, and *IL2RB*) associated with inflammation in human airways, many of which had not previously been associated with asthma, so the biological mechanisms influencing the development of disease are still being evaluated (Zhang, Moffatt, & Cookson, 2012).

10.3.3.4. Genes Associated with Lung Function, Airway Remodeling and Disease Severity

Four polymorphisms (rs1042711, rs1042713, rs1042714, and rs1800888) in the beta-adrenergic receptor B2 (*ADRB2*) gene have been associated with reduced lung function in children with asthma. Children with a particular *ADRB2* polymorphism had a significantly lower risk of reduced lung function whether or not they were exposed to asthma triggers, such as tobacco

TABLE 10.5. *Examples of Genetic Mutations Associated with Respiratory Infections.*

Disorder	Signs & Symptoms	Genetic Mutation
MECP2 duplication syndrome	Males, weak muscle tone in infancy, poor or absent speech, seizures, delayed development of motor skills, recurrent respiratory infections	Extra copy of *MECP2*, q arm of X chromosome in each cell. Inherited in Xlinked pattern.
Mucolipidosis III alpha/beta (lysosomal disorder)	Begin age 3, heart valve abnormalities, mild clouding of the cornea, coarse facial features, frequent ear & respiratory infections, intellectual disability or leaning problems	*GNPTAB* coding for GlcNAc-1-phosphotransferase. Mutations disrupts "tagging" of enzyme for delivery to lysosomes.
Fucosidosis	Impaired growth; abnormal bone development, seizures, spasticity, angiokeratomas, distinctive "coarse" facial, recurrent respiratory infections and abnormally large abdominal organs	*FUCA1* codes for alpha-L-fucosidase. Mutation reduces or eliminates activity of the enzyme causing incomplete breakdown of glycolipids and glycoproteins. Accumulation causes malfunction, especially in brain.
Larsen syndrome	Infants born with clubfeet and dislocations of the hips, knees, and elbows, prominent forehead, midface hypoplasia, ocular hypertelorism, respiratory problems, apnea, and frequent respiratory infections	*FLNB* gene codes for filamin B protein to build cytoskeleton. Mutations cause change in amino acids or delete a small section of the protein sequence resulting in an abnormal protein. This new protein has atypical function which impairs ossification.
Trichothiodystrophy (TTD)	Sparse, brittle hair that is easily broken, developmental delays, significant intellectual disability, recurrent respiratory infections, short stature, sensitive to UV rays causing severe sunburn after few minutes in the sun. Many do not sweat.	Mutations in one of three genes: *ERCC2, ERCC3*, or *GTF2H5*. Proteins from these genes have a role in transcription. Mutations will impair both DNA repair and gene transcription.
Nijmegen breakage syndrome	Short stature, microcephaly, distinctive facial features, recurrent respiratory tract infections, increased risk of cancer, intellectual disability, and other health problems	*NBN* codes for the nibrin protein. It is associated with DNA repair. Mutations cause short version of the nibrin protein with defective areas preventing it from effectively responding to DNA damage. Inherited in autosomal recessive pattern.
X-linked retinitis pigmentosa	Progressive vision loss, chronic respiratory and sinus infections, recurring otitis media, and hearing loss	*RPFR* gene with mutations causing malfunction of the cilia. Located on Xp21.1.

Adapted from *Genetics Home Reference* (November 25, 2013). Respiratory Infections. Retrieved November 30, 2013, from http://ghr.nlm.nih.gov/search?query=respiratory+infections.

TABLE 10.6. Examples of Genes Associated with Asthma.

Genetic Analysis Approaches	Identified Genes
Candidate-gene association	*IL10, CTLA4, IL13, IL4, CD14, HAVCR1, LTC4S, LTA, TNF, HLA-DRB1, HLA-DQB1, HLA-DPB1, FCER1B, IL18, STAT6, CMA1, IL4R, FLG, SPINK5, CC16, NOS1, CCL11, CCL5, GSTM1, ADRB2, GPRA, NAT2, GSTP1, ACE, TBXA2R, TGFB1, ADAM33, GSTT1*
Genome-wide linkage	*DPP10, GPRA, HLAG, ADAM33, PHF11, CYFIP2, IRAK3, COL6A5, OPN3/CHML*
Genome-wide association	*ORMDL3, CHI3L1, ILIRL1, IKZF2, GATA2, IL5, SH2B3, TLE4, PDE4D, PDE11A, RAD50, HLA-DR/DQ, ADRA1B, PRNP, DPP10, IL1RL1/IL18R1, HLA-DQ, IL33, SMAD3, IL2RB, ORMDL3/GSDMB, HLA-DPA/HLA-DPB1, DENND1B, IL6R, CII ORF30/LRRC32, USP38-GAB1, TSLP/WDR36, NOTCH4/HLA-DRA/HLA-DQA2/IKZF4, LOC338591, IKZF4/CDK2, GSDMB, IL1RL1, TSLP, IL33, PYHIN1, C11orf71, CRCT1, ORMDL3, C11orf30/LRRC32, TMEM232/SLCA25A46, HLA region, FCER1A, IL13, HLA-A, STAT6/NAB2, DARC, HLA-DQA2, FCER1A, STAT6, RAD50, CHRNA3/5, FAM13A, RAB4B/EGLN2/MIA/CYP2A6, HHIP, GPR126, ADAM19, AGER-PPT2, FAM13A, PTCH1, PID1, HTR4, INTS12-GSTCD-NPNT, TNS1, GSTCD, AGER, THSD4, MFAP2, TGFB2, HDAC4, RARB, MECOM, SPATA9, ZKSCAN3, NCR3, ARMC2, C10orf11, LRP1, CCDC38, MMP15, CFDP1, KCNE2, DLEU7*

Adapted from Vercelli, 2008; March, Sleiman, & Hakonarson, 2013.

smoke exposure, sex, and animal dander (Torjussen *et al.*, 2013).

10.3.4. Lung Cancer

More men and women die each year from lung cancer in the U.S. than from any other type of cancer, and lung cancer is the 2nd most commonly diagnosed cancer (after non-melanoma skin cancer) in America. In 2010, more than 200,000 people were diagnosed with lung cancer, and 150,000 died from the disease. The average five-year survival rate is less than 10%, a sad statistic that has not changed in over 15 years. Lung cancer is also an "equal opportunity" disease, killing men and women at roughly equivalent rates irrespective of race or ethnicity (U.S. Cancer Statistics Working Group, 2013).

The vast majority (85–90%) of lung cancer cases can be traced back to voluntary or involuntary (secondhand) tobacco exposure (National Comprehensive Cancer Network [NCCN], 2014), but emerging research has shown that genetic predisposition may be important as well (Brennan, Hainaut, & Boffera, 2011). First-, second-, and third-degree relatives of affected individuals were all at increased risk for developing lung cancer, particularly when exposed to tobacco smoke, and the risk was even higher in relatives of patients with early-onset disease (Jons-

son *et al.*, 2004). Identifying the gene variants associated with an increased risk for lung cancer can help clarify the natural history of the disease and assist clinicians in developing personalized screening and prevention plans (Brennan *et al.*, 2011).

Germline mutations associated with lung cancer have been identified in several large GWASs (Jonsson *et al.*, 2004, Yamamoto *et al.*, 2014, Cote *et al.*, 2012). *TP53* mutations have been associated with a number of different cancers, including sarcomas, breast cancer, brain tumors, leukemia, adrenocortical cancer, and lung cancer. *TP53*, described as "the guardian of the genome," is a tumor suppressor gene that plays a critical role in regulating the cell cycle, killing abnormally developing cells, and preventing cancer (National Library of Medicine, 2007). Early genomic research noted that lung tumor cells often had acquired mutations in oncogenes (such as *KRAS*) and tumor suppressor genes (such as *TP53*). These researchers noted that in cancer cells, a specific region on the short arm of chromosome 17 often had both a point mutation and a deletion. At around the same time, a germline mutation at 17p13.1 was identified in individuals with Le Fraumini, a cancer syndrome that significantly increases an individual's risk for developing cancer at an early age, including lung carcinoma in the absence of tobacco exposure (Gibbons, Byers, & Kurie 2014).

Glutathione S-transferase M1 and T1 (GSTM1 and GSTT1 respectively) are members of a family of enzymes that promote the excretion of carcinogens found in tobacco smoke. These carcinogens include acetaldehyde, polycyclic aromatic hydrocarbons, 2-naphthylamine, and nicotine. The GSTM1 and GSTT1 enzymes have also been found to induce isothiocyanates found in cruciferous vegetables and may confer protection against lung cancer. That said, however, emerging evidence has also shown that GSTM1 and GSTT1 enzymes can form toxic byproducts as well, possibly increasing the risk for lung cancer, so they may not be completely benign. Three alleles have been identified in *GSTM1* (*0, *A, and *B), and two alleles have been identified in *GSTT1* (*1 and *0), making this a complex condition with many possible genetic combinations (Rotunno *et al.*, 2012). Many people have been found to carry either a *GSTM1* or *GSTT1* mutation, but some people have deletions in both genes *GSTM1* and *GSTT1*, some have deletions in either *GSTM1* or *GSTT1*, or others are missing *GSTM1* with normal function in *GSTT1*. Any of these genotypes can alter lung cancer risk estimates. The more *GSTT1* deletions were present, the higher the lung cancer risk, particularly in men. There is some question if the same mutations may actually be *protective* in people who have never smoked and in women, possibly because the down-regulated genes produce fewer genotoxic chemicals (Rotunno *et al.*, 2012).

Ethnicity and smoking history have been correlated with the development of lung cancer and three chromosomes sites (Yang, Holloway, & Fong, 2013). GWASs conducted in Caucasian smokers have found strong associations between genes in three chromosomal regions: the long arm of chromosome 15 (*CHRNA3* and *CHRNA3*) and the short arms of chromosomes 5 (*TERT*) and 6 (*BAT3-MSH5*). Studies in other ethnic groups have not found the same associations. In Asian smokers, these same chromosomal regions appear to be important in the development of lung cancer, but other regions may be more important, particularly in Asian females who have never smoked. In these patients, risk loci have also been found on the long arm of chromosomes 19 (*CYP2A6*) and 3 (*TP63*) (Yang *et al.*, 2013).

Other genes have also been associated with an increased risk for lung cancer in smokers, including the gene associated with retinoblastoma (*RB1*) (Foulkes, 2008), and the *CHEK2* gene, which is also associated with a number of other cancers (Brennan *et al.*, 2011). Approximately 10% of lung cancer occurs in people who deny ever smoking or who report smoking fewer than 100 cigarettes during their lifetime (Subramanian & Govindan, 2007). Ethnic differences in lung cancer risk among nonsmokers are startling; the percentage of lung cancers associated with non-smoking in Asia is upwards of 40% (Govindan *et al.*, 2012). In the U.S., some nonsmokers with lung cancer have been found to have a mutation in the *GPC5* gene, thought to function as a tumor suppressor, located on the long arm (*q*) of chromosome 13 (Li, Sheu, & Ye, 2010; Li & Yang, 2011).

There are two major types of lung cancers, small cell lung cancer (SCLC) and non-small cell lung cancer (NSCLC), categorized by how the cancer cells look under a microscope. NSCLC is the most common type, is less aggressive, and

TABLE 10.7. Asthma Related Genes Identified in Four Different Categories.

Functions of Gene Products	Identified Genes
Innate immunity and immunoregulation	CD14, TLR2, TLR4, TLR6, TLR10, NOD1, NOD2, IL10, TGFB1, STAT3, MHC Class II molecules, PDGER2
T helper 2– (T$_H$2-) cell differentiation and effector functions	TBX21, IL12B, GATA3, IL4, IL13, STAT6, FCERIB, IL5, IL5RA, IL4RA
Epithelial biology and mucosal immunity	CCL5, CCL11, CCL24, DEFB1, CC16, FLG, SPINK5
Lung function, airway remodeling and disease severity	ADRB2, TNF, TGB1, LTC4S, GSTP1, GSTM1, TBXA2R, ALOX5, TNFB, TNC, NOS1

Adapted from Vercelli, 2008; March, Sleiman, & Hakonarson, 2013.

TABLE 10.8. *Predictive and Prognostic Biomarkers Associated with Non-small Cell Lung Cancer (NSCLC) Types.*

Biomarker	Genetic Effect	Lung CA Type	Predictive	Prognostic	Therapy
AKT 1[a]	~1% frequency in tumors but E17K mutations in AKT1 = 88%	NSCLC	Unknown		Unknown, but found with EGFR and ALK wild-type driver mutations.
ALK fusion oncogene[a,b]	Fusion between ALK and other genes	NSCLC-Adenocarcinoma Mixed squamous cell histology (non-smokers, small biopsy specimens or mixed histology)	✓	✓	ALK TKIs; HSP90 inhibitors; EGFR TKIs Anti-EGFR antibodies unknown
ALK[a,b]	Gene rearrangements. Non-overlapping with other NSCLC oncogenic mutations				Resistant to TKI therapy
BRAF[a,b]GG (466V) (G469L) (Y472C) (L597V) (V600E)	Driver mutation & gene rearrangement Usually found in tumors with EGFR, ALK and other driver mutations	NSCLC	✓		
DDR2-New[b] (S768R)	Mutation	NSCLC-Squamous	Unknown	Unknown	Unknown
EGFR[b]	Wild-type	NSCLC	Less sensitive	No role	
EGFR[a]	Exon 19 deletion Exon 21 L858R mutation (Sensitizing EGFR mutations)	NSCLC-Adenocarcinoma Mixed squamous cell histology (non-smokers, small biopsy specimens or mixed histology)	Predicts treatment benefit from EGFR-tyrosine kinase therapy		Activate TK domain; sensitive to small mole TKIs (erlotinib, geftinib & afatinib)
EGFR[b]	Point mutations at Exon 21 (L86IQ) & Exon 18 (G719X)		✓		
EGFR[b]	Acquired T790M mutation				Acquire resistance to TKI therapy

(continued)

TABLE 10.8 (continued). Predictive and Prognostic Biomarkers Associated with Non-small Cell Lung Cancer (NSCLC) Types.

Biomarker	Genetic Effect	Lung CA Type	Predictive	Prognostic	Therapy
ERCC1	Endonuclease			High levels predictive of better survival, independent of therapy	
HER2	Driver mutation & gene rearrangement (Exon 20 insertion)	NSCLC	✓		Response unknown at this time
KRAS	Mutations-Most common Transform immortalized cells, promote proliferation, and survival	NSCLC- 25% adenocarcinomas Associated w/ cigarette smoking	✓	Prognostic of poor survival. Mutation has better survival than wildtype	Resistant to platinum/vinorelbine therapy & EGFR TKI therapy. KRAS specific targeted therapy not available
KRAS[a,b]	Oncogenes				✓
MET[a,b]	Gene amplification	NSCLC	✓ Increased sensitivity to MET TKIs		Confers decreased sensitivity to EGFR TKIs
RET fusions[a,b]	Gene rearrangement on 10q11.2	NSCLC-adenocarcinoma			Unknown response to RET TKIs
ROS1[a,b]	Gene rearrangement on 6q22 Non-overlapping with EGFR & KRAS mutations or ALK fusions	NSCLC	✓		

Predictive = indicative of therapeutic outcome; Prognostic=suggests patient survival independent of treatment received.
Created from the following:
aMy Cancer Genome, N.D.
bNCCN Guidelines—NSCLC (2014). Predictive and prognostic biomarkers. NCCN Guidelines version 3.2014.

has higher survival rates, depending on the stage at diagnosis. SCLC is less common, comprising approximately 15% of all lung cancers. It typically starts in the bronchi, is aggressive, often metastasizes, and is more common in males and smokers (Seidel, 2013; Kalemkerian, Akerley, Bogner, et al, 2013).

There is currently no designated role for genetics in the detection, personalized management or prognosis of SCLC. A few studies in cell lines or mouse models have targeted *PTEN* mutations and *PIK3CA* activating mutations in SCLC, but the relevance of these signaling pathways remains unclear. A recent study revealed if the *PTEN* gene is inactivated, at least in the mouse model, SCLC accelerates, which suggests a therapeutic option for a subset of patients (Cui *et al.*, 2014).

More is known about the genes involved in the development and regulation of NSCLC, perhaps because the cancer is more common or because people with NSCLC tend to live longer than those with SCLC. NSCLC is divided histologically into adenocarcinoma, squamous cell cancer, and large-cell lung cancer (Brennan *et al.*, 2011). Adenocarcinoma more commonly arises from mutations that activate *EGFR* (epidermal growth factor receptor) genes, which stimulate cell growth; from proliferation; or from mutations that alter *KRAS* (V-Ki-ras2 Kirsten Rat Sarcoma viral oncogene) genes, which regulate tissue signaling, an important first step in the development of cancer. Interestingly, *KRAS* and *EGFR* mutations are usually mutually exclusive, and the presence of one or the other has implications for management (Suda, Tomizawa, & Mitsudomi, 2010). Patients with *EGFR* mutations are more likely to have a family history of lung cancer (He *et al.*, 2013), are less likely to have smoked, and are more likely to be diagnosed with adenocarcinoma than patients without the mutation (He *et al.*, 2013). *KRAS* mutations are more commonly found in smokers, in women, and in patients of Asian ethnicity (Davidson, Gazdar, & Clarke, 2013). The presence of an *EGFR* mutation can also help predict how a patient will respond to certain chemotherapy agents. Tumors that have acquired an *EGFR* mutation are likely (60%) to respond to erlotinib (Tarceva), whereas tumors that have acquired a *KRAS* mutation (and have normal *EGFR* genes) are unlikely (5%) to respond (Suda *et al.*, 2010).

Squamous cell tumors often contain many different mutations (copy number variants, rearrangements, etc.); in one study, 11 genes, including *TP53*, were consistently seen in nearly all specimens (Hammerman, Lawrence, Voet, & Jing, 2012). Many of these mutations are involved in regulating important cell functions, such as immune regulation (*HLA-A* class I major histocompatibility genes), cell signaling (*NFE2L2* and *KEAP1*), cell differentiation, kinase pathways (*CDKN2A* and *RB1*) (Hammerman *et al.*, 2012), chromatin modifications, and DNA repair pathways (*DACH1, CFTR, RELN, ABCB5,* and *HGF*). Many of these mutations are being identified in genes not previously considered important in the development of lung cancer, so this research is creating exciting new opportunities for therapy.

10.4. CASE STUDY

A 22-year-old, nonsmoking, adult, white male of Northern European ancestry was admitted from the emergency room to the inpatient medical unit of the hospital with a diagnosis of bilateral pneumothorax after a 3-day history of intermittent chest tightness and dyspnea that had progressively worsened within the last several hours. Past medical and surgical history are unremarkable, and the patient is taking no prescription or over-the-counter medications and denies a history of drug or alcohol use. Physical assessment revealed bilateral decreased breath sounds, hyper-resonant percussion notes, and numerous pinpoint papules on his forehead, face, neck, upper trunk, and back. Chest x-ray revealed pneumothoraces and several bullae. A chest computed tomography (CT) scan revealed several other pneumothoraces and multiple pulmonary cysts bilaterally.

Family health history revealed the following: father age 59 years had a history of recurrent pneumothoraces at the ages of 28, 41, 44, and 46 years of age; paternal aunt also had a history of pneumothorax at age of 38 and died at age 54 from renal cancer; paternal grandmother died at age 46 of an undiagnosed "respiratory problem" (she was a nonsmoker). Based on this history, the family history was further expanded to include a three-generational pedigree (see Figure 10.4). Additional information identified the patient's

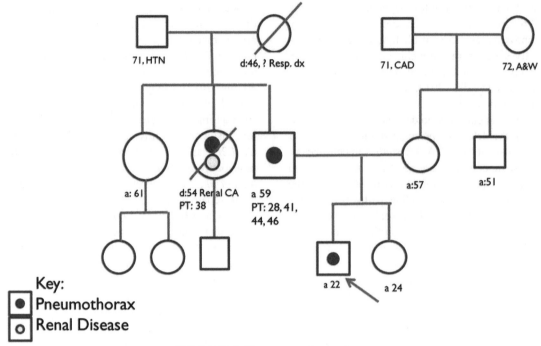

FIGURE 10.4. Three-generation pedigree

sibling, a sister age 24 years, without a history of pneumothorax and whose medical and surgical history are currently unremarkable; another paternal aunt age 61 years with smoking history but no pneumothorax and unremarkable medical and surgical history; and three paternal first cousins with no history of respiratory problems and unremarkable medical and surgical history. The maternal lineage was noncontributory.

With the patient's current history of lung cysts; pneumothorax coupled with dermatologic feature of papules on the face, neck, and upper extremity; a paternal family history significant for renal cancer; and multiple family members with pneumothoraces, BirtHogg-Dube syndrome (BHDS) was suspected. The patient was counseled on the syndrome and after informed consent, genetic testing was done to determine if there was a mutation in the folliculin (*FLCN*) gene. Results from the genetic testing identified one of the common germline mutations, at c.1285dupC (a C insertion in the exon 11 causing a frameshift), in the *FLCN* gene. Other paternal family members were tested, and the proband's sister and father were also found to have deleterious mutations. Because the living aunt was not positive, her children were not tested.

10.4.1. Birt-Hogg-Dube Syndrome

BHDS, a rare autosomal dominant genetic syndrome (Nickerson *et al.*, 2002) is associated with mutations in the *FLCN* gene. *FLCN*, which acts as a tumor suppressor, encodes for the folliculin protein, which interacts with both the mechanistic target of rapamycin (mTOR) and AMP-activated protein kinase (AMPK) signaling pathways (Toro, 2008). Genetic testing using sequence analysis can detect up to 88% of mutations in affected individuals, but some individuals with BHDS features have not been found to have a known *FLCN* mutation (Toro, 2008).

BHDS is a genodermatosis characterized by follicular hamartomas, kidney tumors, and spontaneous pneumothorax (Toro, 2008). Individuals with a *FLCN* mutation have a 30 to 50 fold increased risk over the general population for spontaneous pneumothorax and a 7 to 9 fold increased risk for renal neoplasias. They often have pulmonary cysts and renal tumors that are typically bilateral and multifocal (Stamatakis, Metwalli, Middleton, & Linehan, 2013). Although different types of renal tumors have been associated with BHDS, the types most commonly seen in affected individuals are hybrid chromophobe/

oncocytic tumors (67%), chromophobe tumors (23%), or oncocytoma, a benign renal tumor (3%) (Toro, 2008). Clear cell and papillary renal carcinomas have also been reported, but these occur less frequently (Toro, 2008). Other less common clinical features of BHDS include parotid oncocytoma, multiple lipomas, angiolipomas, intestinal polyposis, neural tissue tumors, parathyroid adenomas, and large connective tissue nevi. Most clinical manifestations emerge during in the third decade of life, with an average age of onset of twenty-five years (Toro *et al.*, 2007).

Initial evaluation should include a detailed skin examination and high-resolution CT scan or chest CT scan to assess for pulmonary cysts; if pneumothorax symptoms are present, a chest x-ray and chest CT scan should be done to confirm the diagnosis (Toro, 2008). If renal disease is not the presenting symptom, baseline screening (magnetic resonance imaging [MRI], abdominal or pelvic CT scan, with or without ultrasound) for renal tumors should be initiated promptly and repeated every 36 to 48 months. If renal tumors are present, they should be closely followed until the largest tumor reaches 3 cm, at which point nephron-sparing surgery is recommended. Most renal tumors associated with BHD syndrome tend to be indolent, and if localized and confined to the kidney, adjuvant therapy is not recommended (Stamatakis *et al.*, 2013). A variety of different *FLCN* mutations and clinical manifestations have been seen in Japanese individuals and individuals of European descent, indicating that there may be significant racial/ethnic variability in both mutations and phenotype (Kunogi *et al.*, 2010).

10.5. REFERENCES

Alcaïs, A, Quintana-Murci, L., Thaler, D. S., Schurr, E., Abel, L., & Casanova, J-L. (2010). Life-threatening infectious diseases of childhood: Single-gene inborn errors of immunity? *Annals of the New York Academy of Sciences, 1214*, 18–33. doi: 10.1111/j.1749-6632.2010.05834.x

Boon, M., Jorissen, M., Proesmans, M., & De Boeck, K. (2013). Primary ciliary dyskinesia, an orphan disease. *European Journal of Pediatrics, 172*(2), 151–162. doi: 10.1007/s00431-012-1785-6.

Boyle, M. P., & De Boeck, K. (2013). A new era in the treatment of cystic fibrosis: correction of the underlying CFTR defect. *The Lancet Respiratory Medicine, 1*(2), 158–163. doi:10.1016/S2213-2600(12)70057-7Cite

Brantly, M. L., Chulay, J. D., Wang, L., Mueller, C., Humphries, M., Spencer, L. T., . . . & Betts, M. R. (2009). Sustained transgene expression despite T lymphocyte responses in a clinical trial of rAAV1-AAT gene therapy. *Proceedings of the National Academy of Science, 106*, 16363–16368.

Brennan, P., Hainaut, P., & Boffetta, P. (2011). Genetics of lung-cancer susceptibility. *Lancet Oncology, 12*(4):399–408.

Bunyavanich, S., Silberg, J. L., Lasky-Su, J., Gillespie, N. A., Lange, N. E., Canino, G., & Celedón, J. C. (2013). A twin study of early-childhood asthma in Puerto Ricans. *PloS one, 8*(7), e68473.

Cantero-Recasens, G., Fandos, C., Rubio-Moscardo, F., Valverde, M. A., & Vicente, R. (2010). The asthma-associated ORMDL3 gene product regulates endoplasmic reticulummediated calcium signaling and cellular stress. *Human Molecular Genetics, 19*(1), 111121. doi: 10.1093/hmg/ddp471

Casanova, J-L., & Abel, L. (2013). The genetic theory of infectious diseases: A brief history and selected illustrations. *Annual Review of Genomics and Human Genetics, 14*, 215–243. doi: 10.1146/annurev-genom-091212-153448

Castro-Rodriguez, J. A. (2011). The asthma predictive index: Early diagnosis of asthma. *Current opinion in allergy and clinical immunology, 11*(3), 157–161.

Chapman, S. J., and Hill, A. V. S. (2012) Human genetic susceptibility to infectious disease, *Nature Reviews Genetics, 13*, 175–188. doi:10.1038/nrg3114

Choy, D. F., Modrek, B., Abbas, A. R., Kummerfeld, S., Clark, H. F., Wu, L. C., . . . & Arron, J. R. (2011). Gene expression patterns of Th2 inflammation and intercellular communication in asthmatic airways. *The Journal of Immunology, 186*(3), 1861–1869.

Cohen-Cymberknoh, M., Shoseyov, D., & Kerem, E. (2011). Managing cystic fibrosis: strategies that increase life expectancy and improve quality of life. *American Journal of Respiratory and Critical Care Medicine, 183*, 1463–1471. doi: 10.1164/rccm.201009-1478CI. Epub 2011 Feb 17

Collaco, J. M., Blackman, S. M., McGready, J., Naughton, K. M., & Cutting, G. R. (2010). Quantification of the relative contribution of environmental and genetic factors to variation in cystic fibrosis lung function. *Journal of Pediatrics, 157*, 802–807. doi: 10.1016/j.jpeds.2010.05.018. Epub 2010 Jun 30

Cote, M., Liu, M., Bonassi, S., Neri, M., Schwartz, A.G., Christiani, D. C., . . . & Hung, R.J. (2012). Increased risk of lung cancer in individuals with a family history of the disease: A pooled analysis from the International Lung Cancer Consortium. *European Journal of Cancer, 48*, 1957–1968. DOI: 10.1016/j.ejca.2012.01.038

Cui, M., Augert, A., Rongione, M., Conkrite, K., Parazzoli, S., Nikitin, A., Ingolia, N., & MacPherson, D. (2014). PTEN is a potent suppressor of small cell lung cancer. *Molecular Cancer Re-*

search. Published OnlineFirst January 30, 2014, doi: 10.1158/1541-7786.MCR-13-0554

Cutting, G. R. (2010). Modifier genes in Mendelian disorders: The example of cystic fibrosis. *Annals of the New York Academy of Sciences, 1214*, 57–69. DOI: 10.1111/j.1749-6632.2010.05879.x.

Davidson, M. R., Gazdar, A. F., & Clarke, B.E. (2013). The pivotal role of pathology in the management of lung cancer. *Journal of Thoracic Disease, 5*(Suppl5): S463–S478.

Davies, J., Alton, E., & Griesenbach, U. (2005). Cystic fibrosis modifier genes. *Journal of the Royal Society of Medicine, 45* (98), 47–54.

DeMeo D. L., & Silverman, E. K. (2004). Alpha-1 antitrypsin deficiency: 2. Genetic aspects of alpha-1 antitrypsin deficiency: phenotypes and genetic modifiers of emphysema risk. *Thorax, 59*, 259–264. DOI: 10.1136/thx.2003.006502

DeMeo, D., Hersh, C., Hoffman, E., Litonjua, A., Lazarus, R., Sparrow, D., . . . & Silverman, E. (2007). Genetic determinants of emphysema distribution in the National Emphysema Treatment Trial. American *Journal of Respiratory & Critical Care Medicine, 176*(1), 42–48. DOI: 10.1164/rccm.200612-1797OC

Dorfman, R., Sandford, A., Taylor, C., Huang, B., Frangolias, D., Wang, Y., . . . & Zielenski, J. (2008). Complex two-gene modulation of lung disease severity in children with cystic fibrosis. *The Journal of Clinical Investigation, 118*, 1040–1049. DOI: 10.1172/JCI33754

Drumm, M.L., Konstan, M. W., Schluchter, M. D., Handler, A., Pace, R., Zou, F., Zariwala, M., ... & Fargo, D. (2005). Genetic modifiers of lung disease in cystic fibrosis. *The New England Journal of Medicine, 353*, 1443–1453. DOI: 10.1056/NEJMoa051469

Durham, A.L., Wiegman, C., Adcock, I.M. (2011). Epigenetics of asthma, Biochimica et Biophysica Acta (BBA) *Biochemistry of Asthma, 1810*(11), 1103–1109 10.1016/j.bbagen.2011.03.006

Eisele, N.A. & Anderson, D.M. (2011). Host defense and the airway epithelium: frontline responses that protect against bacterial invasion and pneumonia, *Journal of Pathogens, 2011*, Article ID 249802, 16 pages, doi:10.4061/2011/249802

Foulkes, W.D. (2008). Inherited susceptibility to common cancers. *New England Journal Medicine, 359*(20):2143–2153.

Frisbie, W.P., Song, S.E., Powers, D.A. & Street, J.A. (2004). The increasing racial disparity in infant mortality: respiratory distress syndrome and other causes. *Demography, 41*, 773–800.

Fry, J.S., Hamling, J.S. & Lee, P.N. (2012). Systematic review with meta-analysis of the epidemiological evidence relating FEV1 decline to lung cancer risk. *BMC Cancer; 12*: 498–513. doi: 10.1186/1471-2407-12-498.

Garrod, A.E. (1931). Garrod's Inborn Factors in Disease, Oxford University Press, USA.

Georas, S. N., Guo, J., De Fanis, U., & Casolaro, V. (2005). T-helper cell type-2 regulation in allergic disease. *European respiratory journal, 26*(6), 1119–1137.

Gibbons, D.L., Byers, L.A., & Kurie, J.M. (2014). Smoking, p53 Mutation, and Lung Cancer. *Molecular Cancer Research, 12*(1), 3–13.

Gibson, R. L., Burns, J. L., & Ramsey, B. W. (2003). Pathophysiology and management of pulmonary infections in cystic fibrosis. *American Journal of Respiratory and Critical Care Medicine, 168*, 918–951. DOI: 10.1164/rccm.200304-505SO

Govindan, R., Ding, L., Griffith, M., Subramanian, J., Dees, N. D., Kanchi, K. L., . . . & Wilson, R. K. (2012). Genomic landscape of non-small cell lung cancer in smokers and never-smokers. *Cell, 150*(6), 1121–1134.

Guggino, W. B., & Stanton, B. A. (2006). New insights into cystic fibrosis: molecular switches that regulate CFTR. *Nature Reviews, 7*, 426–436. DOI:10.1038/nrm1949

Hammerman, P.S., Lawrence, M.S., Voet, D. & Jing, R. (2012). Comprehensive genomic characterization of squamous cell lung cancers. *Nature, 489*(7417): 519–525. DOI: 10.1038/nature11404

Haas, D.M., Lehmann, A.S., Skaar, T., Philips, S., McCormick, C.L., Beagle, K., Hebbring, S.J., Dantzer, J., Li, L. and Jung, J. (2012) The impact of drug metabolizing enzyme polymorphisms on outcomes after antenatal corticosteroid use. *American Journal of Obstetrics and Gynecology, 206*(5):447.e17–e24. doi:10.1016/j.ajog.2012.02.016.

Haas, D.M., Dantzer, J., Lehmann, A.S., Philips, S., Skaar, T., McCormick, C.L., Hebbring, S.J., Jung, J. and Li, L. (2013) The impact of glucocorticoid polymorphisms on markers of neonatal respiratory disease after antenatal betamethasone administration. *American Journal of Obstetrics and Gynecology, 208*(3):215.e1-6. doi: 10.1016/j.ajog.2012.12.031.

Haupt, M.E., Kwasny, M.J., Schechter, M.S., & McColley, S.A. (2014). Pancreatic Enzyme Replacement Therapy Dosing and Nutritional, *The Journal of Pediatrics*, Outcomes in Children with Cystic Fibrosis, available online 20 February 2014, ISSN 0022-3476, http://dx.doi.org/10.1016/j.jpeds.2014.01.022

He, Y., Li, S., Ren, S., Cai, W., Li, X., Zhao, C., Li, J., Chen, X., Gao, G., Li, W. & Zhou, F. (2013). Impact of family history of cancer on the incidence of mutation in epidermal growth factor receptor gene in non-small cell lung cancer patients. *Lung Cancer, 81*, 2, 162–166. Retrieved November 7, 2013 from http://dx.DOI.org/10.1016/j.lungcan.2013.05.004

Hersh, C., Hansel, N., Barnes, K., Lomas, D., Pillai, S., Coxson, H., & . . . Silverman, E. (2009). Transforming growth factor-beta receptor-3 is associated with pulmonary emphysema. *American Journal* of Respiratory Cell and Molecular Biology, 41(3), 324–331. DOI:10.1165/rcmb.2008-0427OC[TG40]

Huffnagle, G.B. (2014). Increase in dietary fiber dampens allergic responses in the lung. Nature Medicine, 20(120), doi.org/10.1038/nm.3472

Jafer, A. T., Mahmood, A. A., Fatah, M. A., & Jasim, M. A. (2007). Guidelines for the diagnosis and management of asthma.

Jonsson, S., Thorsteinsdottir, U., Gudbjartsson, D. F., Jonsson, H. H., Kristjansson, K., Arnason, S., . . . & Stefansson K. (2004). Familial risk of lung carcinoma in the Icelandic population. JAMA, 292:2977-83.

Kavvadia, V., Greenough, A., Dimitriou, G. & Hooper, R. (1998). Influence of ethnic origin on respiratory distress syndrome in very premature infants. Archives of Pediatrics and Adolescent Medicine, 78, F25–28.

Kelly, E., Greene, C.M., Carroll, T.P., McElvaney, N.G. and O'Neill, S.J. (2010). Alpha-1 antitrypsin deficiency Respiratory Medicine, 104(6). 763–772. doi: 10.1016/j.rmed.2010.01.016

Knowles, M. R., & Drumm, M. (2012). The Influence of Genetics on Cystic Fibrosis Phenotypes. Cold Spring Harbor Perspectives in Medicine, DOI:10.1101/cshperspect.a009548

Kong, X., Cho, M., Anderson, W., Coxson, H., Muller, N., Washko, G., & . . . Pillai, S. (2011). Genome-wide Association Study Identifies BICD1 as a Susceptibility Gene for Emphysema. American Journal of Respiratory & Critical Care Medicine, 183(1), 43–49. DOI:10.1164/rccm.201004-0541OC

Kunogi, M., Kurihara, M., Ikegami, T., Kobayashi, T., Shindo, N., Kumasaka, T., . . . & Seyama, K. (2010). Clinical and genetic spectrum of Birt-Hogg-Dube' syndrome patients in whom pneumothorax and/or multiple lung cysts are the presenting feature. Journal of Medical Genetics, 47(4), 281–287. DOI: 10.1136/jmg.2009.070565.

Li, Y. & Yang, P. (2011). GPC5 gene and its related pathways in lung cancer. Journal of Thoracic Oncology, 6(1): 2–5. DOI: 10.1016/S1470-2045(10)70042-5

Li, Y., Sheu, C. Ye, Y. et al. (2010). Genetic variants and risk of lung cancer in never smokers: a genome-wide association study. Lancet Oncology, 11:321–330.

March, M. E., Sleiman, P. MA., & Hakonarson, H. (2013). Genetic polymorphisms and associated susceptibility to asthma. International Journal of General Medicine, 6, 253–265. DOI: 10.2147/IJGM.S28156. Print 2013.

Mason, R. J., Broaddus, V. C., Martin, T. R., King Jr, T. E. & Schraufnagel, D. E. (2010). Murray and Nadel's Textbook of Respiratory Medicine. Philadelphia, Pa.: Saunders Elsevier.

Moffatt, M. F., Kabesch, M., Liang, L., Dixon, A. L., Strachan, D., Heath, S., Depner, M., . . . & Cookson, W. O., (2007). Genetic variants regulating ORMDL3 expression contribute to the risk of childhood asthma. Nature, 448(7152), 470–473. DOI:10.1038/nature06014

Mogayzel, P. J., & Flume, P. A. (2011). Update in cystic fibrosis 2010. American Journal of Respiratory and Critical Care Medicine, 183, 1620–1624. DOI: 10.1164/rccm.201102-0275UP

Mukherjee, A. B., & Zhang, Z. (2011). Allergic Asthma: Influence of Genetic and Environmental Factors. The Journal of Biological Chemistry, 286(38), 32883–32889. DOI: 10.1074/jbc.R110.197046.

National Comprehensive Cancer Network (NCCN) (2014). Non-Small cell lung cancer. NCCN Guidelines, PREV-1, Version 2, 2014. Accessed November 7, 2013, from www.nccn.org/professionals/physician_gls/pdf/nscl.pdf#page9

National Library of Medicine. (2007) Genetics Home Reference [Internet]. Bethesda (MD): The Library; 2014 March 10, 2014. TP53; [reviewed: August 2007 cited 2014 Mar 10]; Available from: http://ghr.nlm.nih.gov/gene/TP53

Nkadi, P.O., Merritt, T.A., and Pillers, D.A. (2009). An overview of pulmonary surfactant in the neonate: genetics, metabolism, and the role of surfactant in health and disease, Molecular Genetics and Metabolism; 97(2): 95–101. doi:10.1016/j.ymgme.2009.01.015

Perin, P., & Potočnik, U. (2014). Polymorphisms in recent GWA identified asthma genes CA10, SGK493, and CTNNA3 are associated with disease severity and treatment response in childhood asthma. Immunogenetics, 1–9.

Riley, J.C. (2005). Estimates of Regional and Global Life Expectancy, 1800–2001. Population and Development Review, 31, (3), pp. 537–543. Retrieved November 26, 2013 from http://www.jstor.org.libproxy.clemson.edu/stable/pdfplus/3401478.pdf.

Rogan, M. P., Stolta, D. A., & Hornick, D. B. (2011). Cystic fibrosis transmembrane conductance regulator intracellular processing, trafficking, and opportunities for mutation-specific treatment. Chest. 139, 1480–1490. DOI: 10.1378/chest.10-2077.

Rosenkranz, R., Rosenkranz, S., & Neessen, K. (2012). Dietary factors associated with lifetime asthma or hayfever diagnosis in Australian middle-aged and older adults: a cross-sectional study. Nutrition journal, 11(1), 84.

Rotunno, M., Lam, T. K., Vogt, A., Bertazzi, P. A., Lubin, J. H., Caporaso, N. E., & Landi, M. T. (2012). GSTM1 and GSTT1 copy numbers and mRNA expression in lung cancer. Molecular Carcinogenesis, 51(S1), E142-E150.

Sharafkhaneh, A., Hanania, N. A., & Kim, V. (2008). Pathogenesis of Emphysema: From the Bench to the Bedside. Proceedings of the American Thoracic Society, 5, 475–477. DOI: 10.1513/pats.200708-126ET.

Siri, D. Farah, H. & Hogarth, D.K. (2013[TG42]). Distinguishing alpha1-antitrypsin deficiency from asthma. *Annals of Allergy and Asthma Immunology. 111*, 458–464. doi: 10.1016/j.anai.2013.09.019

Sosnay, P.R., Siklosi, K.R., Van Goor, F., Kaniecki, K., Yu, H., Sharma, N.,et al.& Cutting, G.R., (2013). Defining the disease liability of variants in the cystic fibrosis transmembrane conductance regulator gene. *Nature Genetics, 45*(10), 1160–69. doi:10.1038/ng.2745

Stamatakis, L., Metwalli, A., Middleton, L. & Linehan, W. (2013). Diagnosis and management of BHD-associated kidney cancer. *Familial Cancer, 12*, 397-402. DOI: 10.1007/s10689-013-9657-4

Stoller, J. K., & Aboussouan, L. S. (2012). A Review of alpha 1-Antitrypsin Deficiency. *American Journal of Respiratory and Critical Care Medicine, 185*(3), 246–259. DOI: 10.1164/rccm.201108-1428CI.

Stoller JK, Lacbawan FL, Aboussouan LS. Alpha-1 Antitrypsin Deficiency. 2006 Oct 27 [Updated 2014 May 1]. In: Pagon RA, Adam MP, Ardinger HH, *et al.*, editors. *GeneReviews®* [Internet]. Seattle (WA): University of Washington, Seattle; 1993-2014. Available from: http://www.ncbi.nlm.nih.gov/books/NBK1519/

Subramanian, J. & Govindan, R. (2007). Lung cancer in never smokers: a review. *Journal of Clinical Oncology, 25*:561–570.

Suda, K., Tomizawa, K., & Mitsudomi, T. (2010). Biological and clinical significance of KRAS mutations in lung cancer: an oncogenic driver that contrasts with EGFR mutation. *Cancer and Metastasis Reviews, 29*(1), 49–60.

Sutherland, M.J. and Ware, S.M. (2009). Disorders of left-right asymmetry: heterotaxy and situs inversus, American Journal of Medical Genetics Part C. *Seminars in Medical Genetics 151C*(4):307–17. doi: 10.1002/ajmg.c.30228.

Toro JR. Birt-Hogg-Dubé Syndrome (2008). In: Pagon RA, Adam MP, Bird TD, *et al.*, editors. GeneReviews™ [Internet]. Seattle (WA): University of Washington, Seattle; 1993–2014. Available from: http://www.ncbi.nlm.nih.gov/books/NBK1522/

Toro, J., Pautler,S., Stewart, L., Glenn, G., Weinrich, M., Toure, O., Wei,M., . . . & Linehan, W. (2007).

Lung cysts, spontaneous pneumothorax, and genetic associations in 89 families with Birt-Hogg-Dube' syndrome. *American Journal of Respiratory and Critical Care Medicine, 175*(10), 1044–1053. DOI: 10.1164/rccm.200610-1483OC

Torjussen, T.M., Munthe-Kaas, M.C., Mowinckel, P., Carlsen, K.H., Undlien, D.E. & Lodrup-Carlsen, K.C. (2013). Childhood lung function and the association with beta2-adrenergic receptor haplotypes. *Acta Paediatr, 102*, 727–531. DOI: 10.1111/apa.12221

Vercelli, D. (2008). Discovering susceptibility genes for asthma and allergy. *Nature Reviews, 8*, 169–183. DOI: 10.1038/nri2257.

Wan, E. S., & Silverman, E. K. (2009). Genetics of COPD and Emphysema. *CHEST, 136* (3), 859–866. DOI: 10.1378/chest.09-0555.

Yamamoto, H., Higasa, K., Sakaguchi, M., Shien, K., Soh, J., Ishimura, K., . . . Toyooka, S. (2014). Novel Germline Mutation in the Transmembrane Domain of HER2 in Familial Lung Adenocarcinomas, *Journal National Cancer Institute, 106*:1–4. DOI:10.1093/jnci/djt338

Yang, I. A., Holloway, J. W., & Fong, K. M. (2013). Genetic susceptibility to lung cancer and co-morbidities. *Journal of Thoracic Disease, 5*(Suppl 5), S454. doi:10.3978/j.issn.2072-1439.2013.08.06

Zahran, H.S., Bailey, C. Garbe, P. (2011). Vital Signs: Asthma Prevalence, Disease Characteristics, and Self-Management Education—United States, 2001–2009. Morbidity and Mortality Weekly Report, *Center for Disease Control. 60*(17), 547–552. http://www.cdc.gov/mmwr/pdf/wk/mm6017.pdf

Zariwala MA, Knowles MR, Leigh MW. (2013). Primary Ciliary Dyskinesia, In: Pagon RA, Adam MP, Bird TD, *et al.*, editors. *GeneReviews*™, University of Washington, Seattle, Available from: http://www.ncbi.nlm.nih.gov/books/NBK1122/

Zhang, Y., Moffatt, M. F., and Cookson, W. O. (2012). Genetic and genomic approaches to asthma: new insights for the origins. *Current Opinion in Pulmonary Medicine, 18*(1), 6–13. doi: 10.1097/MCP.0b013e32834dc532

Genomics of Complex Cardiovascular Diseases

JENNIFER R. DUNGAN, Ph.D, RN
ALLISON A. VORDERSTRASSE, DNSC, APRN
SARA M. JORDAN, BA, BSN, RN
ERICA A. JULIAN, RN, BSN

Objectives:

- Explain the difference between genetics and genomics related to common, complex cardiovascular disease (CVD).
- Identify key genetic and genomic contributions to coronary artery disease (CAD) and essential hypertension (EH).
- Distinguish phenotypes and intermediate phenotypes common to CAD and EH.
- Describe fundamental characteristics of genome-wide association, transcriptomics, and metabolomics that advance the understanding of common, complex CVDs.
- Discuss the criteria for appraising clinical utility of genomic testing platforms.

11.1. INTRODUCTION

Genomics refers to the global evaluation of a multitude of genetic factors across the entire DNA code (genome), rather than the targeted investigation of individual genetic markers. In contrast to the rare, single-gene (e.g., monogenic, Mendelian) cardiovascular disorders presented in Part 2 of this chapter, the common, complex forms of CVD have many genes contributing to disease (polygenic), as well as gene-by-gene and genebyenvironment interactions and epigenetic modifications. Complex disease genes are considered susceptibility variants, rather than causal mutations. They do not follow traditional inheritance patterns and are subject to population effects.

Moreover, different mechanisms may be at play in different individuals or groups, leading to varying forms of disease and subsequently, different clinical manifestations, treatment response, and outcomes. This clinical heterogeneity requires scientists to refine (narrow) phenotype definitions for complex diseases, in order to improve likelihood of isolating genetic variation associated with the trait. Some examples of coronary artery disease (CAD) and hypertension (HTN) phenotypes are atherosclerosis, left-main arterial disease, systolic HTN, and salt-sensitive HTN. Furthermore, there are numerous intermediate (sub-/endo-) phenotypes that characterize lowerlevel processes involved in disease (e.g., lipid metabolism, plasma renin activity) that may themselves be mediated by genetic factors and that are under study. This extensive clinical heterogeneity leads to a high likelihood of genetic heterogeneity. Simply, for every "version" of a disease (phenotype), different genes can lead to the same disease (locus heterogeneity), and different mutations/alleles within the same gene can also lead to the same disease (allelic heterogeneity). It is this wide variation in genetic contribution that makes it more difficult to isolate the major genetic factors involved in the variable expression of CAD and HTN.

Although the clinical risk factors and epidemiology for complex diseases may be well established, the genetic and genomic factors involved have only begun to be explored following the completion of the Human Genome Project, and with the development of high throughput "omics" platforms. Targeted genetic studies have been important in testing hypothesis-driven studies of common, complex diseases; but the rapid advancement in "omics" science has allowed for untargeted, "agnostic" approaches to uncover novel genetic underpinnings, which would have never likely been hypothesized. This chapter presents two exemplars of common, complex, CVDs (CAD; essential hypertension) and the state of the science for genetic contributions identified largely through "omics" approaches, reflecting on nursing implications throughout. In supplement to Chapter 5, which reviews pharmacogenetics, important pharmacogenetic implications relevant to CAD and HTN are highlighted.. Finally, existing genomic testing platforms available in CAD and HTN are presented and their current clinical utility is discussed. The chapter concludes with future directions in genomics of complex CVD.

11.2. CORONARY ARTERY DISEASE (OR CORONARY HEART DISEASE)

CAD is defined as narrowing of the coronary arteries due to plaque buildup, which can obstruct the flow of blood (and oxygen) to the heart. This can lead to ischemia/angina (chest pain) because the heart muscle is not receiving adequate oxygen. If blood flow is completely blocked (or prolonged vasospasm occurs), a myocardial infarction (MI, heart attack) can result. Clinical risk factors for CAD have been well-established and include high LDL, low HDL, obesity, family history, excessive alcohol use, physical inactivity, elevated blood pressure, diabetes, smoking, race/ethnicity (notably, African Americans), and older age (older than age 45 years for men and postmenopausal for women) (Go et al., 2014). These risk factors are very common among adults in the United States (U.S.), leading to a high burden of CAD. Approximately 15.4 million adults older than age 20 have CAD (6.4%); by sex, 7.9% of men and 5.1% of women are affected (Go et al., 2014). Approximately 620,000 people in the U.S. this year will have a "new" (first) heart attack; an estimated 150,000 silent MIs occur each year; and an estimated 295,000 will have a recurrent heart attack. The average age for first MI is 64.9 years for men and 72.3 years for women (Go et al., 2014). Advancements in treatment and prevention of CVD have led to a decline in morbidity and mortality; however, CVD remains the leading cause of death in both men and wom-

en in the U.S. (Roger et al., 2012). A majority (380,000 out of 600,000 deaths annually) are attributed specifically to CAD (Go et al., 2014). Those of "white" ethnicity account for 25.1% of heart disease–related deaths, whereas African-Americans account for 24.5%, Asians/Pacific Islanders 23.2%, Hispanics 20.8%, and American Indians/Alaska Natives 18% (Go et al., 2014).

11.3. GENETIC BACKGROUND

The heritability of CAD and CAD risk factors has been established at about 40% (Ganesh et al., 2013). This informs us that about 40% of the variability in CAD could be due to individual genomic variability. Environmental and modifiable risk factors account for much of the remaining influence on CVD development. In twin studies, the concordance rate is approximately 44% in monozygotic and 14% in dizygotic twins (Allen, Harvald, & Shields, 1967). The relative risk associated with a positive family history of CAD ranges from 1.5 to 2.4 across multiple studies and varies slightly by sex (Schildkraut, Myers, Cupples, Kiely, & Kannel, 1989). In the Framingham Heart Study, men with a family history of CAD had a 2.6-fold increased risk for CAD, and women had a 2.3-fold increased risk (Lloyd-Jones et al., 2004). These findings support a potential role for genetic contribution to CAD.

11.4. GENOME-WIDE ASSOCIATION STUDIES (GWAS) FOR CAD

With the advances in genetic technologies and research approaches, many variants associated with complex chronic diseases have been identified through genome wide association studies (GWAS). Evaluating thousands to millions of genetic markers across the genome in large cohorts of unrelated cases and controls, GWAS explore both common and rare genetic variants for association with disease. For more information about GWAS, see Table 11.1. Currently there are over 100 variants associated with CAD; with 50 of them identified as both significantly associated with CAD and replicated in other populations (Roberts, 2014). Ganesh and colleagues (2013) recently compiled a list of major CAD candidate genes identified by GWAS, with candidates from nearly every chromosome (refer to Table 1 in Ga-

TABLE 11.1. Online GWAS Resources.

Source	Description	Citation
National Human Genome Research Institute (NHGRI): GWAS Fact Sheet	Webpage explaining GWAS approach and relevance to investigating complex diseases	http://www.genome.gov/20019523
NHGRI Catalog of Published GWAS	Curated catalog of published GWAS containing only studies meeting genome-wide levels of statistical significance and details of their results	Hindorff LA, MacArthur J (European Bioinformatics Institute), Morales J (European Bioinformatics Institute), Junkins HA, Hall PN, Klemm AK, and Manolio TA. A Catalog of Published Genome-Wide Association Studies. Available at: www.genome.gov/gwastudies
HuGE Navigator	An integrated, searchable knowledge base of genetic associations and human genome epidemiology	Wei Yu, Ajay Yesupriya, Anja Wulf, Lucia A Hindorff, Nicole Dowling, Muin J Khoury and Marta Gwinn GWAS Integrator: a bioinformatics tool to explore human genetic associations reported in published genome-wide association studies. *European Journal of Human Genetics.* (25 May 2011) | doi:10.1038/ejhg.2011.91 http://hugenavigator.net/HuGENavigator/gWAHitStartPage.do?

nesh *et al.*, 2013). A majority are common variants, occurring in over 50% of the population. In addition, most contribute a minimal increase in risk, leading researchers to explore whether additive or combined risk is conferred by multiple variants. With the exception of the A and B blood groups, these variants act through atherosclerosis pathways (Roberts, 2014).

11.5. THE 9P21 CANDIDATE LOCUS FOR CAD

By far the strongest and most validated candidate gene marker in CAD is the 9p21 loci (gene location), which became the first risk factor to be identified since 1964 (Roberts & Stewart, 2012). Two simultaneous investigative groups identified this variant via GWAS analyses in 2007. McPherson and colleagues (2007) of the Ottawa Heart Genomic Study evaluated six independent samples containing about 23,000 participants from four white populations. Helgadottir and colleagues (2007) evaluated 1,607 cases and 6,728 controls from Iceland. Both groups identified the 9p21 genetic marker and, through replication and further fine-mapping of the ge-

netic region, found that the risk allele was comprised of a single haplotype (specific combination of alleles among different single nucleotide polymorphisms [SNPs]) approximately 58,000 base pairs long, located in a noncoding region near *CDKN2A* and *CDNK2B* (see Figure 11.1). About 75% of the population carries the 9p21 risk variant, yet AfricanAmericans do not confer an increased risk for CAD with the variant (Roberts & Stewart, 2012). Loci at 9p21 related to CAD have been validated in multiple studies. Having one copy of the 9p21 variant is associated with a 25% increased risk for CAD and a 50% increased risk with two copies; for those with premature CAD (< 55 years in men and < 60 years in women), the 9p21 risk variant is associated with a two-fold increase in risk, similar to that of smoking and cholesterol (Roberts & Stewart, 2012). Support for the candidacy of 9p21 is strengthened by the fact that its effect on risk is independent of all other known risk factors (Roberts & Stewart, 2012); yet, the improvement in risk prediction with 9p21 is nominal (Evaluation of Genomic Applications in Practice and Prevention [EGAPP], 2010). The hypothesized mechanism of action for 9p21 could include cell

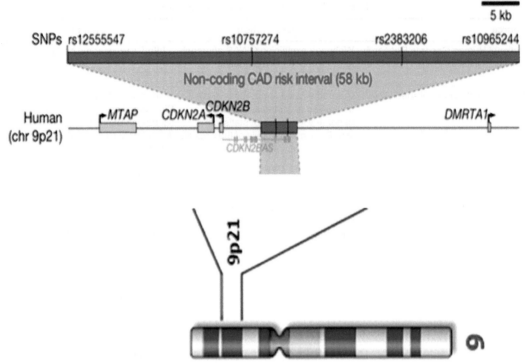

FIGURE 11.1. 9p21 loci schematic, indicating location of the 9p21 variant on the short arm of chromosome 9 (bottom, center), and expanded view of the 58kb region, with corresponding SNPs across region and proximal genes (*MTAP, CDKN2A, CDKN2B, DMRTA1*). Adapted with permission from (KREATECH Diagnostics, 2014; Visel *et al.*, 2010). Chromosome 9 (bottom image) used with permission from KREATECH Diagnostics, Inc., 2014.

cycle kinase inhibitors or atherogenesis, specifically at the vessel wall (Ardissino *et al.*, 2011; Dandona *et al.*, 2010; Reilly *et al.*, 2011). Several independent investigators have shown that 9p21 is a risk factor not only for CAD but also for abdominal aortic and intracranial aneurysms, platelet reactivity, and stroke (Helgadottir *et al.*, 2008; Musunuru *et al.*, 2010). There is now some thought that the risk conferred by the variants on the 9p21 loci may be context-dependent and associated with hypertension (Lusk *et al.*, 2014).

Aside from the 9p21 GWAS investigations, the most notable GWAS come from the Coronary Artery Disease Genome Wide Replication and Meta-Analysis (CARDIoGRAM) and Coronary Artery Disease (C4D) Genetics Consortium groups. The CARDIoGRAM Consortium evaluated over 22,000 cases and 64,000 controls of European ancestry across 14 CAD/MI GWAS, identifying 13 novel susceptibility loci for CAD and confirming 10 of 12 existing candidate associations with CAD (Schunkert *et al.*, 2011). The candidate genes are *PPAP2B, ANKS1A, TCF21,*

ZC2HC1, ABO, CYP17A1/CNNM2/NT5C2, ZNF259/APOA5-A4-C3-A, COL4A1/COL4A2, HHIPL1, ADAMTS7, SMG6, SRR, RASD1/ SMCR3/PEMT, and *UBE2Z/GIP/ATP5G1/SNF8* (for more detail, it is recommended to search the genes in GeneCards [Weizmann Institute of Science, 2014]). Four additional novel loci were identified by the C4D Consortium (Coronary Artery Disease Genetics Consortium, 2011), composed of two European ($n = 8,424$) and two South Asian ($n = 6,996$) cohorts, annotating to *LIPA, ADAMTS7-MORF4L1, KIAA1462,* and a gene-rich locus on chromosome 7q22. Furthermore, these two consortia later combined efforts and samples to conduct a large-scale replication (approximately 42,000 cases and about 66,000 controls of European and South Asian ancestry)—leading to discovery of 15 new novel loci, as well as replicating > 30 previously identified loci for CAD (CARDIoGRAMplusC4D Consortium, 2013). An estimated 11% of the additive heritability of CAD was explained by a combination of their 46 SNPs meeting genome-wide significance plus 104 other independently associated CAD variants (CARDIoGRAMplusC4D Consortium, 2013). GWAS has made significant contributions to discovery and replication of candidate genes in CAD.

The results of these GWAS are compelling but should be taken with a few notes of caution. First and foremost, GWAS have a high risk of falsepositive associations, owing to the immense number of multiple statistical comparisons (over 25,000 associations could be identified as significant at $p < 0.05$ because of chance alone if 500,000 SNPs are genotyped). Thus, the accepted threshhold level of significance for GWAS is set between $p < 10^{-7}$ and $p < 10^{-8}$ to reduce the risk of Type I error. Additionally, the candidate loci and/or genes identified herein may not be the "causative" variants for the disease associations. Because of the nature of GWAS and the property of linkage disequilibrium (coinheritance) between markers, the identified variants may be proxies for the true susceptibility variants. This is often referred to as "indirect association" (Figure 11.2). Only with further functional studies and sequencing of the candidate genes can the directly associated variant be determined. Modest effect sizes are another limitation of GWAS, reflecting their inability to explain large proportions of the estimated genetic heritability (reasons for which are explained in detail by Manolio *et al.*, 2009).

11.6. EARLY-ONSET CAD

Indirect genetic association. Genotyped SNPs often lie in a region of high linkage disequilibrium with an influential allele. The genotyped SNP (gray arrow seen in Figure 11.2) will be statistically associated with disease as a surrogate for the disease SNP (red arrow seen in Figure 11.2) through an indirect association (dashed line seen in Figure 11.2). Adapted material from Bush & Moore, 2012, covered under the Creative Commons Attribution License.

Early-onset disease tends to confer genetic enrichment—owing to reduced cumulated environmental effects early in life—and CAD is no exception. The Genetics of Early Onset Cardiovascular Disease (GENECARD) study was the first exploratory genetic linkage study to deter-

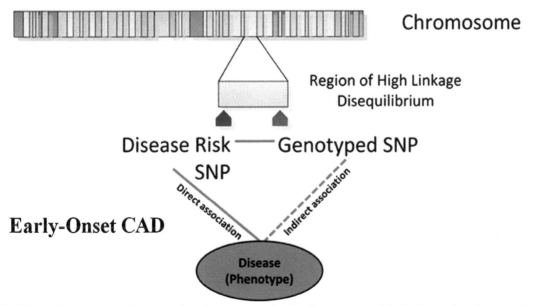

FIGURE 11.2. Indirect genetic association. Genotyped SNPs often lie in a region of high linkage disequilibrium with an influential allele. The genotyped SNP will be statistically associated with disease as a surrogate for the disease SNP through an indirect association. Adapted with permission from Bush & Moore, 2012.

mine genetic markers in early onset CVD (at or before age 50 years in men and age 55 years in women) (Hauser *et al.*, 2003). Investigators identified genome-wide significant peaks mapped to 1q25 and 3q13 and later identified the candidate genes (*GATA2*: Connelly *et al.*, 2006; FAM5C: Connelly *et al.*, 2008; and PLA2G7: Sutton *et al.*, 2008) within these regions that contributed to the association signals (Hauser *et al.*, 2004).

11.7. ATHEROSCLEROSIS/ ARTERIOSCLEROSIS

Most of the genes associated with CAD are also associated with atherosclerosis. This follows in line with the pathophysiology of the disease processes, because atherosclerosis is the leading cause of heart disease and MI. Recent findings offer compelling insight into potential genetic underpinnings of the atherosclerotic/ arteriosclerotic disease processes. Yoshino and colleagues (2014) evaluated intermediate phenotypes specific to microvascular dysfunction (e.g., atherosclerosis, calcification, vasoreactivity, inflammation, and/or angiogenesis) and found significantly associated SNPs within *VEGFA* and *CDKN2B-AS1* genes among 643 patients without coronary heart disease (CHD). Sex-specific variants were identified in *MYH15*, *VEGFA*, and *NT5E* for men only (Yoshino *et al.*, 2014). Evidence is building for matrix metalloproteinase (*MMP*) genetic involvement in atherosclerosis development and coronary events. Preliminary evidence was recently reported for sex-specific associations between *MMP* gene polymorphisms and plaques in femoral or carotid bifurcations (Panayiotou *et al.*, 2013). Specifically, men had a 4.5-fold increased risk of any bifurcation-type plaque when they carried the *MMP9 279Q* allele (odds ratio [OR] = 4.5, 95% CI = 2.0–10.2, $p < 0.001$); being a carrier of the *MMP7-181A* allele conferred about 2.6 times increased risk of plaque in the femoral bifurcation (OR = 2.62, 95% CI = 1.36–4.99, $p < 0.004$) (Panayiotou *et al.*, 2013). Female carriers of the *MMP12-82G* allele conferred nearly 2 times increased risk for presence of femoral plaques (OR = 1.9, 95% CI = 1.14–3.16, $p = 0.014$). In a cohort of 1,572 Han Chinese individuals, the *MMP3* 5A allele occurred at higher frequency in patients with acute coronary syndrome (ACS) than in ACS-free controls, conferring nearly three-fold increased risk of an ACS event (adjusted OR = 2.297, 95% CI = 1.12–4.78, $p = 0.026$) (Xu *et al.*, 2013). Also, having any copy of the T allele for the *MMP9 -1562C/T* polymorphism was associated with increased risk for CAD (OR = 1.43, 95% CI = 1.05–1.94, $p = 0.025$) (Xu *et al.*, 2013). The 5A/6A variant in *MMP3* and C677T variant in *MTHFR* were associated with advanced stenosis (> 75%) in arterial vessels of 412 young adults (age < 45 years) (Sakowicz, Fendler, Lelonek, Sakowicz, & Pietrucha, 2013).

11.8. DYSLIPIDEMIAS

There are about 157 variants associated with lipid levels: 55 with HDL, 37 with LDL, 54 with total cholesterol, and 24 with triglycerides (Roberts, 2014). Importantly, these associations have already led to drug development, such as *PCSK9* inhibition. More than 25 GWAS for various lipid phenotypes have been conducted to date (Ganesh *et al.*, 2013). Among the most compelling research is the demonstration that *SORT1* polymorphism (rs12740374) mediates a causal relation between LDL-cholesterol and CAD (Musunuru *et al.*, 2010). Through meticulous experiments, investigators demonstrated that this SNP created a transcription factor binding site that altered hepatic expression of *SORT1*, which in turn altered plasma LDL cholesterol levels and was associated with increased risk for MI in humans (Musunuru *et al.*, 2010). The *APOE* gene has noted candidacy in CAD, with *APOE4* forms often more common among those with CVD (MI and stroke) than among controls. Zende and colleagues (2013) recently documented higher total cholesterol, LDL, and triglycerides in those with the *e4* allele as well. Among patients with hyperlipidemias, higher lipoprotein concentrations were found in those with at least one *APOE4* allele and G allele at *NPC1L1* (Lupattelli *et al.*, 2013). The authors also reported that HDL and these alleles were independent predictors of lipoprotein levels (Lupattelli *et al.*, 2013).

11.9. EVENTS: MYOCARDIAL INFARCTION AND SURVIVAL

MI is often the presenting symptom for CAD and contributes significantly to the overall disease- and health-care burden. The Myocardial Infarction Genetics Consortium has conducted a number of GWAS for early-onset MI. Six novel and three replicated loci were significantly associated with early-onset MI in over 6,000 subjects and replicated in about 19,500 subjects (Kathiresan *et al.*, 2009). They also found a missense variant in *PCSK9* conferring reduced risk for (protection against) early-onset MI (Kathiresan & Myocardial Infarction Genetics Consortium, 2008). Sakowicz and colleagues (2013) reported association of both Leu125Val *PECAM1* and *A1/A2 FVII* with early-onset MI in their aforementioned described study. The GRACE Genetics Study found a single variant upstream of the *ABO* gene (rs579459) independently associated with recurrent MI (adjusted hazard ratio [HR] = 2.25, CI = 1.37–3.71; *p* = 0.001) as well as a composite endpoint for recurrent MI or cardiac death (adjusted HR = 1.80, CI = 1.09–2.95; *p* = 0.021) within 5 years after an index ACS (Wauters *et al.*, 2013). This SNP also correlates with Type A blood group (Wauters *et al.*, 2013). Through a targeted approach, Li and colleagues (2014) conducted a meta-analysis that shows that *LTA* C804A may be associated with an increased susceptibility to MI, whereas *LTA* A252G and G10A may confer a significant increased susceptibility to MI only in Asians.

Mortality risk may be further explained by genetic factors. Arking and Sotoodehnia (2012) review the state of the science for sudden cardiac death (SCD) candidate genes, highlighting *SCN5A, NOS1AP, CXADR, BAZ2B*, and *TKT/ CACNA1D, PRKCD* (Arking & Sotoodehnia, 2012). Of note, *BAZ2B* maintained genome-wide level significance in the largest GWAS to date; *NOS1AP* has support of multiple replications and has been shown to modify long QT syndrome phenotypes (Arking & Sotoodehnia, 2012). Six novel sudden cardiac arrest candidates and eight known SCD candidates were validated through GWAS by Aouizerat and colleagues (Aouizerat *et al.*, 2011). Multiple fatty acid gene variants were associated with survival to admission and survival to discharge in out-of-hospital SCD (C.O. Johnson *et al.*, 2012). Dungan, Hauser, Qin, & Kraus (2013) characterized a novel phenotype for survivorship in CAD (survival likelihood in the context of significant CAD), demonstrating unique genetic effects on survival that were sig-

nificant in CAD cases but not in controls. They reported a 24% increased risk of all-cause mortality in 1,155 CAD cases with each addition of the G allele for the rs1462845 *LSAMP* variant (*p* = 0.044). The authors also reported a potential protective genetic effect on survivorship among two other *LSAMP* SNPs and discussed the potential for survival bias in case-control genetic associations (Dungan *et al.*, 2013).

Although GWAS is considered a genomic approach (evaluating a multitude of gene variants across all chromosomes), it still isolates effects in the genetic structure (or code). Individual targeting of candidate genes, as well as GWAS investigations, have proven useful in identifying potential genetic variation in CAD, yet a majority of the genetic contribution remains at-large—referred to as "missing heritability." Other "omic" approaches focus on quantifying how genes are being expressed at a given time and the metabolites produced from homeostatic and diseasedriven processes. The advances being made in transcriptomics and metabolomics is the topic of the next section.

11.10. GENE EXPRESSION/ TRANSCRIPTOMICS

As described in Chapter 1, transcription is the process of transcribing (copying) DNA through the generation of single-stranded messenger ribonucleic acid (mRNA) copies, which are in turn used to direct protein synthesis. In comparison to the nearly 22,500 genes in the human genome, there are approximately 100,000 known mRNA transcripts, which then direct the synthesis of approximately 100,000 proteins. The abundance of mRNA present at a given point in time is a reflection of the activity level of a gene—specifically, whether the gene is being up- or down-regulated in response to the body's homeostatic demands—often termed "gene expression." In contrast to the stability of one's genetic code (DNA base pairs and genotypes do not change), gene expression is a dynamic, moment-to-moment process quantifying the genes' activity level (or, expression) among different cells and tissues. Often, where individual genetic markers fail to explain the "missing heritability" in a trait, gene expression studies may be conducted with the basic hypothesis that the transcription process, rather than the code itself, is the culprit for the disease. Gene expression findings can provide support for understanding signaling and mechanisms in disease processes and can be identified with targeted gene expression studies in tissue and blood. Tissue is the preferred source of investigation, as mRNA levels tend to be more accurately reflected and less prone to influence of circulating factors within the blood. Thus, gene expression studies for CAD and HTN are traditionally conducted in animal models or human blood samples. Some exceptions involve harvesting arterial tissue from surgical patients to determine gene expression differences between cases and controls (as in hypertensive and normotensives (Dungan *et al.*, 2009). A major limitation of gene expression studies is the interindividual and time-variant nature of mRNA levels; profiles or signatures represent only a snapshot in time of a largely dynamic process.

The "transcriptomic" method involves evaluating thousands to millions of transcripts (unique mRNA templates) on a single microarray chip (one for each subject) for which individual variation in each transcript can be analyzed and compared. An alternate method is to generate collective gene expression "signatures" (i.e, profiles) characterizing unique patterns of up- and down-regulation. The three main approaches for gene expression studies are class comparison, class prediction, and class discovery. For example, a class comparison study may seek to determine whether genes are differentially expressed between people with and without the disease (e.g., CAD or HTN cases vs. controls). A class prediction study would generate an expression profile for the cases and test its capability of accurately predicting disease in another group of subjects/ samples. Finally, a class discovery approach is a means to discover novel or subphenotypes based on gene expression patterns. The key here is that the class/phenotype is not pre-determined; the expression signature is the defining characteristic between samples. A common exemplar is to identify expression patterns among tumor types in order to characterize the tumor. Gene expression studies can also serve to validate a candidate gene, in which significant expression differences or patterns are exhibited in a design relevant to the original genetic association finding.

A recent transcriptomic study utilizing a class comparison approach involved analysis of a subset of Framingham Heart Study participants with CHD and their age-matched controls ($n = 188$, each group) (Joehanes *et al.*, 2013). A cluster analysis of the 35 differentially expressed genes meeting less than 5% false discovery rate revealed three distinct gene clusters associated with coronary disease in whole blood samples (two clusters related to increased red blood cell production and one cluster to attenuated T cell and natural killer cell activity) (Joehanes *et al.*, 2013). Their use of an exome-based expression platform added support to hypotheses regarding the roles of immunity and erythropoiesis in the pathophysiology of CAD. Some exemplar studies by Sinnaeve (Sinnaeve *et al.*, 2009) and Wingrove (Wingrove *et al.*, 2008) have yielded compelling findings of expression signatures generated from peripheral blood mononuclear cells that correlate with the extent of coronary stenosis. Using an extreme phenotype approach, Sinnaeve and colleagues (2009) compared CAD cases with greater than 50% stenosis to controls with no appreciable disease on coronary angiography. A signature containing expression patterns for 160 individual genes was significantly correlated with a clinical CAD severity scale (Duke CAD index; $p < 0.003$), was highly predictive in a polynomial regression model of disease severity ($r^2 = 0.764$ ($p < 0.001$), had strong predictability metrics in multiple leave-one-out cross validation samples, and also predicted severity of atherosclerosis in human aorta tissue samples (Sinnaeve *et al.*, 2009). Transcripts showing "prominent" differential expression annotated to genes involved in cell growth, apoptosis, and inflammation (Sinnaeve *et al.*, 2009). This study was important in generating proof of principal that gene expression patterns in peripheral blood paralleled that of aortic tissue. A smaller-scale expression array analysis was conducted by Wingrove and colleagues (2008), for which 14 genes' expression patterns were associated with both presence and extent of CAD ($p < 0.001$). Many of the genes were involved in modulating monocyte or macrophage function (Wingrove *et al.*, 2008). These studies were designed to generate data in support of genomic-based, noninvasive testing for CAD. Their results—and that of others—influenced the development of the CORUS® CAD (CardioDx Inc., Palo Alto, CA) blood-based gene expression array for predicting likelihood of obstructive CAD. The invasive procedure, coronary angiography (i.e., cardiac catheterization) is the current goldstandard in CAD diagnosis. CORUS CAD was developed in the hopes of harnessing genomics to prevent adverse events associated with catheterization (e.g., bleeding, infection, MI, stroke, death) and reduce hospital length of stay and health care costs. The details of this test and its estimated clinical utility are discussed in the "Genomic Platforms and Their Clinical Utility" section. With inherent limitations in the platform itself and in blood-based gene expression profiling as a whole, and the growing support for noninvasive computed tomography (CT) angiographies (Redberg & Walsh, 2008), the clinical uptake of this novel testing may be limited.

11.11. METABOLOMICS

Metabolomics is the study of small molecules that are the byproducts of metabolism. For example, ethanol is the metabolite produced by alcohol; the breakdown of pyruvic acid produces lactic acid. There are about 7,000 known metabolites, and, like mRNA, they are time-variant and dynamic—having a broad range of concentration and a great deal of chemical diversity among cells, tissues, and organisms (Shah *et al.*, 2010a). Metabolites are measured by various techniques, such as liquid/gas chromatography with mass-spectrometry or nuclear magnetic resonance with spectral separation of molecules by their mass-to-charge ratios (Shah *et al.*, 2010a). Metabolomic pertubations are hypothesized to reflect underlying disease as "intermediate phenotypes proximal to gene function" (Yu *et al.*, 2014; p. e1004212) and have the potential to serve as future biomarkers.

Shah and colleagues (2009) established that metabolite profiles are highly heritable in families predominant for early-onset CVD. Shah and colleagues (2012) have also conducted one of the largest metabolomics studies of CAD to date in 2,023 cardiac catheterization patients. The five factors (principal components groups) independently associated with mortality consisted of medium-chain acylcarnitines, short- and long-chain dicarboxylacylcarnitines, branched-chain amino acids, and fatty acids, three of which predicted

a composite endpoint for death or MI. These results supported earlier findings by Shah and colleagues (2010b) from a smaller study implicating branched-chain amino acids as associated with CAD case status and dicarboxylaclycarnitines as predicting death or MI (Shah *et al.*, 2010b).

11.12. PHARMACOGENOMICS RELATED TO CAD MANAGEMENT

A review of the basics of pharmacogenetics and key examples is presented in Chapter 5. This section in Chapter 11 focuses on the most notable developments in pharmacogenetics, recently reviewed by Ong *et al.* (2012), relevant to associations between statins (hydroxymethylglutarylCoA [HMG-CoA] reductase inhibitors; HMGCR) and *LDLR, HMGCR*, and *SLCO1B1* gene polymorphisms. The pharmacodynamics of statins involve increasing *LDLR* gene expression, which reduces the amount of endogenous LDL cholesterol produced, thereby reducing plasma cholesterol (Goldstein & Brown, 2009). Haplotypes in *LDLR* (haplotype L5) and *HMGCR* (haplotypes H2 and H7) (Krauss *et al.*, 2008; Mangravite *et al.*, 2010; Poduri *et al.*, 2010) and variants in *CYP3A4* (Kajinami, Brousseau, Ordovas, & Schaefer, 2004; A. Wang *et al.*, 2005) have been shown to decrease or vary the effectiveness of statins in lowering LDL cholesterol. The 3-SNP *HMGCR* haplotype (H7) is associated with 11% to 19% less LDLlowering capacity in multiple, independent, and ethnically diverse studies (Chasman *et al.*, 2004; Donnelly *et al.*, 2008; Krauss *et al.*, 2008; Mangravite *et al.*, 2010; Medina, Gao, Ruan, Rotter, & Krauss, 2008; Poduri *et al.*, 2010; Roden *et al.*, 2011). A single *SLOC1B1* SNP (rs4363657) was shown by the SEARCH consortium (SEARCH [NCT00124072], 2012) to have nearly 17-fold (homozygous) and 4.5-fold (heterozygous) increased risk for simvastatin-induced myopathy or rhabdomyolysis in the context of an 80 mg/day dose, prompting the U.S. Food and Drug Administration (FDA) to issue a recommendation that the medication be titrated up only to the 80mg/day dose in patients taking it for at least 12 months (United States [U.S.] Food and Drug Administration [FDA], 2013). (*Note:* They do not recommend genetic testing for the rs4364657 variant at this time.) Ong and colleagues (2012) explain that existing studies are evaluating the predictive ability of genomic markers for CAD for patients on statin therapy (Ong *et al.*, 2012).

11.13. ESSENTIAL HYPERTENSION

Hypertension is a major health problem experienced by nearly 40% of adults globally (World Health Organization [WHO], 2008) and 33% of Americans (Go *et al.*, 2014). Essential (primary/idiopathic) hypertension (EH) accounts for 95% of these cases, defined as systolic blood pressure (BP) above 140 mmHg and/or a diastolic BP above 90 mmHg (Eighth Joint National Committee Guidelines in James *et al.*, 2014), for which no secondary causes (renal, vascular, neurologic, pulmonary, pregnancy, stress, pheochromocytoma, aldosteronism, or familial mutation) are present. Single-gene (monogenic/Mendelian), familial mutations are known to be causal in less than 5% of HTN cases (Basson, Simino, & Rao, 2012; Toka, Koshy, & Hariri, 2013). The remaining 95% of cases comprise complex forms of HTN, for which genetic contributions are poorly understood; however, rapid advances in human genome science are improving the ability to identify underlying genetic variation associated with predisposition to this more common, widespread phenotype. This mostly "silent" disease remains undiagnosed in many individuals because of lack of or vague symptoms and can be difficult to manage medically (only 53% of those with documented HTN are controlled to target BP levels) (Go *et al.*, 2014). As such, HTN contributes to significant health burden as a major risk factor for MI, stroke, heart failure, and kidney disease. The death rate due to HTN was estimated at 18.8% per 100,000 people in 2010 (Murphy, Xu, & Kochanek, 2013). HTN costs the U.S. health care system about $47.5 billion each year. By 2030, 41.4% of the U.S. population is projected to have HTN (Go *et al.*, 2014), increasing the HTN-associated comorbidities, health costs, and mortality burden. HTN is largely preventable through reduction of modifiable risk factors, such as obesity, sedentary lifestyle, smoking, excessive salt intake, excessive alcohol use, and stress. Yet, nonmodifiable risk factors such as age greater than 45 years, sex, race (AfricanAmericans at highest risk), underlying kidney conditions, and positive family history, contribute strongly to the development of HTN and often interact with modifiable factors to further heighten the risk of disease.

11.14. GENETIC BASIS FOR ESSENTIAL HYPERTENSION

Earliest evidence for genetic contribution to EH came from clinical observations of familial aggregation of blood pressure traits, which was later quantified in pedigree studies demonstrating an estimated heritability of HTN between 30% and 60% (Williams *et al.*, 1990). Extensive twin studies also established concordance rates (correlations for presence of trait in both twins) for monozygotic (MZ) and dizygotic (DZ) twins. The seminal research reporting blood pressure concordance in twins was led by Stocks and estimated MZ concordance at 0.81 and 0.44 for same-sex DZ twins (Ward, 1990). The relative risk (likelihood that a trait present in one family member will occur in a subsequent generation) increases as the number of firstdegree relatives increases, such that having normotensive parents confers only 4% risk of HTN in offspring; having one parent confers 10% to 20% increased risk, and having two hypertensive parents confers the greatest risk at 25% to 45% (Lucassen, 1999). This supports use of standard family history risk assessment for primary hypertension, particularly to identify probands having at least one parent with documented HTN in order to target prevention strategies. Taken together, these results support that an underlying genetic predisposition is likely in many people, yet a large proportion of the genetic risk is unexplained. Although many people may harbor genetic predisposition to essential HTN, environmental and behavioral risk factors contribute significantly to the disease process.

11.15. EARLY CANDIDATE GENES IN HYPERTENSION

Focusing on the pathophysiologic mechanisms involved in HTN has helped identify a number of major susceptibility candidate genes. The most consistent and replicated findings have come from genetic variation in the renin-angiotensin-aldosterone system (RAAS). Briefly, the hypertensive disease process is characterized by dysfunction of the RAAS and sympathetic nervous system and the dysregulation of adducin and natriuretic hormones, leading to vasoconstriction (increasing peripheral resistance) and renal salt/water retention (increasing blood volume).

The strongest candidate genes involved in RAAS to date are renin (*REN*), angiotensinogen (*AGT*), and angiotensin II type 1 receptor (*AGTR1*). As a whole, these candidate genes have significant associations with EH phenotypes; yet, none have been identified as causative, most contribute small effects to the proportion of risk (*OR*s between 1 and 2), and many of them remain to be replicated or confirmed. In addition, few of the genetic markers associated with these candidate genes have clinical tests indicated for screening in HTN (see Genetic Testing Registry [GTR], 2014), with weak clinical validity or clinical utility for use in EH at this time. We review some key findings for these candidate genes that highlight their strong potential for involvement in HTN.

Renin, the initiating enzyme of the RAAS, aids in regulating blood pressure via sodium homeostasis. Altered renin activity has been associated with HTN, salt sensitivity, and BP responsiveness to antihypertensive treatments (Stanton, Dicker, & O'Brien, 2009; Williams, Moore, & Hollenberg, 1991). The renin gene is located on the long arm of chromosome 1 (1q32) and individual SNPs within this gene have been associated with blood pressure (Mansego *et al.*, 2008; Moore *et al.*, 2007), plasma renin activity (Hasimu *et al.*, 2003), and susceptibility to HTN (Ahmad, Saleheen, Bokhari, & Frossard, 2005; Chiang *et al.*, 1997; Frossard, Malloy, Lestringant, & Kane, 2001) in various ethnicities, with inconsistent findings (Berge & Berg, 1994; Chamarthi, Williams, & Williams, 2010; Fu *et al.*, 2001). A recent analysis of tagging SNPs informative for the entire *REN* gene confirmed polymorphisms that are associated with increased risk for HTN in the HyperPATH cohort of 570 hypertensive and 222 normotensive white subjects (Sun *et al.*, 2011). They found that carriers of the A allele of SNP rs6693964 in the *REN* gene had nearly two-fold increased risk of HTN (*OR* = 1.98, *p* = 0.0001). A three-SNP haplotype, H2A:ACG (that included rs6693964) was also correlated with plasma renin activity level and suggested that carriers of this haplo-

type may be more responsive to high-dose antirenin (aliskiren) treatment, because aliskiren has shown greatest antihypertensive effects in those with highest baseline plasma renin levels (Hopkins *et al.*, 2002; Stanton *et al.*, 2009). The results of this study were strengthened by the HyperPATH study's strict clinical control of dietary salt intake, body posture, and hypertensive medications, often cited as major confounders that weaken internal validity.

A plethora of work has been conducted to evaluate the role of the angiotensinogen (AGT) gene in essential HTN. Historically, the *AGT* gene has had the most support for its hypothesized role in HTN—meeting stringent criteria in early studies. Mapped to chromosome 1q42.4, *AGT* encodes pre-angiotensinogen. In response to lowered BP, renin cleaves this protein, producing angiotensin I, which is then cleaved by angiotensin-converting enzyme (ACE) to form angiotensin II—causing a cascade of events leading to increased blood volume, pressure, and pH. Mutations in *AGT* have been associated with HTN susceptibility, some of which can cause renal tubular dysgenesis, a rare and severe autosomal recessive disorder of renal tubular development, for which genetic testing is indicated (National Institutes of Health, 2014). The most common *AGT* variant is rs699 (Met235Thr), a germline missense mutation for which the C allele (present among approximately 30% of the population) encodes threonine instead of a methionine, an amino acid change associated with increased plasma angiotensin levels, BP, and risk for hypertension disorders (first reported by Jeunemaitre *et al.*, 1992). Despite the known protein change and moderate frequency in the population, this variant has inconsistent associations. Across many studies, where positive associations are found, the amount of risk explained by this single variant in EH is minimal (*OR*s less than 2). The rs5051 (aka, A-6G) variant is associated with renal tubular dysgenesis and preeclampsia and is often in tight linkage (coinherited) with the rs699 mutation. Furthermore, epistatic (gene-by-modifier gene interactions) may be important in *AGT*'s involvement with HTN, as Tsai *et al.* (2003) reported evidence of intergenic interactions between *AGT* and *ACE* gene polymorphisms (Tsai *et al.*, 2003).

The *AGTR1* gene has been found in multiple

studies and populations to have polymorphic association with EH and other BP phenotypes, as well as with renal tubular dysgenesis. The gene is mapped to chromosome 3q24 and encodes for the angiotensin receptor II-subtype 1, the enzyme that converts angiotensinogen-I to angiotensinogen–II, mediating both BP and volume. Several *AGTR1* variants are known, including at least 15 insertion/deletion polymorphisms, over 260 SNPs, two of which are nonsynonymous (protein-changing) SNPs within the coding region: Ala163Thr and Ala244Ser (Mottl, Shoham, & North, 2008). Because these are missense mutations with lack of clear association with EH, they are likely to represent "silent" mutations with unknown or varied significance. A detailed review of the literature surrounding genetic association with *AGTR1* variants and various HTN phenotypes are available from Mottl and colleagues (2008) as well as more recently by Katsuya and Morishita (2013). Early reports of *AGTR1* gene association with EH (Bonnardeaux *et al.*, 1994) and early-onset EH in people with two affected parents (Wang, Zee, & Morris, 1997) led to a significant focus on a SNP with an A-to-C base pair change at nucleotide 1166 (1166A>C); however, there has since been a great deal of variation in findings across polymorphisms in *AGTR1*, limiting the clinical utility of genetic testing for EH.

The RAAS-related genes represent a mere fraction of the candidate genes suspected in EH. Basson *et al.* (2012) provide a detailed review of the 50 most strongly implicated candidate genes—citing both confirmed and refuted associations in the literature—which are involved in the following pathways: aldosterone signaling, renal ion channel, ion channel regulation, vasoconstriction, and inflammation. Of note are genes involved in pharmacologic targeting of antihypertensive agents: *ACE* (ACE inhibitors), *ADRA1A, ADRB1, ADRB2, ADRB3* (alpha- and beta-adrenergic receptor blockers), *AGTR1* (angiotensin-II receptor-1 blockers), *CYP11B2* (aldosterone antagonists), and *SLC12A3* (loop diuretics). Interestingly, *CYP11B* is the only variant considered a candidate for EH that also has a known causative role in a monogenic (Mendelian) form of HTN (familial hyperaldosteronism (Toka *et al.*, 2013). In addition, many of these candidate genes have also been implicated in several other common cardiovascular and renal diseases, highlighting the potential for pleiotropic effects in which one gene influences multiple traits.

11.16. GENOME WIDE ASSOCIATIONS FOR ESSENTIAL HYPERTENSION

The aforementioned candidate genes were individually targeted for investigation because of hypothesized relations with the pathophysiologic mechanisms involved in regulation of BP or renal handling of fluid and sodium. Alternately, genome-based, agnostic approaches (for which there is no a priori assumption of candidate genes) have led to identification of novel genes for EH, primarily through population-based GWAS. Ganesh and colleagues (2013) released a Scientific Statement from the American Heart Association in 2013 that reviews the genetics and genomics of CVD and include a compilation (see Table 3 in Ganesh, *et al.*, 2013) of candidate genes for HTN identified through GWAS. Summarized here are the major GWAS conducted through consortia via meta-analyses, in which multiple cohort studies of HTN compiled data to improve power to detect small genetic effect sizes. Following this summary are highlights of additional limitations of the HTN based GWAS presented.

The Global BP Gen consortium evaluated 2.5 million SNPs in 34,433 subjects of European ancestry, identifying eight genetic loci (locations) that were all associated with systolic BP (SBP), diastolic BP (DBP), and HTN (Newton-Cheh *et al.*, 2009). The candidate genes corresponding to these loci are *CYP17A1, CYP1A2, FGF5, MTHFR, c10orf107, ZNF652,* and *PLCD3* (Newton-Cheh *et al.*, 2009). Five of the SNPs were replicated in the independent sample of 15 cohorts; six were significant in an in-silico analysis (computer-simulated predictions) conducted with CHARGE consortia data; and two were replicated in an extension sample of 12,889 Indian-Asian subjects (Newton-Cheh *et al.*, 2009). The individual effect sizes of these genetic variants on BP traits are extremely small, explaining less than 1% of the variation in SBP, DBP, and HTN (and less than 3% of the genetic variance as noted by Ganesh *et al.*, 2013). However, these effects confer 1 mm Hg per allele SBP or 0.5 mm Hg per allele DBP (Newton-Cheh *et al.*, 2009). The authors explain that the collective observed effects—consistent with reduction of SBP by 2 mm Hg—can translate into an estimated 6% reduction in stroke and 5% reduction in CHD (Lewington *et al.*, 2002; Stamler *et al.*, 1989). Simultaneously, the CHARGE Consortium reported further replication of three of these variants among their own list of 43 SNPs for SBP, DBP, and HTN, all with *p*-values less than 4×10^{-7} in their GWAS of over 29,000 people of European Ancestry in the CHARGE Consortium of six cohorts (Levy *et al.*, 2009). Their SNP variants annotated to the following candidate genes: *ATP2B1, C18orf1, CASZ2, SH2B3, ATXN2, TRAFD1, TBX3/TBX5,* and *PLEKHA7* (Levy *et al.*, 2009). These two studies were the first confirmed associations of common genetic variants and BP traits (NewtonCheh *et al.*, 2009) and represent a significant leap forward in understanding the genetic architecture of this complex, polygenic, multifactorial disease.

In 2011, a multistage follow-up of these GWAS was conducted by The International Consortium for Blood Pressure Genome-Wide Association (ICBPGWA), evaluating 200,000 individuals of European descent for SBP and DBP. They identified 16 significant loci, six of which contained previous candidate genes for HTN and 10 of which were completely novel (ICBPGWA *et al.*, 2011). Importantly, they found that nine of the loci replicated in approximately 30,000 East Asians, six of the loci replicated in approximately 24,000 South Asians, and lack of replication was seen in approximately 20,000 Africans (ICBPGWA *et al.*, 2011). Furthermore, a weighted clinical risk score generated from the effect sizes of the 29 genetic variants (13 previously identified by Newton-Cheh *et al.*, 2009 and Levy *et al.*, 2009, plus their 16) was significantly associated with SBP in all three ethnic ancestry populations (ICBPGWA *et al.*, 2011). In the European ancestry cohort, a genetic risk score (weighted by mean SBP and DBP) increased the odds of HTN in women by 23%, with just one standard deviation (SD) increase in the genetic risk score (ICBPGWA *et al.*, 2011). Comparing the top and bottom quintiles of the risk score, differences in SBP and DBP (4.6 mm Hg and 3.0 mm Hg, respectively) (ICBPGWA *et al.*, 2011) reflect population-averaged BP treatment effects for a single antihypertensive agent (Burt *et al.*, 1995). Moreover, the 29-SNP risk score was sig-

nificantly associated with left ventricular wall thickness ($p = 6.0 \times 10^{-6}$), incidence of stroke ($p = 3.3 \times 10^{-5}$), and CAD ($p = 8.1 \times 10^{-29}$), but was not significant for kidney disease or renal phenotypes (ICBPGWA *et al.*, 2011). These findings highlight the important potential for genetic risk scores (rather than single-gene variants) to aid in predicting disease and outcomes. In addition, the investigation of haplotypes (see example above for the *REN* gene) may also be more informative than any single variant. In 2014, another meta-analysis of GWASs involving 87,736 individuals of European ancestry replicated findings from 27 variants of the previous studies and identified 11 novel loci (encompassing 31 candidate genes) for BP traits (Tragante *et al.*, 2014). The unique contribution of this study included cross-referencing small molecule and drug databases to determine that nine of the 11 novel variants were potential therapeutic targets for future antihypertensive drug discovery (Tragante *et al.*, 2014).

In the section on CAD GWAS, we provided cautionary notes regarding GWAS limitations and interpretation. For a thorough review of GWASs in HTN and the limitations therein, we recommend review of Ehret (2010). The modest effect sizes represent a welldocumented issue with GWAS; however, as previously described, sometimes modest effects in HTN can lead to significant population impact (Lewington *et al.*, 2002; Whelton *et al.*, 2002). Another limitation of the HTN GWASs presented was the primary focus on people of European ancestry in the discovery phases with replication in non-Whites. Ehret and colleagues replicated some of the European-associated variants in East and South Asians but failed to replicate any of the variants in AfricanAmericans (ICBPGWA *et al.*, 2011). There is a multitude of literature supporting unique genetic variants contributing to HTN in various ethnic groups. Genomic variation among different ethnicities may help to explain differences in clinical heterogeneity. Given the significantly greater impact of HTN morbidity and mortality in AfricanAmericans, the study of black and other non-European populations for discovery analysis is needed on the same consortia scale as conducted for whites, but remains to be seen. Furthermore, sex-by-gene effects have also been identified and require continued research. Considering both ethnicity and sex has the potential to shed new light as well. In a study conducted by Wang and colleagues (2006), polymorphic variation in *AGT* was associated with SBP and DBP only in African-American males in a multi-ethnic evaluation of 581 youth. As a whole, these GWAS investigations have provided significant insight into molecular and pathophysiologic underpinnings towards a better understanding of the etiology of this complex disease.

11.17. GENE EXPRESSION/ TRANSCRIPTOMICS

As previously described in this chapter, transcriptomics is the study of gene expression patterns across a multitude of transcripts in the genome, for which three main gene expression approaches are class comparison, class prediction, and class discovery. Korkor and colleagues (2011) took a class comparison approach, evaluating peripheral blood cells in a small sample of 18 Chinese subjects for differences in gene expression between nine normotensive and nine hypertensive subjects. They provided preliminary evidence of 31 up-regulated and 18 down-regulated genes having ≥ 2- or < 0.5-fold differences in expression between the two groups (Korkor *et al.*, 2011). The differences were initially identified through microarray analysis and validated through targeted reverse-transcriptase polymerase chain reaction (RT-PCR). Many of which were involved in pathways for inflammation and immunity and/or indirectly related to the RAA system, bradykinin, and other known pathways involved in HTN. Of note, three of the differentially expressed transcripts corresponded to previously identified candidate genes *ERAP1, SLC4A1*, and *ZNF652* (Tragante *et al.*, 2014). Marques and colleagues (2011) were the first to report a transcriptomic, class comparison approach to analyze mRNA and micro-RNA (miRNA) expression in human renal medulla and cortex tissue samples. Array data from 15 untreated hypertensive and 7 normotensive white males of European-ancestry demonstrated significant expression differences (array and RT-PCR validation) in known candidate genes as well as novel markers with biologically plausible connections to HTN (Marques *et al.*, 2011). Of interest was evidence of *REN* overexpression in HTN with downregulation of *REN*-binding miRNAs, pro-

viding preliminary mechanistic evidence to solidify the role of *REN* gene in HTN. Limitations of this study included small sample size, reduced internal validity because of use of renal cancer subjects, and poor generalizability due to inclusion of only male Chinese subjects (Marques *et al.*, 2011). Despite the many limitations of gene expression microarray studies, evaluating the transcriptome has great potential to provide further insight into genetic contribution to HTN.

11.18. METABOLOMICS

Earlier in this chapter is a description of the foundation of metabolomics approaches as focused on quantifying small-molecule metabolites and their associations with disease. To date, few metabolomics studies have been conducted in HTN (the least in human samples), and Nikolic and colleagues (2014) compiled a recent overview of metabolomics in HTN and review of the literature. We briefly highlight some key findings below.

Akira and colleagues (2008) identified metabolic perturbations related to the citric acid cycle in urine of six spontaneously hypertensive rats (SHR) compared with control animals. Two additional studies using SHR models reported free fatty acids (FFAs, such as oleic, linoleic, hexadecanoid, and steric acids) were significantly increased in SHR and correlated with increased BP levels (Aa *et al.*, 2010; Lu *et al.*, 2008). In humans, various FFAs detected in serum were significantly increased in a sample of elderly hypertensive subjects ($n = 34$) compared with controls ($n = 29$). Increased FFA, glucose, galactose, and decreased fructose levels were reported in another comparison between hypertensive and normotensive subjects, further underscoring the concomitant prevalence of impaired glucose tolerance and HTN (Liu *et al.*, 2011). There are biologically plausible hypotheses connecting FFA dysregulation in HTN through pathways involved in neurovascular tone and membrane phospholipid structure and/or membrane ion transport. Furthermore, these results are in support of previous investigations implicating FFAs as independent risk factors for the development of HTN, even after controlling for common confounders (Fagot-Campagna *et al.*, 1998).

Suspecting that metabolic differences may

hold the key to understanding the disproportionate prevalence of HTN in AfricanAmericans and hypothesized difference in etiologic mechanisms, Zheng and colleagues (2013) conducted a metabolomics analysis in nearly 900 black normotensives from the Atherosclerosis Risk in Communities Study. Their longitudinal sample, enriched with older females (ages 45 to 64 years), observed a 38% (*n* = 344) incidence rate of HTN over 10 years follow-up. Increase in 4-hydroxyhippurate (product of gut microbial fermentation) was associated with HTN, such that every increase of 1 SD conferred a 17% increased risk of disease, remaining significant even after controlling for baseline BP values (Zheng *et al.*, 2013). A principal component for a sex steroids pattern was also associated with risk of incident HTN in both men and women (Zheng *et al.*, 2013).

"Omics" approaches have offered unique insights into CAD and HTN phenotypes and are helping to rapidly advance the science around mechanisms driving etiologies, manifestations, treatment responses, and outcomes in these clinically and genetically heterogenous traits. The immense impact of CAD and HTN from individuals to health care systems at large in the context of recent genomic advances and consumer interest in genomics has led to an open market for testing platforms in these areas. In the next section, we present some of the currently available genomic testing platforms for CAD and EH and discuss their clinical validity and utility.

11.19. PHARMACOGENETICS RELATED TO MANAGEMENT OF ESSENTIAL HYPERTENSION

A review of the basics of pharmacogenetics is presented in Chapter 5. Here, we briefly describe exemplars in the pharmacogenetics of EH, recently reviewed by Ong and colleagues (2012). Beta blockers and diuretics are first-line drugs in the treatment of EH. Individually, the Ser49Gly and Arg389Gly polymorphisms of the beta-1 adrenergic receptor (*ADRB1*) gene have been associated with differential BP lowering levels across multiple clinical studies (Johnson & Liggett, 2011; Johnson *et al.*, 2003; Liu *et al.*, 2003; Pacanowski *et al.*, 2008). In combined haplotype analyses, the combination of both variants improved outcome and lowered death rate in hy-

pertensives treated with atenolol compared with verapamil-treated hypertensives (Pacanowski *et al.*, 2008). The alpha-adducin (*ADD1*) variant Gly460Trp was positively associated with response to thiazide diuretics (Pacanowski *et al.*, 2008; Roden *et al.*, 2011), and increased risk for MI/stroke in thiazide-treated hypertensives (Psaty *et al.*, 2002); however, lack of significant associations for this polymorphism were reported by the ALLHAT (2009) and INVEST (2011) Trials. Despite the conflicting reports, adducin has been isolated as a novel antihypertensive drug target, with a Phase II drug—ouabain—demonstrating positive efficacy in lowering BP (Citterio, Lanzani, Manunta, & Bianchi, 2010; Lanzani *et al.*, 2010).

11.20. GENOMIC PLATFORMS AND THEIR CLINICAL UTILITY

Genetic testing allows for diagnosis, screening, risk assessment, prognosis, and prediction of treatment response or adverse events. Genetic testing is evolving from testing only for specific, familial mutations to screening a patient's whole genome for changes associated with complex diseases, most of which are also significantly influenced by environmental factors. Currently, some genomic platforms have been developed for providers to use in conjunction with other routine or related tests (such as lipid levels or BP readings). Companies offering genetic testing related to complex diseases, such as CAD or EH, promise to report an estimate of risk or susceptibility for a patient within days or weeks after the provider sends in a patient's blood, saliva, or stool sample. Most of these platforms are SNP arrays, meaning that the laboratory uses high-throughput technology to detect genotypes for thousands to millions of genetic variants called single nucleotide polymorphisms (SNPs) in the DNA. Most of these SNP arrays use Sanger sequencing or polymerase chain reaction (PCR), both of which have an analytical specificity and sensitivity of 99%. Many of these SNP arrays are available as cardiac panels that are custom-built arrays containing SNPs common in the population, as well as rare mutations implicated in several different cardiac disorders, such as aneurysms, cardiomyopathies, arrhythmias, and Mendelian (single-gene) disorders like Marfan syndrome or familial hypercholesterolemia. Table 11.2 provides details for the platforms we present.

Some companies focus their genetic testing panels on Mendelian disorders, such as the Ambry Genetics (Ambry Genetics™, Aliso Viejo, CA) panel for Marfan syndrome (Ambry Genetics, 2014) or the GeneDx (GeneDx, Gaithersburg, MD) panels for specific cardiac diseases (hereditary hemorrhagic telangiectasia or Noonan syndrome, as examples) (GeneDx, 2014). Until June 2013, Ambry Genetics had been offering a Pan Cardio Panel, which used next-generation sequencing to detect mutations associated with cardiomyopathies or arrhythmias. They stopped offering this test in order to update and re-release this panel, which they reported had an average analytical sensitivity of 97% across all genes tested in the panel (Ambry Genetics, 2014). Neither their panel nor any of Gene Dx panels included testing for complex diseases.

Some companies offer panels that test for mutations associated with complex diseases, coagulation factors, and drug response and metabolism (see Chapter 5). Examples of these panels include the Cardiogenomic Plus Profile™ from Genova Diagnostics, Inc. (Asheville, NC), the Cardiovascular Risk Panel from GENETiKS® (Istanbul); and the Cardiac Panel from Applied Genetics Laboratories, Inc. (Melbourne, FL). Other tests, such as the Health Diagnostic Laboratory, Inc. (Richmond, VA), Cardiac Risk Panel, include both genetic testing and traditional biomarkers as part of a comprehensive panel. All of these companies claim that they provide this testing in order to allow providers to determine patient susceptibility to CVD and/or improve pharmacogenomics outcomes by concomitantly testing for FDA-approved pharmacogenomics tests. Thus, companies market genetic testing as a way to provide a more complete profile of a patient's risk.

MTHFR and *APOE* are the two most common genes associated with CAD included in these panels. For example, GENETiKS tests for 12 mutations in their panel, of which two are mutations in *MTHFR* and two are in *APOE* (GENETiKS, 2014). Applied Genetics Laboratories Inc. (Melbourne, FL), Genova Diagnostics, Inc. (Asheville, NC), and Health Diagnostic Laboratories, Inc. (Richmond, VA), also include *MTHFR* and *APOE* in their panels. *MTHFR* encodes

for an enzyme called methylenetetrahydrofolate reductase, which is involved in a complex process that converts homocysteine to methionine (FN4). Mutations in this gene (the most common of which are C677T and A1298C) can inactivate the enzyme or impair its function, leading to accumulation of homocysteine in the bloodstream. These elevated homocysteine levels may irritate blood vessels and put homozygous carriers at risk for atherosclerosis and venous thrombosis (Varga, Sturm, Misita, & Moll, 2005). Mutations in *MTHFR* may affect homocysteine levels, but a recent meta-analysis of over 48,000 CHD cases and nearly 68,000 controls refuted the association with the common C677T polymorphism (rs1801133) in *MTHFR* with minute effects sizes and lack of significant associations (Clarke *et al.*, 2012). Moreover, nurses can inform patients that adequate dietary folate intake can "essentially cancel out" any risk for cardiac disease associated with elevated homocysteine levels (National Library of Medicine [NLM], 2014).

APOE encodes for apolipoprotein E, which is involved in packaging and transporting cholesterol and fats in the bloodstream to the liver for processing. Thus, apolipoprotein E is involved in maintaining normal levels of cholesterol in the bloodstream. There are three alleles of this protein (*e2*, *e3*, and *e4*), the most common of which is *e3* (FN7). Having at least one copy of the *e4* allele may be associated with an increased risk for developing atherosclerosis because this version of the protein is not as efficient or functional in transporting cholesterol and fatty acids to the liver, thus leading to a build up of those substances in the arteries. This build up can in turn lead to a narrowing of the vessels and increase the risk for having an MI or stroke (NLM, 2014).

Genetic testing for HTN is limited and is only included in the Cardiogenomic Plus Profile from Genova Diagnostics, Inc. (Asheville, NC), which tests for SNPs on *GNB3* and *AGTR1* (Genova Diagnostics, 2014) (see summary of *AGTR1* above in the "Early Candidate Genes in Hypertension" section). Pathway Genomics® (Pathway Genomics Corp., San Diego, CA) also lists HTN as a condition tested for in their comprehensive Cardiac DNA Insight™ panel, but the specific markers tested are not listed (Pathway Genomics Corporation, 2014). *GNB3* encodes for a beta protein that is involved in a complex process

TABLE 11.2. *Comparison of Genomic Platforms for Cardiovascular Disorders.*

Company	Platform Name	Type of Platform	Associated Disease(s)	Genes
Ambry Genetics	Pan Cardio Panel (currently unavailable)	SNP array with additional next-generation sequencing	Cardiomyopathies, dilated cardiomyopathy, hypertrophic cardiomyopathy, arrhythmias, long QT syndrome, Brugada syndrome	ABCC9, ACTC1, ACTN2, AKAP9, ANK2, ANKRD1, BAG3, CACNA1C, CACNA2D1, CACNB2, CALR3, CASQ2, CAV3, CRYAB, CSRP3, DES, DMD, DSC2, DSG2, DSP, EMD, EYA4, FXN, GATA4, GLA, GPD1L, ILK, JAG1, JPH2, JUP, KCNE1, KCNE2, KCNE3, KCNH2, KCNJ2, KCNJ8, KCNQ1, LAMP2, LDB3/ZASP, LMNA, MYBPC3, MYH6, MYH7, MYL2, MYL3, MYOM1, MYOZ2, MYPN, NEBL, NEXN, NKX2.5, PDLIM3, PKP2, PLN, PRKAG2, PTPN11, RAF1, RBM20, RYR2, SCN1B, SCN3B, SCN4B, SCN5A, SGCD, SNTA1, TAZ, TBX1, TBX5, TCAP, TMEM43, TMPO, TNNC1, TNNI3, TNNT2, TPM1, TTN, TTR, TXNRD2, VCL
Applied Genetics	Cardiac Panel	SNP array	Coronary artery disease, stroke, thrombosis, drug metabolism	MTHFR, APOE (atherosclerosis), Factor V (Leiden), Factor II (thrombosis), CYP 2C19, CYP 2D6, CYP 3A4-3A5, CYP2C9/VKORC1 (drug metabolism)
GeneDx	Specific to associated condition for which test is ordered e.g., Noonan Syndrome Panel)	SNP array, deletion/duplication analysis, next-generation sequencing based on specific panel ordered	Depends on panel ordered (many panels for single-gene disorders)	Varies based on selected panel
Genova Diagnostics	Cardiogenomic Plus Profile	SNP array	Hypercholesteremia, atherosclerosis, obesity, hypertension, myocardial infarction, thrombosis, endothelial dysfunction, stroke	APOE, CETP, SELE (atherosclerosis); MTHFR (methylation); GNB3, AGTR1 (hypertension); GP3a, PAI-1, Factor 5, Factor 2 (coagulation)

(continued)

TABLE 11.2 (continued). Comparison of Genomic Platforms for Cardiovascular Disorders.

Company	Platform Name	Type of Platform	Associated Disease(s)	Genes
Genetiks	Cardiovascular Risk Panel	SNP array and deletion/insertion analysis	Thrombosis, ischemic stroke, myocardial infarction, atherosclerosis, hypertension	Factor V G1691A (Leiden), Factor V H1299R (R2), *PAI-1 4G-5G*, Prothrombin G20210A, Factor XIII V34L (thrombosis), Fibrinogen -455 G-A (ischemic stroke), GPIIIa L33P (HPA-1) (myocardial infarction), *MTHFR C677T, MTHFR A1298C, ApoB R3500Q, ApoE* (E2, E3, E4) (atherosclerosis), *ACE I/D* (hypertension)
Health Diagnostics	Cardiac Risk Panel	SNP array and traditional biomarker tests (LDL, HDL, triglycerides, BNP, fibrinogen, immune complex assay, VLCFA, insulin)	Coronary artery disease	Unknown
Pathway Genomics	Cardiac DNA Insight	SNP array	Hypertension, atrial fibrillation, coronary artery disease, myocardial infarction, peripheral arterial disease, venous thrombosis, cholesterol regulation, drug metabolism	Unknown
Cardio Dx	CORUS CAD	Gene expression	Coronary artery disease	Unknown (23 genes total)
23andMe	Personal Health Overview	SNP array	Many single-gene and complex disorders, of which results are given for coronary heart disease and hypertension among other cardiac-related health conditions	CAD, Established report: 9p21, *PHACTR1, CXCL12, SMARCA4, MRPS6, MIA3, WDR12, MRAS, LPA, ZC3HC1, ABO, CNNM2, APOA5, COL4A2, HHIPL1 CAD*, Preliminary report: *ADTRP, ANRIL, BRAP, LGALS2, LDLR, MIA3* HTN: Preliminary report: *UMOD, STK39, CNNM2, MTHFR, FGF5, EDN1, CSK*

Sources: Company web sites.

of transmembrane signaling (NLM, 2014). The C825T mutation in this gene has been associated with EH, although the evidence of its association is still inconclusive. This mutation is thought to increase the activity of signal transduction, thus leading to vascular hypertrophy from increased vasoconstriction signaling (Pereira *et al.*, 2014).

Other than the SNP array panels, there is one gene expression test available on the market called CORUS CAD from CardioDx® (Redwood City, CA). This test measures the amount of up- or down-regulation of 23 genes thought to be associated with CAD and gives the provider results within 72 hours. This test is not scanning for specific mutations in the genome as the SNP arrays do, but rather is examining the activity of specific genes and how that activity reflects a patient's current state of obstructive coronary disease. Therefore, this test is a point-in-time assessment of a patient's likelihood of CAD, calculated with a prediction algorithm from the 23 genes' expression levels, and taking patient age and sex into account (Elashoff *et al.*, 2011). Results submitted to the provider only contain a "score" from 1 to 40 and percent likelihood of obstructive CAD, not the individual gene expression results for each mRNA transcript. Unfortunately, CardioDx also does not report which 23 genes are included in their gene expression profile, citing proprietary rights to this information and preventing further insight into underlying pathologic mechanisms. They do assert that the test's clinical validity has been proved in two major studies, known as PREDICT (Rosenberg *et al.*, 2010) and COMPASS (Thomas *et al.*, 2013). Notably, the two reports estimate high 85% to 89% sensitivity, moderate 43% to 52% specificity, strong negative predictive values between 83% and 96%, and moderate positive predictive value of 46% at prespecified threshholds of a score < 15 (corresponding to 20% likelihood of obstructive CAD) (Rosenberg *et al.*, 2010; Thomas *et al.*, 2013). The CORUS CAD platform was developed and validated using predominantly white patients who did not have diabetes, inflammatory disease, or autoimmune disease (Vargas, Lima, Kraus, Douglas, & Rosenberg, 2013), thus limiting its clinical applicability. Vargas, along with original investigators of the platform, recently published a clinical utility evaluation (Vargas *et al.*, 2013), self-appraising a Level 1 clinical

utility status based on EGAPP working group's framework for evaluating evidence of genomic testing (Teutsch *et al.*, 2009). Further studies are needed to determine clinical utility of CORUS CAD in more clinically generalizable samples.

The EGAPP Working Group is an independent review group that periodically evaluates evidence regarding genomics for clinical utility and has published guidelines for clinical utility appraisal (Teutsch *et al.*, 2009). EGAPP does not currently recommend for or against genomic testing for CAD, because the limited evidence showed weak to moderate clinical validity and test specificity and sensitivity. This recommendation stems from their research, which found that using these genomic markers in combination with traditional risk factors did not lead to improved outcomes for patients and that further evidence is needed on the clinical validity of these tests (EGAPP, 2010). One major insurance provider cites this EGAPP recommendation as the reason it does not provide coverage for the entire cost of genetic cardiac panels (Blue Cross Blue Shield, 2014). The insurance company states that improved health outcomes could still be made with lifestyle changes, such as diet changes, increased exercise, and smoking cessation. Furthermore, it claims that genetic testing is "investigational" instead of necessary. In order to encourage providers to order genetic testing, however, each company offers its own provider brochures, patient brochures, and test information sheets with citations of research to support their decision to test for a specific variant (Applied Genetics Laboratories Incorporated, 2011). With their tests, companies also provide access to a genetic counselor or provide information on how to reach a genetic counselor.

Instead of the provider-ordered genetic testing, patients can also access their personal genetic information through 23andMe, Inc. (Mountainview, CA), a direct-to-consumer (DTC) genetics testing company that allows consumers to purchase access to their own genetic health risk information. In November 2013, the FDA issued a letter to 23andMe requiring them to stop issuing consumers the genetic health risks report until the company complied with providing FDA-requested materials (U.S. FDA, 2014b). Acting in oversight of DTC testing, the FDA was concerned about the genetic risk information being provided to consumers and the validity and utility of their platform and risk algorithms. It is anticipated that 23andMe will be authorized to reinstate the health risks portion of their platform in the near future. Using visual aids and interactive, color-coded graphs, 23andMe provides consumers with a risk assessment report for various health conditions, a large proportion of which are complex diseases. Although 23andMe reports ORs for SNPs and lists references from the literature, the lay population may not fully understand the results or may feel overwhelmed by the amount of information presented. Moreover, patients may overestimate ("genetic determinism") or underestimate their risk for developing a disease based on the results. When exploring their results, some patients may focus solely on the genetic aspect of their risk and fail to consider family history and environmental influences. The reactions of consumers also depend on their knowledge concerning their own health, the science of genetics, and their family history. Some patients may have trouble understanding the scientific evidence provided. 23andMe provides links to the articles on which they base their assertions, but consumers who do not have a strong background in science may find those articles confusing. To help explain these findings to a patient, 23andMe offers the assistance of a genetic counselor (at an additional fee), just as other companies offer genetic counseling assistance to providers.

Some patients may bring their results to their provider for interpretation and discussion. 23andMe lists the genes and SNPs included in their panels for each disease, so providers can clearly see what is being tested. For example, 23andMe includes 15 genes in its panel for CAD (none of which are tested as part of the other panels previously discussed, but some of which may be proxy markers for known candidate gene regions) and 7 genes in its panel for EH. It lists the specific SNPs tested within those genes and cites research related to that SNP to support why they are included in the panel. 23andMe also denotes the strength of evidence for CAD as "established" while the evidence for HTN is only "preliminary." Even if the "established," whereas evidence is still not fully understood or developed, 23andMe uses it as the best evidence in the literature at this time. The evidence for

HTN is labeled as "preliminary," meaning that it "includes results of studies that still need to be confirmed by the scientific community," thus communicating that the result may not even be correct (23andMe, 2014). They make no recommendations based on preliminary evidence, which may leave some patients wondering what to do with this information. Providers themselves need to be able to understand the significance or evidence related to those SNPs in order to incorporate that information into the patient's plan of care and help the patient understand the information (Jordan & Timberlake, 2013).

Unfortunately, much of the data for clinical utility and validity are not available for many of these platforms. As clinicians, we are trained to look for clinical validity of these tests, but this information is not reported at this time. Perhaps as more clinicians order or use the test, companies will gather more data and release that information. Because the evidence is not strong yet, the use of these platforms will depend on provider knowledge, preference, and patient accessibility. More trials for clinical utility, as well as trials on the specific genes tested, will prove useful. No proteomic or metabolic tests are available for cardiac disease at this time.

11.21. NURSING IMPLICATIONS RELATED TO GENOMIC TESTING PLATFORMS

In determining risk for CAD or HTN, evaluating the standard modifiable and nonmodifiable risk factors (clinical, environmental, behavioral) that are known independent predictors for disease remains critical. For now, the best "genetic" maker in these complex diseases is a good family history assessment to evaluate potential risk based on firstdegree relatives' (parents and siblings) presence of early-onset disease or events (MI, severe, refractory hypertensive episodes), indicating a potential for stronger genetic contribution for the individual (CAD: men $\leq$ 50 years, women $\leq$ 55 years for CAD [Hauser et al., 2004]; HTN: age < 45 years for whites, age < 35 years for AfricanAmericans [Wilk et al., 2004]). Clinicians could find these tests useful, however, if family history is unknown, a sudden cardiac-related death occurs in a family, or a complex history of CVD exists within a family (Ambry

Genetics, 2014). Additionally, clinical heterogeneity and genetic heterogeneity are important considerations when evaluating the results of one of these platforms for a specific patient. The fact that these platforms test for certain genetic markers does not necessarily signify that those markers are the strongest indicators for a disease, or that patients who have the same mutations will present with the same health condition clinically. Additionally, much of the evidence provided for the markers tested is inconclusive at this time and is the focus of current research.

Providers could also use this additional genetic information to motivate patients to make lifestyle changes, such as consuming fewer saturated fats or increasing the amount of time they exercise per week. The genetic data provided in these cardiac panels can provide educational information for the provider and patient that may inform the patient's personal healthcare plan despite the fact that the clinical validity of these tests is still not reported. Genomic platforms can add another dimension to a patient's profile and inform clinical decisions, but providers and patients need to be aware of the other influences on a patient's health and the limitations of genetic data. The clinical utility of these tests for the broad population remains to be supported by current evidence, but nurses need to be aware of the potential benefits and limitations of these platforms and stay abreast of future guidelines that may be developed for their implementation. If clinical implementation were supported for CAD or HTN, the American Heart Association and/or the EGAPP working groups would be the most likely proponents.

11.22. CONCLUSIONS

Unlike the single-gene, Mendelian cardiovascular disorders presented in part two of this chapter, the genetic architecture underlying the etiology and pathophysiology of common, complex cardiovascular phenotypes such as CAD and HTN is less established. Strong candidate genes exist for CAD and HTN, only few of which have been replicated through large consortia datasets (9p21 in CAD and 13 HTN candidates from the CHARGE and Global BP Gen Consortia). More emphasis and resources need to be placed on elucidating unique genomic contribution in ethnically diverse groups and/or understand popu-

lation effects that warrant further investigation. GWASs and other "omics" approaches such as transcriptomics and metabolomics have invigorated the scientific potential to better understand these complex, polygenic diseases. Genomic risk scores are being generated and tested for improvement over existing clinically-based risk scores or improved risk reclassification. Some of these advances have shifted the market towards making genomic testing for CAD and HTN available to both clinicians and consumers. A majority of the existing platforms offer SNP arrays to evaluate common and rare markers in various susceptibility and causative genes. Only one gene expression platform exists.

Attention to red flags in the family history is an essential assessment of the nursing role (red flags presented in Chapter 2). Nonetheless, patients should be addressed with existing standards of care for risk screening, prevention, risk factor management, and treatment guidelines. Furthermore, nurses should be aware of the potential for stronger evidence to build in the area of pharmacogenetics related to CAD and HTN, such that new FDA labels could be issued for recommending genetic testing concomitant with prescribing therapeutics. The FDA currently has approximately 161 pharmacogenomics-based labels issued for pharmacologic agents (cardiovascular and non-cardiovascular related). For a complete list, see U.S. FDA (2014a).

11.23. FUTURE DIRECTIONS

We have highlighted the immense scientific benefit of consortia-based science in cardiovascular genomics, and significant advances in other "omics" continue to be made. Genome sequencing (determining each base pair code in an individual's genome or exome) is gaining efficiency and affordability, improving the capability of elucidating genomic differences in CVDs. An advancing field of transcriptomics is now focused on miRNAs, which are small, noncoding RNA molecules typically no more than 22 nucleotides in length that essentially repress gene expression and are involved in other transcriptional processes. A recent review by Sayed and colleagues (Sayed, Xia, Salma, Yang, & Peng, 2014) highlights the early work in characterizing miRNA activity associated with AMI, ACS, stable CAD, heart failure, atherosclerosis, EH, and stroke. This field may prove tantamount in future understanding of complex, common disease pathology. The future of genomics also includes more systems-biology approaches to designing research. Schallom and colleagues (2011) describe the systems-biology approach as a holistic, multi-disciplinary, evidence-based integration of systems and astutely mirror the nursing foundation in this approach (Schallom, Thimmesch, & Pierce, 2011). Nurse scientists can harness this approach in their primary and collaborative research related to "omics" sciences. Some institutions are developing infrastructure to support large-scale systems biology science, such as the launching of the Systems Approach to Biomarker Research (SABRe) by investigators of the Framingham Heart Study (Joehanes *et al.*, 2012). Nurses are poised to be at the forefront of implementation science in CVD (see Vorderstrasse, Ginsburg, Kraus, Maldonado, & Wolever, 2013) aimed at studying the processes and impact of implementing genomics-based health care and new genomic-clinical risk algorithms among health care systems and patients. Nurses who understand genomics, its limitations, and potential benefits will be leaders in meeting the genomic needs of patients, families, and communities.

11.24. REFERENCES

23andMe, Incorporated. (2014). Health risks: High blood pressure (hypertension). Retrieved from https://www.23andme.com/you/journal/pre_hypertension/overview/

Aa, J. Y., Wang, G. J., Hao, H. P., Huang, Q., Lu, Y. H., Yan, B., . . . & Kang, A. (2010). Differential regulations of blood pressure and perturbed metabolism by total ginsenosides and conventional antihypertensive agents in spontaneously hypertensive rats. *Acta Pharmacologica Sinica, 31*(8), 930–937. doi: 10.1038/aps.2010.86

Ahmad, U., Saleheen, D., Bokhari, A., & Frossard, P. M. (2005). Strong association of a renin intronic dimorphism with essential hypertension. *Hypertension Research, 28*(4), 339–344. doi: 10.1291/hypres.28.339

Akira, K., Masu, S., Imachi, M., Mitome, H., Hashimoto, M., & Hashimoto, T. (2008). 1H NMR-based metabonomic analysis of urine from young spontaneously hypertensive rats. *Journal Pharmaceutical and Biomedical Analysis, 46*(3), 550–556. doi: 10.1016/j.jpba.2007.11.017

Allen, G., Harvald, B., & Shields, J. (1967). Measures of twin concordance. *Acta Genetica et Statistica Medica, 17*(6), 475–481.

ALLHAT (NCT00000542). (2009). Clinical Trials: Antihypertensive and Lipid-Lowering Treatment to Prevent Heart Attack Trial (ALLHAT). Retrieved July 1, 2014, from http://clinicaltrials.gov/ct2/show/NCT00000542?term=ALLHAT&rank=3

Ambry Genetics. (2014). Pan cardio panel. Retrieved July 1, 2014, from http://www.ambrygen.com/test/pan-cardio-panel

Aouizerat, B. E., Vittinghoff, E., Musone, S. L., Pawlikowska, L., Kwok, P. Y., Olgin, J. E., & Tseng, Z. H. (2011). GWAS for discovery and replication of genetic loci associated with sudden cardiac arrest in patients with coronary artery disease. *BMC Cardiovascular Disorders, 11*, 29. doi: 10.1186/1471-2261-11-29

Applied Genetics Laboratories, Incorporated. (2011). Cardiac panel. Retrieved from http://www.applied-genetics.com/tests/?content_id=55&&panel=cardiac

Ardissino, D., Berzuini, C., Merlini, P. A., Mannuccio Mannucci, P., Surti, A., Burtt, N., . . . & Vascular Biology, Investigators. (2011). Influence of 9p21.3 genetic variants on clinical and angiographic outcomes in early-onset myocardial infarction. *Journal of the American College of Cardiology, 58*(4), 426–434. doi: 10.1016/j.jacc.2010.11.075

Arking, D. E., & Sotoodehnia, N. (2012). The genetics of sudden cardiac death. *Annual Review of Genomics and Human Genetics, 13*, 223–239. doi: 10.1146/annurev-genom-090711-163841

Basson, J., Simino, J., & Rao, D. C. (2012). Between candidate genes and whole genomes: Time for alternative approaches in blood pressure genetics. *Current Hypertension Reports, 14*(1), 46–61. doi: DOI 10.1007/s11906-011-0241-8

Berge, K. E., & Berg, K. (1994). No effect of a BglI polymorphism at the renin (REN) locus on blood pressure level or variability. *Clinical Genetics, 46*(6), 436–438.

Blue Cross Blue Shield. (2014). Corporate medical policy: Cardiovascular disease risk tests. Retrieved from http://www.bcbsnc.com/assets/services/public/pdfs/medicalpolicy/cardiovascular_disease_risk_tests.pdf

Bonnardeaux, A., Davies, E., Jeunemaitre, X., Fery, I., Charru, A., Clauser, E., . . . & Soubrier, F. (1994). Angiotensin II type 1 receptor gene polymorphisms in human essential hypertension. *Hypertension, 24*(1), 63–69.

Burt, V. L., Cutler, J. A., Higgins, M., Horan, M. J., Labarthe, D., Whelton, P., . . . & Roccella, E. J. (1995). Trends in the prevalence, awareness, treatment, and control of hypertension in the adult US population. Data from the health examination surveys, 1960 to 1991. *Hypertension, 26*(1), 60–9.

Bush, W. S., & Moore, J. H. (2012). Chapter 11: Genome-wide association studies. *PLoS Computer*

Biology, 8(12), e1002822. doi: 10.1371/journal.pcbi.1002822

CARDIoGRAMplusC4D Consortium. (2013). Large-scale association analysis identifies new risk loci for coronary artery disease. *Nature Genetics, 45*(1), 25–33. doi: 10.1038/ng.2480

Chamarthi, B., Williams, J. S., & Williams, G. H. (2010). A mechanism for salt-sensitive hypertension: Abnormal dietary sodium-mediated vascular response to angiotensin-II. *Journal of Hypertension, 28*(5), 1020–1026. doi: 10.1097/HJH.0b013e3283375974

Chasman, D. I., Posada, D., Subrahmanyan, L., Cook, N. R., Stanton, V. P., Jr., & Ridker, P. M. (2004). Pharmacogenetic study of statin therapy and cholesterol reduction. *JAMA, 291*(23), 2821–2827. doi: 10.1001/jama.291.23.2821

Chiang, F. T., Hsu, K. L., Tseng, C. D., Lo, H. M., Chern, T. H., & Tseng, Y. Z. (1997). Association of the renin gene polymorphism with essential hypertension in a Chinese population. *Clinical Genetics, 51*(6), 370–374.

Citterio, L., Lanzani, C., Manunta, P., & Bianchi, G. (2010). Genetics of primary hypertension: the clinical impact of adducin polymorphisms. *Biochimica et Biophysica Acta, 1802*(12), 1285–1298. doi: 10.1016/j.bbadis.2010.03.014

Clarke, R., Bennett, D. A., Parish, S., Verhoef, P., Dotsch-Klerk, M., Lathrop, M., ... & Mthfr Studies Collaborative Group. (2012). Homocysteine and coronary heart disease: Metaanalysis of MTHFR case-control studies, avoiding publication bias. *PLoS Medicine, 9*(2), e1001177. doi: 10.1371/journal.pmed.1001177

Connelly, J. J., Shah, S. H., Doss, J. F., Gadson, S., Nelson, S., Crosslin, D. R., ... & Gregory, S. G. (2008). Genetic and functional association of FAM5C with myocardial infarction. *BMC Medical Genetics, 9*, 33. doi: 10.1186/1471-2350-9-33

Connelly, J. J., Wang, T., Cox, J. E., Haynes, C., Wang, L., Shah, S. H., ... & Gregory, S. G. (2006). GATA2 is associated with familial early-onset coronary artery disease. *PLoS Genetics, 2*(8), e139. doi: 10.1371/journal.pgen.0020139

Coronary Artery Disease Genetics Consortium. (2011). A genome-wide association study in Europeans and South Asians identifies five new loci for coronary artery disease. *Nature Genetics, 43*(4), 339–344. doi: 10.1038/ng.782

Dandona, S., Stewart, A. F., Chen, L., Williams, K., So, D., O'Brien, E., ... & Roberts, R. (2010). Gene dosage of the common variant 9p21 predicts severity of coronary artery disease. *Journal of the American College of Cardiology, 56*(6), 479–486. doi: 10.1016/j.jacc.2009.10.092

Donnelly, L. A., Doney, A. S., Dannfald, J., Whitley, A. L., Lang, C. C., Morris, A. D., ... & Palmer, C. N. (2008). A paucimorphic variant in the HMG-CoA reductase gene is associated with lipid-lowering response to statin treatment in diabetes: a GoDARTS

study. *Pharmacogenetics and Genomics, 18*(12), 1021–1026. doi: 10.1097/FPC.0b013e3283106071

Dungan, J. R., Conley, Y. P., Langaee, T. Y., Johnson, J. A., Kneipp, S. M., Hess, P. J., & Yucha, C. B. (2009). Altered beta-2 adrenergic receptor gene expression in human clinical hypertension. *Biological Research for Nursing, 11*(1), 17–26. doi: 10.1177/1099800409332538

Dungan, J. R., Hauser, E. R., Qin, X., & Kraus, W. E. (2013). The genetic basis for survivorship in coronary artery disease. *Frontiers in Genetics, 4*, 191. doi: 10.3389/fgene.2013.00191

Ehret, G. B. (2010). Genome-wide association studies: contribution of genomics to understanding blood pressure and essential hypertension. *Current Hypertension Reports, 12*(1), 17–25. doi: 10.1007/s11906-009-0086-6

Elashoff, M. R., Wingrove, J. A., Beineke, P., Daniels, S. E., Tingley, W. G., Rosenberg, S., ... Topol, E. J. (2011). Development of a blood-based gene expression algorithm for assessment of obstructive coronary artery disease in non-diabetic patients. *BMC Med Genomics, 4*, 26. doi: 10.1186/1755-8794-4-26

Evaluation of Genomic Applications in Practice and Prevention [EGAPP]. (2010). Recommendations from the EGAPP Working Group: Genomic profiling to assess cardiovascular risk to improve cardiovascular health. *Genetics in Medicine, 12*, 839–843. doi: doi:10.1097/GIM.0b013e3181f872c0

Fagot-Campagna, A., Balkau, B., Simon, D., Warnet, J. M., Claude, J. R., Ducimetiere, P., & Eschwege, E. (1998). High free fatty acid concentration: An independent risk factor for hypertension in the Paris Prospective Study. *International Journal of Epidemiology, 27*(5), 808–813.

Frossard, P. M., Malloy, M. J., Lestringant, G. G., & Kane, J. P. (2001). Haplotypes of the human renin gene associated with essential hypertension and stroke. *Journal of Human Hypertension, 15*(1), 49–55.

Fu, Y., Katsuya, T., Asai, T., Fukuda, M., Inamoto, N., Iwashima, Y., ... Ogihara, T. (2001). Lack of correlation between Mbo I restriction fragment length polymorphism of renin gene and essential hypertension in Japanese. *Hypertension Research, 24*(3), 295–298.

Ganesh, S. K., Tragante, V., Guo, W., Guo, Y., Lanktree, M. B., Smith, E. N., ... & Asselbergs, F. W. (2013). Loci influencing blood pressure identified using a cardiovascular genecentric array. *Human Molecular Genetics, 22*(8), 1663–1678. Doi:10.1093/hmg/dds555

GeneDx. (2014). Cardiology Genetics: Cardiology Genetic Testing Services Retrieved July 1, 2014, from http://www.genedx.com/test-catalog/cardiology/

Genetic Testing Registry [GTR]. (2014). Genetic Testing Registry. Retrieved July 1, 2014, from National Center for Biotechnology Information (NCBI) http://www.ncbi.nlm.nih.gov/gtr/

GENETiKS. (2014). Cardiovascular Risk Panel. Retrieved July 1, 2014, from http://www.genetiks.com.tr/en/news-details/cardiovascular-risk-panel

Genova Diagnostics. (2014). CardioGenomic Plus Profile. Retrieved from http://www.gdx.net/product/cardio-genomic-plus-genomic-testing

Go, A. S., Mozaffarian, D., Roger, V. L., Benjamin, E. J., Berry, J. D., Blaha, M. J., . . . Turner, M. B. (2014). Heart disease and stroke statistics—2014 update: a report from the American Heart Association. *Circulation, 129*(3), e28-e292. doi: 10.1161/01.cir.0000441139.02102.80

Goldstein, J. L., & Brown, M. S. (2009). The LDL receptor. *Arteriosclerosis, Thrombosis, and Vascular Biology, 29*(4), 431–438. doi: 10.1161/ATVBAHA.108.179564

Hasimu, B., Nakayama, T., Mizutani, Y., Izumi, Y., Asai, S., Soma, M., . . . Ozawa, Y. (2003). Haplotype analysis of the human renin gene and essential hypertension. *Hypertension, 41*(2), 308–312.

Hauser, E. R., Mooser, V., Crossman, D. C., Haines, J. L., Jones, C. H., Winkelmann, B. R., . . . Kraus, W. E. (2003). Design of the Genetics of Early Onset Cardiovascular Disease (GENECARD) study. *American Heart Journal, 145*(4), 602–613. doi: 10.1067/mhj.2003.13

Hauser, E. R., Crossman, D. C., Granger, C. B., Haines, J. L., Jones, C. J., Mooser, V., . . . Kraus, W. E. (2004). A genomewide scan for early-onset coronary artery disease in 438 families: the GENECARD Study. *American Journal of Human Genetics, 75*(3), 436–447. doi: 10.1086/423900

Helgadottir, A., Thorleifsson, G., Manolescu, A., Gretarsdottir, S., Blondal, T., Jonasdottir, A., . . . Stefansson, K. (2007). A common variant on chromosome 9p21 affects the risk of myocardial infarction. *Science, 316*(5830), 1491–1493. doi: 10.1126/science.1142842

Helgadottir, A., Thorleifsson, G., Magnusson, K. P., Gretarsdottir, S., Steinthorsdottir, V., Manolescu, A., . . . Stefansson, K. (2008). The same sequence variant on 9p21 associates with myocardial infarction, abdominal aortic aneurysm and intracranial aneurysm. *Nature Genetics, 40*(2), 217–224. doi: 10.1038/ng.72

Hopkins, P. N., Hunt, S. C., Jeunemaitre, X., Smith, B., Solorio, D., Fisher, N. D., . . . Williams, G. H. (2002). Angiotensinogen genotype affects renal and adrenal responses to angiotensin II in essential hypertension. *Circulation, 105*(16), 1921–1927.

International Consortium for Blood Pressure Genome-Wide Association Studies, Ehret, G. B., Munroe, P. B., Rice, K. M., Bochud, M., Johnson, A. D., . . . Johnson, T. [ICBPGWA *et al.*] (2011). Genetic variants in novel pathways influence blood pressure and cardiovascular disease risk. *Nature, 478*(7367), 103–109. doi: 10.1038/nature10405

INVEST Trial, (NCT00133692). (2011). ClincialTrials

INVEST: INternational VErapamil SR Trandolapril STudy. Retrieved from http://clinicaltrials.gov/ct2/show/NCT00133692?term=INVEST&rank=4

James, P. A., Oparil, S., Carter, B. L., Cushman, W. C., Dennison-Himmelfarb, C., Handler, J., . . . Ortiz, E. (2014). 2014 evidence-based guideline for the management of high blood pressure in adults: report from the panel members appointed to the Eighth Joint National Committee (JNC 8). *JAMA, 311*(5), 507–520. doi: 10.1001/jama.2013.284427

Jeunemaitre, X., Soubrier, F., Kotelevtsev, Y. V., Lifton, R. P., Williams, C. S., Charru, A., . . . *et al.* (1992). Molecular basis of human hypertension: role of angiotensinogen. *Cell, 71*(1), 169–180.

Joehanes, R., Johnson, A. D., Barb, J. J., Raghavachari, N., Liu, P., Woodhouse, K. A., . . . Levy, D. (2012). Gene expression analysis of whole blood, peripheral blood mononuclear cells, and lymphoblastoid cell lines from the Framingham Heart Study. *Physiological Genomics, 44*(1), 59–75. doi: 10.1152/physiolgenomics.00130.2011

Joehanes, R., Ying, S., Huan, T., Johnson, A. D., Raghavachari, N., Wang, R., . . . Munson, P. J. (2013). Gene expression signatures of coronary heart disease. *Arteriosclerosis, Thrombosis, and Vascular Biology, 33*(6), 1418–1426. doi: 10.1161/ATVBAHA.112.301169

Johnson, J. A., & Liggett, S. B. (2011). Cardiovascular pharmacogenomics of adrenergic receptor signaling: clinical implications and future directions. *Clinical Pharmacology & Therapeutics, 89*(3), 366–378. doi: 10.1038/clpt.2010.315

Johnson, J. A., Zineh, I., Puckett, B. J., McGorray, S. P., Yarandi, H. N., & Pauly, D. F. (2003). Beta 1-adrenergic receptor polymorphisms and antihypertensive response to metoprolol. *Clinical Pharmacology & Therapeutics, 74*(1), 44–52. doi: 10.1016/S0009-9236(03)00068-7

Johnson, C. O., Lemaitre, R. N., Fahrenbruch, C. E., Hesselson, S., Sotoodehnia, N., McKnight, B., . . . Rea, T. D. (2012). Common variation in fatty acid genes and resuscitation from sudden cardiac arrest. *Circulation: Cardiovascular Genetics, 5*(4), 422–429. doi: 10.1161/CIRCGENETICS.111.961912

Jordan, S., & Timberlake, S. (2013, December 1, 2013). Direct-to-consumer genomics call for provider education, Opinion Editorial, The Herald Sun. Retrieved from http://www.heraldsun.com/opinion/guestcolumnists/x201537343/Direct-to-consumer-genomics-call-for-provider-education

Kajinami, K., Brousseau, M. E., Ordovas, J. M., & Schaefer, E. J. (2004). CYP3A4 genotypes and plasma lipoprotein levels before and after treatment with atorvastatin in primary hypercholesterolemia. *American Journal of Cardiology, 93*(1), 104–107.

Kathiresan, S., & Myocardial Infarction Genetics Consortium. (2008). A PCSK9 missense variant associated with a reduced risk of early-onset myocardial infarction. *New England Journal of*

Medicine, 358(21), 2299–2300. doi: 10.1056/NEJMc0707445

Kathiresan, S., Voight, B. F., Purcell, S., Musunuru, K., Ardissino, D., Mannucci, P. M., . . . Altshuler, D. (2009). Genome-wide association of early-onset myocardial infarction with single nucleotide polymorphisms and copy number variants. *Nature Genetics, 41*(3), 334–341. doi: 10.1038/ng.327

Katsuya, T., & Morishita, R. (2013). Gene polymorphism of angiotensin II type 1 and type 2 receptors. *Current Pharmaceutical Design, 19*(17), 2996–3001.

Korkor, M. T., Meng, F. B., Xing, S. Y., Zhang, M. C., Guo, J. R., Zhu, X. X., & Yang, P. (2011). Microarray analysis of differential gene expression profile in peripheral blood cells of patients with human essential hypertension. *International Journal of Medical Sciences, 8*(2), 168–179.

Krauss, R. M., Mangravite, L. M., Smith, J. D., Medina, M. W., Wang, D., Guo, X., . . . Rotter, J. I. (2008). Variation in the 3-hydroxyl-3-methylglutaryl coenzyme a reductase gene is associated with racial differences in low-density lipoprotein cholesterol response to simvastatin treatment. *Circulation, 117*(12), 1537–1544. doi: 10.1161/CIRCULATIONAHA.107.708388

Lanzani, C., Citterio, L., Glorioso, N., Manunta, P., Tripodi, G., Salvi, E., . . . Bianchi, G. (2010). Adducin- and ouabain-related gene variants predict the antihypertensive activity of rostafuroxin, part 2: clinical studies. *Science Translational Medicine, 2*(59), 59ra87. doi: 10.1126/scitranslmed.3001814

Leica Biosystems, Amsterdam (2014). p16 (INK4A, 9p21)—for Tissue. Retrieved July 1, 2014, from http://www.kreatech.com/products/repeat-freetmposeidontm-fish-probes/solid-tumors/p16-ink4a-9p21-for-tissue.html

Levy, D., Ehret, G. B., Rice, K., Verwoert, G. C., Launer, L. J., Dehghan, A., . . . van Duijn, C. M. (2009). Genome-wide association study of blood pressure and hypertension. *Nature Genetics, 41*(6), 677–687. doi: 10.1038/ng.384

Lewington, S., Clarke, R., Qizilbash, N., Peto, R., Collins, R., & Prospective Studies, Collaboration. (2002). Age-specific relevance of usual blood pressure to vascular mortality: a meta-analysis of individual data for one million adults in 61 prospective studies. *Lancet, 360*(9349), 1903–1913.

Li, N., Liu, R., Zhai, H., Li, L., Yin, Y., Zhang, J., & Xia, Y. (2014). Polymorphisms of the LTA gene may contribute to the risk of myocardial infarction: a meta-analysis. *PLoS One, 9*(3), e92272. doi: 10.1371/journal.pone.0092272

Liu, J., Liu, Z. Q., Tan, Z. R., Chen, X. P., Wang, L. S., Zhou, G., & Zhou, H. H. (2003). Gly389Arg polymorphism of beta1-adrenergic receptor is associated with the cardiovascular response to metoprolol. *Clinical Pharmacological Therapeutics, 74*(4), 372–379. doi: 10.1016/S0009-9236(03)00224-8

Liu, Y., Chen, T., Qiu, Y., Cheng, Y., Cao, Y., Zhao, A., & Jia, W. (2011). An ultrasonication-assisted extraction and derivatization protocol for GC/TOFMS-based metabolite profiling. *Analytical and Bioanalytical Chemistry, 400*(5), 1405–1417. doi: 10.1007/s00216-011-4880-z

Lloyd-Jones, D. M., Nam, B. H., D'Agostino, R. B., Sr., Levy, D., Murabito, J. M., Wang, T. J., . . . O'Donnell, C. J. (2004). Parental cardiovascular disease as a risk factor for cardiovascular disease in middle-aged adults: a prospective study of parents and offspring. *JAMA, 291*(18), 2204–2211. doi: 10.1001/jama.291.18.2204

Lu, Y., A, J., Wang, G., Hao, H., Huang, Q., Yan, B., . . . Hao, K. (2008). Gas chromatography/time-of-flight mass spectrometry based metabonomic approach to differentiating hypertension- and age-related metabolic variation in spontaneously hypertensive rats. *Rapid Communication in Mass Spectrometry, 22*(18), 2882–2888. doi: 10.1002/rcm.3670

Lucassen, A. (1999). Genetics of Multifactorial Diseases. In P. Rose & A. Lucassen (Ed.), *Practical Gentics for Primary Care* (pp. 145–165). Oxford: Oxford University Press.

Lupattelli, G., Pisciotta, L., De Vuono, S., Siepi, D., Bellocchio, A., Melis, F., . . . Mannarino, E. (2013). A silent mutation of Niemann-Pick C1-like 1 and apolipoprotein E4 modulate cholesterol absorption in primary hyperlipidemias. *Journal of Clinical Lipidology, 7*(2), 147–152. doi: 10.1016/j.jacl.2012.12.003

Lusk, C. M., Dyson, G., Clark, A. G., Ballantyne, C. M., Frikke-Schmidt, R., Tybjaerg-Hansen, A., . . . Sing, C. F. (2014). Validated context-dependent associations of coronary heart disease risk with genotype variation in the chromosome 9p21 region: the Atherosclerosis Risk in Communities study. *Human Genetics*. doi: 10.1007/s00439-014-1451-3

Mangravite, L. M., Medina, M. W., Cui, J., Pressman, S., Smith, J. D., Rieder, M. J., . . . Krauss, R. M. (2010). Combined influence of LDLR and HMGCR sequence variation on lipid-lowering response to simvastatin. *Arteriosclerosis, Thrombosis, and Vascular Biology, 30*(7), 1485–1492. doi: 10.1161/ATVBAHA.110.203273

Manolio, T. A., Collins, F. S., Cox, N. J., Goldstein, D. B., Hindorff, L. A., Hunter, D. J., . . . Visscher, P. M. (2009). Finding the missing heritability of complex diseases. *Nature, 461*(7265), 747–753. doi: 10.1038/nature08494

Mansego, M. L., Redon, J., Marin, R., Gonzalez-Albert, V., Martin-Escudero, J. C., Fabia, M. J., . . . Chaves, F. J. (2008). Renin polymorphisms and haplotypes are associated with blood pressure levels and hypertension risk in postmenopausal women. *Journal of Hypertension, 26*(2), 230–237. doi: 10.1097/HJH.0b013e3282f29865

Marques, F. Z., Campain, A. E., Tomaszewski, M., Zukowska-Szczechowska, E., Yang, Y. H., Charchar,

F. J., & Morris, B. J. (2011). Gene expression profiling reveals renin mRNA overexpression in human hypertensive kidneys and a role for microRNAs. *Hypertension, 58*(6), 1093–1098. doi: 10.1161/HYPERTENSIONAHA.111.180729

McPherson, R., Pertsemlidis, A., Kavaslar, N., Stewart, A., Roberts, R., Cox, D. R., . . . Cohen, J. C. (2007). A common allele on chromosome 9 associated with coronary heart disease. *Science, 316*(5830), 1488–1491. doi: 10.1126/science.1142447

Medina, M. W., Gao, F., Ruan, W., Rotter, J. I., & Krauss, R. M. (2008). Alternative splicing of 3-hydroxy-3-methylglutaryl coenzyme A reductase is associated with plasma low-density lipoprotein cholesterol response to simvastatin. *Circulation, 118*(4), 355–362. doi: 10.1161/CIRCULATIONAHA.108.773267

Moore, N., Dicker, P., O'Brien, J. K., Stojanovic, M., Conroy, R. M., Treumann, A., . . . Stanton, A. V. (2007). Renin gene polymorphisms and haplotypes, blood pressure, and responses to renin-angiotensin system inhibition. *Hypertension, 50*(2), 340–347. doi: 10.1161/HYPERTENSIONAHA.106.085563

Mottl, A. K., Shoham, D. A., & North, K. E. (2008). Angiotensin II type 1 receptor polymorphisms and susceptibility to hypertension: a HuGE review. *Genetics in Medicine, 10*(8), 560–574. doi: 10.1097GIM.0b013e3181809613

Murphy, S. L., Xu, J. Q., Kochanek, K. D. . (2013). Deaths: Final data for 2010. *National Vital Statistics Report, 61*(4).

Musunuru, K., Strong, A., Frank-Kamenetsky, M., Lee, N. E., Ahfeldt, T., Sachs, K. V., . . . Rader, D. J. (2010). From noncoding variant to phenotype via SORT1 at the 1p13 cholesterol locus. *Nature, 466*(7307), 714–719. doi: 10.1038/nature09266

National Institutes of Health. (2014). Genetic and Rare Disease Information Center (GARD). Retrieved July 1, 2014 from http://rarediseases.info.nih.gov/gard

National Library of Medicine [NLM]. (2014). MedlinePlus. Retrieved from http://www.nlm.nih.gov/medlineplus/druginfo/natural/1017.html

Newton-Cheh, C., Johnson, T., Gateva, V., Tobin, M. D., Bochud, M., Coin, L., . . . Munroe, P. B. (2009). Genome-wide association study identifies eight loci associated with blood pressure. *Nature Genetics, 41*(6), 666-676. doi: 10.1038/ng.361

Nikolic, S. B., Sharman, J. E., Adams, M. J., & Edwards, L. M. (2014). Metabolomics in hypertension. *Journal of Hypertension, 32*(6), 1159–1169. doi: 10.1097/HJH.0000000000000168

Ong, F. S., Deignan, J. L., Kuo, J. Z., Bernstein, K. E., Rotter, J. I., Grody, W. W., & Das, K. (2012). Clinical utility of pharmacogenetic biomarkers in cardiovascular therapeutics: a challenge for clinical implementation. *Pharmacogenomics, 13*(4), 465–475. doi: 10.2217/pgs.12.2

Pacanowski, M. A., Gong, Y., Cooper-Dehoff, R. M., Schork, N. J., Shriver, M. D., Langaee, T. Y., . . . Investigators, Invest. (2008). beta-adrenergic receptor gene polymorphisms and beta-blocker treatment outcomes in hypertension. *Clinical & Pharmacology Therapeutics, 84*(6), 715–721. doi: 10.1038/clpt.2008.139

Panayiotou, A. G., Griffin, M. B., Tyllis, T., Georgiou, N., Bond, D., Humphries, S. E., & Nicolaides, A. N. (2013). Association of genotypes at the matrix metalloproteinase (MMP) loci with carotid IMT and presence of carotid and femoral atherosclerotic plaques. *Vascular Medicine, 18*(5), 298–306. doi: 10.1177/1358863x13502698

Pathway Genomics Corporation. (2014). Cardiac DNA Insight. Retrieved from https://www.pathway.com/dna-reports/cardiac-dna-insight

Pereira, T. V., Kimura, L., Suwazono, Y., Nakagawa, H., Daimon, M., Oizumi, T., . . . Mingroni-Netto, R. C. (2014). Multivariate meta-analysis of the association of G-protein beta 3 gene (GNB3) haplotypes with cardiovascular phenotypes. *Molecular Biology Reports, 41*(5), 3113–3125. doi: 10.1007/s11033-014-3171-0

Poduri, A., Khullar, M., Bahl, A., Sehrawat, B. S., Sharma, Y., & Talwar, K. K. (2010). Common variants of HMGCR, CETP, APOAI, ABCB1, CYP3A4, and CYP7A1 genes as predictors of lipid-lowering response to atorvastatin therapy. *DNA Cell Biology, 29*(10), 629–637. doi: 10.1089/dna.2009.1008

Psaty, B. M., Smith, N. L., Heckbert, S. R., Vos, H. L., Lemaitre, R. N., Reiner, A. P., . . . Rosendaal, F. R. (2002). Diuretic therapy, the alpha-adducin gene variant, and the risk of myocardial infarction or stroke in persons with treated hypertension. *JAMA, 287*(13), 1680–1689.

Redberg, R. F., & Walsh, J. (2008). Pay now, benefits may follow—The case of cardiac computed tomographic angiography. *New England Journal of Medicine, 359*(22), 2309–2311. doi: 10.1056/NEJMp0805920

Reilly, M. P., Li, M., He, J., Ferguson, J. F., Stylianou, I. M., Mehta, N. N., . . . Rader, D. J. (2011). Identification of ADAMTS7 as a novel locus for coronary atherosclerosis and association of ABO with myocardial infarction in the presence of coronary atherosclerosis: two genome-wide association studies. *Lancet, 377*(9763), 383–392. doi: 10.1016/S0140-6736(10)61996-4

Roberts, R., & Stewart, A. F. (2012). Genes and coronary artery disease: where are we? *Journal of the American College of Cardiology, 60*(18), 1715–1721. doi: 10.1016/j.jacc.2011.12.062

Roberts, R. (2014). Genetics of coronary artery disease. *Circulation Research, 114*(12), 1890–1903. doi: 10.1161/CIRCRESAHA.114.302692

Roden, D. M., Johnson, J. A., Kimmel, S. E., Krauss, R. M., Medina, M. W., Shuldiner, A., & Wilke, R. A. (2011). Cardiovascular pharmacogenomics. *Cir-*

culation Research, 109(7), 807–820. doi: 10.1161/CIRCRESAHA.110.230995

Roger, V. L., Go, A. S., Lloyd-Jones, D. M., Benjamin, E. J., Berry, J. D., Borden, W. B., . . . Stroke Statistics, Subcommittee. (2012). Heart disease and stroke statistics—2012 update: A report from the American Heart Association. *Circulation, 125*(1), e2-e220. doi: 10.1161/CIR.0b013e31823ac046

Rosenberg, S., Elashoff, M. R., Beineke, P., Daniels, S. E., Wingrove, J. A., Tingley, W. G., . . . Investigators, Predict. (2010). Multicenter validation of the diagnostic accuracy of a blood-based gene expression test for assessing obstructive coronary artery disease in nondiabetic patients. *Annals of Internal Medicine, 153*(7), 425–434. doi: 10.7326/0003-4819-153-7-201010050-00005

Sakowicz, A., Fendler, W., Lelonek, M., Sakowicz, B., & Pietrucha, T. (2013). Genetic polymorphisms and the risk of myocardial infarction in patients under 45 years of age. *Biochemical Genetics, 51*(3-4), 230–242. doi: 10.1007/s10528-012-9558-5

Sayed, A. S., Xia, K., Salma, U., Yang, T., & Peng, J. (2014). Diagnosis, Prognosis and Therapeutic Role of Circulating miRNAs in Cardiovascular Diseases. *Heart, Lung, and Circulation, 23*(6), 503–510. doi: 10.1016/j.hlc.2014.01.001

Schallom, L., Thimmesch, A. R., & Pierce, J. D. (2011). Systems biology in critical-care nursing. *Dimensions of Critical Care Nursing, 30*(1), 1–7. doi: 10.1097/DCC.0b013e3181fd0169

Schildkraut, J. M., Myers, R. H., Cupples, L. A., Kiely, D. K., & Kannel, W. B. (1989). Coronary risk associated with age and sex of parental heart disease in the Framingham Study. *American Journal of Cardiology, 64*(10), 555–559.

Schunkert, H., Konig, I. R., Kathiresan, S., Reilly, M. P., Assimes, T. L., Holm, H., . . . Samani, N. J. (2011). Large-scale association analysis identifies 13 new susceptibility loci for coronary artery disease. *Nature Genetics, 43*(4), 333–338. doi: 10.1038/ng.784

SEARCH (NCT00124072). (2012). Clinical Trials: Study of the Effectiveness of Additional Reductions in Cholesterol and Homocysteine (SEARCH). Retrieved from http://clinicaltrials.gov/ct2/show/NCT00124072?term=SEARCH&rank=2

Shah, S. H., Hauser, E. R., Bain, J. R., Muehlbauer, M. J., Haynes, C., Stevens, R. D., . . . Kraus, W. E. (2009). High heritability of metabolomic profiles in families burdened with premature cardiovascular disease. *Molecular Systems Biology, 5*, 258. doi: 10.1038/msb.2009.11

Shah, S. H., Bain, J. R., Muehlbauer, M. J., Stevens, R. D., Crosslin, D. R., Haynes, C., . . . Kraus, W. E. (2010). Association of a peripheral blood metabolic profile with coronary artery disease and risk of subsequent cardiovascular events. *Circulation Cardiovascular Genetics, 3*(2), 207–214. doi: 10.1161/CIRCGENETICS.109.852814

Shah, S. H., Granger, C. B., Hauser, E. R., Kraus, W. E., Sun, J. L., Pieper, K., . . . Newby, L. K. (2010). Reclassification of cardiovascular risk using integrated clinical and molecular biosignatures: Design of and rationale for the Measurement to Understand the Reclassification of Disease of Cabarrus and Kannapolis (MURDOCK) Horizon 1 Cardiovascular Disease Study. *American Heart Journal, 160*(3), 371–379.e372. doi: 10.1016/j.ahj.2010.06.051

Shah, S. H., Sun, J. L., Stevens, R. D., Bain, J. R., Muehlbauer, M. J., Pieper, K. S., . . . Newby, L. K. (2012). Baseline metabolomic profiles predict cardiovascular events in patients at risk for coronary artery disease. *American Heart Journal, 163*(5), 844–850 e841. doi: 10.1016/j.ahj.2012.02.005

Sinnaeve, P. R., Donahue, M. P., Grass, P., Seo, D., Vonderscher, J., Chibout, S. D., . . . Granger, C. B. (2009). Gene expression patterns in peripheral blood correlate with the extent of coronary artery disease. *PLoS One, 4*(9), e7037. doi: 10.1371/journal.pone.0007037

Stamler, J., Rose, G., Stamler, R., Elliott, P., Dyer, A., & Marmot, M. (1989). INTERSALT study findings. Public health and medical care implications. *Hypertension, 14*(5), 570–577.

Stanton, A. V., Dicker, P., & O'Brien, E. T. (2009). Aliskiren monotherapy results in the greatest and the least blood pressure lowering in patients with high- and low-baseline PRA levels, respectively. *American Journal of Hypertension, 22*(9), 954–957. doi: 10.1038/ajh.2009.114

Sun, B., Williams, J. S., Pojoga, L., Chamarthi, B., Lasky-Su, J., Raby, B. A., . . . Williams, G. H. (2011). Renin gene polymorphism: its relationship to hypertension, renin levels and vascular responses. *Journal of Renin-Angiotensin-Aldosterone System, 12*(4), 564–571. doi: 10.1177/1470320311405873

Sutton, B. S., Crosslin, D. R., Shah, S. H., Nelson, S. C., Bassil, A., Hale, A. B., . . . Hauser, E. R. (2008). Comprehensive genetic analysis of the platelet activating factor acetylhydrolase (PLA2G7) gene and cardiovascular disease in case-control and family datasets. *Human Molecular Genetics, 17*(9), 1318–1328. doi: 10.1093/hmg/ddn020

Teutsch, S. M., Bradley, L. A., Palomaki, G. E., Haddow, J. E., Piper, M., Calonge, N., . . . Group, Egapp Working. (2009). The Evaluation of Genomic Applications in Practice and Prevention (EGAPP) Initiative: Methods of the EGAPP Working Group. *Genetics in Medicine, 11*(1), 3–14. doi: 10.1097/GIM.0b013e318184137c

Thomas, G. S., Voros, S., McPherson, J. A., Lansky, A. J., Winn, M. E., Bateman, T. M., . . . Rosenberg, S. (2013). A blood-based gene expression test for obstructive coronary artery disease tested in symptomatic nondiabetic patients referred for myocardial perfusion imaging the COMPASS study. *Circulation: Cardiovascular Genetics, 6*(2), 154–162. doi: 10.1161/CIRCGENETICS.112.964015

Toka, H. R., Koshy, J. M., & Hariri, A. (2013). The molecular basis of blood pressure variation. *Pediatric Nephrology, 28*(3), 387–399. doi: 10.1007/s00467-012-2206-9

Tragante, V., Barnes, M. R., Ganesh, S. K., Lanktree, M. B., Guo, W., Franceschini, N., . . . Keating, B. J. (2014). Gene-centric meta-analysis in 87,736 individuals of European ancestry identifies multiple blood-pressure-related loci. *American Journal of Human Genetics, 94*(3), 349–360. doi: 10.1016/j.ajhg.2013.12.016

Tsai, C. T., Fallin, D., Chiang, F. T., Hwang, J. J., Lai, L. P., Hsu, K. L., . . . Tseng, Y. Z. (2003). Angiotensinogen gene haplotype and hypertension: interaction with ACE gene I allele. *Hypertension, 41*(1), 9–15.

United States Food and Drug Administration (FDA). (2013). FDA Drug Safety Communication: New restrictions, contraindications, and dose limitations for Zocor (simvastatin) to reduce the risk of muscle injury. Retrieved from http://www.fda.gov/drugs/drugsafety/ucm256581.htm

United States Food and Drug Administration (FDA). (2014a). Table of Pharmacogenomic Biomarkers in Drug Labeling. Retrieved from http://www.fda.gov/drugs/scienceresearch/researchareas/pharmacogenetics/ucm083378.htm

United States Food and Drug Administration [FDA]. (2014b). Inspections, Compliance, Enforcement, and Criminal Investigations: Warning Letter, 23andMe, Inc. Retrieved from http://www.fda.gov/ICECI/EnforcementActions/WarningLetters/2013/ucm376296.htm

Varga, E. A., Sturm, A. C., Misita, C. P., & Moll, S. (2005). Cardiology patient pages. Homocysteine and MTHFR mutations: Relation to thrombosis and coronary artery disease. *Circulation, 111*(19), e289–293. doi: 10.1161/01.CIR.0000165142.37711.E7

Vargas, J., Lima, J. A., Kraus, W. E., Douglas, P. S., & Rosenberg, S. (2013). Use of the Corus(R) CAD Gene Expression Test for Assessment of Obstructive Coronary Artery Disease Likelihood in Symptomatic Non-Diabetic Patients. *PLoS Currents, 5*. doi: 10.1371/currents.eogt.0f04f6081905998fa92b99593478aeab

Visel, A., Zhu, Y., May, D., Afzal, V., Gong, E., Attanasio, C., . . . Pennacchio, L. A. (2010). Targeted deletion of the 9p21 non-coding coronary artery disease risk interval in mice. *Nature, 464*(7287), 409–412. doi: 10.1038/nature08801

Vorderstrasse, A. A., Ginsburg, G. S., Kraus, W. E., Maldonado, M. C., & Wolever, R. Q. (2013). Health coaching and genomics-potential avenues to elicit behavior change in those at risk for chronic disease: protocol for personalized medicine effectiveness study in air force primary care. *Global Advances in Health and Medicine, 2*(3), 26–38. doi: 10.7453/gahmj.2013.035

Wang, A., Yu, B. N., Luo, C. H., Tan, Z. R., Zhou, G., Wang, L. S., . . . Zhou, H. H. (2005). Ile118Val genetic polymorphism of CYP3A4 and its effects on lipid-lowering efficacy of simvastatin in Chinese hyperlipidemic patients. *European Journal of Clinical Pharmacology, 60*(12), 843–848. doi: 10.1007/s00228-004-0848-7

Wang, W. Y., Zee, R. Y., & Morris, B. J. (1997). Association of angiotensin II type 1 receptor gene polymorphism with essential hypertension. *Clinical Genetics, 51*(1), 31–34.

Wang, X., Zhu, H., Dong, Y., Treiber, F. A., & Snieder, H. (2006). Effects of angiotensinogen and angiotensin II type I receptor genes on blood pressure and left ventricular mass trajectories in multiethnic youth. *Twin Research and Human Genetics, 9*(3), 393–402. doi: 10.1375/183242706777591335

Ward, R. (1990). Familal aggregation and genetic epidemiology of blood pressure. . In JH Laragh & BM Brenner (Eds.), *Hypertension: Pathophysiology, Diagnosis, and Management.* New York, NY: Raven Press, Ltd. .

Wauters, E., Carruthers, K. F., Buysschaert, I., Dunbar, D. R., Peuteman, G., Belmans, A., . . . Fox, K. A. (2013). Influence of 23 coronary artery disease variants on recurrent myocardial infarction or cardiac death: the GRACE Genetics Study. *European Heart Journal, 34*(13), 993–1001. doi: 10.1093/eurheartj/ehs389

Weizmann Institute of Science. (2014). GeneCards. Retrieved from http://www.genecards.org/

Whelton, P. K., He, J., Appel, L. J., Cutler, J. A., Havas, S., Kotchen, T. A., . . . National High Blood Pressure Education Program Coordinating, Committee. (2002). Primary prevention of hypertension: clinical and public health advisory from The National High Blood Pressure Education Program. *JAMA, 288*(15), 1882–1888.

Wilk, J. B., Djousse, L., Arnett, D. K., Hunt, S. C., Province, M. A., Heiss, G., & Myers, R. H. (2004). Genome-wide linkage analyses for age at diagnosis of hypertension and early-onset hypertension in the HyperGEN study. *American Journal of Hypertension, 17*(9), 839–844. doi: 10.1016/j.amjhyper.2004.06.003

Williams, G. H., Moore, T. J., & Hollenberg, N. K. (1991). Dysregulation of aldosterone secretion and its relationship to the pathogenesis of essential hypertension. *Endocrinology Metabolism Clinics of North America, 20*(2), 423–447.

Williams, R. R., Hunt, S. C., Hasstedt, S. J., Hopkins, P. N., Wu, L. L., Berry, T. D., . . . Kuida, H. (1990). Genetics of hypertension: what we know and don't know. *Clinical and Experimental Hypertension, 12*(5), 865–876.

Wingrove, J. A., Daniels, S. E., Sehnert, A. J., Tingley, W., Elashoff, M. R., Rosenberg, S., . . . Kraus, W. E. (2008). Correlation of peripheral-blood gene expression with the extent of coronary artery stenosis. *Circulation: Cardiovascular Genetics, 1*(1), 31–38. doi: 10.1161/CIRCGENETICS.108.782730

World Health Organization (WHO). (2008). Raised blood pressure: Situation and trends. Retrieved from http://www.who.int/gho/ncd/risk_factors/blood_pressure_prevalence_text/en/

Xu, X., Wang, L., Xu, C., Zhang, P., Yong, F., Liu, H., . . . Shi, Y. (2013). Variations in matrix metalloproteinase-1, -3, and -9 genes and the risk of acute coronary syndrome and coronary artery disease in the Chinese Han population. *Coronary Artery Disease, 24*(4), 259–265. doi: 10.1097/MCA.0b013e32835ea3af

Yoshino, S., Cilluffo, R., Best, P. J., Atkinson, E. J., Aoki, T., Cunningham, J. M., . . . Lerman, A. (2014). Single nucleotide polymorphisms associated with abnormal coronary microvascular function. *Coro-*

nary Artery Disease, 25(4), 281–289. doi: 10.1097/mca.0000000000000104

Yu, B., Zheng, Y., Alexander, D., Morrison, A. C., Coresh, J., & Boerwinkle, E. (2014). Genetic determinants influencing human serum metabolome among African Americans. *PLoS Genetics, 10*(3), e1004212. doi: 10.1371/journal.pgen.1004212

Zende, P. D., Bankar, M. P., Kamble, P. S., & Momin, A. A. (2013). Apolipoprotein e gene polymorphism and its effect on plasma lipids in arteriosclerosis. *Journal of Clinical and Diagnostic Research, 7*(10), 2149–2152. doi: 10.7860/jcdr/2013/6195.3455

Zheng, H., Xu, H., Cui, B., Xie, N., Wang, Z., & Luo, M. (2013). Association between polymorphism of the G-protein beta3 subunit C825T and essential hypertension: an updated meta-analysis involving 36,802 subjects. *Biological Research, 46*(3), 265–273. doi: 10.4067/s0716-97602013000300007

Single Gene Cardiovascular Disorders

SARAH RACE, RN, MSN, CNS
MEGAN GROVE, MS, LCGC

Objectives:

- Understand importance of genetic counseling in provision of care for single gene cardiovascular disorders.
- Distinguish between structural and nonstructural inherited single gene cardiovascular disorders.
- Discuss importance of family history taking in inherited single gene cardiovascular disorders.
- Describe two of the most common inherited single gene cardiovascular disorders.
- Discuss future genomic technologies and how they are affecting inherited cardiovascular care and research.

11.25. INTRODUCTION

Many common cardiovascular conditions such as coronary artery disease (CAD) and hypertension (HTN) are generally caused by a combination of environmental influences and genetic factors, with each individual genetic factor typically having only small effects on an individual's risk of developing disease. In contrast, there are many inherited single gene cardiovascular conditions, often following a Mendelian inheritance pattern, in which the condition is largely a result of one variant in just one gene. The focus of this section of the cardiac chapter will be on these single gene cardiovascular conditions. Genetic testing has been used clinically for many years in single gene cardiovascular disorders. Previously, the list of disease associated genes was small, and genetic testing may have only included a search of one gene. The number of genes associated with each disease has grown, and many genetic testing laboratories now offer multigene panels involving the major genes associated with each of these conditions. In most cases, genetic testing will not alter management or change the diagno-sis of a patient, but rather it will offer value to the patient's family to help identify at-risk relatives before the onset of disease and to offer an additional method of screening. Rarely, genetic testing can be attempted to help guide clinical diagnosis in complex or ambiguous cases.

Although genetic testing is clinically available for single gene disorders in the cardiovascular field, there is still much to be learned. For instance, reduced penetrance and variable expressivity, which occur in many of the single gene cardiovascular conditions, have yet to be explained at the genetic level. Also, in many of these single gene cardiovascular conditions, genetic testing is currently only able to identify the underlying disease causing mutation in approximately 30% to 60% of the cases (Ackerman *et al.*, 2011; Gersh *et al.*, 2011; Pugh *et al.*, 2014). It has become clear through large scale sequencing studies that everyone has a large amount of rare, benign variation in his or her genomes (Ashley *et al.*, 2010). These variants often fall within disease associated genes, making it difficult to discern what variations are contributing to the patient's condition and which are benign (Dunn,

Caleshu, Cirino, Ho, & Ashley, 2013). More research needs to be done, not only to discover new mutations and new genes that are implicated in these conditions, but also to strengthen the data surrounding variants that are of uncertain significance and to provide more knowledge into the roles of epigenetic factors that affect disease expression.

11.26. GENETIC TESTING IN SINGLE GENE CARDIOVASCULAR DISORDERS

The medical community, as well as the public, are becoming more aware of the availability of genetic testing. It is powerful to be able to offer this option to individuals as they gather information about their diagnoses. What is important for the treating provider to realize is that genetic testing is not as straightforward as sending regular blood testing like a basic metabolic panel on a patient and getting the result back. There are many layers of care that must be considered prior to sending a genetic test, when considering the result and when discussing this result with the client. More information about the genetic counseling process is located in Chapter 3. It is essential that a genetic counselor or a well-trained genetics nurse be involved in each step of this process to help guide both the patient and the treating provider through the process.

Prior to deciding to pursue genetic testing, the individual should be given counseling to understand the potential benefits, limitations, and possible results of the test, as well as the potential risks of having this type of testing done. For instance, although there is legislation such as the Genetic Information Nondiscrimination Act (GINA) to prevent genetic discrimination by health care insurance companies, GINA does not apply to life insurance, disability insurance, or longterm care (Genetic Alliance, 2010). Life insurance companies could theoretically use genetic testing results to exclude an individual from a policy even though the individual has not shown any clinical sign of the condition in question. Ensuring the individual is ready for such realities of genetic testing prior to having it is essential.

Associating a genetic variant that has been identified on a genetic test and the condition in question can be challenging and can sometimes result in falsepositives (Dunn *et al.*, 2013). The level of confidence that a particular genetic variant is disease causing is based on the weight of several pieces of evidence. For instance, for the genetics community to be confident that a genetic variant is truly implicated in disease, a variant is typically required to definitively track with disease in several unrelated families and it needs to be absent from ethnically matched "control" individuals without inherited single gene cardiovascular conditions such as those found in the 1000 Genomes Project or the NHLBI Exome Sequencing Project (The 1000 Genomes Project Consortium, 2012). Once results from genetic testing have been reported, the genetic provider may wish to perform an independent variant analysis to ensure they and their colleagues are in agreement with the report provided from the genetic testing company. Bioinformatic programs such as PolyPhen2 and SIFT, as well as genetic databases, such as 1000 Genomes (Roberts, Marian, Dandona, & Stewart, 2013) should be consulted to add information such as evolutionary conservation and the nature of the genetic variant. Additionally, genetic mutation databases should be searched, because these may include information such as whether the particular genetic variant has been previously reported in the literature to be in association with disease. These sources should be considered carefully, because these databases have been shown to carry false positive disease associations (Bell *et al.*, 2011).

A proper counseling session should be booked for the individual to receive the results of his or her testing, and ideally a letter should be provided to share with family members so relatives understand the family screening recommendations. If a causative mutation has been found, at-risk relatives will be able to consider if genetic screening would be of value to their individual situations. Often this decision will involve an individual who is currently under the age of 18 years. The medical system gives the decision-making authority to the parents of these individuals; however, the issues involved with genetically testing a child should be discussed extensively, with consideration for the wishes and understanding of the child prior to initiating predictive genetic testing.

At this time, the benefit of genetic testing is typically used for the genetic screening of family members. Until more progress is made in personalized medicine, genetic testing results will rarely influence treatment for the individual in single gene cardiovascular conditions. Occasionally, a situation arises in which clinical diagnosis of an individual is not possible because the presenting evidence is not strong enough to confirm one specific diagnosis. In these cases, in which symptoms may be attributable to several conditions, genetic testing can be useful in determining diagnosis. The physician and the genetic counselor or nurse would consider which condition is most suspected and they would send this genetic testing panel to see if a causative variant could be determined. Occasionally, there isn't one particular panel that is most appropriate and in this case, a pan cardio panel can be considered. A pan-cardio panel includes genes related to all different types of known single gene cardiovascular conditions, and it would encompass all possible diagnoses being considered.

With increased technological advances, there are also the options of sending whole exome sequencing or whole genome sequencing. The difficulty with these types of tests has already become less about the cost of the sequencing, but rather centralized around the cost of the interpretation and amount of data that are returned. Although clinical whole exome sequencing is becoming increasingly common to assist with identification of the underlying causes of undiagnosed genetic conditions, whole genome sequencing has primarily been seen in the research setting. This will likely change as the technology continues to improve. At this time, it is important to understand that although these new genomic technologies are powerful, they also still have their limitations. An exome or genome is not yet necessarily always indicated as a firstline test. The ability to identify genetic variants is highly dependent on "depth of coverage" or the number of sequence reads that line up at each position of the genome. Genomic sequencing tests, although impressive in their ability to look at all protein-coding regions and other regions of the genome, are not yet able to provide complete coverage of all disease associated genes. Thus, if there is a high suspicion for a particular cardiovascular condition, sending a targeted panel where there can be complete coverage across the known disease genes is important to ensure a comprehensive look at these genes. Then, if no variants are identified, exome or genome sequencing may al-

low the clinical team to look at additional genes that are not yet included on clinical panels.

Another use for pan-cardio panels, whole exome, or whole genome sequencing is when there is a diagnosis known, but no genetic variant has been found. This additional testing is usually reserved for severe phenotypes in which there is high clinical utility in being able to provide genetic screening for the family. It is also useful to consider the family for which the information is be provided, as segregation analysis may be needed to determine which of the many variants are significant when this amount of data is sequenced. Segregation analysis in this context is a method utilized to sift through the genetic data to select and identify important variants within families (Cirulli & Goldstein, 2010). More detail on genomic technologies can be found in Chapter 17.

11.27. ROLE OF FAMILY HISTORY TAKING IN INHERITED SINGLE GENE CARDIOVASCULAR DISORDERS

Knowing the family history of an individual with a single gene cardiovascular condition presenting for evaluation is as important as knowing the medical history of this individual. The pedigree is a very important clinical tool, because it assists with risk assessment and diagnosis, while helping to guide management (Morales, Cowan, Dagua, & Hershberger, 2008). In ambiguous cases, the family pedigree may provide important information that can help confirm diagnosis. Sudden death or symptoms in relatives can increase the level of suspicion of a particular condition, whereas a pedigree without supporting family history may lower suspicion (Dunn *et al.*, 2013). The pedigree can help to identify individuals at increased risk and may allow for risk reduction by implementing lifestyle changes, introducing medical intervention, and/or increasing surveillance for disease (Genetic Alliance, 2009). A proper pedigree may also help inform whether genetic testing should even be considered, because if there are no first-degree relatives who would benefit from the results, it may not be something that is of interest to the individual. Detailed information about conducting a pedigree and a risk assessment is located in Chapter 2.

11.28. STRUCTURAL INHERITED SINGLE GENE CARDIOVASCULAR DISORDERS

Structural cardiovascular disorders refer to conditions in which the structure of the heart is in some way abnormal and these abnormalities affect its function. These disorders can be a result of environmental influence (e.g., mercury exposure), environmental influence combined with genetic predisposition (e.g., coronary atherosclerosis leading to MI), or single gene mutations. There are many forms of Mendelian like conditions that affect the function of the heart. The most common is hypertrophic cardiomyopathy (HCM), which will be discussed in detail later in this chapter.

11.28.1. Familial Dilated Cardiomyopathy

Familial dilated cardiomyopathy (DCM) is a diffuse disorder involving cardiomyocytes, in which the left ventricle becomes dilated and systolic function is diminished (Ku, Feiger, Taylor, & Mestroni, 2003). Affected individuals may experience heart failure and/or arrhythmia and are at an increased risk for thromboembolism (stroke or systemic embolus). Unlike HCM, individuals with DCM have normal left ventricular wall thickness (Vernengo, Lilienbaum, Agbulut, & Rodríguez, 2013). There is much overlap in the genetics of HCM and DCM, because they have both been associated with mutations in the contractile unit of cardiac myocytes. However, there are also many genes that have been implicated in DCM that have not been seen in HCM. Despite the large number of genes that have been associated with DCM, 31 autosomal and 2 X-linked genes, a genetic explanation is still only possible for approximately 30% to 35% of individuals diagnosed with familial DCM (Hershberger & Siegfried, 2011). There are many unanswered questions in terms of the genetic nature of this condition, including which variants are the most relevant and whether other genetic mechanisms (epigenetics, copy number variants, etc.) influence the development of DCM (Hershberger & Morales, 2013). Adding to the complexity of the situation, DCM is also highly variable in severity, expressivity, and age of onset (Hershberger & Morales, 2013). Being able to isolate one genetic variable as the cause is not sufficient to explain to atrisk individuals how the disease course will progress. Much work is needed in this area of inherited cardiomyopathies, because understanding the genetic underpinnings of DCM will help with early identification and intervention, and potentially prevention of heart failure in the future (Hershberger, Morales, & Siegfried, 2010).

11.28.2. Muscular Dystrophy

Approximately 1 in every 4,700 males is born with a mutation in the dystrophin (*DMD*) gene (Dooley, Gordon, Dodds, & MacSween, 2010). The dystrophin gene is located on the short arm of the X chromosome (Xp21.2-p21.1), and it encodes for dystrophin protein. Dystrophin, found primarily in muscle and nerve cells, binds the cytoskeleton of muscle fibers to proteins in the extracellular matrix, maintaining muscle fiber strength and preventing muscle fiber injury. Individuals who cannot produce normal dystrophin experience progressive generalized muscle weakness and wasting (atrophy). A range of phenotypes is seen in this disorder, and these are related to how much of the protein the mutated gene is capable of producing. The development of cardiomyopathy in individuals with muscular dystrophy is not well understood but is thought to be caused by mutations in the muscle promoter region and/or first exon of the *DMD* gene, alterations in gene regions particularly important to cardiac muscle function, reduced expression of cardiac sodium channels causing conduction abnormalities, or the degeneration of cardiomyocytes leading to cardiac tissue fibrosis (Romfh & McNally, 2010). In a particularly aggressive form of muscular dystrophy, Duchenne Muscular Dystrophy, the incidence of cardiomyopathy increases with age, with 25% of patients affected by age 6 years, 59% by age 10 years, and 100% by age 18 years (Romfh & McNally, 2010). Few affected individuals live beyond the third decade of life, with death commonly occurring from respiratory and/or cardiovascular complications (Darras *et al.*, 2011).

11.28.3. Connective Tissue Disorders

Connective tissue disorders are a group of

conditions affecting the connective tissue of the body. There are hundreds of these conditions; however, a handful of them have shown to be related to single gene mutations. Marfan syndrome (MFS) is caused by an autosomal dominant mutation in the *FBN1* gene that effects the eyes, heart, and musculoskeletal systems. MFS is highly variable, even within families, ranging from isolated AAA to manifestations in infancy with severe and rapidly progressive disease. The hallmark feature of Marfan (60% of patients) is myopia (nearsightedness) severe enough to cause retinal detachment, but other ocular manifestations such as glaucoma and early onset cataracts are common in affected patients as well (Dietz, 2011). Musculoskeletal manifestations include bony overgrowth, causing disproportionately long extremities, pectus excavatum or carinatum, and scoliosis, and significant hypermobility and joint laxity. Although ocular and musculoskeletal symptoms cause morbidity in this population, the primary cause of death is from cardiovascular malformations, including ruptured aortic aneurysms, mitral or tricuspid valve prolapse, and pulmonary artery enlargement. The diagnosis is most commonly made based on family history and clinical features, because *FBN1* genetic testing is not particularly sensitive. Some families may have unusual or uncommon *FBN1* mutations or mutations in genes that regulate FBN1 function (promoters). When diagnosis is made early and disease manifestations are managed appropriately, life expectancy can be normal in patients with MFS (Dietz, 2011).

Loeys-Dietz syndrome (LDS) is an autosomal dominant genetic syndrome with features very similar to that of MFS. First described in 2005, LDS is caused by mutations in either transforming growth factor beta receptor 1 (*TGFBR1*) [Type 1] or transforming growth factor beta receptor 2 (*TGFBR2*) [Type 2] genes causing arterial (cerebral, thoracic, and abdominal arterial aneurysms and/or dissections), and craniofacial (widely spaced eyes, bifid uvula/cleft palate, craniosynostosis) anomalies (Loeys *et al.*, 2006). Approximately 75% of affected individuals have Type I and have both arterial and craniofacial features. Those with Type II have virtually identical risk for arterial manifestations but have fewer or milder craniofacial anomalies. The clinical hallmark of LDS is rapidly progressive arterial aneu-

rysms (mean age at death 26.1 years) and a significantly increased risk for uterine rupture and death during pregnancy (Loeys & Dietz, 2013).

Ehlers-Danlos syndrome (EDS) is caused by defects in genes encoding for type V collagen, most commonly *COL5A1* or *COL5A2* genes. Approximately half of affected individuals inherit mutations and the other 50% are caused by de novo mutations that occur during embryogenesis. Most forms are inherited in an autosomal dominant fashion; however, there are a few that are inherited in an autosomal recessive manner. The diagnosis is primarily based on clinical findings because even when inherited from a parent, the phenotype varies so widely between individuals that the family history may appear to be negative. Parents of an affected child should therefore be closely examined as well, to make sure that subtle disease manifestations have not been missed in that generation. Clinical manifestations include hyperelastic skin, easy bruising, abnormal wound healing, hypermobile joints with recurrent dislocations, and chronic joint pain. Although most of the morbidity is associated with dermatologic and musculoskeletal anomalies, other, more lethal, clinical manifestations include mitral and tricuspid valve prolapse, aortic root dilatation, and spontaneous rupture of large arteries (Malfait, Wenstrup, & De Paepe, 1993).

11.28.4. Congenital Heart Disease

Structural cardiovascular anomalies have been associated with at least 20 distinct genetic disorders. One of the most common disorders associated with congenital cardiac anomaly is 22q11.2 Deletion Syndrome, which occurs in approximately 1 in 4,000 to 6,395 births (Devriendt, Fryns, Mortier, van Thienen, & Keymolen, 1998). Although the syndrome occurs in all racial and ethnic groups in the U.S., the prevalence is reported to be slightly higher among Hispanics (1 in 3,800) than in whites, African Americans, and Asians (1 in 6,000) (Botto *et al.*, 2003). Approximately 90% of all cases are caused by a microdeletion of the chromosome at 22q11.2 that spans over three million base pairs (3 Mb) eliminating 32 genes; the remaining cases are caused by a smaller (1.5 Mb) deletion encompassing 24 genes. The vast majority (93%) of cases occur spontaneously (de novo), and the remainder are inherited in an autosomal dominant manner; thus, the 22q11.2 loci is an example of a "hot spot" in the human genome (McDonaldMcGinn, Emanuel, & Zackai, 2013).

The diagnosis is usually made early in life during a workup to evaluate the cause of congenital anomalies, such as cleft palate and congenital cardiac malformations. Congenital cardiac anomalies are a major feature of the syndrome and include conotruncal defects (transposition of the great arteries, double outlet of the right ventricle, tetralogy of Fallot, truncus arteriosus), ventricular septal defects (VSD), and right aortic arch (Ardinger & Ardinger, 2002). Some children with significant cardiovascular anomalies (such as isolated right sided aortic arch) may be asymptomatic and remain undiagnosed until adulthood, whereas others may have relatively minor anomalies (bicuspid aortic valve, aberrant subclavian arteries, or anomalous origin of the common carotid) that are difficult to detect in infancy (Shprintzen et al., 2005). Although most affected individuals have anomalies, the diagnosis is often challenging because no single feature is consistently reported in every individual with VCFS (Horowitz, Shifman, Rivlin, Pisante, & Darvasi, 2005).

11.29. NONSTRUCTURAL SINGLE GENE CARDIOVASCULAR DISORDERS

As the name implies, nonstructural single gene cardiovascular disorders encompass conditions that do not affect the actual structure of the heart. This category includes inherited lipidologies (disorders of the blood cholesterol) and channelopathies (disorders of the conduction system of the heart). The most common inherited lipidology that is caused by a mutation in a single gene is familial hypercholesterolemia. This condition will be extensively discussed later in this chapter. Familial hyperchylomicronemia is a very rare lipid disorder occurring in 1 in every 1 million individuals. It is an autosomal recessive condition that results in elevated chylomicrons. The remaining lipidologies, familial combined HLD, familial dysbetalipoproteinemia, familial endogenous hypertriglyceridemia, and primary mixed hypertrygliceridemia all have as yet unknown genetic causes (Fredrickson & Lees, 1965) and may fall into the mulitgenic/genomic disease category.

11.29.1. Cardiac Channelopathies

Cardiac channelopathies are conditions caused by a defect in the ion channel, most commonly related to mutations in the genes encoding the ion channels. Many different systems can be affected by defects in the ion channel, including the nervous system, respiratory system, urinary system, and cardiovascular system (Kim, 2014). Disorders caused by defects of ion channels in the cardiovascular system include long QT syndrome (LQTS), Brugada syndrome, and catecholaminergic polymorphic ventricular tachycardia (CPVT).

LQTS mutations can be inherited in either an autosomal dominant or autosomal recessive fashion. Autosomal dominant LQTS is heterogeneous with at least 13 different cardiac ion channelopathy subtypes (numbered LQT 1-13) associated with it (Modell, Bradley, & Lehmann, 2012). LQT1 (*KCNQ1* gene) and LQT2 (*KCNH2* gene) mutations account for nearly 90% of all identifiable cases of LQT, with the LQT3 (*SCN5A*) mutation comprising 5% to 10% of the cases and LQT4-13 mutations making up ≤ 1% of the remaining cases (Perrin & Gollob, 2012). Autosomal recessive LQTS mutations are rare but often have a more severe phenotype and may have noncardiac manifestations such as syndactyly or congenital neural deafness. LQTS can also be caused without the presence of genetic mutations by medications and other health conditions that cause changes in serum potassium or sodium levels. A list of medications that prolong the QT interval can be found online, and individuals with LQTS should be cautioned to avoid using these medications.

Brugada syndrome refers to a condition in which cardiac conduction abnormalities can result in ventricular arrhythmias and sudden death. Brugada syndrome typically presents during adulthood, with the most common presentation being a 40-year-old male with malignant arrhythmias and syncopal episodes (Brugada, Campuzano, Brugada, Brugada, & Hong, 2005). Diagnosis is made by electrocardiogram (ECG), which shows elevation of the J wave with negative T wave and ST segment changes with or without the administration of a sodium channel blocker (Brugada *et al.*, 2005). Brugada syndrome is inherited in an autosomal dominant manner. Variants in 16 genes have been associated with this syndrome: *SCN5A, SCN1B, SCN2B, SCN3B, GPD1L, CACNA1C, CACNB2, CACNA2D1, KCND3, KCNE3, KCNE1L (KCNE5), KCNJ8, HCN4, RANGRF, SLMAP,* and *TRPM4.* Only 25% to 35 % of Brugada syndrome is accounted for by variants in these genes; therefore, further locus heterogeneity is likely. In cases of Brugada syndrome, in which a genetic variant is known, mutations in *SCN5A* account for 15% to 30%. *SCN5A* is responsible for the creation of a protein in the sodium channel abundant in cardiac tissue. Mutations in this gene have been associated with both Brugada syndrome and LQTS. Mutations associated with a gain of function are typically seen in LQTS, and those with a loss of function are associated with Brugada syndrome (Brugada *et al.*, 2005).

CPVT is characterized by episodic syncope or sudden death occurring during exercise or acute emotion. Diagnosis is made based on the determination that the episodes are a result of the heart going into a fast ventricular tachycardia (VT) while being unable to show evidence of structural abnormalities. If the VT self terminates, the episode is a syncopal event. If the VT does not terminate but rather degrades into a ventricular fibrillation, the individual will suffer an SCD if resuscitation is not available. The onset of symptoms is usually between ages 7 and 12 years, but it can be as late as the fourth decade of life (Napolitano, Priori, & Bloise, 2004). The resting ECG is usually normal in an individual with CPVT. Diagnosis is made using an exercise stress test, in which the VT is provoked by adrenergic activation (Napolitano *et al.*, 2004). There are four genes that are currently associated with CPVT: *RYR2, CASQ2, TRDN*, and *CALM1*. All four are related to calcium regulation in the sarcoplasmic reticulum of cardiac myocytes. *RYR2* and *CALM1* are inherited in an autosomal dominant manner, and *CASQ2* and *TRDN* are inherited in an autosomal recessive manner (Napolitano *et al.*, 2004).

11.29.2. Examples of the Two Most Common Single Gene Cardiovascular Conditions

11.29.2.1. Hypertrophic Cardiomyopathy

Hypertrophic Cardiomyopathy is an inherited

cardiomyopathy that results in the thickening of the walls of the left ventricle. It affects approximately 1 in 500 individuals (Maron et al, 2003). The presentation of this thickening is highly variable between individuals both in "width" of the thickness and the area of the left ventricle that is affected, even amongst individuals who carry the same mutation. This is known as variable expressivity. A diagnosis of HCM is made when the thickness of the left ventricular wall at any point is greater than or equal to 1.5 cm. Thicknesses between 1.3 cm and 1.5 cm are also larger than normal, and these cases need to be evaluated closely for other indications of HCM that could confirm diagnosis, such as systolic anterior motion (SAM) of the mitral valve, fibrosis, or abnormal electrical conduction.

There is not a "typical" appearance to the HCM heart. The area of the heart affected by the thickening may be very discrete or it may encompass all of the walls of the left ventricle; it may result in left ventricular outflow track (LVOT) obstruction or it may not impede blood flow through the aortic valve at all. Most commonly, the thickening of the left ventricle is seen in the septum (the wall between the right and left ventricles). Thickening in the proximal area of the septum, the area just below the aortic valve, often results in left ventricular outflow tract obstruction, blockage of the blood leaving the heart. Obstruction may also be caused or worsened if the leaflet of the mitral valve is pulled towards the septum during systole (systolic anterior motion of the mitral valve). During the physical assessment of the patient, the obstruction can be heard as a midsystolic murmur on auscultation of the individual's heart sounds. Thickening may also be seen further down the septum, where it does not interfere with the blood flow from the heart, a nonobstructive form of HCM. Other nonobstructive forms of HCM are known as apical HCM, in which the thickening is isolated to the apical area of the heart or the "bottom" of the heart, and concentric HCM, in which the thickening is seen in all of the walls of the left ventricle.

The systolic function of the HCM heart is typically either normal or enhanced (Maron *et al.*, 2003). Often the reported ejection fraction (EF) on an echocardiogram is either at the high end of normal or above. A very small number of individuals diagnosed with HCM will progress and develop systolic dysfunction. The diastolic function is typically what is impaired in the HCM heart. What this means is the thick walls of the left ventricle have lost the ability to relax during diastole, resulting in a decreased ability of the left ventricle to fill with blood (Maron & Salberg, 2006). This decreased ability to fill with blood often results in more severe symptoms any time blood volume is compromised.

The other abnormalities that are commonly seen in individuals diagnosed with HCM are arrhythmias. HCM hearts are at increased risk for both atrial and ventricular arrhythmias. This increased risk for arrhythmia may be related to the myocyte disarray that has been observed in cardiac tissue of HCM patients (Maron et al., 2003). Usually myocytes are aligned in a parallel way throughout the cardiac muscle. In myocardial disarray, the myocytes are arranged in a disorganized pattern creasing areas of scar or fibrosis (Maron & Salberg, 2006). Atrial fibrillation can be difficult to tolerate if the individual is particularly reliant on the atrial contraction for filling. VT can be life-threatening if it degrades into ventricular fibrillation. If the individual has any indication of experiencing this arrhythmia, an internal cardiac defibrillator should be recommended for primary prevention.

There are other conditions that cause similar thickening of the walls of the left ventricle, which may complicate the diagnosis of HCM. Situations resulting in pressure overload (hypertension, aortic stenosis), storage disorders (Fabry disease, amyloidosis, Noonan syndrome), thyroid disease, iron overload, and participation in competitive athletics need to be considered when evaluating an individual for HCM (Cirino & Ho, 2008; Maron & Salberg, 2006). Clinical testing, including blood work, ECG, echocardiogram, cardiac magnetic resonance imaging (MRI), and sometimes genetic testing, are used to confirm diagnosis of HCM.

HCM is inherited in an autosomal dominant manner, with mutations found primarily in the cardiac sarcomere genes. The sarcomere is a unit that repeats over and over throughout the cardiac myocyte (the heart's muscle cell). It is ultimately responsible for contraction of the muscle in the heart, which results in blood flowing around the body (Klabunde, 2007). The majority of the genes connected with HCM are those that encode proteins in the myofilaments of the sarcomeres. There are two main myofilament-encoding genes that are most commonly associated with HCM, myosin heavy chain (*MYH7*) and myosin binding protein C3 (*MYBPC3*). *MYH7* encodes a protein that is the major component of the thick filament in the sarcomere (the beta heavy chain subunit of cardiac myosin). *MYBPC3* encodes a protein that is involved with structural support and helps to regulate muscle contractions (Genetics Home Reference, 2014). There are a total of nine myofilament-encoding genes including *MYH7* and *MYBPC3* implicated in HCM, and the estimated prevalence for myofilament HCM is 35% to 65% (Bos, Towbin, & Acherman, 2009). Other genes associated with HCM are related to the structure of the Z-disc. The Z-disc is found between each sarcomere, and during contraction these lines are drawn closer together. The estimated prevalence for Z-disc HCM is between 1% and 5% (Bos et al., 2009). Other genes that have been implicated in HCM are those that encode proteins involved in the calcium channels of the cardiac myocyte.

Not surprisingly, the symptomatic presentation of HCM is as variable as the phenotypic presentation. Individuals may be asymptomatic and discover their condition by accident during routine physical examination or ECG, whereas others present with severe shortness of breath or chest pain and others may be diagnosed after an aborted cardiac arrest. There are several common symptoms associated with HCM: shortness of breath, lightheadedness, dizziness or syncope, palpitations, and chest pain.

Shortness of breath is often noted by the individual with HCM to occur either during exertion or after a big meal. Physiologically, it is felt that the small left ventricular cavity and the decreased ability of the left ventricle to relax and fill, the LVOT obstruction, or some combination of these two principles are the reason for the symptom of shortness of breath (Maron & Salberg, 2006).

The cause of lightheadedness, dizziness, and/or syncope are related to two separate physiologic conditions. One individual may have one or the other, or both may be present. The first and most important cause to consider is the possibility of ventricular arrhythmia. HCM is one of the leading causes of SCD, especially in young athletes (Maron et al., 2003). The cause of SCD in these cases is VT. Careful evaluation of individuals with HCM must be made in order to determine if they are at risk for SCD. There have been five risk factors proposed that increase the likelihood of the individual experiencing ventricular arrhythmia. They are width of the ventricular wall approaching 3.0 cm, syncope (not related to vasovagal episodes), family history of SCD, ventricular tachycardia as seen on Holter monitoring, and inappropriate BP rise with exercise. In the U.S., only one of these five risk factors needs to be present along with the diagnosis of HCM for the treating provider to recommends an internal cardiac defibrillator (ICD). In Europe, two of the five are needed to make this recommendation. The presence of delayed gadolinium excretion (DGE) on cardiac MRI is also now being considered as a risk factor with an increasing amount of DGE being linked to a higher likelihood of developing VT (Maron, 2012). DGE has not yet been incorporated into clinic guidelines, however, and is used at the discretion of the treating provider until more data are available.

Another possible cause of lightheadedness is related to obstruction. The level of obstruction is measured on echocardiogram by looking at the pressure change pre- and postaortic valve. This value is reported as the gradient and it is a dynamic value. This means the level of the gradient will change under different conditions. While at rest, the gradient is typically lower than when the individual is exercising. Fluid status will also play a part in this value, with the gradient being higher when the individual is dehydrated as opposed to when he or she is well hydrated.

Palpitations are described as skipped beats or fluttering. They are typically as benign as preatrial or preventricular contractions, but can be as concerning as runs of nonsustained VT. Each individual diagnosed with HCM needs to also be evaluated for risk factors increasing likelihood of developing these potentially fatal arrhythmias and appropriate recommendations for ICD placement should be made.

The final symptom of chest pain is not well understood. It is felt that the thickening of the muscle wall causes the micro-vasculature of the coronary circulatory system to be constricted, resulting in similar chest pain to that felt with occlusive CAD. It may also be that the thickened tissue does not have sufficient vasculature to adequately supply oxygen and nutrients to the tissue.

Hypertrophic cardiomyopathy panels are available for testing through all of the major genetic testing laboratories. The HCM panel currently sequences 18 genes, including *ACTC (ACTC1), CAV3, GLA, LAMP2, MTTG, MTTI, MTTK, MTTQ, MYBPC3, MYH7, MYL2, MYL3, PRKAG2, TNNC1, TNNI3, TNNT2, TPM1,* and *TTR* (Genedx HCM Sequencing Panel, n.d.). These 18 genes include the sarcomeric genes, the Z-disc genes, and calcium channel genes, as well as genes implicated in syndromes that have left ventricular hypertrophy (LVH) associated with them. Mutations in *PRKAG2* result in a glycogen storage disorder, *LAMP2* mutations cause Danon's disorder, mutations in *GLA* are associated with Fabry's disease, and mutations in *TTR* are associated with amyloidosis.

First-degree relatives of individuals diagnosed with HCM should all have ECG and echocardiogram screenings every five years to evaluate for any signs of LVH. Children should be screened once prior to age 10 years, yearly from age 12 to 18 years, and then every five years through adulthood (Maron, 2010). If there is a genetic test result available to use for screening, the benefits and limitations of genetic screening should be discussed with the first-degree family members, and they should be allowed to decide if they would like to pursue this option. The provider for these individuals may want to consider also having those who test negative for the variant have one ECG and echocardiogram prior to releasing them from routine surveillance.

11.29.2.2. Familial Hypercholesterolemia

Familial hypercholesterolemia (FH) is an autosomal dominant disorder that affects 1 in 200 to 500 in the general population. Populations at higher risk are Afrikaners in South Africa (1:72 to 100), French Canadians (1:270), Christian Lebanese (1:85), Tunisia (1:165), and South Aftican Ashkenazi Jews (1:67) (Youngblom & Knowles, 2014). FH is characterized by LDL levels > 190 mg/dL (normal < 130 mg/dL) and excess cholesterol deposits in tissue and vasculature. In addition to elevated LDL levels, clinical findings often include xanthomas (patches of yellowish cholesterol buildup) around the eye or on tendons of joints and/or corneal arcus (white, gray, or blue opaque ring in the corneal margin).

Unlike the normal population, LDL levels in the FH individual are elevated from birth, and thus this individual is at risk for early coronary vascular events.

FH is caused by mutations in one of four genes, apolipoprotein B (*APOB*), low density lipoprotein receptor (*LDLR*), proprotein convertase subtilisin/kexin 9 (*PCSK9*), or low density lipoprotein receptor adapter protein 1 (*LDLRAP1*) or a gene yet to be discovered (Hopkins, Toth, Ballantyne, & Rader, 2011).

Apolipoprotein B exists in two versions, a short version called apolipoprotein B-48, and apolipoprotein B-100. The *APOB* gene encodes both of these proteins. Apolipoprotein B-48 is produced in the intestine and is used to form chylomicrons, which carry fat and cholesterol into the circulation. Apolipoprotein B-100 is produced in the liver and is packaged into very low density lipoprotein (VLDL) for release into the circulation. VLDL along with chylomicrons from the intestine function to deliver triglycerides to cells in the body. As the triglycerides are removed by the cells, they become denser and are remodeled into LDL (cholesterol, lipoproteins and the liver, n.d.).

LDL is responsible for delivering cholesterol to the cells in the body. Cholesterol is used in membranes or for the synthesis of steroid hormones. LDL attaches to the LDL receptor on the surface of cells via the apolipoprotein B protein. The is responsible for bringing LDL into the cell, where it is broken down to release cholesterol to be used, stored, or removed from the body (Genetic Home Reference, 2014b). A loss of function mutation in either gene can interfere with the binding of the LDL particle. LDLRAP1 is found on the surface of cells along with the LDLR, and it plays a critical role in moving the LDL into the cell (Genetic Home Reference, 2014c). A mutation in any of these three genes that causes a loss of function results in a decreased ability to clear LDL from the circulation.

The *PCSK9* protein functions to control the number of LDL receptors found on the surface of cells by breaking down LDL receptors before they are able to be incorporated into the cell membrane (Genetic Home Reference, 2014d). A mutation in *PCSK9* that causes a gain of function results in an increased number of LDL receptors being broken down and an increase in circulating LDL.

Individuals with FH typically do not realize they have this condition. Apart from the clinical findings mentioned above, there is no outward sign that there are increased levels of circulating LDL causing increased atherosclerotic disease. The first indication that FH is present in a family is often the occurrence of an MI in a family member at a young age. Untreated heterozygous individuals will likely experience their first coronary vascular event around the age of 50 for men and around the age of 60 for women (Hopkins *et al.*, 2011). Untreated homozygotes will likely die around the age of 20 of MI (Raal & Santos, 2012).

In the U.S., the diagnosis of FH is usually made on the basis of lipid testing and physical examination. Despite the fact that genetic testing is considered the gold standard for diagnosis of FH, it is often not routinely sent in the U.S. (Knowles, 2013). Only three of the genes mentioned above are currently found on the FH panel at the clinical genetic testing laboratories. Mutations in *LDLR* account for 85% of the cases of FH with a genetic diagnosis, whereas mutations in *APOB* account for about 10% and mutations in *PCSK9* account for about 5% of cases (Youngblom & Knowles, 2014). The yield or the likelihood of finding a mutation is about 85% in definite FH cases and about 50% in possible FH cases. One value for the use of genetic testing is for confirmation of diagnosis when the clinical manifestations are not strong enough to give a definite diagnosis, but where FH is being considered. The major reason for performing genetic testing in FH is to be able to perform cascade screening on the family members of the affected individual. Cascade screening involves testing the proband's first-degree relatives for the known causative mutation. Should any of those individuals be found to also have the mutation, their first-degree relatives are then screened for the mutation. This process continues ideally until all of the branches of the family know their status of having FH. Cascade screening is particularly effective in FH as the penetrance of the condition is around 90% (Youngblom & Knowles, 2014). The goal of cascade screening to identify all those family members who carry the mutation and get them on lipidlowering medication to reduce their lifetime exposure to elevated cholesterol.

First line management for lipid reduction in all

cases of hyperlipidemia is changing environmental factors. Diet and weight control are important in the control of cholesterol in FH as well, but this is not going to be sufficient to reach the goal level of lipid reduction. The goal is to reduce the LDL to 50% of the nontreated level. Typically, even for the heterozygous FH population, which have half of their low density lipoprotein receptor (LDLR) capabilities functioning, more than just hydroxymethylglutaryl CoA (HMG-CoA) reductase inhibitors (statins) are required. Other agents that can be added are bile acid sequestrants, ezetimibe, and/or niacin (Brown *et al.*, 2001).

Because individuals with homozygous FH do not have any functioning LDLR, they will need to consider more rigorous treatment if they are to reach the goal for their cholesterol levels. LDL apheresis, the extracorporeal, mechanical removal of LDL and lipoprotein (a) from the blood, is one option (Lee, Datta, Ong, Rees, & Halcox, 2011). This involves a procedure much like dialysis, and there are now five main methods. The procedure takes roughly 2 to 4 hours, and the individual needs to have treatment roughly every 2 weeks to prevent atherosclerotic disease. This procedure can also be considered for homozygous familial hypercholesterolemia (HoFH) individuals who are unable to meet their goal LDL by pharmacologic means. The high cost of treatment and its invasive nature are two limiting factors to the use of this treatment (Lee *et al.*, 2010).

Two new medications that have recently been approved for use for HoFH by the FDA are lomitapide and mipomerson. Lomitapide is a once-daily tablet that works to inhibit microsomal triglyceride transfer protein (MTP or MTTP). This protein is part of VLDL assembly in the liver. In a Phase III trial, lomitapide was shown to decrease plasma levels of LDL by 50% over a 26week period (Perry, 2013) The medication was shown to be well tolerated; however, there are side effects of GI upset, elevated levels of aminotransferase, and increased levels of hepatic fat (Cuchel et al, 2007). GI upset was typically related to frequent stool and was often related to intake of a highfat meal. Patients taking this medication need to be counseled to reduce their calories from fat to less than 10% of their diet.

Mipomersen is a once-weekly subcutaneous injection (SC) that has also been recently ap-

proved for use in HoFH. It is an antisense oligonucleotide that inhibits the synthesis of apolipoprotein B (APOB) in the liver (Hughes, 2011). APOB is required for creation of VLDL for delivery of triglycerides to the cells in the body. The Phase III trial showed almost a 50% reduction in LDL levels using this medication over 24 weeks. The main side effects are flu-like symptoms, injection site discomfort, and, as with lopitamide, increased hepatic fat (Hughes 2011).

11.30. FUTURE GENOMIC TECHNOLOGIES IN INHERITED SINGLE GENE CARDIOVASCULAR CARE

The biggest shift in the provision of genetic care in single gene conditions is the rapidly decreasing cost and time needed to sequence DNA. It took approximately 13 years and several billion dollars to sequence the first human genome. This can now be accomplished in as little as one week, as reported in some case projects, and the cost is approaching $1,000 (Wetterstrand, 2014). The barrier to providing individuals the information in their genome is no longer related to the ability to obtain the information. Exome and whole genome sequencing are beginning to be offered clinically, in specific situations, to help identify the causal variant affecting families. The limiting factor in doing this testing is the time that needs to be taken to sift through the variants that are found, and properly assess whether or not this could be a contributing factor to disease. As is performed for variants found on genetic testing panels, different types of evidence, such as bioinformatic programs and genetic databases, need to be considered to filter out variants that are likely not causal (Roberts *et al.*, 2013). This process takes time, although while these filtering mechanisms can reduce the number of potentially causative variants, the reality is that this process will likely not leave just one potential candidate, and further in vitro and in vivo studies will be needed to delineate the biological and functional significance of the variants (Roberts *et al.* 2013).

Pharmacogenomics is another area in which there is hope to find medical therapy to either halt or slow progression of disease. Transgenomic mice have been used to test the effectiveness of different medications in slowing the progres-

TABLE 11.3. Resources for Cardiac Singlegene Disorders.

Organization	Purpose	Website
2011 ACCF/AHA Guideline for the Diagnosis and Treatment of Hypertrophic Cardiomyopathy	Guideline for the diagnosis and treatment of hypertrophic cardiomyopathy	http://circ.ahajournals.org/content/124/24/e783.full.pdf+html?sid=2790d961-a7a4-4b7a-b7ce-188081ad6573
The Cardiomyopathy Association	Provides information and support to families affected by cardiomyopathy	http://www.cardiomyopathy.org
Hypertrophic Cardiomyopathy Association	Provides support, advocacy and education to patients, family members, the medical community, and the public about hypertrophic cardiomyopathy	http://4hcm.org
FH Foundation	To raise awareness and save lives by increasing the rate of early diagnosis and encouraging proactive treatment for individuals with familial hypercholesterolemia	http://thefhfoundation.org/

sion of fibrosis in HCM (Bos *et al.*, 2009). There is a currently a wave of research going into the production of pluripotent stem (iPS) cells. Researchers are now able to successfully reprogram patient-derived fibroblasts into iPS cells (Webster, Yan, & Marsden, 2013). The hope is that in creating these cells, pharmacologic treatments could be tested on them and the patient could be given personalized medical therapy.

Transcriptomics is one of the blossoming fields in the "-omics" generation. It is essentially a technique that allows for the visualization of the mRNA that has been produced from the genome at any one time, and applications are available online from the Center for Omics Science via the following link: http://omicscentre.com/services-applications/genomics-and-transcriptomics/ (Center for Omic Science, n.d.). Microarray chips can be used to compare expression levels of mRNA of affected cells and healthy controls. This technique has been used to identify genes that were either up-regulated or down-regulated from that of healthy controls in both HCM and DCM (Bos *et al.*, 2009). Now the challenge is to determine why these changes occur and how they can be prevented or reversed.

Finally, although not the final chapter in cardiovascular genomics, microRNA (miRNA) is emerging as an important piece of cardiac development in heart disease. MiRNAs are cellular regulators composed of approximately 22 noncoding RNA molecules. They function to silence genes through post-transcriptional regulation by binding to complementary mRNA (Rooji *et al.*,

2006). These molecules play an important role in cardiac development, organogenesis, and early embryonic patterning, as well as seeming to be important in cardiac remodeling and the development of hypertrophy (Bos *et al.*, 2009). Determining which miRNA molecules are up-regulated in relation to disease and isolating the signaling for miRNA production will lead us closer to understanding the varied penetrance found in many single gene cardiovascular disorders, as well as potentially a method of reducing gene expression leading to disease.

11.31. SUMMARY

Single gene disorders in cardiovascular disease are complex, and the testing is not always straightforward. New technologies may provide insights into early identification and interventions for individuals and families affected with these disorders. Table 11.3 contains selected resources for families and health care providers caring for individuals with cardiovascular disorders.

11.32. REFERENCES

Ackerman, M. J., Priori, S. G., Willems, S., Berul, C., Brugada, R., Calkins, H., . . . Zipes, D. P. (2011). HRS/EHRA expert consensus statement on the state of genetic testing for the channelopathies and cardiomyopathies this document was developed as a partnership between the Heart Rhythm Society (HRS) and the European Heart Rhythm Association (EHRA). *Heart Rhythm, 8*(8), 1308–39. doi: 10.1016/j.hrthm.2011.05.020

Alders, M., & Mannens, M. (2003). Romano-Ward syndrome. In R. A. Pagon, M. P. Adam, & H.H. Ardinger (Eds.), *GeneReviews*. Seattle (WA): University of Washington, Seattle.

Ardinger, H. H., & Ardinger Jr, R. H. (2002). Historical perspectives of velo-cardio-facial syndrome. *Progress in Pediatric Cardiology, 15*(2), 89–92.

Ashley, E. A., Butte, A. J., Wheeler, M. T., Chen, R., Klein, T. E., Dewey, F. E., . . . Altman, R. B. (2010). Clinical assessment incorporating a personal genome. *Lancet, 375*(9725), 1525–1535.

Bell, C. J., Dinwiddie, D. L, Miller, N. A., Hateley, S. L., Ganusova, E. E., Mudge, J., . . . Kingsmore, S. F. (2011). Carrier testing for severe childhood recessive diseases by next-generation sequencing. *Science of Translocational Medicine, 3* (65), 65ra4. doi: 10.1126/scitranslmed.3001756

Bos, J. M., Towbin, J. A., & Acherman, M. J. (2009). Diagnostic, prognostic, and therapeutic implications of genetic testing for hypertrophic cardiomyopathy. *Journal of the American College of Cardiology, 54*(3), 201–211.

Botto, L. D., May, K., Fernhoff, P. M., Correa, A., Coleman, K., Rasmussen, S. A., . . . Campbell, R. M. (2003). A population-based study of the 22q11.2 deletion: phenotype, incidence, and contribution to major birth defects in the population. *Pediatrics, 112*(1), 101–107.

Brown, B.G., Zhao, X.Q., Chait, A., Fisher, L.D., Cheung, M.C., & Morse, J.S. (2001). Simvastatin and niacin, antioxidant vitamins, or the combination for the prevention of coronary disease. *New England Journal of Medicine, 345*(22), 1583–92.

Brugada, R., Campuzano, O., Brugada, P., Brugada, J., & Hong, K. (2005 Mar 31 [Updated 2014 Apr 10]). Brugada Syndrome. In: R. A. Pagon, M. P. Adam, H. H. Ardinger, S. E. Wallace, A. Amemiya, L. J. H. Bean, . . . K. Stephens (Eds.) *GeneReviews®* [Internet]. Seattle (WA): University of Washington, Seattle; 1993–2014. Available from: http://www.ncbi.nlm.nih.gov/books/NBK1517/

Center for Omic Science. (n.d.). Retrieved from http://omicscentre.com/services applications/genomics-and-transcriptomics/

Cholesterol, lipoproteins and the liver. (n.d.) Retrieved from http://courses.washington.edu/conj/bess/ cholesterol/liver.html.

Cirino, A.L., & Ho, C. (2008, Aug 5 [Updated 2014 Jan 16]). Hypertrophic Cardiomyopathy Overview. In: Pagon, R.A., Adam, M.P., Ardinger, H.H., *et al.*, (Eds.). *GeneReviews®* [Internet]. Seattle (WA): University of Washington, Seattle; 1993–2014. Available from: http://www.ncbi.nlm.nih.gov/books/NBK1768/

Cirulli, E., & Goldstein, D. (2010). Uncovering the role of rare variants in common Disease through whole genome sequencing. Nature Reviews: *Genetics, 11*, 415–425. doi:10.1038/nrg2779

Cuchel, M., Bloedon, L.T., Szapary, P.O., Kolansky, D.M., Wolfe, M.L., & Sarkis, A. (2007). Inhibition of microsomal triglyceride transfer protein in Familial Hypercholesterolemia. *New England Journal of Medicine, 356*(2), 148–156.

Devriendt, K., Fryns, J. P., Mortier, G., van Thienen, M. N., & Keymolen, K. (1998). The annual incidence of DiGeorge/velocardiofacial syndrome. *Journal of Medical Genetics, 35*(9), 789–790.

Dietz, H.C. Marfan Syndrome. (2001 Apr 18; [Updated 2014 Jun 12]). In: Pagon, R.A., Adam, M.P., Ardinger, H.H., *et al.*, (Eds.) *GeneReviews®* [Internet]. Seattle (WA): University of Washington, Seattle; 1993-2014. Available from: http://www.ncbi.nlm.nih.gov/books/NBK1335/

Dooley, J., Gordon, K. E., Dodds, L., & MacSween, J. (2010). Duchenne muscular dystrophy: a 30-year population-based incidence study. *Clinical Pediatrics, 49*(2), 177–179.

Dunn, K.E., Caleshu, C., Cirino, A.L., Ho, C.Y., & Ashley, E.A. (2013). A clinical approach to inherited hypertrophy: the use of family history in diagnosis, risk assessment, and management. *Circulation Cardiovascular Genetics, 6*, 118–131.

Fredrickson, D.S., & Lees, R.S. (1965) A System for Phenotyping Hyperlipoproteinemia. *Circulation, 31*, 321–327. doi: 10.1161/01.CIR.31.3.321

Genedx HCM Sequencing Panel. (n.d.). Retrieved from http://www.genedx.com/test catalog/available-tests/hcm-sequencing-panel/.

Genetic Alliance. (2009). *Understanding Genetics: A New York, Mid-Atlantic Guide for Patients and Health Professionals*. Washington, DC: Genetic Alliance. Retrieved from http://www.geneticalliance.org/publications/understandinggenetics

Genetic Alliance. (2010). Genetic Information Non-Discrimination Act. Retrieved from

Genetic Alliance website: http://www.ginahelp.org

Genetic Home Reference. (2014a). Genes: MYBPC3. Retrieved from http://ghr.nlm.nih.gov/gene/MYBPC3

Genetic Home Reference. (2014b). Genes: LDLR. Retrieved from http://ghr.nlm.nih.gov/gene/LDLR

Genetic Home Reference. (2014c). Genes: LDLRAP1. Retrieved from http://ghr.nlm.nih.gov/gene/LDLRAP1

Genetic Home Reference. (2014d). Genes: PCSK9. Retrieved from http://ghr.nlm.nih.gov/gene/PCSK9

Gersh, B.J., Maron, B.J., Bonow, R.O., Dearani, J.A., Fifer, M.A., Link, M.S., . . . Yancy, C.M., American College of Cardiology Foundation/American Heart Association Task Force on Practice Guidelines; American Association for Thoracic Surgery; American Society of Echocardiography; American Society of Nuclear Cardiology; Heart Failure Society of America; Heart Rhythm Society; Society for Cardiovascular Angiography and Interventions; Society of Thoracic Surgeons. (2011). 2011 ACCF/AHA guideline for the diagnosis and treatment of hypertrophic cardiomyopathy: executive summary: a report of the American College of Cardiology Foundation/American Heart Association Task Force on Practice Guidelines. *Circulation, 124*(24), 2761–96. doi: 10.1161/CIR.0b013e318223e230

Hershberger, R.E., & Morales, A. (2007 Jul 27 [Updated 2013 May 9]). Dilated Cardiomyopathy Overview. In: Pagon, R.A., Adam, M.P., Ardinger, H.H., *et al.*, (Eds.) *GeneReviews®* [Internet]. Seattle (WA): University of Washington, Seattle; 1993–2014. Available from: http://www.ncbi.nlm.nih.gov/books/NBK1309/

Hershberger, R. E., Morales, A., & Siegfried, J. D. (2010). Clinical and genetic issues in dilated cardiomyopathy: a review for genetics professionals. *Genetics in Medicine, 12*(11), 655–667.

Hershberger, R. E., & Siegfried, J. D. (2011). Update 2011: clinical and genetic issues in familial dilated cardiomyopathy. *Journal of American College of Cardiology, 57*(16), 1641–1649.

Hopkins, P.N., Toth, P.P., Ballantyne, C.M., & Rader, D.J. (2011). Familial hypercholesterolemias: prevalence, genetics, diagnosis and screening recommendations from the National Lipid Association Expert Panel on Familial Hypercholesterolemia. *Journal of Clinical Lipidology, 5*(S), 9–17.

Horowitz, A., Shifman, S., Rivlin, N., Pisante, A., & Darvasi, A. (2005). A survey of the 22q11 microdeletion in a large cohort of schizophrenia patients. *Schizophrenia Ressource, 73*(2-3), 263–267.

Hughes, S. (2011). Mipomersen shows large LDL reduction, side effects an issue. Retrieved from http://www.medscape.com/viewarticle/754273

Kim, J. (2014). Channelopathies. *Korean Journal of Pediatrics, 57*(1), 1–18.

Klabunde, R.E. (2007). Cardiac Myocytes. Retrieved from http://www.cvphysiology.com/Cardiac%20Function/CF020.htm.

Knowles, J.W. (2013, September). Focus on Familial Hypercholesterolemia. Paper presented at the In Our Genes: Living with Inherited Heart Disease Patient Day, Palo Alto, CA.

Ku, L., Feiger, J., Taylor, M. & Mestroni, L. (2003). Familial Dilated Cardiomyopathy. *Circulation, 108*, e118-e12.

Lee W.P., Datta B.N., Ong B.B., Rees A., & Halcox J. (2011). Defining the role of lipoprotein apheresis in the management of familial hypercholesterolemia. *American Journal of Cardiovascular Drugs. 11*(6), 363–70.

Loeys, B.L., & Dietz, H.C. (2008 Feb 28, [Updated 2013 Jul 11]). Loeys-Dietz Syndrome. In: Pagon, R.A., Adam, M.P., Ardinger, H.H., *et al.*,(Eds.). *GeneReviews®* [Internet]. Seattle (WA): University of Washington, Seattle; 1993–2014.Available from: http://www.ncbi.nlm.nih.gov/books/NBK1133/

Loeys, B. L., Schwarze, U., Holm, T., Callewaert, B. L., Thomas, G. H., Pannu, H., . . . Dietz, H.M. (2006). Aneurysm syndromes caused by mutations in the TGF-beta receptor. *New England Journal of Medicine, 355*(8), 788–798.

Malfait, F., Wenstrup, R., & De Paepe, A. (2007 May 29 [Updated 2011 Aug 18]). Ehlers-Danlos Syndrome, Classic Type. In: Pagon, R.A., Adam, M.P., Ardinger, H.H., *et al.*, (Eds.). *GeneReviews®* [Internet]. Seattle (WA): University of Washington, Seattle; 1993–2014. Available from: http://www.ncbi.nlm.nih.gov/books/NBK1244/

Maron, B. J. (2010). Contemporary insights and strategies for risk stratification and prevention of sudden death in hypertrophic cardiomyopathy. *Circulation, 121*(3), 445–456.

Maron B.J., McKenna W.J., Danielson G.K., Kappenberger, L. J., Kuhn, H. J., Seidman, C. E., . . . Wigle, E.D. (2003). American College of Cardiology/European Society of Cardiology Clinical Expert Consensus Document on Hypertrophic Cardiomyopathy: A report of the American College of Cardiology Foundation Task Force on Clinical Expert Consensus Documents and the European Society of Cardiology Committee for Practice Guidelines. *Journal of American College of Cardiology, 42*(9), 1687–1713.

Maron, B.J., & Salberg, L. (2006). Hypertrophic Cardiomyopathy; For patients, their families and interested physicians. Malden, MA: Blackwell publishing.

Maron, M.S. (2012). Clinical utility of cardiovascular magnetic resonance in hypertrophic cardiomyopathy. *Journal of Cardiovascular Magnetic Resonance, 14*(13), http://www.jcmr-online.com/content/14/1/13.

McDonald-McGinn, D.M., Emanuel, B.S., & Zackai, E.H. (1999, Sep 23 [Updated 2013 Feb]) 2822q11.2 Deletion Syndrome.]. In: Pagon, R.A., Adam. M.P., Ardinger, H.H., *et al.*, (Eds.). *GeneReviews®* [Internet]. Seattle (WA): University of Washington, Seattle; 1993-2014. Available from: http://www.ncbi.nlm.nih.gov/books/NBK1523/

McDonald-McGinn, D. M., & Zackai, E. H. (2008). Genetic counseling for the 22q11.2 deletion. *Developmental Disability Research Reviews, 14*(1), 69–74.

Modell, S. M., Bradley, D. J., & Lehmann, M. H. (2012). Genetic testing for long QT syndrome and the category of cardiac ion channelopathies. *PLoS Currents, 4*, e4f9995f9969e9996c9997. doi: 10.1371/4f9995f69e6c7

Morales, A., Cowan, J., Dagua, J., & Hershberger, R. E. (2008). Family history: an essential tool for cardiovascular genetic medicine. *Congestive Heart Failure, 14*(1), 37–45.

Napolitano, C., Priori, S.G., & Bloise R. (2004 Oct 14 [Updated 2014 Mar 6]). Catecholaminergic Polymorphic Ventricular Tachycardia.. In: Pagon, R.A., Adam, M.P., Ardinger, H.H., *et al.*, (Eds.). *GeneReviews®* [Internet]. Seattle (WA): University of Washington, Seattle; 1993–2014. Available from: http://www.ncbi.nlm.nih.gov/books/NBK1289/

Perrin, M. J., & Gollob, M. H. (2012). The genetics of cardiac disease associated with sudden cardiac death: a paper from the 2011 William Beaumont Hospital Symposium on molecular pathology. *Journal of Molecular Diagnostics, 14*(5), 424–436.

Perry, C.M. (2013) Lomitapide: a review of its use in adults with homozygous familial hypercholesterolemia. *American Journal of Cardiovascular Drugs, 13*(4), 285–96.

Pugh, T.J., Kelly, M.A., Gowrisankar, S., Hynes, E., Seidman, M.A., Baxter, S.M., & Funke, B.H. (2014, Feb). The landscape of genetic variation in dilated cardiomyopathy as surveyed by clinical DNA sequencing. *Genetics in Medicine*, doi: 10.1038/gim.2013.204. Retrieved from http://www.nature.com/gim/journal/vaop/ncurrent/full/gim2013204a.html

Raal, F.J., & Santos, R.D. (2012). Homozygous familial hypercholesterolemia: Current perspectives on diagnosis and treatment. *Atherosclerosis, 223*, 262–268.

Roberts, R., Marian, A.J., Dandona, S., & Stewart, A. (2013). Genomics in Cardiovascular Disease. *Journal of the American College of Cardiology, 61*(20), 2029–2037.

Romfh, A., & McNally, E. M. (2010). Cardiac assessment in Duchenne and Becker muscular dystrophies. *Current Heart Failure Reports, 7*(4), 212–218. doi: 10.1007/s11897-010-0028-2.

Rooij, E., Sutherland, L., Liu, N., Williams, A.H., McAnally, J., Gerard, R.D., . . . Olson, E.N. (2006). A signature pattern of stress-responsive microRNAs that can evoke cardiac hypertrophy and heart failure. *PNAS, 103*(48), 18255–18260.

Shprintzen, R. J., Higgins, A. M., Antshel, K., Fremont, W., Roizen, N., & Kates, W. (2005). Velocardio-facial syndrome. *Current Opinion in Pediatrics, 17*(6), 725–730.

Spinto, P., Seidman, C., McKenna, W., & Maron, B. (1997). The management of hypertrophic cardiomyopathy. *New England Journal of Medicine, 336*:775–785.

The 1000 Genomes Project Consortium. (2012). An integrated map of genetic variation from 1,092 human genomes. *Nature, 491*, 56–65.

Vernengo, L., Lilienbaum, A., Agbulut, O., & Rodríguez, M. M. (2013). *The Role of Genetics in Cardiomyopathy, Cardiomyopathies*. In P. J. Milei (Ed.). Retrieved from http://www.intechopen.com/books/cardiomyopathies/the-role-of-genetics-in-cardiomyopathy.

Webster, A.L, Yan, M.S., & Marsden, P.A. (2013) Epigenetics and Cardiovascular Disease. *Canadian Journal of Cardiology, 29*, 46–57.

Widdows, S. (2012). Hypertrophic cardiomyopathy. Retrieved June 16, 2014 from http://blog.iridiamedical.com/tag/hcm/.

Wetterstrand, K.A. (2014). DNA Sequencing Costs: Data from the NHGRI Genome Sequencing Program (GSP) Retrieved June 29, 2014 from www.genome.gov/sequencingcosts.

Youngblom, E., & Knowles, J.W. (2014, Jan 2) Familial Hypercholesterolemia. In: Pagon, R.A., Adam M.P., Ardinger, H.H., *et al.*, (Eds.). *GeneReviews*® [Internet]. Seattle (WA): University of Washington, Seattle; 1993–2014. Available from: http://www.ncbi.nlm.nih.gov/books/NBK174884/

The information presented represents the author's own views and does not necessarily represent the views of Stanford Hospital and Clinics, Lucile Packard Children's Hospital and/or Stanford University or its affiliates.

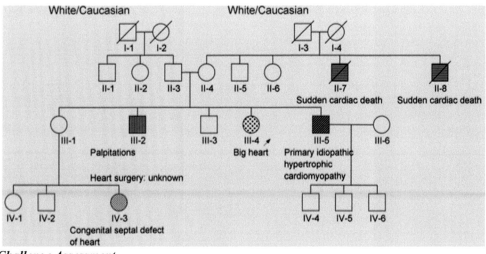

Challenge Assessment

Utilize the above case to determine which individuals should be recommended to pursue cardiac screening. Are there individuals who are at increased risk and warrant more comprehensive cardiac assessment rather than simple cardiac screening? Who are the potential genetic carriers of a mutation that causes HCM?

Chapter 12

Genetics in Hematology

EDWARDA M. BUDA-OKREGLAK, MD, FACP
DIANE C. SEIBERT, Ph.D, ARNP, FAANP, FAAN

Objectives:

- Describe the genetic and molecular basis of inherited red blood cell (RBC) disorders.
- Discuss genetic and molecular basis of inherited white blood cell (WBC) disorders.
- Describe the genetic and molecular basis of inherited platelet disorders.
- Describe the genetic and molecular basis of inherited coagulopathies.
- Discuss inherited and acquired bone marrow failure syndromes.
- Describe the genetic and molecular basis of inherited hematologic neoplasms.

12.1. INTRODUCTION

All blood cells arise from bone marrow–derived hematopoietic pluripotent stem cells, which give rise to the committed hematopoietic progenitors, common myeloid progenitor cells, and common lymphoid progenitor cells (Hoffbrand, Moss, & Pettit, 2011). The common myeloid progenitor gives rise to monocytes and 6 different cell types: erythroid progenitors (forming mature red blood cells [RBCs]); megakaryocyte progenitors (forming platelets); granulocyte progenitors (forming mature neutrophils), monocyte progenitors (giving rise to monocytes and tissue macrophages [histiocytes]), Langerhans cells, and interdigitating dendritic cells); and progenitors for eosinophils and basophils. The common lymphoid progenitor gives rise to 3 different cell types: B-lymphocytes, T-lymphocytes (which traverse the thymus), and natural killer (NK) lymphocytes.

Hundreds of genes are involved in creating and regulating the production of blood products and blood-forming organs, and entire books have been devoted to the topic. This chapter provides an overview of the genetic underpinnings of some of the most common hematologic disorders and is further divided into several subsections for ease of navigation: disorders associated with RBCs, white blood cells (WBCs), and platelets and disorders associated with coagulation, bone marrow failure syndromes, and hematologic neoplasms.

12.2. RED BLOOD CELL DISORDERS

More than 75 gene regions containing at least 121 genes important in RBC production and/or function have been identified in a recent Genome Wide Association Study (GWAS) (van der Harst *et al.*, 2012). This section discusses some of the more common RBC disorders, such as heritable hemolytic anemias, hemoglobinopathies, thalassemias, cell membrane disorders, polycythemias, and iron-related disorders.

12.2.1. Anemia

Anemia, a lower-than-normal hemoglobin (Hb) concentration based on an individual's age and sex (Hoffbrand *et al.*, 2011) may develop when too few RBCs are released from the bone marrow, if cells undergo premature destruction, if they cannot transport or release oxygen (O_2), or if they do not develop normally. Although iron deficiency and acute and/or chronic blood loss, are the most common forms of anemia, the genes associated with an increased risk for iron deficiency or bleeding are not necessarily related to RBC structure or function.

Myoglobin and Hb were the first proteins to be

fully described (Nobel Media, 1962), providing important information about the biochemistry of the hematologic system while also forming the foundation for future biochemical and proteomic research. The ability to visualize a protein's 3 dimensional structure offered scientists the opportunity to explore protein structure and function, and genetic control mechanisms and have paved the way for novel therapies (Schechter, 2008) (See Figure 1.1). Human Hb functions as an O_2 transport vehicle, distributing O_2 to tissues throughout the body and interacting with other gasses, such as carbon dioxide (CO_2), carbon monoxide (CO), and nitric oxide (NO). Recently, Hb chains have been found in nonerythroid cells (e.g., neurons, macrophages, alveolar cells, the lens of the eye and renal cells), where Hb appears to function as an antioxidant and/or an iron metabolism regulator (Biagioli *et al.*, 2009). Human Hb biochemistry changes over time, with many of the most important changes occurring prior to birth. Sometime between the 2nd and 3rd gestational week, human embryos begin forming primitive, nucleated erythrocytes that gather in "blood islands" in the secondary yolk sac and begin to circulate in embryonic blood. As the fetal liver matures, it assumes the task of erythrocyte production until the bone marrow takes over the function at the end of the 32nd gestational week (Zambidis, Peault, Park, Bunz, & Civin, 2005). Embryonic hemoglobin (Hb E) is composed of 3 globin chains: embryonic zetaglobin (an alphalike globin produced only in the yolk sac),

embryonic alpha-globin (produced throughout life), and embryonic epsilon-globin (a beta-globin like globin produced only in the yolk sac). As Hb production transitions to the fetal liver, zeta-globin and epsilon-globin are replaced by alpha-globin and gamma-globin, forming fetal hemoglobin (Hb F) ($\alpha 2\gamma 2$) (Wilber, Nienhuis, & Persons, 2011). After about 2 years of age, approximately 97% of the Hb in circulation is the adult form (adult hemoglobin [Hb A]), composed of 2 alpha globins and 2 beta globins ($\alpha 2\beta 2$) and a very small amount (approximately 1%) of Hb F ($\alpha 2\gamma 2$). Each of these changes in conformation is driven by the amount of O_2 available to the organism; Hb E and Hb F bind much more tightly to available O_2 than Hb A. Although all forms of Hb facilitate O_2 transfer, Hb A is more efficient at drop-off and pick-up of O_2 because it has more relaxed binding kinetics (Hartwell, 2008).

Each of these transitions is directed by a complex conversation between and within genes, much of which is still not completely understood. What is known is that the α-globin gene is on chromosome 16 and β-globin is on chromosome 11. Fetal zeta and epsilon Hbs are downregulated early in embryonic life as alpha and gamma globin genes, which are functionally identical but contain either glycine or alanine in position 136, are up-regulated, causing Hb F to accumulate. Although the alpha genes remain fully functional throughout life, after birth the genes producing gamma globin down-regulate and beta globin up-regulates to form Hb A. In some people, for reasons as yet unknown, gamma globin genes remain active, and Hb F production continues. Although Hb F is somewhat less efficient because it binds more tightly to O_2, most of these adults are asymptomatic. Further research is underway to determine what causes the gamma globin gene to remain active, because hereditary persistence of fetal hemoglobin (HPFH) is seen as potentially useful therapy in treating sickle cell disease (Schechter, 2008).

Hb disorders can be classified as either *qualitative* or *quantitative*. Hemoglobinopathies, the most common of which are hemoglobin S (Hb S), hemoglobin C (Hb C), and hemoglobin E (Hb E), are caused by mutations that cause qualitative alterations in globin amino acid sequences, producing structural and/or functional changes in beta Hb. The thalassemias, beta thalassemia

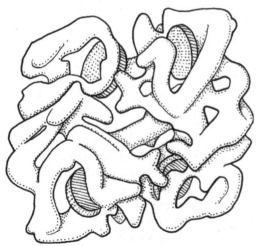

FIGURE 12.1. Hemoglobin Molecule. Drawn by Mark J. Wieber MA, BSN.

(β-thal) and alpha thalassemia (α-thal), result from mutations that cause a quantitative decrease in structurally normal globin proteins. Mutations that decrease the overall production of alpha globins cause α-thal (resulting in a relative excess of beta globins); those that decrease synthesis of beta globins result in β-thal (resulting in a relative excess of alpha globins). All hemoglobinopathies are inherited in an autosomal recessive manner, and genetic testing is necessary to determine the genotype.

12.2.1.1. Sickle Cell Anemia

Sickle cell anemia (also known as homozygous sickle cell disease [SCD] or Hb SS) was the first molecular disease in which every clinical manifestation could be traced back to the Hb molecule and, later, to deleterious Hb mutations (Conley, 1980). The label "*sickle cell syndrome*" encompasses all conditions that contain Hb S, including sickle cell trait, but the term "*sickle cell disease*" includes only those disorders associated with chronic hemolytic anemia and vaso-occlusive pain. SCD therefore is inclusive of homozygous Hb S, which accounts for 60% to 70% of SCD in the U.S. (http://www.genes-r-us.uthscsa.edu), Hb S paired with a thalassemia trait or another mutant Hb in a compound heterozygote, but not Hb S paired with Hb A.

Hb S is caused by a single gene mutation causing amino acid substitution of valine for glutamic acid at the sixth residue of the beta globin chain (Glu6Val), resulting in sickle Hb. When bound to O_2, the Hb S behaves normally, but as Hb S becomes deoxygenated, more and more valine binding sites become bound to nearby molecules, forming long strands of fibrous aggregates, thousands of Hb molecules in length. The long, fibrous strands damage the red cell membrane, causing cellular dehydration and oxidative damage. However, they also stretch across the erythrocyte, making it brittle, distorting its shape (sickling), and increasing the tendency for red cells to adhere to the endothelium, causing venous occlusion, decreased tissue perfusion, and ischemia. The net result of all of these cellular changes is a shortened cellular life span, hemolysis, and chronic inflammation (Bender & Hobbs, 2012; Tymoczko, Berg, & Stryer, 2013). Individuals with one copy of Hb S (sickle cell trait) are usually asymptomatic, are much less likely to develop malaria, and are therefore more likely to reproduce, passing the Hb S mutation to their children (Tymoczko *et al.*, 2013). Individuals who inherit 2 copies of Hb S (Hb S/S) are healthy at birth, but symptoms associated with sickle cell disease (SCD) begin to emerge in early childhood as Hb F is gradually replaced by Hb S. Often the earliest manifestations in children are dactylitis (pain and/or swelling in the hands or feet) and splenic sequestration crisis (splenic engorgement), which causes permanent splenic damage, increasing the risk for acquiring bacterial infections with encapsulated organisms. The most common manifestation of sickle cell crisis is acute and/or chronic pain caused by intermittent venous occlusion, which can damage virtually every organ in the body, but other manifestations include chronic hemolytic anemia, jaundice, cholelithiasis, and delayed growth and sexual maturation (Bender & Hobbs, 2012).

Hb C is caused by a mutation that substitutes lysine for glutamic acid at the 6th amino acid position (Glu6Lys) in the beta globin gene. Individuals with Hb C/C experience chronic hemolytic anemia and splenomegaly but their symptoms are typically milder than Hb S/S and those with Hb C/A are usually asymptomatic.

Hb E, common in Southeast Asia and becoming more common in the Western world, is caused by a mutation that substitutes lysine for glutamic acid at the 26th position (Glu26Lys) in the beta globin gene. Unlike the other hemoglobinopathies, individuals with Hb E/A and Hb E/E have mild or no symptoms, but severe disease is common in Hb E/β-thal compound heterozygotes.

12.2.1.2. Thalassemias

α-thal and β-thal are characterized by a quantitative decrease or complete absence of normal alpha or beta globin chains, and like the hemoglobinopathies described above, the mutation is more prevalent in communities with endemic malaria, because the mutations confer protection against malaria (Weatherall, 1980).

Alpha thalassemia affects nearly 5% of people worldwide, making it one of the most common genetic disorders in humans. Alpha globin genes are located on the short arm of chromosome 16, and each person inherits a maternal chromosome containing 2 alpha globin genes and a paternal chromosome containing 2 alpha globin genes that function as a unit to produce alpha Hb. Alpha thalassemia mutations impair the body's ability to form alpha-globin chains, and free unpaired beta globin chains begin to accumulate, forming unstable beta chain tetramers with poor O_2 disassociation abilities. In embryos, a similar process occurs as free gamma-globin accumulates, forming tetramers with such a strong affinity to O_2 that it is not released for use in peripheral tissues. More than 40 alpha-globin mutations have been described, and disease severity ranges widely depending on the type and number of mutations, but most fall into 1of 2 clinically significant forms, Hemoglobin H disease, and "Hemoglobin Bart's Hydrops Fetalis" (Hb Bart syndrome) (Origa, Moi, Galanello, & Cao, 2013). In Hb Bart syndrome, all 4 genes are nonfunctional, and affected infants often die in utero or during the neonatal period. Common manifestations include severe hypochromic anemia with associated hepatosplenomegaly, extramedullary erythropoiesis and generalized edema, pleural and pericardial effusions, hydrocephaly, and congenital cardiac and urogenital defects (Origa et al., 2013). Although most α-thal mutations do not disrupt Hb E, large deletions and nondeletional mutations such as "Hemoglobin Constant Spring," in which a misplaced stop codon causes 31 extra amino acids to be added to the alpha chain, making the chain unstable, and significantly prolonging globin chain production times, can cause severe symptoms (Vichinsky, 2009). Deletion of 3 alpha globin genes results in Hb H disease (α-thal intermedia) with a wide spectrum of phenotypic presentations, with moderately severe hemolytic anemia, marked microcytosis and hypochromia of RBCs, hepatosplenomegaly, and variable transfusion needs. Alpha thalassemia trait (minor, also called alpha plus) results from the absence of 2 genes (in either cis position, more commonly found in Asian individuals, or the *trans* position, more commonly in patients of African or Mediterranean origin) and mild anemia with microcytic indices. Deletion of a single alpha globin gene results in the silent carrier state, with borderline microcytosis or clinically normal blood counts. Prenatal screening for Hb Bart syndrome is available, offering parents the option to select embryos without the mutation, terminate affected pregnancies, or initiate intrauterine transfusions to improve outcomes in affected infants (Origa et al., 2013). Beta thalassemia is associated with more than 150 mutations on 2 genes located on the short arm of chromosome 11, some of which cause beta+ thalassemia, in which normal beta-globin chains are produced in reduced amounts, and others which cause beta-thalassemia, in which no beta globin chains are produced at all. Unpaired alpha globin chains precipitate, which damages RBCs, causing microcytic hypochromic anemia and hepatosplenomegaly. Individuals with beta°-thalassemia usually become symptomatic in early childhood as Hb F disappears, and if untreated, experience severe failure to thrive and a shortened life expectancy related to iron overload. Individuals with beta+ thalassemia or thalassemia intermedia often present later in life and have less severe disease. Beta thalassemia carriers who have only 1 copy of a β-thal mutation (thalassemia trait) will remain asymptomatic (Cao, Galanello, & Origa, 2013). Pulmonary hypertension is one of the major complications of thalassemia, even when patients are not transfusion dependent. The genotype an individual has inherited appears to be an independent risk factor for pulmonary hypertension and patients with β-thal have an increased risk compared with α-thal or combined α-thal and β-thal (Teawtrakul et al., 2014). Patients with thalassemia who require frequent blood transfusions are at high risk for developing iron overload syndromes and require vigorous chelation therapy to prevent organ failure, which can result in premature death. Allogeneic hematopoietic stem cell (HSC) transplantation with human leukocyte antigen (HLA) identical sibling; a well–matched, unrelated donor; or HLA identical sibling cord blood have been explored and are accepted clinical practice for pediatric patients. Until gene therapy becomes feasible, HSC transplantation remains the only potential cure for thalassemia and other hemoglobinopathies, with more than 90% of patients surviving transplantation and more than 80% of patients being disease-free (Angelucci, 2010).

12.2.1.3. Other Hemoglobinopathies

After ruling out iron deficiency anemia, individuals with severe anemia associated with a hemoglobinopathy should be offered genetic test-ing, because some people with severe symptoms may not have Hb S/S, but have actually inherited 2 different Hb mutations (Hb S/C, Hb S/β-thal, Hb E/β-thal, etc.), called *Compound Heterozy-gotes*, and genetic testing can both identify the specific mutations and forecast phenotype. In order of severity, individuals with Hb S/S often have the most severe manifestations followed by Hb S/β-thal, Hb E/β-thal and then Hb S/C. Other genetic and environmental modifiers include the presence of an β-thal mutation, the type of β-thal mutation, persistence of Hb F, and other environ-mental factors (Bender & Hobbs, 2012).

Several genomic discoveries have been trans-lated into therapies specifically targeting disease manifestations associated with hemoglobinopa-thies, several of which involve novel uses for pharmacologic agents. Hydroxyurea is the most commonly prescribed medication for SCD, be-cause it has several positive effects. It induces Hb F synthesis, which decreases sickling and improves erythrocyte survival; reduces vascular inflammation; lowers WBC and platelet counts; and functions as a potent vasodilator, because it is metabolized into NO.

Other novel drugs under investigation, which may have a future therapeutic role and have also been shown to increase Hb F levels in experi-mental studies, include pomalidomide (Bender & Hobbs, 2012). HDAC inhibitors, which are short chain fatty acids such as butyrate or valproic acid and other potent Hb F inducers, are under inves-tigation. These includes 5-azacytidine, decitabi-ne, and BCL11A inhibitors, which GWASs have suggested may play an important role in Hb F suppression. Naturally occurring BCL11A pro-tein deletion and suppression in knock-out ani-mal models have both been shown to increase Hb F levels, providing significant therapeutic benefit in SCD and β-thal (Bender & Hobbs, 2012).

Bone marrow, HSC transplantation, and cord blood transplantation can be curative in sickle cell anemia, although the risks and morbidity as-sociated with transplants have limited their use to individuals with a history of severe disease (typically cerebrovascular events) who have a matched donor (often a sibling). As overall trans-plant survival rates have improved (90% over-all and 85% disease free), less toxic transplant and immunosuppressive regimens have been developed, and the management of graft-vs.-host disease has advanced, transplant is becoming a more viable option. One of the biggest barriers to transplant is often locating a suitable donor; < 30% have a matched sibling donor and < 60% can find a matched unrelated donor (Bender & Hobbs, 2012).

Gene therapy is appealing, because hemo-globinopathies arise from a single nucleotide change at a clearly defined location on the beta globin gene and affect only RBCs, providing all the benefits of stem cell transplantation without the risks. Earlier approaches to gene therapy had been focused on replacing the abnormal allele, but newer strategies include the insertion of gene activators to stimulate fetal or embryonic genes to re-commence Hb production or using induced pluripotent stem (iPS) cells derived from periph-eral tissue from the affected individual. All of these new techniques are intended to improve the safety and efficiency of gene correction, with the goal of providing a permanent cure (Bender & Hobbs, 2012).

12.2.1.4. Cell Membrane Disorders

All cells are surrounded by a plasma mem-brane that separates the interior of the cell from the environment. RBC cell membranes serve important roles in cellular adhesion and immune recognition and provide structural support, pro-tecting the cells from deformity. Mutations that alter cell membrane structure and/or function are an important cause of hemolytic anemia (see Fig-ure 1.2).

Cell membranes are composed of 3 layers: an outer layer (glycocalyx) rich in carbohydrates, a middle layer composed of equal proportions of cholesterol and phospholipids, and an inner layer that serves as the cell's structural support (skeleton). Mutations affecting membrane en-zymes, phospholipids, and glucose regulation have all been associated with RBC membrane dysfunction. Over 20 enzymes, 2 glucose path-ways (glycolytic and hexosemonophosphate shunt), and 5 membrane phospholipids (phos-phatidylcholine [PC] and sphingomyelin [SM] in the outer layer and phosphatidylethanolamine [PE], phosphoinositol [PI] and phosphatidylser-ine [PS] in decreasing amounts in the inner layer) help regulate RBC membrane (Mohandas & Gal-

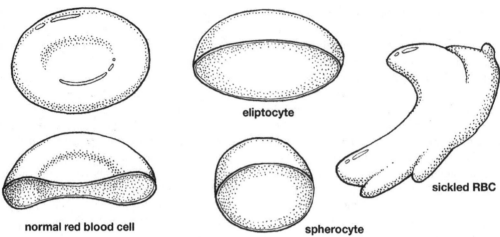

eliptocyte

sickled RBC

normal red blood cell

spherocyte

FIGURE 12.2. Normal and Abnormal Red Cell Configurations. Drawn by Mark J. Wieber MA, BSN.

lagher, 2008; Yazdanbakhsh, Lomas-Francis, & Reid, 2000). Because of the number of possible mutation effects, RBC membrane syndromes are characterized by marked clinical, laboratory, and genetic heterogeneity (Gallagher, 2005).

12.2.1.5. Hereditary Spherocytosis

Hereditary spherocytosis (HS) is more prevalent in Northern European Caucasians, and although HS is inherited predominantly in an autosomal dominant manner, autosomal recessive forms have been reported. Mutations in 5 genes (*ANK1, EPB42, SLC4A1, SPTA1*, and *SPTB*) that encode for cell membrane transport, attachment, or structure proteins are associated with HS, but *ANK1* is responsible for approximately 50% of all cases. HS mutations cause RBCs to become overly rigid, forming spheres (spherocytes) instead of flattened discs, which interfere with their ability to flex when traveling through tiny blood vessels. Abnormal RBCs are removed by the spleen from circulation more rapidly than normal RBCs, resulting in chronic hemolysis, anemia, and splenomegaly (National Library of Medicine, 2014a).

Hereditary elliptocytosis (HE) (also known as ovalocytosis if the RBC shape appears more oval than elliptical) is prevalent in areas where malaria is endemic, because like many of the hemoglobinopathies, it confers resistance to malaria. Virtually all forms of HE are autosomal dominant, with the exception of the hereditary pyropoikilocytosis (HPP), which is autosomal recessive. HE

develops when mutations occur in 1 or more of the genes (*EPB41, SPTA1, SPTB,* and *SLC4A1*) that form the proteins that create the RBCs stable inner membrane layer (cytoskeleton). This causes the RBCs to form elliptical rather than the normal discoid shape. There are 3 major forms of HE: common HE (the most common and extensively researched), spherocytic elliptocytosis, and Southeast Asian ovalocytosis. The clinical severity of HE varies between individuals even within the same families, and it is estimated that only 5% to 10% of individuals develop significant hemolytic anemia (Hoffman, 2005).

Diagnosis of RBC membrane disorders is usually made clinically and should be considered when individuals present with mild or variable refractory hemolytic anemia, particularly if other manifestations such as intermittent jaundice, gallstones, splenomegaly, spherocytes on peripheral blood smear, negative direct Coombs, and increased RBC osmotic fragility are present.

Folic acid supplementation should be considered, especially in those with more severe hemolysis. In hereditary spherocytosis, splenectomy by laparoscopic approach is considered in cases of severe hemolysis or aplastic crises. Although splenectomy may benefit most patients, it may not totally correct the disease. The role of splenectomy remains controversial and requires a detailed discussion between health care providers and the patient as well as the family regarding the potential benefits and long-term risks and complications. Splenectomy is avoided in children less than 5 years of age (Gallagher, 2005).

12.2.1.6. Glucose-6-phosphate Dehydrogenase Deficiency (G6PD)

Glucose-6-phosphate dehydrogenase (G6PD) deficiency is the most common genetic defect in the pentose phosphate pathway (also called the phosphogluconate pathway and the hexose monophosphate shunt), the first step in the production of nicotinamide adenine dinucleotide phosphate (NADPH), which protects cells from damage caused by the accumulation of toxic free radicals. The pentose phosphate pathway plays a critical role in RBCs, because they lack the mitochondria needed to produce NADPH via alternative pathways. Environmental exposure to some infectious organisms, certain drugs, and fava bean ingestion can significantly increase the levels of free radicals. Free radicals cause RBCs to rupture prematurely, leading to hemolytic anemia, the characteristic feature of G6PD deficiency (Howes, Battle, Satyagraha, Baird, & Hay, 2013).

The G6PD gene is located on the X chromosome (Xq28), and unlike most X-linked disorders, symptoms often manifest in females, although males are usually more symptomatic. More than 300 G6PD variants have been described, almost all of which either disrupt the normal structure and function or reduce the overall amount of G6PD enzyme in cells. The variants are organized into categories based on (1) the level of gene function (normal to severely deficient) and (2) whether or not oxidative stress causes hemolytic anemia, and they likely persist because they confer a survival advantage in patients infected with *Plasmodium falciparum* malaria (Howes *et al.*, 2013).

12.2.1.7. Pyruvate Kinase Deficiency (PKD)

Pyruvate kinase deficiency (PKD), the second most common cause of enzyme-deficient hemolytic anemia after G6PD and the most common defect in the glycolytic pathway of RBC metabolism, is a metabolic disorder that is usually inherited in an autosomal recessive manner. More than 200 variants in the *PKLR* gene located on chromosome 1 (1q21) have been associated with PKD, and the disease is most commonly diagnosed in Northern and Eastern Europeans. PKD symptoms range from a mild compensated hemolysis to a significant hemolytic anemia that be-

gins in early childhood, causing failure to thrive.

PKLR directs the production of pyruvate kinase enzymes which play a key role in adenosine triphosphate (ATP) production in the RBC. Mutations that reduce the production or function of pyruvate kinase reduce levels of cellular energy and cause ATP precursors to accumulate, both of which damage RBCs. The deformed cells or echinocytes are often described as "burr cells" on peripheral blood smears. Prematurely destroyed cells are scavenged by the spleen, culminating in hemolytic anemia, splenomegaly, jaundice, and an increased the risk for cholecystitis (Zanella, Bianchi, & Fermo, 2007).

12.2.1.8. Polycythemia

Although anemias, with decreased Hb and O_2-carrying capacity, represent one end of a spectrum of hemoglobin disorders, the other extreme is represented by the polycythemias. Polycythemia is defined as abnormal increase in the Hb concentration for the patient's age and sex (Hoffbrand *et al.*, 2011). It is subdivided into *absolute polycythemia*, characterized by an increase in the red cell mass (RCM) above 125% of normal for the body mass and sex, and *relative polycythemia* (also called pseudopolycythemia), in which affected individuals have a normal RCM but a reduced total plasma volume, frequently the result of injury, illness such as dehydration, or burns. Absolute polycythemia is further subdivided into primary polycythemia (in which the erythroid progenitor cells show an enhanced response to cytokines) or secondary polycythemia (which is driven by factors outside of the erythroid compartment) (Hoffbrand *et al.*, 2011).

Primary polycythemias (also termed erythrocytosis) can be congenital or acquired. Congenital primary erythrocytosis disorders are relatively rare and include those caused by mutations in the erythropoietin (EPO) receptor. The uncommon heritable primary familial and congenital polycythemia/erythrocytosis (PFCP/Erythrocytosis) is caused by autosomal dominant mutations in the erythropoietin receptor (*EPOR*) gene on the short arm of chromosome 19, is characterized by hypersensitivity of red cell progenitors to EPO, and is commonly associated with low serum EPO levels (Huang, Shen, & Bulut, 2010). At least 16 *EPOR* variants have been described, all of which alter erythropoietin receptor structure so that it remains in the "on" or activated position after it binds to EPO. This extended receptor binding time continuously triggers the *JAK/STAT* pathway, leading to triggering the constant formation and maturation of RBCs, even when no more are needed. PFCP is usually benign, but it may confer a survival advantage for humans living at high altitudes, because it increases the O_2-carrying capacity of the blood by more than 50% (Huang *et al.*, 2010).

The far more common acquired primary polycythemia develops when a somatic mutation in the *JAK2* gene is acquired, leading to polycythemia vera (PV), the most common myeloproliferative neoplasm (MPN) in the United States (U.S.). PV is characterized by low or undetectable serum EPO (RBC growth factor) levels and overproduction of RBCs by the bone marrow (myeloproliferation) and is often accompanied by high WBC and platelet counts, because the mutation occurs in a multipotential progenitor cell. The hallmark clinical feature of PV is a markedly elevated hematocrit, usually > 55%. This can result in blood hyperviscosity, splenomegaly, hypercoagulability, and vague symptoms such as headaches, fatigue, weakness, and dizziness. PV affects approximately 2 in every 100,000 individuals and has been seen in individuals of all ages, although the diagnosis is most commonly made in adults older than age 60. The *JAK2* (*V617F*) mutation is the gene variant most commonly (> 90%) associated with PV, but it is not specific for PV and occurs in other MPNs as well. Although *JAK2* (*V617F*) is not inherited, a detailed family health history may reveal multiple affected family members, suggesting that PV is a complex genetic disorder in which genetic and environmental exposures (such as radiation) increase risk. Although transformation to acute leukemia is rare, it is possible, and phlebotomy accompanied by lowdose aspirin therapy is the mainstay of treatment for low- and intermediate-risk patients, with the addition of chemotherapy (hydroxyurea or interferon) for high-risk patients (National Organization for Rare Disorders [NORD], 2013). Recently, the FDA has approved ruxolitinib, a JAK1/2 inhibitor, as treatment for PV patients who have an inadequate response to or cannot tolerate hydroxyurea (FDA News Release, 2014).

Secondary erythrocytosis/polycythemias can be congenital or acquired, but are relatively easy to distinguish, because those with congenital erythrocytosis often have a provocative family history and typically present at a young age. Congenital secondary erythrocytosis is caused by mutations in genes involved in O_2 sensing such as *VHL, PHD2*, or *HIF2A*, or by mutations that alter hemoglobin's affinity for O_2. As O_2 levels drop, cells become hypoxic and hypoxia-inducible factor-alpha (HIF1-α) is released, stimulating erythropoiesis. As O_2 levels return to normal, HIF1-α decays, decreasing the erythropoiesis stimulus. Several substances, including von Hippel Lindau protein (VHL), iron, O_2, and proline hydroxylase are involved in regulating the HIF1-α response to O_2. Individuals who are homozygous for a VHL mutation (*598C/T*) typically have normal or high EPO levels but develop a form of O_2-sensing polycythemia known as Chuvash polycythemia (CP). It is estimated that there are hundreds of CP homozygotes in the population of approximately 2 million Chuvashians living in Russia, most of them in the Republic of Chuvashia. The 598C/T mutation reduces *HIF1-α* degradation rates, increasing active *HIF1* and inappropriately stimulating downstream genes such as EPO, increasing RBC production. Even though most CP homozygotes have *VHL* mutations, they usually do not manifest with characteristic VHL syndrome tumors (spinocerebellar hemangioblastomas, renal carcinomas, and pheochromocytomas), but often develop significant varicosities and are at significantly increased risk for arterial thrombotic events, including stroke and peripheral thrombosis (Gordeuk, Stockton, & Prchal, 2005).

Acquired secondary erythrocytosis can be caused by appropriate serum EPO secretion in response to a physiologic stimulus such as hypoxia (from lack of adequate oxygenation in the blood and pulmonary disorders, including smoking, or obstructive sleep apnea), as well as by inappropriate production of serum EPO, which can be caused by miscellaneous benign and malignant tumors. It can also occur from exogenous EPO or androgen administration.

The recognition of polycythemia is also important so that it may be appropriately treated. Patients with secondary polycythemia and snoring should be referred for evaluation by a sleep medicine for obstructive sleep apnea (OSA) and sleep disordered breathing with nocturnal hypoxemia. Patients with PV need prompt identification, because these patients have an excellent chance of living a normal life span if they are appropriately monitored and treated. Untreated, PV may lead to severe complications, including thromboses, and may shorten life expectancy (Passamonti, 2012).

12.2.2. Iron Overload

Iron is a mineral required by all living cells for DNA synthesis, O_2 transport, and respiration (McCrae & Rao, 2013). In the RBC, a complex of iron in the ferrous state and protoporphyrin is covalently linked to the globin molecule and reversibly binds to the O_2 molecule, enabling RBCs to deliver O_2 to the tissues. Approximately 70% of the body's iron is contained in Hb and myoglobin (UCSF, 2014). Although iron deficiency anemia is the most common hematologic disorder encountered worldwide, iron excess can be toxic as well and there is no physiologic pathway for iron excretion. Therefore, iron metabolism is carefully regulated to ensure that the amount absorbed is equal to the amount lost (McCrae & Rao, 2013).

Hemochromatosis, an iron overload disorder, can be classified as primary (hereditary) or secondary (Beutler, Hoffbrand, & Cook, 2003) or by pathophysiologic defect (alterations in hepcidin-ferroportin actions, erythroid maturation, or iron transport) (Fleming & Ponka, 2012). Hepcidin is a hepatic peptide hormone responsible for regulating iron absorption from the gut and tissue distribution and ferroportin transfers cellular iron to plasma (Ganz, 2011).

TABLE 12.1. *Variations in the Hepcidin-Ferroportin Axis Can Cause the Following Forms of Hereditary Hemochromatosis (HH).*

HH Type	Gene	Inheritance Pattern
Type I	HFE	autosomal recessive
Type IIA	HFE2	autosomal recessive
Type IIB	HAMP	autosomal recessive
Type III	TFR2	autosomal recessive
Type IVA ("atypical HH")	FP (loss of function)	autosomal dominant
Type IVB	FP (gain of function)	autosomal dominant

(Fleming & Ponka, 2012).

Hereditary hemochromatosis (HH) Type I is the most common single-gene disorder in Caucasians of European descent (Leitman, 2013). It is an inherited autosomal recessive ironoverload disorder, caused by a mutation in the HFE gene on chromosome 6, and is associated with increased dietary iron absorption resulting in iron overload in multiple organs, eventually leading to organ failure. Only 2 mutations, *C282Y* and *H63D*, have been clearly associated with the disease, and over 70% of individuals with clinical symptoms are homozygous for *C282Y* and have the most severe phenotype. Compound heterozygotes (*C282Y* and *H63D*) typically have milder disease, and < 10% of heterozygotes with 1 copy of *C282Y* have clinical symptoms, although many have elevated transferrin levels. Individuals who are homozygous for *H63D* are usually asymptomatic (Cherfane, Hollenbeck, Go, & Brown, 2013).

Rare but possibly more severe forms of HH occur with autosomal recessive mutations in *TfR2* gene (Type III) and rare but severe juvenile HH occurs as an early-onset disease caused by autosomal recessive mutations in *HJV* or hepcidin (*HAMP*) genes (Type IIB). With the exception of Type IVA, individuals with HH are hepcidin deficient, with Type I being the mildest. Individuals with Type IVA have normal or elevated hepcidin levels (Ganz, 2011; Fleming & Ponka, 2012).

Although genetic testing for *HFE* is clinically available, it is often more appropriate to screen individuals with clinical manifestations or those with homozygous relatives by drawing a transferrin saturation level. Younger individuals are usually asymptomatic and come to medical attention incidentally or through screening when an older family member is diagnosed with end-organ failure found to be caused by HH. An HH diagnosis should be considered if serum transferrin saturation is > 50% higher than normal in males and > 45% higher than normal in females in the presence of elevated serum ferritin levels. Population screening for HH is controversial, but individuals at increased risk based on family history should be evaluated.

Treatment of iron overload in HH is through depletion of iron stores in adults through lifetime therapeutic phlebotomies aiming to prevent end-organ damage, such as liver, heart, or endocrine failure. Patients are counseled to avoid exogenous iron, alcohol (because of increased risk of liver cirrhosis and hepatic carcinoma), and raw seafood (because of increased risk of *Vibrio* and *Yersinia* infections). Iron chelation therapy is reserved for those individuals who are anemic and unable to tolerate therapeutic phlebotomies (Fleming & Ponka, 2012).

Secondary HH is usually caused by another disease or condition that causes iron overload, although hepcidin malfunction often remains a primary feature (Fleming & Ponka, 2012). Conditions associated with secondary HH include thalassemias, X-linked and autosomal recessive forms of congenital sideroblastic anemia (*ALAS2, SLC25A38, GLRXS, ABCB7*), and congenital dyserythropoietic anemia, which is discussed later in this chapter.

A final category of iron overload includes disorders that impair iron transport from iron stores, resulting in insufficient delivery of transferrin-bound iron needed for the synthesis of heme and, thus, anemia with low hepcidin levels. Other iron overload disorders characterized by iron overload and excess iron absorption include aceruloplasminemia, caused by inadequate release of iron to erythron (*CP*), inadequate uptake of iron by the erythron (*DMT1*), or hypotransferrinemia (*TF*). Chelation therapy, not phlebotomy, is used to treat the iron overload anemias (Fleming & Ponka, 2012).

12.2.3. The Porphyrias

The porphyrias are a group of rare diverse metabolic disorders caused by mutations in the genes that regulate the enzymes involved in the formation of heme, the structure upon which hemoglobin, myoglobin, and cytochrome enzymes are built. If any of the 8 enzymatic steps required to form the heme molecule are altered, porphyrin, the red colored pigment found in heme accumulates, causing symptoms. Several hundred mutations have been identified in the 9 genes encoding for the 8 enzymes, and almost all of them are inherited in an autosomal dominant, autosomal recessive, or X-linked recessive manner. The most common porphyria, cutanea tarda, is not inherited but is caused by a sporadic mutation that occurs during embryogenesis.

Human porphyrias are grouped into 3 types: acute hepatic porphyrias, hepatic cutaneous porphyrias, and erythropoietic cutaneous porphyr-

ias. Clinical symptoms vary by type and may manifest with marked skin photosensitivity and blistering, recurrent abdominal pain, progressive liver failure, mental symptoms, anemia, and discolored teeth and urine, which fluoresce when exposed to ultraviolet light (Balwani & Desnick, 2012). Treatment is based on the porphyrin type, but commonly includes blood transfusions, avoidance of precipitating agents (e.g., alcohol, estrogens, iron supplements), therapeutic phlebotomies, intravenous glucose, and intravenous hemin. Research efforts are underway to develop gene and stem cell replacement to correct specific mutations and hepatic and erythroid transplantation (Balwani & Desnick, 2012).

12.3. WHITE BLOOD CELL (WBC) DISORDERS

WBCs play a crucial role in both acquired and innate immunity in recognizing self from foreign pathogens and in fighting infections.. There are 5 major categories of mature WBCs in peripheral blood: neutrophils, lymphocytes, monocytes, eosinophils, and basophils, in descending proportion (Territo, 2013). Both qualitative and quantitative WBC disorders have been described. In qualitative disorders, the total WBC count is normal, but the WBCs have defects that limit their function. Quantitative disorders are characterized by the affected cell type; there are 2 types, leukocytosis (> 11,000 WBCs/microliter [μL]) and leukopenia (< 4,000 WBCs/μL). There are 5 types of leukocytosis (neutrophilic, lymphocytic, monocytic, eosinophilic, and basophilic) and 2 types of leukopenia (neutropenia and lymphopenia). It is worth noting that leukocytosis is a normal response to infection, but abnormally high WBC levels may also occur as an uncontrolled neoplastic proliferation of abnormal cells, as seen in the leukemias, discussed later in the chapter. Lower neutrophil counts are also common in some ethnic groups (e.g., Africans, African Americans, and Yemenite Jews).

12.3.1. Disorders of Neutrophil Function

Pathologic neutropenia is defined as an absolute neutrophil count (ANC) < 1500/μL and classified as severe (< 500/μL), moderate (500 to 1000/μL), or mild (1000 to 1500/μL). The causes

TABLE 12.2. Identified Genetic Causes of Congenital Neutropenia.

Disorder	Inheritance	Gene
Severe congenital neutropenia	Sporadic and Autosomal dominant	ELA2
	Autosomal dominant	GFL,GSF3R
	Autosomal recessive	HAX1; G6PC3
X-linked congenital neutropenia	X-linked recessive	WAS
Cyclic neutropenia		ELA2
WHIM syndrome/myelokathesis		CXCR4
Shwachman-Diamond syndrome		SBDS
Barth syndrome		TAZ
Glycogen storage disease type Ib		G6PT1
Cartilage hair hypoplasia		RMRP
Pearson syndrome		mDNA deletions
Dyskeratosis congenita	X-Linked	DKC1
	Autosomal dominant	TERC

(Uy & Dokal, 2013).

of neutropenia vary, but patients with neutropenia are at increased risk for bacterial infection. Congenital neutropenia is of special interest, because many genetic lesions have been identified and genetic testing is becoming an important diagnostic tool in the identification of these disorders (Uy & Dokal, 2013).

WHIM syndrome (warts, hypogammaglobulinemia, infections, and myelokathexis) is a rare inherited disorder presenting in childhood with neutropenia, hypogammaglobulinemia, and extensive infection with human papillomavirus (HPV). Although affected children have ANC counts < 1000/μ and often experience recurrent bacterial infections starting in the neonatal period, the bone marrow is generally hypercellular, producing large numbers of mature neutrophils. The identified defect in most individuals is a heterozygous truncating mutation of the *CXCR4*, resulting in enhanced *CXCR4* signaling, which leads to an abnormal retention of the neutrophils in the bone marrow (myelokathexis). Granulocyte colony stimulating factor (GCSF) is effective in improving the neutropenia (Uy & Dokal, 2013), and infusions of immune globulin can reduce the frequency of bacterial infections. Recent clinical trials have demonstrated that plerixafor, a specific *CXCR4* antagonist, can correct the leukopenia and is a potential targeted agent for myelokathexis (Dale *et al.*, 2011; McDermott *et al.*, 2011).

Chediak-Higashi syndrome (CHS) is a rare inherited disorder that presents with oculocutaneous albinism, mild bleeding tendency due to dense-storage pool disease of platelets, severe immunodeficiency, and progressive neurologic defects. The pathognomonic features of CHS are giant inclusion bodies in the neutrophils and other granular cells. There is usually neutropenia and functional defects of neutrophil function. Mutations of the *LYST* gene lead to loss of LYST protein and disruption of vesicular trafficking, resulting in impaired formation of secretory lysozymes in multiple organs, and organ failure. Treatment is allogeneic bone marrow transplant

TABLE 12.3. Congenital Neutropenias Associated With Impaired Vesicular Transport.

Disorder	Inheritance	Gene
Chediak-Higashi syndrome	Autosomal recessive	LYST
Griscelli syndrome, type II	Autosomal recessive	RAB27A
Hermansky-Pudlak syndrome, type II	Autosomal recessive	AP3B1
p14 deficiency	Autosomal recessive	MAPBPIP
Cohen syndrome	Autosomal recessive	VPS13B

(Uy & Dokal, 2013).

TABLE 12.4. Genetic Causes of Congenital Neutropenia Associated with Primary Immunodeficiency.

Disorder	Inheritance	Gene
Hyper IgM syndrome	X-Linked	HIGM1, IKBKG
	Autosomal recessive	AICDA
X-linked agammaglobulinemia	X-Linked	BTK
Reticular dysgenesis	Autosomal recessive	AK2

(Uy & Dokal, 2013).

in suitable patients and supportive measures (Uy & Dokal, 2013).

Genetic disorders of neutrophil function are uncommon causes of recurrent infections in children who have numerically normal WBC counts but abnormal neutrophil function. Myeloperoxidase deficiency (MPO) inherited in an autosomal recessive manner is common, affecting approximately 1 in 400 people, the majority (95%) of whom are asymptomatic. A small minority of affected individuals are at increased risk for recurrent mucocutaneous Candida infections, especially with diabetes mellitus. The defect is due to mutations in the MPO gene, resulting in an inability to convert H_2O_2 to other toxic intermediates, which help neutrophils in their killing activity. Diagnosis can be made with histochemical assay for MPO on neutrophils. No specific treatment is available (Uy & Dokal, 2013).

Leukocyte adhesion deficiency (LAD) is a rare autosomal recessive disorder usually seen in children with history of consanguinity. LAD clinical features include delayed wound healing, recurrent bacterial infections, neutrophilia, and a severe defect in neutrophil chemotaxis and migration from blood to sites of infection. Three distinct forms of LAD are recognized: LAD-I (mutations in ITGB2), LAD-II (mutations in FUCT2), and LAD-III (mutations in FERMT3/KINDLIN3). Definitive treatment is allogeneic HSC transplantation (Uy & Dokal, 2013).

Hyperimmunoglobulin E syndrome (also referred to as Job syndrome) is characterized by defective neutrophil chemotaxis and elevated serum IgE levels and is associated with recurrent bacterial infections (skin boils and sinus or lung infections) and mucocutaneous infections with

Candida albicans, and coarse facies. Mutations in STAT3 have been found in the majority (60% to 70%) of patients; mutations of DOCK8 (encoding dedicator of cytokinesis 8) are present in many autosomal recessive form of this disorder, and homozygous mutations of TYK2 have been reported in 1 case (Uy & Dokal, 2013).

Chronic granulomatous disease (CGD) is the most common disorder of neutrophil phagocyte function, occurring in approximately 1 in 200,000 live births. Mutations in 1 of the NADPH oxidase system components results in a failure to generate the oxidative burst. As a result, the ability of neutrophilic phagocytes to produce reactive bactericidal O_2 species is impaired, causing clinical manifestations of severe recurrent infections in skin, respiratory tract, and lymph nodes, beginning early in life, primarily in boys. Nearly 70% of affected individuals have a mutation in CYBB (Xp21.1), although other mutations are also associated with CGD symptoms, including NCF-1 (7q11.23), which accounts for approximately 20% of cases; NCF-2 (1q25) and CYBA (16q24), which each account for approximately 5% of cases; and G6PD (Xq28), which is rare and accounts for < 0.01% of cases (Lekstrom-Himes & Gallin, 2000; Newburger, 2006). Diagnosis is suggested by the history and confirmed by a laboratory test demonstrating abnormal neutrophil oxidative burst (such as nitroblue tetrazolium test) or more accurately by the quantitative dihydrorhodamine 123 flow cytometry assay. Treatment includes antibiotics and antifungal agents (for prophylaxis and for specific infections), gamma interferon, and HSC transplant (which is curative) (Uy & Dokal, 2013).

12.3.2. Disorders of Histiocytes and Dendritic Cells

Histiocytes are tissue macrophages (responsible for phagocytosis) that originate in the myeloid line in the bone marrow and migrate into the tissues, becoming part of the immune system. Dendritic cells are specialized antigen presenting cells that are found mainly in the skin, lymph nodes, spleen, and thymus (Hoffbrand et al., 2011). Myeloid-derived dendritic cells include Langerhans cells, which are present in the skin and mucosa. One of the other roles played by dendritic cells is to present antigens to T and B lymphocytes (Hoffbrand *et al.*, 2011). Dendritic cells play critical roles in T-cell activation, induction, maintenance of immune tolerance, and maintaining B-cell immune memory (Weider, 2003). Disorders of histocytes and dendritic cells include the hemophagocytic lymphohistiocytosis (HLH), Langerhans cell histiocytosis (LCH), and non–Langerhans cell histiocytoses.

HLH is a rare, potentially life-threatening syndrome of abnormal T-cell activation, low or absent NK-cell activity, elevated soluble CD25, and extreme inflammatory cytokine production. Clinically, it can manifest as a fever, cytopenia, and fulminant multi-organ dysfunction, with splenomegaly, hemophagocytosis (in bone marrow, spleen, lymph nodes, or liver where macrophages can be seen ingesting RBCs or WBCs), low fibrinogen, high ferritin, and high triglyceride levels. It can occur as either familial or sporadic, in association with infections, malignancies, or rheumatologic disorders. Mutations in perforin were first discovered in 1999, and subsequently, 5 HLH familial syndromes and at least 9 HLH-associated gene mutations have been identified (*PRF1, UNC13D, Munc18-2, Rab27a, STX11, SH2D1A, BIRC4*) (Jordan, Allen, Weitzman, Filipovich, & McClain, 2011). Treatment is with aggressive chemotherapy and immunotherapy, as a bridge to allogeneic stem cell transplant (Zhang, Filipovich, Johnson, Marsh, & Villanueva, 2013).

LCH is an abnormal accumulation of Langerhans cells forming granulomas; it primarily affects children but can be found at all ages. LCH is usually considered a sporadic disorder, but familial clustering and occurrence in twins, especially with consanguinity, has been described (Miranda, Khoury, & Medeiros, 2013).

12.3.3. Lysosomal Storage Disorders with Hematologic Manifestations

Lysosomal storage diseases are a group of rare (approximately 50) inherited metabolic disorders resulting from defects in lysosome function. Lysosomes function within the cell to break down other proteins via enzymes and act as a recycling center for the cell. Lysosomal disorders occur when certain lysosomal enzymes are decreased or altogether missing and accumulation of unwanted glycolipids occurs in different organs.

The lysosomal storage diseases with hematologic manifestations include Gaucher disease and Niemann-Pick disease. (Hoffbrand *et al.*, 2011)

Gaucher disease is a rare inherited heteregeneous disorder caused by a glucocerebrosidase deficiency and is more prevalent in the Ashkenazi Jewish population. Three clinical types of Gaucher Disease are identified, with 94% individuals with type 1, 1% with type 2, and 5% with type 3. Gaucher disease results from accumulation of glycolipids (glucosylceramide) in the reticuloendothelial system, with clinical manifestations of splenomegaly, pancytopenia (severe anemia, leukopenia, and thrombocytopenia, in combination or separately), characteristic bone lesions (Erlenmeyer flask), and pathological fractures from bone deposits; mental symptoms may also occur. Diagnosis is made by assaying glucocerebrosidase enzyme activity in peripheral WBCs or other nucleated cells and DNA analysis (Hoffbrand *et al.*, 2011; Pastores & Hughes, 2013). Treatment includes enzyme replacement therapy, substrate reduction therapy, splenectomy in some patients, and other supportive treatment. Gaucher disease is inherited as an autosomal recessive disorder and is associated with the *GBA* gene. Seven mutations have been associated with Gaucher disease, but 4 (*N37OS/N37OS, N37OS/?, N37OS/L444P, NS37OS/84GG*) account for approximately 90% of disease-causing alleles in Ashkenazi Jewish individuals and 50% to 60% of the disease in non-Jewish populations. Prenatal diagnosis for at-risk pregnancies requires prior identification of the specific mutation in the family. Heterozygote carriers do not manifest symptoms, and carrier testing for glucocerebrosidase enzyme activity is unreliable (Pastores & Hughes, 2013).

Three forms of Niemann-Pick disease have been described: Type A, Type B, and Type C. Types A and B are sphingomyelinase deficiency disorders caused by mutations in *SMPD1* (Uy & Dokal, 2013). Type C, the most common form of Niemann-Pick, is an autosomal recessive disorder caused by mutations in either *NPC1* (90% of cases) or *NPC2* (4% of cases) that impair cholesterol esterification, causing cholesterol to accumulate in organs. Heterozygous carriers are unaffected, but affected individuals usually present with massive hepatosplenomegaly and lung and nervous system involvement (Patterson, 2013).

Diagnosis is established by demonstration of reduced ability to esterify intracellular cholesterol in cultured fibroblasts. No specific treatment exists and measures are supportive. Mutations are often unique to the family, and prenatal diagnosis requires prior identification of the disease-causing mutations in the family (Pastores & Hughes, 2013).

12.4. PLATELET DISORDERS

Platelets are very small cells formed by the fragmentation of megakaryocytes produced in the bone marrow and released into the blood stream, where they circulate for 7 to 10 days until they are cleared by the reticuloendothelial system. These cells are critical to the formation of the primary hemostatic plug as part of the normal response to vascular injury. Normal platelet counts are approximately $250 \times 10^9/L$ (with a range of 150 to $450 \times 10^9/L$), and up to onethird of circulating platelets are normally trapped in the spleen, but up to 90% may be trapped during massive splenic enlargement (Hoffbrand et al., 2011). Thrombopoietin (TPO), a hormone constitutively produced by the liver and the kidneys, regulates platelet production via the c-MPL receptor. Disorders of platelets may be categorized into quantitative disorders (thrombocytopenia or thrombocytosis) or qualitative disorders (platelet dysfunction with normal platelet counts).

12.4.1. Disorders of Platelet Numbers

Thrombocytopenia may be caused by a failure of platelet production in the bone marrow, increased platelet destruction, or consumption in the peripheral blood, abnormal trapping of platelets in the spleen, or dilutional thrombocytopenia subsequent to massive transfusion in hemorrhage. Evaluation of a patient with thrombocytopenia should include a CBC and peripheral smear evaluation, to exclude platelet clumping as a cause and evaluate the size and uniformity of platelets and other cells. Bone marrow biopsy helps to determine whether or not the problem is failure of platelet production. Screening for disseminated intravascular coagulation (DIC) or underlying disease (systemic lupus, human immunodeficiency virus [HIV]) may also be useful. Platelet transfusions are indicated with thrombo-

cytopenia, bleeding, and abnormal platelet function (Hoffbrand et al., 2011).

Thrombocytopenia may present as an isolated finding or may be part of a pancytopenia with leukopenia and/or anemia. Patients with mild decrease in platelet counts (arbitrarily defined as platelets 100 to $150 \times 10^9/L$) or moderate decrease (platelets 50 to $100 \times 10^9/L$) may be identified incidentally on a routine CBC and may be asymptomatic. Patients with platelet counts of less than $50 \times 10^9/L$ are more likely to notice easy bleeding or bruising, and those with profound thrombocytopenia (less than $10 \times 10^9/L$) are likely to present with acute spontaneous life-threatening bleeding.

Thrombocytopenia presenting as part of pancytopenia is likely to be due to a generalized bone marrow failure syndrome (eg, megaloblastic process occurring with severe vitamin B12 deficiency; aplastic anemia (AA); neoplasm of the bone marrow, such as leukemia, lymphoma, myeloma, myelofibrosis, or myelodysplastic syndomes (MDS); other bone marrow infiltration, such as metastatic carcinoma or Gaucher's disease; viral infection, such as HIV; and injury to bone marrow due to alcohol, chemotherapeutic drugs, or radiation). Isolated thrombocytopenia may result from a selective depression of megakaryocyte and platelet production due to congenital defects, such as mutation of the c-MPL TPO receptor in congenital amegakaryocytic thrombocytopenia (CAMT) and thrombocytopenia and absent radii (TAR), discussed later in this chapter. Other congenital syndromes associated with thrombocytopenia include the May-Hegglin anomaly and the Wiskott-Aldrich syndrome. May-Hegglin anomaly is a rare autosomal dominant platelet disorder characterized by isolated mild thrombocytopenia with giant platelets (macrothrombocytes), and cytoplasmic neutrophil inclusion (Dohle) bodies, without splenomegaly. The disorder is caused by mutations in the *MYH9* gene, which codes for nonmuscle myosin IIA. It is a relatively benign disorder and the most important distinction is from ITP; examination of the peripheral smear usually yields the clues. Related disorders include Sebastian, Fechner, and Epstein syndromes, which additionally include deafness, nephritis, and/or cataract (McCrae & Rao, 2013). WiskottAldrich syndrome (WAS) is a primary immunodeficiency disorder presenting with eczema, thrombocytopenia, infections, and a high propensity for developing autoimmune and neoplastic disorders. It is caused by a mutation of the *WASP* gene, which regulates signaling in hematopoietic cells. Stem cell transplant at an early age is the treatment of choice for patients with WAS. Recently, lentiviral (LV) hematopoietic stem cell gene therapy has been reported to restore WAS expression in affected patients, resulting in immunologic and hematologic improvement and clinical benefit (Aiuti *et al.*, 2013). X-linked thrombocytopenia (XLT) is a milder variant of WAS presenting in male infants with congenital thrombocytopenia and small platelets and otherwise lack of other clinical findings of WAS. Flow cytometry or western blotting can determine absent or decreased intracellular WASP in hematopoietic cells (Filipovich, Johnson, & Zhang, 2014).

More often, isolated thrombocytopenia is an acquired disorder caused by increased destruction or sequestration of platelets in the circulation, which can be immune mediated and primary or secondary and associated with other systemic disorders or can be caused by drugs, chemicals, or viral infections. Primary immune thrombocytopenia (eg, ITP) is defined as platelet count $< 100 \times 10^9$/L); it is caused by accelerated platelet destruction by anti–glycoprotein IIb/IIIa (anti–GPIIb-IIIa) and anti–glycoprotein Ib-IX (anti–GPIb-IX) antibodies to the platelet receptor, which can be detected in approximately 60% of patients affected, and is accompanied by inadequate platelet production in the bone marrow (McCrae & Rao, 2013). Chronic ITP, which requires treatment for spontaneous bleeding or unacceptably low platelet counts and does not respond to primary therapy (e.g., corticosteroid, IVIG, immunosuppressive drugs, rituximab), may be a candidate for TPO-receptor agonists (thrombomimetics, romiplostim, or eltrombopag) (Liebman & Pullarkat, 2011).

Secondary immune thrombocytopenias can have a variety of causes. Autoimmune disorders (e.g., systemic lupus erythematosus [SLE]), lymphoid neoplasms (e.g., chronic lymphocytic leukemia [CLL] or lymphoma), and infections (e.g., *Helicobacter pylori*, HIV, other viruses, malaria) can be accompanied by immune thrombocytopenia indistinguishable from ITP.

Drug-induced thrombocytopenia constitutes another class of immune-mediated causes of thrombocytopenia. Heparin-induced thrombocytopenia (HIT) is a potentially life-threatening complication of exposure to heparin (most often unfractionated heparin) and is due to platelet-activating IgG antibodies directed against platelet factor 4 (PF4)/heparin complex. Although the resulting thrombocytopenia may be mild or moderate, the activation of platelets and abnormal thrombin generation can cause catastrophic arterial and venous thrombosis with a high mortality rate, approaching 20%, unless promptly recognized and treated (stopping heparin and using an alternate, nonheparin anticoagulant such as direct antithrombin inhibitors) (Cuker & Crowther, 2013).

Drug-induced thrombocytopenia due to quinine or quinidine is a severe, life-threatening immune thrombocytopenia presenting abruptly with platelet count $< 10 \times 10^9$/L with spontaneous petecchiae and mucosal bleeding. It is caused by antibodies that recognize the von Willebrand factor (VWF) or the fibrinogen receptors GPIb/IX or GPIIb/IIIa on the platelet surface. Platelet counts usually recover above the baseline in 1to 2 weeks once the offending drug is stopped, but platelet concentrates are given to patients with dangerous bleeding. Recent in vitro studies have shown that drug-dependent antibodies also inhibit megakaryocyte production (Perdomo *et al.*, 2011).

Post-transfusion purpura (PTP) is a severe life-threatening immune thrombocytopenia occurring 1 to 2 weeks after blood transfusion, most commonly in multiparous women, who are negative for the genetically controlled platelet-specific *PLA1* antigen (absent in 2–3% of the U.S. population) and who have been sensitized by previous pregnancies and multiple blood transfusions (usually following cardiac surgery). PTP results in destruction of transfused as well as autologous platelets because of a complement-fixing antibody against platelet antigen *PLA1* (now called the human platelet antigen-1a or *HPA-1a*) (Shulman, Aster, Leitner, & Hiller, 1961). PTP is a self-limited disorder and resolves in approximately 3 weeks when not treated, but it has a high mortality rate (10–15%) due to bleeding and can be potentially lethal. Transfusion with *PLA1*-negative platelets has been found to be safe and beneficial in patients with PTP; high-dose IVIG and plasmapheresis have also been utilized in some patients (Lippman, Lizak, Foung, & Grumet, 1988).

Neonatal alloimmune thrombocytopenia (NAIT) is a disorder that should be suspected in an otherwise healthy full-term newborn infant who has a low platelet count and bruises or petechiae. NAIT is caused by maternal antiplatelet antibodies formed against the fetal platelet antigens inherited from the father, which cross the placenta and destroy fetal platelets. The antiplatelet antibodies are usually directed against HPA-1α (PLA-1α) and or HPA5β platelet antigens, which the mother lacks, similar to the incompatibility with Rh disease, the latter directed against RBC Rh antigen. Reported incidence is 1:1,100 live births, but is suspected to be higher. Mortality is approximately 10% in affected infants who can present with a spectrum of mild bruising to catastrophic intracranial hemorrhage and neurologic sequelae. A full blood count is necessary to confirm low platelet count and other causes, including sepsis, DIC, placental insufficiency, congenital infection, asphyxia, or maternal ITP, must be excluded. Urgent platelet transfusions of antigen-negative platelets are given for infant platelet counts of $< 30 \times 10^9$/L. Definitive diagnosis of NAIT requires testing of parental platelets for presence or lack of antigens (Groves & Kuschel, 2014).

Nonimmune thrombocytopenia due to increased consumption of platelets can occur with DIC and thrombotic angiopathies (e.g., thrombotic thrombocytopenic purpura [TTP] and hemolytic uremic syndrome [HUS])

DIC is a life-threatening activation of the coagulation pathway, with consumption of coagulation factors and platelets with intravascular deposition of fibrin in the blood vessels, that can cause concurrent bleeding and thrombosis and may lead to organ failure, gangrene of limbs, or even death. DIC may be caused or occur in association with numerous disorders, usually in very ill patients, including infections, malignancies, obstetric complications, severe burns, vascular abnormalities, liver failure, pancreatitis, snake bites, hypothermia, heat stroke, acute hypoxia, and massive blood loss, among others. DIC is known to be associated with decreased levels of natural anticoagulants in the blood (such as Protein C, Protein S, antithrombin, and factor V Leiden), but studies on the genetic risk factors for DIC are scarce and inconclusive (Sommeijer & Reitsma, 2003).

TTP is a life-threatening disorder diagnosed when there is a combination of thrombocytopenia and microangiopathic hemolytic anemia with fragmented RBCs on the peripheral blood smear; it may also be accompanied by fever, variable neurologic symptoms, and renal failure. TTP occurs in familial or acquired forms and is due to deficiency of ADAMTS13 metalloproteinase. which breaks down ultra-large von Willebrand factor multimers (ULVWF). More than 50 mutations in ADAMTS13 have been reported in familial TTP. In the acquired form of TTP, an IgG autoantibody forms, which inhibits the ADAMTS13 and can be formed in response to infection, autoimmune, or connective tissue disease, some drugs, stem cell transplantation, or cardiac surgery. Under high shear stress conditions, the ULVWF multimers bind platelets, causing microvascular thrombosis and endothelial injury in blood vessels and ischemia, which results in microangiopathic hemolytic anemia and thrombocytopenia (Hoffbrand et al., 2011). Plasma ADAMTS13 is absent or very low in TTP and supports the diagnosis, but typically rapid treatment is initiated before results are available. The presence of thrombocytopenia and microangiopathic hemolytic anemia is sufficient to make a diagnosis and initiate treatment. If untreated, mortality may approach 90% and relapses are common. Treatment is with plasma exchange and fresh frozen plasma (FFP) infusions, which remove the ULVWF multimers and the antibody and supply the ADAMTS13. Other agents used include rituximab (anti-CD 20 monoclonal antibody), highdose corticosteroids, IVIG, and immunosuppressive therapy, especially in refractory or relapsed cases. The HUS is a closely related condition and has many features common with TTP, but acute kidney failure is prominent. In typical HUS, the ADAMTS13 levels are normal, and in children, it presents with bloody diarrhea (often caused by Shiga-toxin producing Escherichia coli or Shigella) and requires supportive renal dialysis and blood pressure control rather than plasma exchange. Platelet transfusions are contraindicated in HUS and TTP. Atypical HUS (aHUS) is rare form of thrombotic microangiopathy with hemolysis, thrombocytopenia, and renal failure, where genetic mutations in the alternate pathway of complement are present in more than 60–70% of patients (Nester & Thomas, 2012).

Normally the alternate complement pathway is constitutively active as part of the innate immune system and is usually tightly controlled. Dysregulation of this pathway, often by the loss of function of regulatory proteins, with activation of the terminal complement pathway, leads to endothelial injury, platelet activation, and thrombosis. There are no specific acute markers that distinguish aHUS from TTP and other HUS (typical, secondary, and idiopathic) and treatment is guided by clinical presentation and presumed diagnosis. Treatment has included plasma exchange or plasma infusion therapy as the cornerstone, in which it may be useful to replace complement deficiencies. Recently, eculizumab, a recombinant, humanized, monoclonal antibody that targets C5 complement and provides terminal complement blockade, has been approved for treatment of aHUS. Patients on eculizumab are at risk for infection with encapsulated bacterial organisms and should receive the pneumococcal and *Haemophilus influenzae* vaccinations. Liver and renal transplantation may be appropriate for some patients with aHUS. Genetic testing (for *CFH, CFB, C3, MCP, THBD, CFHR5, CFHR1/2 deletion*, and *MPLA*) should be done early when aHUS is suspected, but treatment should not be delayed. Genetic test results may help to define a more precise treatment of aHUS (Nester & Thomas, 2012).

As mentioned previously, splenomegaly results in increased splenic pooling, which may sequester up to 90% of circulating platelets, causing thrombocytopenia. Platelet life span is normal, and these patients are unlikely to have bleeding unless additional factors are present, such as platelet dysfunction due to drugs or toxins or other hemostatic defects (Hoffbrand *et al.*, 2011).

Massive transfusion syndrome in patients who are transfused with more than 10 units of stored blood over a 24-hour period manifests as thrombocytopenia and abnormal clotting and should be treated with platelet transfusions and FFP (Hoffbrand *et al.*, 2011).

Thrombocytosis, or abnormally increased platelet numbers above 450×10^9/L, especially if sustained, need further evaluation for reactive (most common) or neoplastic etiologies (Bleeker & Hogan, 2011). Thrombocytosis is further discussed under Essential Thrombocytosis in the Myeloproliferative Neoplasms sections.

12.4.2. Disorders of Platelet Function

Normal platelets participate in platelet adhesion, release, and aggregation. Disorders of platelet function can be suspected with skin and mucosal bleeding and a normal platelet count. The defects can be hereditary (rare) or acquired (common). When the platelet count is normal, a platelet closure time (PFA-100) (used in place of bleeding time) detects abnormal platelet function. Platelet aggregation studies are used to define more specific abnormalities, especially in inherited platelet disorders. In the evaluation of suspected von Willebrand disease (VWD), further studies include assay of ristocetin cofactor, VWF, and coagulation factor VIII. The treatment of bleeding due to platelet function defects must be individualized, and the benefits must be balanced with the risk of bleeding and development of platelet alloimmunization. Platelet transfusions are indicated in the management of significant bleeding or preparation for surgical procedures. In other patients, depending on the platelet abnormality, administration of desmopressin (DDAVP) can shorten the bleeding time temporarily (Hoffbrand *et al.*, 2011; McCrae & Rao, 2013).

Acquired platelet defects can be associated with systemic disease (e.g., uremia) or with therapeutic drug use. The cyclo-oxygenase 1 (COX1) is irreversibly inhibited by a single dose of aspirin, which impairs thromboxane A_2 synthesis and acetylates the platelet for the duration of its life span (7 to 10 days), impairing the release reaction and aggregation reaction. Other drugs such as nonsteroidal anti-inflammatoy drugs (NSAIDS) have a shorter duration of action on the platelet, correlating with the NSAID blood level. Dipyridamole inhibits platelet aggregation by blocking the reuptake of adenosine. Clopidogrel inhibits binding of ADP to the platelet receptor. Intravenous drugs such as abciximab, eptifibatide, and tirofiban inhibit the GPIIb/IIIa receptor. Defective platelet function can also be associated with heparin, dextrans, alcohol, and hyperglobulinemia (such as plasma cell neoplasms). Platelet dysfunction can occur in patients with essential thrombocytosis, other myeloproliferative and myelodysplastic disorders, and paroxysmal nocturnal hemoglobinuria (Hoffbrand *et al.*, 2011).

12.4.3. Hereditary Platelet Disorders

12.4.3.1. Bernard-Soulier Syndrome (BSS), Disorder of Platelet Adhesion

BSS is an autosomal recessive familial bleeding disorder due to a defect in the platelet GPIb-V-IX complex, with impaired binding of VWF and adhesion. There is mild to moderate thrombocytopenia and large platelets. Platelet aggregation studies show lack of aggregation with ristocetin. Diagnosis can be established by flow cytometry, demonstrating decreased platelet surface GPIb. Treatment is supportive and individualized depending on the severity of bleeding (McCrae & Rao, 2013).

12.4.3.2. Glanzmann's Thrombasthenia (GT), Disorder of Platelet Aggregation

GT is a rare autosomal recessive bleeding disorder, found more often in the offspring of consanguineous marriages, associated with genetic mutations in GPIIb/IIIA genes. Different genetic mutations in GPIIb/IIIA genes on chromosome 17 result in heterogeneity of thrombasthenia phenotype. Patients affected by GT present with mucocutaneous bleeding, starting in the neonatal period and epistaxis, in which gum bleeding and menorrhagia (in pubertal girls) are common. Deficiency of or functionally defective GPIIb/IIIA leads to impaired binding of fibrinogen and absent platelet aggregation in vitro with all agents tested except for ristocetin. The diagnosis can be established by flow cytometry showing decreased platelet expression of the GPIIb/IIIa complex. Treatment is supportive and individualized depending on the severity of bleeding (Hoffbrand et al., 2011; McCrae & Rao, 2013; Nair, Ghosh, Kulkarni, Shetty, & Mohanty, 2002).

12.4.3.3. Storage Pool Deficiency (SPD) Disorders

SPD disorders refer to deficiencies in platelet granules (either dense granules or delta or alpha-granules) that are associated with a bleeding tendency, prolonged bleeding time, and abnormalities in platelet aggregation.

Patients with dense-SPD have a mild to moderate bleeding tendency, prolonged bleeding time, and impaired second wave of aggregation. Dense-SPD has been associated with other inherited disorders. Hermansky-Pudlak syndrome (HPS) has features of oculocutaneous albinism and increased reticuloendothelial ceroid. At least 7 HPS-causing genes have been identified. Most patients have HPS-1 and are from Puerto Rico, with autosomal recessive inheritance, additional features of granulomatous colitis, and pulmonary fibrosis. Chediak-Higashi syndrome, Wiskott-Aldrich syndrome, and thrombocytopenia with absent radii (TAR) are discussed in other sections (McCrae & Rao, 2013).

Patients with the Gray platelet syndrome are selectively and severely deficient in the alpha-granule proteins and have mild thrombocytopenia, prolonged bleeding time, variable aggregation responses, and a bleeding tendency. Inheritance has been autosomal recessive, autosomal dominant, and sex-linked recessive in some patients (McCrae & Rao, 2013).

12.4.3.4. Other Disorders Affecting Platelet Function

Platelet dysfunction can also occur in patients with essential thrombocytosis, other myeloproliferative neoplasms and myelodysplastic disorders and paroxysmal nocturnal hemoglobinuria Hoffbrand, 2001).

12.5. COAGULATION DISORDERS

Unlike platelet disorders, in which petechial and mucocutaneous bleeding predominates, coagulation disorders are more likely to present with excessive bruising, painful hemarthroses from bleeding into joints, muscle hematomas, and postsurgical hemorrhage. Coagulation disorders can be inherited (rare) or acquired (more common) (Hoffbrand & Moss, 2011).

Of the inherited coagulation disorders, the most frequently encountered are VWD and the hemophilias due to F8 (Factor VIII) deficiency and F9 (Factor IX) deficiency. These factor deficiencies are found in the intrinsic pathway of the coagulation system, and all can have variable abnormalities of the activated partial thromboplastin time (aPTT), with normal prothrombin time (PT) and fibrinogen, normal platelet counts, and normal platelet function in both hemophilia A and B. Platelet function is abnormal in VWD.

VWD is the most common genetic bleeding disorder, estimated to affect 1 in every 100 to 10,000 individuals, and is very heterogeneous in its bleeding severity. Clinical manifestations can range from mild in the most common variant, type 1, which has a partial VWF deficiency, to a more rare type 3, with complete VWF deficiency and severe spontaneous bleeding. Type 2 is further divided into 4 subtypes and bleeding is intermediate in severity (National Library of Medicine, 2014b). Unlike the hemophilias, the clinical presentations of VWD include easy and excessive bleeding or bruising from mucocutaneous surfaces (nose, mouth, gastrointestinal, genitourinary, and/or gynecologic). VWD is inherited as an autosomal dominant in type 1 and in rare cases of type 2 and as an autosomal recessive in type 3 and most cases of type 2; it may affect both men and women. The *VWF* gene is found on chromosome 12, and more than 300 mutations have been identified in the *VWF* gene, making it capable of causing VWD. The VWF is a plasma protein that serves as a carrier protein for F8 and is necessary for platelet adhesion and aggregation in primary hemostasis. Diagnosis of mild VWD may be especially challenging and involves measuring the aPTT coagulation assay (which may be variable), bleeding time (now often replaced by PFA-100), and levels of the ristocetin cofactor, VWF, and F8 and platelet aggregation with ristocetin (which is defective). VWF multimer analysis is used to diagnose different subtypes of VWD. Treatment depends on the severity of the VWD and may be sufficient with DDAVP and antifibrinolytic agents for dental surgery and minor surgical procedures, whereas for those with very low VWF levels, high purity VWF concentrates, FVIII/VWF concentrates, or recombinant VWF may be needed. All patients being considered for major surgical procedures, including those with mild VWD, are at risk for major postsurgical bleeding and should be managed by a hematology coagulation specialist and treated with appropriate factor concentrates (Eby, Frater, & Rand, 2013; Hoffbrand *et al.*, 2011).

The hemophilias are disorders of secondary hemostasis, and congenital deficiencies of Factor VIII (*F8*) and Factor IX (*F9*) result from gene mutations on the X chromosome. They are usually manifested in males, with females being the carriers. Unlike the cutaneous bleeding that occurs in VWD, bleeding in the hemophilias occurs into joints, muscles, or the retroperitoneal space, either spontaneously or after trauma or surgery, depending on the severity of the factor deficiency. Normally both coagulation Factor VIII and Factor IX are made in the liver and circulate in the plasma in an inactive state until a blood vessel injury activates these and other factors in the coagulation cascade, leading to normal hemostasis and cessation of bleeding.

Hemophilia A (classic hemophilia or coagulation Factor VIII deficiency) is the most common inherited hemophilia, occurring in approximately 1 in 4,000 to 5,000 males worldwide, and is caused by mutations in the *F8* gene located on the long arm of X chromosome (Xq28), which causes absence or low levels of plasma Factor VIII. More than 1,300 alterations in *F8* gene have been identified (National Library of Medicine, 2014c). It is inherited as an X-linked recessive but about one-third of hemophilias are spontaneous mutations.

Factor VIII levels of < 1% are associated with the most severe and spontaneous bleeding; levels between 1% and 5% are associated with moderate hemophilias. Individuals with Factor VIII levels between 5% and 40% have mild hemophilias. Treatment is symptomatic and/or prophylactic with recombinant Factor VIII and purified Factor VIII preparations in the moderate and severe hemophilias; DDAVP can be used in the milder hemophilias. The aPTT coagulation assay is usually abnormal, although with mild deficiencies it may be normal and misleading. Measurements of *F8* activity should be performed for confirmation of hemophilia A. All patients being considered for major surgical procedures, including those with mild hemophilia A, are at risk for major postsurgical bleeding and should be managed by a hematology coagulation specialist and treated with appropriate factor concentrates. Carriers of Factor VIII deficiency can be detected with DNA polymerase chain reaction (PCR) probes of peripheral blood leukocytes. Sequencing of the Factor VIII gene in a family or restriction fragment length polymorphism (RFLP) within or close to the Factor VIII gene makes it possible to track the mutant gene. Fetal DNA from chorionic biopsies at 8 to 10 weeks' gestation can be used for analysis. In a minority of cases, fetal blood at 16 to 20 weeks' gestation for low levels of Factor VIII can be tested if DNA analysis is not diagnostic (Hoffbrand et al., 2011).

Hemophilia B (Christmas disease, Factor IX deficiency) occurs in approximately 1 in 20,000 newborn males worldwide (National Library of Medicine, 2014d) and is caused by mutations in the *F9* gene located on the long arm of the X chromosome (Xq27.1-q27.2) and transmitted as an X-linked recessive, which results in abnormal Factor IX, or complete or partial absence of Factor IX coagulant protein. Although mothers are the carriers of both *F8* and *F9* genes, fathers cannot pass the X-linked trait to their sons, but can pass it on to their daughters who can pass it on to their sons. Thus, it may appear to skip a generation. The clinical features of hemophilia B are identical to hemophilia A. The aPTT test is abnormal, and the 2 disorders can be distinguished only by the specific coagulation assays of the Factors IX and VIII. All patients with hemophilia B being considered for major surgical procedures, including those with mild hemophilia, are at risk for major postsurgical bleeding and should be managed by a hematology coagulation specialist and treated with appropriate factor concentrates. Treatment for bleeding or prophylactically for surgery is with high-purity Factor IX concentrate or recombinant Factor IX. Genetic sequence analysis can detect approximately 100% of mutated sequence variants in males affected by hemophilia B and 97% of carrier females. Deletion/duplication analysis can detect gene deletions or rearrangements in approximately 3% when not detectable by sequence analysis (Konkle, Josephson, Nakaya Fletcher, & Thompson, 2011).

Other rare hereditary coagulation disorders include deficiency of fibrinogen; prothrombin (Factor II); Factors V, VII, combined V, and VIII; and Factors X, XI, and XIII. They are inherited as autosomal recessive except for Factor XI deficiency, which has variable penetrance, is seen mainly in Ashkenazi Jews, and can occur in either sex. In Factor XI hemophilia, bleeding does not correlate well with the level of the Factor XI deficiency and occurs after trauma, such as surgery. It is treated with antifibrinolytic agents, Factor XI concentrate, or FFP. Factor XIII deficiency is not detected by the usual screening coagulation tests (PT, aPTT) and produces severe

bleeding, characteristically from the umbilical stump at birth. It is treated with plasma concentrates and recombinant Factors VII and XIII (Hoffbrand et al., 2011).

12.5.1. Acquired Coagulation Disorders

The acquired coagulation disorders constitute a more frequent finding than the inherited disorders, and they usually involve multiple coagulation factor deficiencies. Deficiency of vitamin K leads to a deficiency of Factors II, VII, IX, and X and can be caused by inadequate diet, malabsorption, antibiotics, or therapeutic use of vitamin K antagonists (e.g., warfarin). Warfarin interferes with the action of vitamin K epoxide reductase, which causes a functional vitamin K deficiency and results in decrease in these procoagulant factors and in the naturally occurring anticoagulant proteins (protein C and S). In vitamin K–dependent factor deficiency, usually the PT is prolonged, but both the PT and aPTT coagulation tests can be abnormal, with normal platelet count and fibrinogen levels. Low vitamin K levels in newborn infants is the cause of bleeding in what is known as hemorrhagic disease of the newborn, usually on the second to fourth day of life, and sometimes during the first 2 months. Injections of vitamin K are given either as prophylaxis or for bleeding. In children and older individuals, vitamin K deficiency and a bleeding tendency can result from obstructive jaundice and pancreatic or small bowel malabsorption. Liver disease may lead to multiple coagulation defects because of impaired vitamin K absorption, decreased synthesis of vitamin K–associated factors, reduced Factor V and fibrinogen, and increased plasminogen activator. This may be accompanied by thrombocytopenia because of decreased TPO liver production, hypersplenism, and DIC with pathologic consumption of coagulation factors and platelets, reduced protein C, and alpha-antiplasmin. Impaired removal of activated factors and increased fibrinolytic activity in DIC, may result in fulminant hemorrhage, thrombosis, or both (Hoffbrand et al., 2011).

Acquired coagulopathies and hemophilias are rare but potentially lifethreatening bleeding disorders, with an incidence of approximately 1 per million per year, increasing markedly with age and usually involving Factor VIII antibodies. The most severe forms occur in 5% to 10% and involve alloantibodies to Factor VIII. Acquired coagulopathies may also occur as IgG autoantibodies in nonhemophiliac patients and in postpartum women (rare), some immunologic disorders (e.g., RA), cancer, or older age. The antibodies (also called circulating anticoagulant) inhibit the activity or increase the clearance of Factor VIII, usually causing acute spontaneous and severe bleeding. Coagulation studies will show normal platelet count, normal or prolonged PT, normal thrombin time (TT), and a prolonged aPTT that does not correct upon incubation with normal plasma. Treatment requires a combination of immunosuppression, replacement with Factor VIII, and recombinant VIIa or activated prothrombin complex concentrate (FEIBA) (Hoffbrand *et al.*, 2011). Why a nonhemophiliac individual develops an acquired inhibitor to Factor VIII is not clear, but may involve the presence of certain gene polymorphisms (e.g., *HLA, CTLA4*) and or autoreactive CD4+ T lymphocytes (Mahendra, Padiolleau-Lefevre, Kaveri, & Lacroix-Desmazes, 2012). Antiphospholipid antibodies and the lupus anticoagulant are more often associated with thrombosis rather than bleeding and are discussed below in the "Thrombotic Disorders" section.

12.5.2. Thrombotic Disorders

Thrombotic disorders, also known as thrombophilia, occur in both arterial and venous systems and may be inherited or acquired.

Arterial thrombosis contributes to myocardial infarction and stroke, which together are the leading causes of death in developed countries (Ginsburg, 2005). Several disorders are epidemiologically identified as increasing the risk for artherosclerosis (e.g., diabetes, hypertension, polycythemia, hyperhomocysteinemia, and lupus anticoagulant), but the genetic factors contributing to the risk of arterial thrombosis remain largely unknown. Epidemiologic data suggests that 4 inflammatory markers, fibrinogen, C-reactive protein (CRP), lipoprotein-associated phospholipase A_2, and interleukin-6 (IL-6), serve as predictive markers for coronary heart disease (Hoffbrand *et al.*, 2011). It is hoped that DNA analysis and increasing characterization of the human genome will allow further progress in understanding and clinical application of the genetic basis of atherothrombotic diseases (Lotta, 2010).

Venous thrombosis can occur as an inherited or an acquired disorder. Heritable risk factors for venous thrombosis are well defined. Gain of function mutations in thrombosis are more prevalent than loss of function mutations and include Factor V Leiden (FVL) mutation and prothrombin gene mutation (*PTM20210*).

FVL gene mutation (activated protein C resistance) is the most common inherited thrombophilia with an increased risk for venous thromboembolism (VTE). It is considered a genetic polymorphism of the *Factor V gene* found in approximately 3–7% of Caucasians and is due to the FVL mutation (*Arg506Gln*), which causes activated protein C (APC) resistance and reduced ability of APC to inactivate Factor Va, which increases the risk of thrombosis. Heterozygous individuals for FVL mutation have an approximately 5- to 8-fold increased risk of VTE, but only 10% of carriers experience thrombosis during their lifetime. Homozygous individuals with the mutation have a 30- to 140-fold risk of thrombosis over the general population and an increased risk of rethrombosis. The absolute risk of thrombosis is influenced by many other factors (e.g., exogenous estrogen use and smoking) (Hoffbrand *et al.*, 2011). Diagnosis is made through the APC resistance assay or the molecular genetic testing for *FVL* gene with PCR (Kujovich, 2010).

Prothrombin gene mutation (PTM), *G20210A*, is the second most common inherited thrombophilia after FVL mutation. It is autosomal dominant and due to the G20210A allele in the *F2* gene, leading to increased prothrombin levels and increased thrombosis, which can present as a deep vein thrombosis (DVT) or pulmonary embolism . Heterozygous individuals have a 2- to 5-fold increased risk for thrombosis. Risk for VTE is increased by coexisting genetic abnormalities ,such as FVL, or acquired thrombophilia, such as antiphospholipid antibodies. Testing is through PCR. For those who have had a VTE, the duration of anticoagulant treatment is tailored to the individual's need (Kujovich, 2011).

Loss of function mutations in thrombosis include antithrombin deficiency, Protein C deficiency, and Protein S deficiency, which are the body's endogenous anticoagulants. All of these mutations are highly thrombogenic and lead to recurrent venous thrombosis starting early in life, typically requiring prolonged and lifelong anticoagulation.

Antithrombin deficiency is inherited as autosomal dominant and occurs in about 1 in 2,000 to 3,000 individuals. It is caused by mutations in the *SERPINC1* gene. Homozygous mutations are usually incompatible with life (National Library of Medicine, 2014e). Antithrombin percent activity is measured through the coagulation assay. Antithrombin concentrates are used to prevent thrombosis during surgery or childbirth (Hoffbrand *et al.*, 2011).

Protein C deficiency is inherited as autosomal dominant with variable penetrance and is caused by mutations in the *PROC* gene (Protein C deficiency, ghr.nlm.nih.gov, published 2014) Heterozygotes usually have protein C levels approximately 50% of normal; skin necrosis can develop after initiating treatment with warfarin (due to reduction in Protein C). Rare cases of severe Protein C deficiency due to homozygosity can present as purpura fulminans or DIC in newborns. Activated Protein C (APC) is used in severe genetic Protein C deficiency (Hoffbrand *et al.*, 2011).

Protein S deficiency is inherited as autosomal dominant and is caused by mutations in the *PROS1* gene. Protein S is a cofactor of Protein C and has similar clinical features, including risk for thrombosis and risk for skin necrosis with warfarin therapy.

ABO blood group. Individuals with non-O (A or B) blood groups have been observed to have a higher risk of thrombosis and embolism, which is thought to be related to genetically regulated higher plasma levels of VWF and Factor VIII in those individuals (Hoffbrand *et al.*, 2011).

Acquired hypercoagulable states with risk factors for thrombosis include the antiphospholipid antibody syndrome, JAK2 mutations (found in myeloproliferative neoplasms), PNH, cancer and its treatment, estrogens, and heparin.

Antiphospholipid syndrome (APS) is an acquired thrombophilic disorder manifesting with venous or arterial thrombosis and/or recurrent pregnancy loss in the presence of acquired antiphospholipid autoantibodies. Laboratory testing is used to identify the lupus anticoagulant

antibody (LAC), the anticardiolipin antibodies, and antibodies to beta-2-glycoprotein Ib (B2G-PIb). It can occur as idiopathic or in association with autoimmune disorders, such as connective tissue diseases (including SLE), lymphoproliferative disorders, and postviral infections or with certain drugs. Individuals presenting with thrombosis are anticoagulated, and the duration of anticoagulation may depend on resolution or persistence of the APS. A rare variant is the catastrophic antiphospholipid syndrome (CAPS), in which many organs are affected by microthrombi. CAPS is treated with a combination of anticoagulation, corticosteroids, and plasmapheresis/plasma exchange (Shiel, 2014).

Other combined inherited and acquired hypercoagulable states include hyperhomocysteinemia and polymorphisms in MTHFR. Screening for MTHFR mutation and for hyperhomocysteinemia is not advised because several randomized trials failed to show a benefit of reducing homocysteine levels with vitamin therapy on reducing the risk of recurrent thrombotic events.

In summary, younger individuals presenting with thrombosis or embolism should be evaluated for the possibility of an inherited thrombophilia. Those who present with thrombosis in unusual locations, cerebral venous sinus thrombosis, or abdominal thrombosis should be evaluated for the possibility of *JAK2* mutations (associated with MPN), antiphospholipid syndrome, or paroxysmal nocturnal hemoglobinuria (PNH), which are discussed in other sections. Diagnostic genetic PCR testing is readily available for FVL and PTM, independent of anticoagulant treatment. Coagulation assays measuring the percent activity are available for antithrombin, Protein C, and Protein S but should not be performed during active anticoagulation.

Regarding treatment, the presence of inherited thrombophilia has no effect on the intensity or the duration of anticoagulation when a patient presents with VTE. Thromboprophylaxis for individuals with no personal history of VTE is currently not routinely recommended but should be given to asymptomatic pregnant women such as those who are homozygous for FVL or the PTM, compound heterozygotes, or other forms of thrombophilia and positive family history of DVT. Not all patients with FVL or PTM mutation need to continue with lifelong anticoagulation after an episode of VTE, unless they have recurrent or lifethreatening thrombosis. However, after an episode of thrombosis, strongly thrombophilic disorders such as antithrombin deficiency, Protein C, and Protein S deficiency necessitate prolonged anticoagulation, often lifelong, to prevent recurrence of life-threatening, or potentially fatal, VTE. The duration of secondary prophylaxis with therapeutic anticoagulation may also depend on secondary contributing factors (e.g., obesity, immobility, and antiphospholipid antibodies) and to what extent these are reversible or modifiable.

Screening for thrombophilia of asymptomatic individuals is not recommended because of excessive cost and limited utility, but is commonly performed. At present, there is no sufficient evidence that knowledge of genetic susceptibility can lead to lifestyle changes that would modify the risk for the development of VTE.

12.6. INHERITED BONE MARROW FAILURE SYNDROMES (IBMFS)

The IBMFS are a heterogeneous group of disorders characterized by failure of the bone marrow to produce cells in adequate quantities or normal function for circulation in the peripheral blood. The bone marrow is located in the long bones of the body, such as the hips, upper leg, and sternum, and this is where the precursors of the RBCs, WBCs, and platelets are made and where they mature before being released into the blood stream. Lack of adequate RBCs leads to anemia, which may require repeated blood transfusions. Low WBCs can result in recurrent and life-threatening infections, and very low platelets may lead to life-threatening bleeding and need for prolonged platelet transfusion support. The IBMFS are a collection of rare genetic disorders that may present with pancytopenia (combination of neutropenia, anemia, and thrombocytopenia) or selective anemia, neutropenia, or thrombocytopenia. The true incidence and natural history of the IBMFS is largely unknown and may vary by different countries and populations and may be influenced by the degree of consanguinity in a particular population. Patients usually present in early childhood, but some may not be diagnosed until adulthood; may manifest abnormal or dysmorphic physical findings; and may be prone to

hematologic malignancies or solid tumors (Dokal & Vulliamy, 2010).

The diagnosis of IBMFS typically requires the presentation of 1 or more cytopenias, due to failure of production, confirmed by a bone marrow examination, high clinical suspicion for characteristic hematologic and physical findings (when present), and exclusion of acquired bone marrow failure disorders. It requires informed genetic counseling for both the affected individual and the family. Some of the well-characterized IBMFS are presented here. Although the IBMFS are rare disorders, a diagnosis with one of these syndromes can have profound implications for the treatment and management of these patients and has given further insights into cell cycle regulation and development of both normal and cancer cells.

Treatment options for IBMFS may include supportive measures (RBC or platelet transfusion) and hematopoietic stem cell transplantation. Stem cell transplantation is the only curative option for IBMFS-associated hematologic manifestations, but may be limited by the suitability of recipient and the availability of donors. Patients with IBMFS may require long-term surveillance for the development of both hematologic (e.g., acute leukemia, MDS) and nonhematologic (e.g., squamous cell carcinomas) malignancies.

12.6.1. IBMFS Associated with Pancytopenia

Fanconi anemia (FA), Dyskeratosis congenital (DC), and Schwachman-Diamond syndrome (SDS) typically present with pancytopenia (low WBC, RBC, and platelet counts) as hematologic abnormalities.

FA is the most common of these rare disorders and is caused by over 13 *FA* genes leading to a defect in DNA repair, inherited as autosomal recessive or X-linked recessive. Affected individuals may have abnormal physical findings (cutaneous, musculoskeletal, and urogenital) that may include short stature, triangular face, abnormal thumbs, and pancytopenia resulting from bone marrow failure (hypocellular bone marrow leading to progressive AA and failure to produce sufficient normal cells) and usually come to medical attention as children, but on rare occasions may also present as adults. Normal cells have a number of repair mechanisms to replace damaged

DNA sequences with normal molecules during the cell cycle and replication of the cell. Defects in DNA repair in individuals with FA lead to genetic instability and, thus, a propensity to develop blood cancers at an early age; an association with the *BRCA* genes leads to susceptibility to breast, ovarian, and prostate cancers. Diagnosis is made through chromosomal breakage testing (diepoxybutane [DEB] or mitomycin C [MMC]). Telomere shortening is also thought to play a role in FA. These individuals tolerate chemotherapy and radiation therapy poorly, and bone marrow or hematologic stem cell transplantation is the only curative option for the hematologic abnormalities (Giralt & Radich, 2013).

Dyskeratosis congenita (DC) is classically characterized by the triad of abnormal skin pigmentation, nail dystrophy, and mucosal leukoplakia in the setting of low blood counts (pancytopenia) and a hypocellular (or empty) bone marrow. It can be inherited as X-linked recessive, autosomal dominant, and autosomal recessive subtypes and 6 DC genes have been identified (*DKC1, TERC, TERT, NOP10, NHP2,* and *TINF2*). Affected individuals have been described with a variety of abnormalities affecting other organ systems, and bone marrow failure (from low blood counts and its complications) is the major cause of mortality, along with additional predisposition to malignancy and fatal pulmonary complications (Dokal & Vulliamy, 2010). How many times a cell can reproduce is regulated by telomeres, which are located at the ends of chromosomes, and short telomeres lead to accelerated senescence and death of a cell. The defect in DC is principally in telomere maintenance, and cells from these individuals have very short telomeres. Diagnosis is made by measuring the telomere length by PCR, flow cytometry, or Southern blot.

Schwachman-Diamond syndrome (SDS) typically presents in very young children (median age of 1 year), with findings of neutropenia, anemia, thrombocytopenia, and bone marrow dysfunction (aplasia) and accompanied by exocrine pancreatic insufficiency with malabsorption, skeletal abnormalities, and failure to thrive. It is inherited as autosomal recessive, most commonly with a mutation in *SBDS* gene, which has an important role in ribosome biogenesis (Dokal & Vulliamy, 2010). Patients have also been shown to have short telomeres and a predisposition to MDS and leukemia.

Screening is for pancreatic insufficiency (with findings of decreased serum trypsinogen at any age and decreased isoamylase after age 3 years).

12.6.2. IBMFS Presenting Primarily with Anemia

Congenital dyserythropoietic anemias (CDA) are a heterogenous group of anemias characterized by ineffective erythropoiesis, with increased multinucleated erythroid precursors and excess iron stores in the bone marrow and anemia in the peripheral blood. The differential diagnosis of dyserythropoietic anemias includes hemoglobinopathies, hereditary sideroblastic anemias, *GATA1* mutations, and MDS (myleodysplastic syndromes) (Giralt & Radich, 2013).

CDA type I is a rare autosomal recessive disorder due to a germline mutations in *CDAN1* with reduced levels of erythrocyte membrane protein 4.1, which presents with moderate hemolytic anemia, with macrocytosis and iron overload in children or adolescents (even without blood transfusions). Some individuals may have dysmorphic features, such as syndactyly, absent or hypoplastic distal phalanges or nails, and sensorineural deafness. Bone marrow examination shows increased erythroid precursors (hyperplasia), binucleated erythroblasts (early RBC precursors), and distinctive internuclear chromatin bridging (Giralt & Radich, 2013). The anemia typically responds to interferon-alpha therapy, for unclear reasons.

CDA type II is also autosomal recessive, more common than CDA type I, and formerly known as HEMPAS (hereditary erythroblastic multinuclearity with a positive acidified serum test); it presents in children with a variable mild hemolytic anemia and iron overload and can be misdiagnosed as hereditary spherocytosis. Peripheral blood smear shows anisocytosis (variations in size of RBCs) and poikilocytosis (changes in shape of RBC cells), and the bone marrow shows multinucleated giant red cell precursors. The RBC membrane in these patients shows abnormal glycosylation associated with a defect in Golgi processing in erythroblasts; abnormal migration on SDS gels may be useful diagnostically (Giralt & Radich, 2013). The *SEC23B* gene has been identified in CDA type II (Fleming & Ponka, 2012; Renella & Wood, 2009).

CDA type III is a rare autosomal dominant disorder of mild anemia, peripheral blood smear findings similar to severe β-thal, and bone marrow findings of multinucleated erythroid precursors (gigantoblasts). Abnormality on chromosome 15q21 was found in 1 kindred, but the causative gene is unknown. Several other forms of CDA have been reported but have not been genetically characterized (Giralt & Radich, 2013).

Diamond-Blackfan anemia (DBA) usually presents in early infancy with anemia and red cell aplasia in the bone marrow and can be accompanied by somatic abnormalities, which can include short stature and neck, widely spaced eyes (hypertelorism), abnormal thumbs, cleft lip or palate, and urogenital or cardiac abnormalities. Predisposition to hematologic malignancies (MDS, leukemia) and solid tumors (osteosarcoma) has been observed. It is a disorder of defective ribosomal biogenesis. At least 9 genes have been identified; inheritance can be autosomal dominant (involving gene *RPS19* in 25%) or autosomal recessive (gene *SBDS*). Screening is through testing for elevated RBC adenosine deaminase (ADA) levels (Dokal & Vulliamy, 2010; Giralt & Radich, 2013).

Severe congenital neutropenias (SCN) are a group of disorders belonging to the IBMFS, which in this case selectively involve the WBCs and are characterized by early onset of severe neutropenia ($< 0.2 \times 10^9$/L), pyogenic infections (e.g., frequent fevers, mouth sores, recurrent pharyngitis, and otitis) and a bone marrow maturation arrest (at the promyelocyte stage). Inheritance pattern is either autosomal dominant or autosomal recessive in approximately 50% of cases (and half may be new mutations). SCN autosomal dominant usually is due to mutations of the gene coding for neutrophil elastase, *ELA2* (sporadic and autosomal dominant), or *GFL* gene or *CSF3R* gene. Small proportion may be autosomal recessive and have mutations in *HAX1* gene or *G6PC3* gene, whereas X-linked recessive SCN may be associated with the *WAS* gene (Uy & Dokal, 2013). The screening test is bone marrow examination for promyelocyte arrest of the myeloid cells. Patients with SCN will respond to treatment with granulocyte colony stimulating factor (GCF). They have an increased risk of MDS and leukemia.

CAMT (congenital amegakaryocytic thrombocytopenia) is a very rare IBMFS in which an otherwise normal infant presents after birth with petecchiae, bruising, or bleeding and very low platelet count. The key findings are in the bone marrow, which shows absent or greatly decreased megakaryocytes. Inheritance is autosomal recessive and CAMT is due to biallelic mutations in MPL gene, which encodes the TPO receptor. Patients are at increased risk for developing pancytopenia, AA, MDS, and leukemia. Treatment is supportive with platelet transfusions. TPO levels are typically high, and platelet count is not responsive to treatment with TPO. Bone marrow failure may be cured with hematopoietic stem cell transplantation (Giralt & Radich, 2013).

TAR (thrombocytopenia absent radii) is a syndrome presenting with low platelet count in an infant at birth, who has absent radii but with thumbs present and with other somatic abnormalities. Key is bone marrow examination finding of low or absent megakaryocytes. It may be inherited as an autosomal recessive, and chromosome 1q21.1 microdeletion is necessary but not sufficient to cause the syndrome (Alter, 2007; Giralt & Radich, 2013).

12.7. ACQUIRED BONE MARROW FAILURE SYNDROMES (ABMFS)

The acquired bone marrow failure syndromes to be discussed here will be limited to AA, PNH, and MDS.

Aplastic anemia (AA) incidence is rare in the U. S. and Europe (306 individuals per million population per year) but it is 3 to 4 times higher in China, Southeast Asia, and Mexico (Giralt & Radich, 2013). AA peaks in children and younger adults and then again in patients > 60 years old. The etiology of acquired AA can be idiopathic, the result of a T-cell–mediated autoimmune process or in association with pregnancy, or PNH. Secondary AA can occur in association with viruses (Epstein-Barr virus [EBV], cytomegalovirus [CMV]), hepatitis, idiosyncratic (chloramphenicol), other medications, chemicals, or radiation. Irrespective of the cause, the hematologic manifestations are very similar, with clinical presentations of anemia, leukopenia, and thrombocytopenia and easy bruising or bleeding and infections, accompanied by a very hypocellular, or empty, bone marrow. The cytogenetics are usually normal at diagnosis, but these patients frequently harbor or acquire abnormal clones, such as the PNH clone. The diagnosis is crucial because, without therapy, these patients will succumb to bleeding or infections. Spontaneous remissions can be seen within 2 months in cases of drug induced AA, in which the offending agent is stopped. Therapy of choice for severe AA in children and adolescents (< 20 years old) is with sibling allogeneic HSC transplant and all potential transplant patients should be HLA typed. Patients are treated with supportive measures, transfusions are kept to a minimum, and, when needed, irradiated, leukocyte-depleted blood products are used to decrease the chances of posttransplantation GVHD. Immunosuppressive therapy (ATG and cyclosporine) has been used successfully in some patients and has been the initial treatment in those patients who lack a sibling donor or who are older. Growth factors and Epo are tried but usually without success in typical AA (Giralt & Radich, 2013).

Paroxysmal nocturnal hemoglobinuria (PNH) is an acquired disorder of the hematopoietic stem cell clone, due to a somatic mutation in the *PIGA* gene, which results in deficiency in the GPI-linked proteins in blood and bone marrow cells. The cell membrane has 2 classes of associated proteins: transmembrane proteins and GPI-anchored proteins. The phosphatidylinositol glycan anchor biosynthesis, class A (*PIGA*) gene codes for a protein that is necessary to produce the glycophosphotidylinositol (GPI) anchor molecule, which attaches many different proteins to the cell membrane. In PNH, defect in the enzyme coded by the mutant *PIGA* gene prevents the synthesis of the GPI-anchored proteins in the membranes of all affected cells. Abnormalities in *PIGA* gene in PNH include deletions, insertions, missense, nonsense, and splice mutations. It is thought that symptoms of PNH result from deficiency of specific GPI proteins, such as those that protect cells from complement-mediated lysis. PNH is characterized clinically by chronic intravascular hemolytic anemia, bone marrow failure (with hypocellular marrow), and a propensity for thrombosis in unusual places (such as hepatic vein). Patients with intravascular hemolysis have elevated lactate dehydrogenase (LDH), absent haptoglobin, and positive urine hemosiderin and eventually become iron deficient. The diagnosis of PNH is made by a very sensitive flow cytometry fluorescein-labeled proaerolysin (FLAER) assay and is defined by the absence of 2 constitutive GPI-anchored proteins, such as CD55, CD59, CD66b, or CD16. Treatment of PNH depends on severity and includes steroid therapy and supportive measures in mild forms of PNH and more recently incorporates eculizumab treatment in severe PNH. Eculizumab is a humanized monoclonal antibody to the C5 terminal complement component, and its action stops hemolysis and reduces the need for transfusions in > 50% of patients. At the same time, terminal components of complement are important for protection against meningitis, and binding of the complement increases meningitis risk. Patients must be vaccinated against *Neisseria meningitides* prior to being treated with eculizumab, although the protection afforded by the vaccine may not be complete. Bone marrow transplantation appears to be the only curative treatment of PNH, but is not appropriate for all patients (Giralt & Radich, 2013).

Myelodysplastic syndromes (MDS) are a heterogeneous group of acquired clonal disorders, predominantly in older individuals, resulting in ineffective hematopoiesis and most often resulting in macrocytic anemia, which can be accompanied by thrombocytopenia and leukopenia/neutropenia. The median age at diagnosis of MDS is approximately 70 years of age. MDS is rare in pediatric patients and, if present, is usually associated with Down syndrome (also known as trisomy 21, with the finding of an extra chromosome 21) or a congenital bone marrow failure syndrome and defects with DNA repair. The bone marrow in MDS is often hypercellular for age, but approximately 10% have a hypocellular marrow; dysplasia (abnormal development) is present in specific cell lineages and other causes must be excluded (such as B12 and folate deficiency, HIV infection, copper deficiency, alcohol abuse, and medication effects) (Giralt & Radich, 2013).

12.8. HEMATOLOGIC NEOPLASMS

Disorders of uncontrolled neoplastic proliferation of WBCs, which begin in the bone marrow and peripheral blood, are the leukemias. Leukemias start in the hematopoietic stem cell in the bone marrow and usually affect the WBC series (although on rare occasions, the leukemia may begin in a red cell [erythroid] or platelet precursor [megakaryocyte]), crowding out the normal bone marrow elements. Leukemias are generally divided into myeloid and lymphoid lineage and can be acute or chronic. Acute leukemias usually present as emergencies with signs of infection, anemia, or bleeding (due to low platelets or DIC) and progress rapidly. The bone marrow is typically hypercellular with replacement by the abnormal immature cells (blasts) and paucity of normal blood cells. Chronic leukemias usually present with increased mature WBCs and, early on, may still have adequate other normal cells and progress more slowly. Discussion here will be limited to the 5 major types of leukemia, which are acute myeloid leukemia (AML), acute promyelocytic leukemia (APL), acute lymphocytic leukemia (ALL), chronic myeloid leukemia (CML), and chronic lymphocytic leukemia (CLL). The leukemias and other hematopoietic malignancies are classified according to the *WHO (World Health Organization) Classification of Tumours of Haematopoietic and Lymphoid Tissues*, which was published in 2008 based on recommendations of the Working Group that convened for an Editorial and Consensus Conference at the International Agency for Research on Cancer (IARC) in Lyon, France (Swerdlow *et al.*, 2008).

12.8.1. Acute Myeloid Leukemia

AML is a genetically very heterogeneous hematologic malignancy of clonal myeloid blasts in the peripheral blood, bone marrow, and other tissues, with an incidence of 3 to 4 per 100,000 individuals per year (Schlenk & Dohner, 2013). It is characterized by multiple acquired somatic genetic lesions, including chromosomal rearrangements and submicroscopic gene mutations (Schlenk & Dohner, 2013; Vardiman *et al.*, 2009). The gene profile of AML is the most important determining factor in its outcome and is used to stratify it into different risk groups. Based on recommendations from an international expert panel, on behalf of the European LeukemiaNet (ELN), AML is classified into 4 genetic groups: Favorable, Intermediate-I, Intermediate-II, and Adverse (Dohner *et al.*, 2010).

More than 25% of patients with AML have no identifiable mutations in genes thought to be associated with leukemia, but further genomic and epigenetic analysis implicates mutations to be present in these cytogenetically normal AML (CN-AML) cells (Cancer Genome Atlas Research, 2013). Other mutations of genes such as *FLT3, JAK2, RAS,* or *KIT* that encode proteins involved in signal transduction pathways may be required for the proliferation and/or survival

TABLE 12.5. Acute Myeloid Leukemia (AML) Genetic Profile in Determining Outcome of Acute Myeloid Leukemias and Their Associated Genes.

Genetic Group and Outcomes	Genes
Favorable	*t(8;21)(q22;q22)/ RUNX1-RUNX1T1* *inv(16)(p13.1q22) or t(16;16)(p13.1;q22)/ CBFB-MYH11'* *Mutated NPM1 without FLT3-ITD (CN-AML)* *Mutated CEBPA (CN-AML)*
Intermediate – I	*Mutated NPM1 and FLT3-ITD (CN-AML)* *Wild-type NPM1 and FLT3-ITD (CN-AML)* *Wild-type NPM1 without FLT3-ITD (CN-AML)*
Intermediate – II	*t(9;11)(p22;q23)/ MLLT3-MLL* *Others not classified as "favorable or adverse"*
Adverse	*inv(3)(q21q26.2) or t(3;3)(q21;q26.2);/ RPN1-EVI1* *t(6;9)(p23;q34)/ DEK-NUP214* *t(v;11)(v;q23)* *MLL rearranged;* • *–5 or del(5q)* • *–7; abnl(17p)* *3 or more cytogenetic abnormalities, in the absence of one of the WHO-designated recurring translocations or inversions*

(The Cancer Genome Atlas Research Network, 2013).

of the neoplastic clone in AML (Vardiman *et al.*, 2009). The *nucleophosmin* (*NPM*) gene nucleotide insertion is found in 35% of cases of AML and confers a favorable prognosis, whereas internal tandem duplication (ITD) or point mutations in the *FLT-3* gene occur in 30% of patients with AML and normal cytogenetics and confer an unfavorable prognosis (Hoffbrand *et al.*, 2011). Secondary AML is more often associated with *11q23* translocations involving the *MLL* gene. Although the results of all the genetic studies are usually not available at the time of initiation of therapy for AML, the findings play a crucial role in subsequent treatment, which may include targeted therapy or need for HSC transplantation.

12.8.2. Acute Promyelocytic Leukemia (APL)

APL is an especially aggressive subset of AML, which is often associated with a distinct presentation and a potentially fatal coagulopathy (DIC). The translocation of the promyelocytic leukemia (*PML*) gene on chromosome 15 adjacent to the retinoic acid receptor alpha (*RARA*) gene on chromosome 17 [*t*(*15;17*)(*q22;q12*)] produces a *PML-RARA*–fusion gene; the identification of this leukemic subtype, together with a high clinical suspicion, is used to guide the expeditious initiation of treatment with targeted therapy using all trans retinoic acid (ATRA) and/ or arsenic trioxide (ATO) in this leukemia, with or without chemotherapy. Successful treatment of APL has led to previously unprecedented cure rates (National Comprehensive Cancer Network, 2014b).

12.8.3. Acute Lymphocytic Leukemia (ALL)

ALL is a hematologic malignancy with complex and diverse genetic changes that presents with uncontrolled growth of immature lymphoid cells in the bone marrow, peripheral blood, and other organs; it is the most common cancer in children but is rare in adolescents and adults (Harrison & Longo, 2013). The age-adjusted incidence of ALL in the U.S. is 1.6 per 100,000 individuals per year (National Comprehensive Cancer Network, 2014a). The overall survival rate in children is 85%, whereas long-term survival is only 45% in adults. The cytogenetics and molecular genetics of ALL vary consider-

ably with age of presentation and provide useful risk stratification for treatment. Good risk subgroup is associated with high hyperdiploidy (51 to 65 chromosomes) and t(*12;21*)(*p13;q22*)/ *ETV6-RUNX1* (which is seen almost exclusively in young children). Poor risk group usually presents with higher age and Philadelphia chromosome (Ph) translocation, *t(;22)(q34;q11)/BCR-ABL1*; rearrangements of the *MLL* gene at *11q23* and hypodiploidy (less than 44 chromosomes), a rare variant t(*17;19*)(*q22;p13/TCF3-HLH*; and complex karyotype of 5 or more abnormalities (Harrison & Longo, 2013). Several other newly identified abnormalities have been reported, including intrachromosomal amplification of chromosome 21 (*iAMP21*); alternative *ABL1* translocation and rearrangements involving *PDGFRB*, *CRLF-2* overexpression and *JAK2* mutations; and high incidence of germline *TP53* mutations. Identification of these abnormalities has already resulted in major success with targeted therapy (as in *BCR-ABL1*-positive ALL treatment with TKIs) and is likely to lead to the development of new and better risk-associated treatment strategies and incorporation of novel agents (Harrison & Longo, 2013).

12.8.4. Chronic Myeloid Leukemia (CML)

CML is characterized by the Philadelphia chromosome (Ph) due to a balanced reciprocal translocation between chromosomes 9 and 22 [*t(9;22)*] resulting in the BCR-ABL1 fusion gene (National Comprehensive Cancer Network, 2014c). This gives rise to the constitutive tyrosine kinase activation, which is responsible for all the manifestations of CML, including high myeloid white cell count, splenomegaly, and nonspecific hypercatabolic systemic symptoms. CML accounts for 15% of adult leukemias, with a median age of diagnosis of 67 years, although it can be found to occur in all age groups, including pediatrics. Close to 6000 people are expected to be diagnosed with this disorder in 2014 (National Comprehensive Cancer Network, 2014c). The majority of patients with CML present in the chronic phase, but if untreated, will progress to the accelerated phase and the blast phase. The selective tyrosine kinase inhibitors (TKIs) (starting with the first generation TKI imatinib) have revolutionized the treatment of CML and have changed the natural history of the disease and made long-term survival possible. Clonal evolution and genetic changes in CML occur especially in high-risk patients or in the transition from the chronic phase to the accelerated phase, necessitating the use of second or third generation TKIs or other novel agents. Bone marrow transplant still remains the only potential curative option in those patients who fail other treatments.

12.8.5. Chronic Lymphocytic Leukemia (CLL)

CLL is the most common leukemia in Western countries and is quite rare in East Asia. It occurs with an incidence of approximately 6 per 100,000 persons per year in North America. Clinically, it presents with an increased white cell count composed predominantly of mature lymphocytes, which may be admixed with larger and atypical cells and may be accompanied by enlargement of lymph nodes due to progressive accumulation of these leukemic cells in the peripheral blood, bone marrow, and lymphoid tissue. The diagnosis of CLL, based on National Cancer Institute–sponsored (NCIsponsored) Working Group guidelines, requires a lymphocyte count of at least 5000/mm^3 and a characteristic B-cell–surface phenotype, which can be detected with high-sensitivity flow cytometry showing the presence of *CD19, CD5,* and *CD23*; weak expression of *CD20* and *CD79b*; and either kappa or lambda immunoglobulin light chains (Rawstron *et al.*, 2008). An increase in the clonal blood lymphocytes and an absolute lymphocyte count less than 5000/mm^3 and no lymphadenopathy is classified as monoclonal Blymphocytosis (MBL), a precursor of CLL. The clinical course of CLL is variable. Some patients may have an indolent course and will not require treatment for many years, whereas others may have aggressive disease and required therapy within a short period after a diagnosis. Genomic aberrations and mutations in CLL are diverse and are being increasingly used to understand prognosis and guide treatment (as with *TP53* biomarker loss). Cytogenetic abnormalities, which have been used to stratify patients with CLL into 5 prognostic groups from the longest survival times to the shortest, are as follows: del(13q), normal karyo-

type, tris(12), del(11q), and del(17p) (Mertens & Stilgenbauer, 2014). Additional novel molecular-based prognostic markers include the mutational status of immunoglobulin heavy variable (*IgVH*) gene (favorable when mutated), interphase FISH abnormalities, expression of the surface marker CD38 (expression correlating with unfavorable), the intracytoplasmic protein ZAP-70 (unfavorable when high) (Furman, 2010), and expression of the CD49d surface marker (unfavorable when high) (Bulian *et al.*, 2014). The most common genetic mutations detected in CLL were *NOTCH1, SF3B1,* and *MYD88*; these may be incorporated into the biomarkers in the future and help define when treatment should be initiated (Mertens & Stilgenbauer, 2014).

12.8.6. Myeloproliferative Neoplasms (MPN)

MPNs are a group of disorders characterized by increased clonal proliferation of one or more components of the myeloid series (e.g., erythroid, granulocytic, megakaryocytic, or mast cell) in the bone marrow (with spilling out into the peripheral blood), and in many cases the liver and spleen (Levine & Tiu, 2013). Their classification has been undergoing an evolution, but most frequently they are separated into the *BCR-ABL1* positive (which is CML) and the *BCRABL1* negative disorders. Here the discussion will focus on the classic *BCR-ABL1* negative diseases and their acquired somatic mutations. Polycythemia (rubra) vera (PV) has already been discussed and will be briefly mentioned here. PV is associated with the *JAK2 V617F* mutation (either heterozygous or homozygous) or, less frequently, the *JAK2 exon* 12 mutation, in almost all patients. The disorder for approximately 30% of patients with PV will progress to myelofibrosis, and for 5% it will transform into AML (Hoffbrand *et al.*, 2011).

Essential thrombocytosis (ET), also called essential thrombocythemia, results from the proliferation of megakaryocytes, which leads to overproduction of platelets and abnormally large platelets, with main clinical features of thrombosis and hemorrhage. A sustained platelet count of > 450 × 10^9/L needs further evaluation to exclude secondary causes of thrombocytosis (e.g., iron deficiency, inflammatory or malignant disorder) versus ET, which affects an estimated

1 to 24 persons per 1 million people worldwide. Approximately 50% of cases of ET will have a mutated *JAK2 V617F* and 4% will have mutation in *MPL* gene; other mutations occur in the *THPO* and *TET2* genes. Mutations in the *JAK2, MPL,* and *THPO* genes lead to abnormal activation of the *JAK/STAT* signaling pathway; the function of the *TET2* gene is less clear. Rarely, ET can be inherited as an autosomal dominant and is then called familial essential thrombocythemia; 1 copy of the gene is sufficient to cause the disorder. The majority of time, ET is a somatically acquired disorder (National Library of Medicine, 2014f). ET patients have the best prognosis for long-term survival. The disorder for 10% to 20% of patients with ET will progress to myelofibrosis. Treatment is usually needed in those with high-risk factors (older, prior thrombosis, JAK2 mutation).

Primary myelofibrosis is associated with the *JAK2 V617F* mutation in about 50% of cases, around 15% with the *TET-2* mutation, and a few with the *MPL W151L/K* mutation and is associated with the worst prognosis. Half the patients have other nonspecific cytogenetic abnormalities. About one-third of patients have a previous history of PV or ET (Hoffbrand *et al.*, 2011). Patients typically present with anemia due to fibrosis in the marrow and massive splenomegaly. Recent studies of ruxolitinib, a *JAK1/JAK2* inhibitor, in patients with myelofibrosis and massive splenomegaly, as well as without clinically significant splenomegaly, have shown significant clinical benefit and survival advantage, which led to the approval of this drug for clinical use (Benjamini, Jain, Estrov, Kantarjian, & Verstovsek, 2012; Verstovsek *et al.*, 2012).

Systemic mastocytosis (SM) is an abnormal clonal neoplastic proliferation of mast cells (which are tissue basophils) in the bone marrow, skin, and other organs. It is associated with the somatic *KIT D816V* mutation, which is detected in the majority of patients with this condition. The release of histamine and prostaglandins is responsible for the clinical symptoms (e.g., flushing, pruritus, and urticaria pigmentosa). Serum tryptase is increased and is used to monitor treatment. The majority of patients have an indolent course, although some may have an aggressive course and their disorder may progress to AML (Hoffbrand *et al.*, 2011).

12.8.7. Neoplasms of Plasma Cells

Plasma cells are mature B-lymphocytes that are terminally differentiated and function to secrete immunoglobulins, which are critical to humoral immunity. Plasma cells can be detected in small numbers in the bone marrow and are also found in the spleen and lymph nodes (Minges Wols, 2006). Multiple myeloma is a malignant neoplasm of plasma cells that abnormally accumulate in the bone marrow and, in the majority of cases, are marked by an abnormal elevation of an immunoglobulin, associated with anemia, bone destruction, increased seepage of calcium into the blood stream, and kidney failure. Approximately 24,050 new myeloma cases are estimated to be diagnosed in 2014 in the U. S. (Siegel, Ma, Zou, & Jemal, 2014). Myeloma most often affects individuals ages 60 years or older, and the majority of these will be over age 75 years, although younger individuals can be affected as well. Symptomatic myeloma is preceded by monoclonal gammopathy (MGUS), frequently by many years, before it becomes overt, and may be indolent (smoldering or asymptomatic). When it presents with end-organ damage, it is classified as Stage I, II, or III and treatment is begun. The treatment of myeloma has evolved rapidly with the introduction of new and more effective drugs (such as the imids and the proteasome inhibitors) and has resulted in an increased 5-year survival rate, but with eventual relapse of the disease. Specific chromosomal abnormalities have been identified in myeloma patients, and cytogenetic markers have been used for risk stratification. In addition to bone marrow metaphase cytogenetics, FISH is obtained for *del(13), del(17p13), t(4:14), t(11:14), t(14:16),* and *1q21* amplification. The majority of these abnormalities are correlated with poor prognosis except for *t(11:14),* which has been associated with improved survival. Genomic tools, such as gene expression profiling (GEP), have the potential to provide additional prognostic information in the near future to direct patient management based on risk (National Comprehensive Cancer Network, 2014d).

12.8.8. Lymphomas

Lymphomas are a group of several related cancers of the lymphoid tissue that may have originated in the B-cell (most common) or the T-cell. Lymphomas are very heterogenous disorders and may have an indolent, intermediate, or aggressive course; they are classified into Hodgkin lynmphoma (HL) or non-Hodgkin lymphoma (NHL). Some of the more frequent genetic abnormalities found in NHL will be mentioned here. Follicular lymphoma is an indolent NHL that is associated with the *t(14;18)* and BCL2 oncogenes. Mantle cell lymphoma is a B-cell NHL that is characterized by *t(11:14)* and *Cyclin D1* (also called *cyclin B1*) oncogenes. Burkitt lymphoma is an extremely aggressive B-cell (hyphenate) NHL in which *t(8;14)* [or alternatively *t(2;8)* or *t(8;22)*] with translocation of *C-myc* oncogene is used to confirm the diagnosis in the appropriate clinical setting. The *C-myc* oncogene is characteristic, but not specific, and can be found in other aggressive NHLs including some diffuse large B-cell lymphomas (DLBCL) (Swerdlow *et al.*, 2008).

12.9. REFERENCES

Aiuti, A., Biasco, L., Scaramuzza, S., Ferrua, F., Cicalese, M. P., Baricordi, C., . . . & Naldini, L. (2013). Lentiviral hematopoietic stem cell gene therapy in patients with Wiskott-Aldrich syndrome. *Science, 341*(6148), 1233151. doi: 10.1126/science.1233151

Alter, B. P. (2007). Diagnosis, genetics, and management of inherited bone marrow failure syndromes. *Hematology Am Soc Hematol Educ Program, 29–* 39. doi: 10.1182/asheducation-2007.1.29

Angelucci, E. (2010). Hematopoietic stem cell transplantation in thalassemia. *Hematology Am Soc Hematol Educ Program, 2010*, 456–462. doi: 10.1182/ asheducation-2010.1.456

Balwani, M., & Desnick, R. J. (2012). The porphyrias: Advances in diagnosis and treatment. *Blood, 120*(23), 4496–4504. doi: 10.1182/ blood-2012-05-423186

Bender, M. A., & Hobbs, W. (2012). Sickle cell disease. In R. A. Pagon, M. P. Adam, T. D. Bird, C. R. Dolan, C. T. Fong, & K. Stephens (Eds.), *GeneReviews.* Seattle (WA).

Benjamini, O., Jain, P., Estrov, Z., Kantarjian, H. M., & Verstovsek, S. (2012). Therapeutic effects of ruxolitinib in patients with myelofibrosis without clinically significant splenomegaly. *Blood, 120*(13), 2768–2769. doi: 10.1182/blood-2012-07-446849

Beutler, E., Hoffbrand, A. V., & Cook, J. D. (2003). Iron deficiency and overload. *ASH Education Program Book, 2003*(1), 40-61.

Biagioli, M., Pinto, M., Cesselli, D., Zaninello, M., Lazarevic, D., Roncaglia, P., . . . & Gustincich,

S. (2009). Unexpected expression of alpha- and beta-globin in mesencephalic dopaminergic neurons and glial cells. *Proceedings of the National Academy of the Sciences of the United States of America, 106*(36), 15454–15459. doi: 10.1073/ pnas.0813216106

Bleeker, J. S., & Hogan, W. J. (2011). Thrombocytosis: Diagnostic evaluation, thrombotic risk stratification, and risk-based management strategies. *Thrombosis, 2011*, 536062. doi: 10.1155/2011/536062

Bulian, P., Shanafelt, T. D., Fegan, C., Zucchetto, A., Cro, L., Nuckel, H., . . . & Gattei, V. (2014). CD49d is the strongest flow cytometry-based predictor of overall survival in chronic lymphocytic leukemia. *Journal of Clinical Oncology, 32*(9), 897–904. doi: 10.1200/JCO.2013.50.8515

Cao, A., Galanello, R., & Origa, R. (2013). Beta-thalassemia. In R. A. Pagon, M. P. Adam, T. D. Bird, C. R. Dolan, C. T. Fong, R. J. H. Smith, & K. Stephens (Eds.), *GeneReviews.* Seattle (WA).

Cherfane, C. E., Hollenbeck, R. D., Go, J., & Brown, K. E. (2013). Hereditary hemochromatosis: Missed diagnosis or misdiagnosis? *The American Journal of Medicine, 126*(11), 1010–1015. doi: 10.1016/j. amjmed.2013.07.013

Conley, C. L. (1980). Sickle-cell anemia: The first molecular disease. *Blood: Pure and eloquent.* New York: McGraw-Hill. pp. 319–371.

Cuker, A., & Crowther, M. A. (2013). *2013 Clinical Practice Guideline on the Evaluation and Management of Adults with Suspected Heparin-Induced Thrombocytopenia (HIT).* Washington DC: American Society of Hematology. Retrieved from www. hematology.org/practiceguidelines

Dale, D. C., Bolyard, A. A., Kelley, M. L., Westrup, E. C., Makaryan, V., Aprikyan, A., . . . & Hsu, F. J. (2011). The CXCR4 antagonist plerixafor is a potential therapy for myelokathexis, WHIM syndrome. *Blood, 118*(18), 4963–4966. doi: 10.1182/ blood-2011-06-360586

Dohner, H., Estey, E. H., Amadori, S., Appelbaum, F. R., Buchner, T., Burnett, A. K., . . . & Bloomfield, C. D. (2010). Diagnosis and management of acute myeloid leukemia in adults: Recommendations from an international expert panel, on behalf of the European LeukemiaNet. *Blood, 115*(3), 453–474. doi: 10.1182/blood-2009-07-235358

Dokal, I., & Vulliamy, T. (2010). Inherited bone marrow failure syndromes. *Haematologica, 95*(8), 1236–1240. doi: 10.3324/haematol.2010.025619

Eby, C. S., Frater, J. L., & Rand, J. H. (2013). Laboratory hematology. In K. McCrae & D. Steensma (Eds.), *American Society of Hematology Self-Assessment Program* (5th ed.). Retrieved from http:// www.ash-sap.org/content/current

FDA News Release, December 4, 2014. FDA approves a new use for Jakafi (ruxolitinib) to treat patients with polycythemia vera.

Filipovich, A. H., Johnson, J., & Zhang, K. (2014).

WAS-Related Disorders. In R. A. Pagon, M. P. Adam, T. D. Bird, C. R. Dolan, C. T. Fong, R. J. H. Smith, & K. Stephens (Eds.), *GeneReviews®*. Seattle (WA).

Fleming, R. E., & Ponka, P. (2012). Iron overload in human disease. *New England Journal of Medicine, 366*(4), 348–359. doi: 10.1056/NEJMra1004967

Furman, R. R. (2010). Prognostic markers and stratification of chronic lymphocytic leukemia. *Hematology Am Soc Hematol Educ Program, 2010*, 77–81. doi: 10.1182/asheducation-2010.1.77

Gallagher, P. G. (2005). Red cell membrane disorders. *Hematology Am Soc Hematol Educ Program,* 13–18. doi: 10.1182/asheducation-2005.1.13

Ginsburg, D. (2005). Genetic risk factors for arterial thrombosis and inflammation. *Hematology Am Soc Hematol Educ Program*, 442–444. doi: 10.1182/asheducation-2005.1.442

Giralt, S. A., & Radich, J. P. (2013). Clinical bone marrow and stem cell transplantation. In K. McCrae & D. Steensma (Eds.), American Society of Hematology Self-Assessment Program (5th ed.). Retrieved from http://www.ash-sap.org/content/current

Gordeuk, V. R., Stockton, D. W., & Prchal, J. T. (2005). Congenital polycythemias/erythrocytoses. *Haematologica, 90*(1), 109–116.

Groves, A., & Kuschel, C. (2014). Neonatal Alloimmune Thrombocytopenia (NAIT). Retrieved 26 March 2014, from http://www.adhb.govt.nz/newborn/guidelines/Blood/Platelets/NAIT.htm

Harrison, T. R., & Longo, D. L. (2013). Acute lymphocytic leukemia. *Harrison's manual of medicine* (18th ed., pp. p.). New York: McGraw-Hill Medical.

Hartwell, L. (2008). *Genetics: From genes to genomes* (3rd ed.). Boston: McGraw-Hill Higher Education.

Hoffbrand, & Moss, P. A. H. (2011). Coagulation disorders. Essential Hematology (6th ed.).

Hoffbrand, Moss, P. A. H., & Pettit, J. E. (2011). *Essential haematology* (6th ed.). Malden, Mass.: Wiley-Blackwell.

Hoffman, R. (2005). *Hematology: Basic principles and practice*. 4th ed.

Howes, R. E., Battle, K. E., Satyagraha, A. W., Baird, J. K., & Hay, S. I. (2013). G6PD deficiency: Global distribution, genetic variants and primaquine therapy. *Advances in Parasitology, 81*, 133–201. doi: 10.1016/B978-0-12-407826-0.00004-7

Huang, L. J., Shen, Y. M., & Bulut, G. B. (2010). Advances in understanding the pathogenesis of primary familial and congenital polycythaemia. *British Journal of Haematology, 148*(6), 844–852. doi: 10.1111/j.1365-2141.2009.08069.x

Jordan, M. B., Allen, C. E., Weitzman, S., Filipovich, A. H., & McClain, K. L. (2011). How I treat hemophagocytic lymphohistiocytosis. *Blood, 118*(15), 4041–4052. doi: 10.1182/blood-2011-03-278127

Konkle, B. A., Josephson, N. C., Nakaya Fletcher, S. M., & Thompson, A. R. (2011). Hemophilia B. In R. A. Pagon, M. P. Adam, T. D. Bird, C. R. Dolan, C. T. Fong, R. J. H. Smith & K. Stephens (Eds.), *GeneReviews®*. Seattle (WA).

Kujovich, J. L. (2010). Factor V Leiden Thrombophilia. In R. A. Pagon, M. P. Adam, T. D. Bird, C. R. Dolan, C. T. Fong, R. J. H. Smith & K. Stephens (Eds.), *GeneReviews®*. Seattle (WA).

Kujovich, J. L. (2011). Prothrombin-Related Thrombophilia. In R. A. Pagon, M. P. Adam, T. D. Bird, C. R. Dolan, C. T. Fong, R. J. H. Smith & K. Stephens (Eds.), *GeneReviews®*. Seattle (WA).

Leitman, S. F. (2013). Hemochromatosis: the new blood donor. A*SH Education Program Book, 2013*(1), 645–650.

Lekstrom-Himes, J. A., & Gallin, J. I. (2000). Immunodeficiency diseases caused by defects in phagocytes. *N Engl J Med, 343*(23), 1703–1714. doi: 10.1056/NEJM200012073432307

Levine, R. L., & Tiu, R. V. (2013). Myeloproliferative neoplasms. In K. McCrae & D. Steensma (Eds.), *American Society of Hematology Self-Assessment Program* (5th ed.). Retrieved from http://www.ash-sap.org/content/current.

Liebman, H. A., & Pullarkat, V. (2011). Diagnosis and management of immune thrombocytopenia in the era of thrombopoietin mimetics. *Hematology Am Soc Hematol Educ Program, 2011*, 384–390. doi: 10.1182/asheducation-2011.1.384

Lippman, S. M., Lizak, G. E., Foung, S. K., & Grumet, F. C. (1988). The efficacy of PlA1-negative platelet transfusion therapy in posttransfusion purpura. *West J Med, 148*(1), 86–88.

Lotta, L. A. (2010). Genome-wide association studies in atherothrombosis. *Eur J Intern Med, 21*(2), 74–78. doi: 10.1016/j.ejim.2009.11.003

Mahendra, A., Padiolleau-Lefevre, S., Kaveri, S. V., & Lacroix-Desmazes, S. (2012). Do proteolytic antibodies complete the panoply of the autoimmune response in acquired haemophilia A? *Br J Haematol, 156*(1), 3–12. doi: 10.1111/j.1365-2141.2011.08890.x

McCrae, K. R., & Rao, A. K. (2013). Disorders of platelet number and function. In K. McCrae & D. Steensma (Eds.), *American Society of Hematology Self-Assessment Program* (5th ed.). Retrieved from http://www.ash-sap.org/content/current.

McDermott, D. H., Liu, Q., Ulrick, J., Kwatemaa, N., Anaya-O'Brien, S., Penzak, S. R., . . . Murphy, P. M. (2011). The CXCR4 antagonist plerixafor corrects panleukopenia in patients with WHIM syndrome. *Blood, 118*(18), 4957–4962. doi: 10.1182/blood-2011-07-368084

Mertens, D., & Stilgenbauer, S. (2014). Prognostic and predictive factors in patients with chronic lymphocytic leukemia: relevant in the era of novel treatment approaches? *J Clin Oncol, 32*(9), 869–872. doi: 10.1200/JCO.2013.53.8421

Minges Wols, H. A. (2006). *Plasma cells.* eLS.

Miranda, R. N., Khoury, J. D., & Medeiros, L. J. (2013). *Langerhans Cell Histiocytosis Atlas of lymph node pathology* (pp. 445–447). New York: Springer.

Mohandas, N., & Gallagher, P. G. (2008). Red cell membrane: past, present, and future. *Blood, 112*(10), 3939–3948. doi: 10.1182/blood-2008-07-161166

Nair, S., Ghosh, K., Kulkarni, B., Shetty, S., & Mohanty, D. (2002). Glanzmann's thrombasthenia: updated. *Platelets, 13*(7), 387–393. doi: 10.1080/0953710021000024394

National Comprehensive Cancer Network. (2014a). Acute Lymphoblastic Leukemia (Version 3.2013). Retrieved 27 March 2014, from http://www.nccn.org/professionals/physician_gls/PDF/aml.pdf

National Comprehensive Cancer Network. (2014b). Acute Myeloid Leukemia (Version 1.2014). Retrieved 27 March 2014, from http://www.nccn.org/professionals/physician_gls/PDF/aml.pdf

National Comprehensive Cancer Network. (2014c). Chronic Myelogenous Leukemia (Version 3.2014). Retrieved 27 March 2014, from http://www.nccn.org/professionals/physician_gls/PDF/aml.pdf

National Comprehensive Cancer Network. (2014d). Multiple Myeloma (Version 2.2014). Retrieved 27 March 2014, from http://www.nccn.org/professionals/physician_gls/PDF/aml.pdf

National Library of Medicine (U.S.). (2014a). Genetics Home Reference [Internet]. Bethesda (MD): The Library; 2014 Jun 30. Hereditary spherocytosis; [reviewed 2013 Sep; cited 2014 March 26]; [about 7 screens]. Available from: http://ghr.nlm.nih.gov/condition/hereditary-spherocytosis

National Library of Medicine (U.S.). (2014b). Genetics Home Reference [Internet]. Bethesda (MD): The Library; 2014 Jun 30. Von Willebrand disease; [reviewed 2012 Dec; cited 2014 March 26]; [about 7 screens]. Available from: http://ghr.nlm.nih.gov/condition/von-willebrand-disease

National Library of Medicine (U.S.). (2014c). Genetics Home Reference [Internet]. Bethesda (MD): The Library; 2014 Jun 30. F8; [reviewed 2010 May; cited 2014 March 26]; [about 8 screens]. Available from: http://ghr.nlm.nih.gov/gene/F8

National Library of Medicine (U.S.). (2014d). Genetics Home Reference [Internet]. Bethesda (MD): The Library; 2014 Jun 30. Hemophilia; [reviewed 2012 August; cited 2014 March 26]; [about 7 screens]. Available from: http://ghr.nlm.nih.gov/condition/hemophilia

National Library of Medicine (U.S.). (2014e). Genetics Home Reference [Internet]. Bethesda (MD): The Library; 2014 Jun 30.). Hereditary antithrombin deficiency; [reviewed 2013 Feb; cited 2014 March 26]; [about 7 screens]. Available from: http://ghr.nlm.nih.gov/condition/hereditary-antithrombin-deficiency

National Library of Medicine (U.S.). (2014f). Genetics Home Reference [Internet]. Bethesda (MD): The Library; 2014 Jun 30. Essential-thrombocythemia; [reviewed 2011 Dec; cited 2014 March 26]; [about 7 screens]. Available from: http://ghr.nlm.nih.gov/condition/essential-thrombocythemia

National Organization for Rare Disorders (NORD). (2013, 8 May 2013). Polycythemia Vera. Retrieved 5 January 2014, 2014, from http://rarediseases.org/rare-disease-information/rare-diseases/byID/236/viewFullReport

Nester, C. M., & Thomas, C. P. (2012). Atypical hemolytic uremic syndrome: what is it, how is it diagnosed, and how is it treated? *Hematology Am Soc Hematol Educ Program, 2012,* 617–625. doi: 10.1182/asheducation-2012.1.617

Newburger, P. E. (2006). Disorders of neutrophil number and function. *Hematology Am Soc Hematol Educ Program,* 104–110. doi: 10.1182/asheducation-2006.1.104

Nobel Media. (1962). *The Nobel Prize in Chemistry 1962.* Retrieved 8 Dec 2013, 2013, from http://www.nobelprize.org/nobel_prizes/chemistry/laureates/1962/index.html

Origa, R., Moi, P., Galanello, R., & Cao, A. (2013). Alpha-Thalassemia. In R. A. Pagon, M. P. Adam, T. D. Bird, C. R. Dolan, C. T. Fong, R. J. H. Smith & K. Stephens (Eds.), *GeneReviews.* Seattle (WA).

Passamonti, F. (2012). How I treat polycythemia vera. *Blood, 120*(2), 275–284. doi: 10.1182/blood-2012-02-366054

Pastores, G. M., & Hughes, D. A. (2013). Gaucher Disease. In R. A. Pagon, M. P. Adam, T. D. Bird, C. R. Dolan, C. T. Fong, R. J. H. Smith & K. Stephens (Eds.), *GeneReviews®.* Seattle (WA).

Patterson, M. (2013). Niemann-Pick Disease Type C. In R. A. Pagon, M. P. Adam, T. D. Bird, C. R. Dolan, C. T. Fong, R. J. H. Smith & K. Stephens (Eds.), *GeneReviews®.* Seattle (WA).

Perdomo, J., Yan, F., Ahmadi, Z., Jiang, X. M., Stocker, R., & Chong, B. H. (2011). Quinineinduced thrombocytopenia: drug-dependent GPIb/IX antibodies inhibit megakaryocyte and proplatelet production *in vitro. Blood, 117*(22), 5975–5986. doi: 10.1182/blood-2010-10-314310

Rawstron, A. C., Bennett, F. L., O'Connor, S. J., Kwok, M., Fenton, J. A., Plummer, M., . . . Hillmen, P. (2008). Monoclonal B-cell lymphocytosis and chronic lymphocytic leukemia. *N Engl J Med, 359*(6), 575–583. doi: 10.1056/NEJMoa075290

Renella, R., & Wood, W. G. (2009). The congenital dyserythropoietic anemias. *Hematol Oncol Clin North Am, 23*(2), 283–306. doi: 10.1016/j.hoc.2009.01.010

Schechter, A. N. (2008). Hemoglobin research and the origins of molecular medicine. *Blood, 112*(10), 3927–3938. doi: 10.1182/blood-2008-04-078188

Schlenk, R. F., & Dohner, H. (2013). Genomic applications in the clinic: use in treatment paradigm of acute myeloid leukemia. *Hematology Am Soc He-*

matol Educ Program, 2013, 324–330. doi: 10.1182/asheducation-2013.1.324

Shiel, W. C. (2014). *Antiphospholipid Syndrome*. Retrieved 26 March 2014, from http://www.medicinenet.com/antiphospholipid_syndrome/article.htm

Shulman, N. R., Aster, R. H., Leitner, A., & Hiller, M. C. (1961). Immunoreactions Involving Platelets. V. Post-Transfusion Purpura Due to a Complement-Fixing Antibody against a Genetically Controlled Platelet Antigen. A Proposed Mechanism for Thrombocytopenia and Its Relevance in "Autoimmunity". *J Clin Invest, 40*(9), 1597–1620. doi: 10.1172/JCI104383

Siegel, R., Ma, J., Zou, Z., & Jemal, A. (2014). Cancer statistics, 2014. *CA: a cancer journal for clinicians, 64*(1), 9–29.

Sommeijer, D. W., & Reitsma, P. H. (2003). Genetic risk factors fo rDisseminated Intravascular Coagulation. In H. ten Cate & M. Levi (Eds.), *Molecular Mechanisms of Disseminated Intravascular Coagulation*: Landes Bioscience.

Swerdlow, S. H., Campo, E., Harris, N. L., Jaffe, E. S., Pileri, S. A., Stein, H., . . . Vardiman, J. W. (2008). *WHO Classification of Tumours of Haematopoietic and Lymphoid Tissues* (4th Ed.): World Health Organization.

Teawtrakul, N., Ungprasert, P., Pussadhamma, B., Prayalaw, P., Fucharoen, S., Jetsrisuparb, A., . . . Chuncharunee, S. (2014). Effect of genotype on pulmonary hypertension risk in patients with thalassemia. *Eur J Haematol*. doi: 10.1111/ejh.12261

Territo, M. (2013). Overview of White Blood Cell Disorders. *Home Health Handbook*. Retrieved 26 March 2014, from http://www.merckmanuals.com/home/blood_disorders/white_blood_cell_disorders/overview_of_white_blood_cell_disorders.html

The Cancer Genome Atlas Research Network. (2013). Genomic and epigenomic landscapes of adult de novo acute myeloid leukemia. *N Engl J Med, 368*(22), 2059–2074. doi: 10.1056/NEJMoa1301689

Tymoczko, J. L., Berg, J. M., & Stryer, L. (2013). *Biochemistry, a short course* (Second edition. ed.).

Uy, G. L., & Dokal, I. (2013). Myeloid disorders and congenital marrow failure syndromes. In K. McCrae & D. Steensma (Eds.), American Society of Hematology Self-Assessment Program (5th ed.). Retrieved from http://www.ash-sap.org/content/current.

van der Harst, P., Zhang, W., Mateo Leach, I., Rendon, A., Verweij, N., Sehmi, J., . . . Chambers, J. C. (2012). Seventy-five genetic loci influencing the human red blood cell. *Nature, 492*(7429), 369–375. doi: 10.1038/nature11677

Vardiman, J. W., Thiele, J., Arber, D. A., Brunning, R. D., Borowitz, M. J., Porwit, A., . . . Bloomfield, C. D. (2009). The 2008 revision of the World Health Organization (WHO) classification of myeloid neoplasms and acute leukemia: rationale and important changes. *Blood, 114*(5), 937–951. doi: 10.1182/blood-2009-03-209262

Verstovsek, S., Kantarjian, H. M., Estrov, Z., Cortes, J. E., Thomas, D. A., Kadia, T., . . . Passamonti, F. (2012). Long-term outcomes of 107 patients with myelofibrosis receiving JAK1/JAK2 inhibitor ruxolitinib: survival advantage in comparison to matched historical controls. *Blood, 120*(6), 1202–1209. doi: 10.1182/blood-2012-02-414631

Vichinsky, E. P. (2009). Alpha thalassemia major--new mutations, intrauterine management, and outcomes. *Hematology Am Soc Hematol Educ Program*, 35–41. doi: 10.1182/asheducation-2009.1.35

Weatherall, D. (1980). The story of Thalassemia. *Wintrobe MM: Blood pure and Eloquent.* Mc Graw-hill, New York, 373.

Weider, E. (2003). *Dendritic Cells: A Basic Review:* MD Anderson Cancer Center.

Wilber, A., Nienhuis, A. W., & Persons, D. A. (2011). Transcriptional regulation of fetal to adult hemoglobin switching: new therapeutic opportunities. *Blood, 117*(15), 3945–3953. doi: 10.1182/blood-2010-11-316893

Yazdanbakhsh, K., Lomas-Francis, C., & Reid, M. E. (2000). Blood groups and diseases associated with inherited abnormalities of the red blood cell membrane. *Transfus Med Rev, 14*(4), 364-374. doi: 10.1053/tmrv.2000.16232

Zambidis, E. T., Peault, B., Park, T. S., Bunz, F., & Civin, C. I. (2005). Hematopoietic differentiation of human embryonic stem cells progresses through sequential hematoendothelial, primitive, and definitive stages resembling human yolk sac development. *Blood, 106*(3), 860–870. doi: 10.1182/blood-2004-11-4522

Zanella, A., Bianchi, P., & Fermo, E. (2007). Pyruvate kinase deficiency. *Haematologica, 92*(6), 721–723.

Zhang, K., Filipovich, A. H., Johnson, J., Marsh, R. A., & Villanueva, J. (2013). Hemophagocytic Lymphohistiocytosis, Familial. In R. A. Pagon, M. P. Adam, T. D. Bird, C. R. Dolan, C. T. Fong, R. J. H. Smith & K. Stephens (Eds.), *GeneReviews®*. Seattle (WA).

Chapter 13

Genetics and Genomics of Neurologic Disorders

SHEILA A. ALEXANDER, Ph.D, RN

Objectives:

- Differentiate selected single gene disorders that affect the nervous system, including their prevalence, pathophysiology, genetic etiologies, symptoms, diagnosis, treatment, and management of care.
- Discuss appropriate food sources that can be used for patients who are diagnosed with phenylketonuria.
- Describe the impact of genomics on common complex disorders that affect the nervous system.
- Utilize selected resources to obtain information on neurological genetic and genomic conditions.

13.1. INTRODUCTION TO THE NERVOUS SYSTEM

The nervous system is a complex system with significant input into the functioning of the human body. Specialized cells communicate with one another and other cells of the body using electrical impulses and neurotransmitters. This communication drives sensory perception, thought, memory, muscle movement, reflexes, and homeostasis of the body. The transcription and translation of genes drives the biologic functioning of all body systems including the nervous system. Individual genetic variability impacts the function of the nervous system leading to common traits and specific disorders. Disorders of the nervous system can affect either the central nervous system (CNS) or the peripheral nervous system (PNS). Genetic disorders more frequently affect the CNS. This chapter focuses on select, single gene neurologic disorders, including phenylketonuria, Friedrich's ataxia, neurofibromatosis, Huntington disease, Fragile X, and congenital deafness. It also focuses on common complex

disorders, such as multiple sclerosis, Parkinson's disease, and amyotrophic lateral sclerosis. In addition to the specific genetic variants and mutations driving these disorders and diseases, information on frequency, incidence, pathophysiology, symptoms, diagnosis, and treatments has been provided.

13.2. SINGLE GENE DISORDERS OF THE NERVOUS SYSTEM

13.2.1. Phenylketonuria

April, a 30-year-old Caucasian female, and her husband Joe, a 35-year-old Caucasian male, have two sons named Charlie and Tommy. Charlie is 3-years-old and has no health problems. Tommy is 6 days old, born the previous Tuesday. Tommy's birth was uneventful, and both he and April were discharged from the hospital four days ago on Thursday. On Friday, a nurse from the hospital called April to schedule an appointment for today, Monday, to follow up on Tommy's newborn screening. The nurse informed April that Tommy

---

Sheila A. Alexander, PhD, RN, Assistant Professor, Acute & Tertiary Care, School of Nursing, Critical Care Medicine, School of Medicine, University of Pittsburgh, 336 Victoria Building, 3500 Victoria Street, Pittsburgh, PA 15261, E-mail: salexand@pitt.edu

had a positive screen for phenylketonuria (PKU), and the test needed to be repeated. April requested more information, but the nurse told her she was not able to provide more information until they had the second set of test results. After this telephone call, April went to the internet to seek out more information about PKU. She learned that children with this disorder do not metabolize protein properly. They must avoid protein to prevent severe mental retardation. She was concerned about the protein in her breast milk and attempted to call the nurse at the hospital, but the office was closed. She spent the weekend reading up on this disease process and worrying that her breast milk was poisoning her newborn son. Tommy's second phenylketonuria test was taken on Monday, and on Tuesday April received the news that he had phenylketonuria. April, Joe, and Tommy had their first visit to the phenylketonuria clinic on Wednesday, eight days after Tommy's birth. At this visit, April was educated about phenylketonuria. She learned the genetic cause of the disorder, the pathology involved, the diet, and amino acid supplement that Tommy would need for the rest of his life. She was relieved to learn that her breast milk had not likely caused any damage since the negative effects of protein intake are caused by long-term exposure to phenylalanine and not the brief eight-day period he had been receiving protein in breast milk. Tommy, April, and Joe attended frequent visits to the clinic for the next two years to monitor his phenylalanine blood levels, growth, and development. During this time, April and Joe continued to learn more about the diet Tommy must follow and received a large book listing phenylalanine levels for all the foods he may eat. As Tommy began to eat foods, they learned to manage his diet, and Tommy developed normally.

Phenylketonuria (PKU) is an autosomal recessive disorder. The phenylalanine hydroxylase gene (*PAH*) provides instructions for making an enzyme called phenylalanine hydroxylase (PAH), the first step in processing the amino acid phenylalanine (PHE) (United States [U.S.] National Library of Medicine, 2013). There are over 500 mutations in the *PAH* gene (U.S. National Library of Medicine, 2013). Mutations in other genes involved in phenylalanine breakdown can also cause PKU, but these are extremely rare and little is known about them (National Insti-

tute of Child Health and Human Development [NICHD], 2006). Mutations in the *PAH* gene result in either low levels or nonfunctioning PAH enzyme. Without adequate enzyme, PHE is not broken down, accumulates in the CNS, and leads to severe profound mental retardation and other symptoms.

PKU incidence varies significantly by race, ethnicity, and population. In the U.S., the frequency of the disorder is 1:15,000. However, the frequency of U.S. Caucasians is 1:10,000 (Bickel *et al.*, 1981) compared with lower reported rates of 1:50,000 among U.S. blacks (Hofman, Steel, Kazazian, & Valle, 1991). The incidence of PKU in other countries varies. For example, the incidence of the disorder is 1:2,600 in Turkey, 1:200,000 in Finland, and 1:125,000 in Japan (Bickel *et al.*, 1981; Williams, Mamotte, & Burnette, 2008).

PHE is an essential amino acid (see Figure 13.1), meaning it has to be ingested. Many foods contain proteins that are metabolized into essential amino acids: meats, poultry, fish, soy, beans, nuts, seeds, dairy, and to a lesser extent, some fruits and vegetables. PHE is also found in many sugar free products since aspartame is broken down into PHE in the body. PHE is absorbed into the bloodstream from the intestine. The PHE in the blood passes through the liver, where PAH is made. PAH transfers one oxygen atom to the carbon ring on the PHE, and a hydrogen atom binds to that oxygen to make tyrosine (see Figure 13.2). Any PHE that has not been converted to tyrosine exits the liver and travels throughout the body for use by individual cells in protein production. Excess PHE is normally cleared through the transaminase pathway, generating phenylketones.

In people with PKU, the PAH enzyme is not made at all, rapidly broken down, faulty, and un-

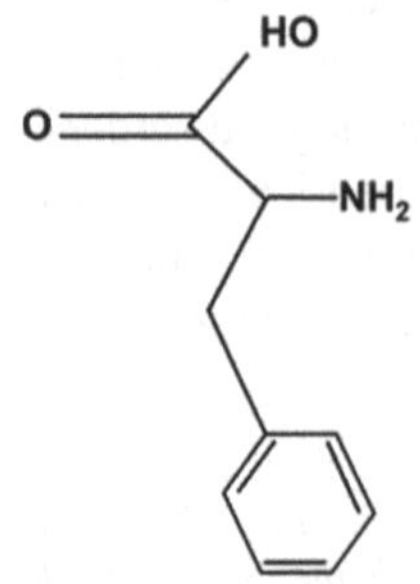

FIGURE 13.1. Phenylalanine chemical structure.

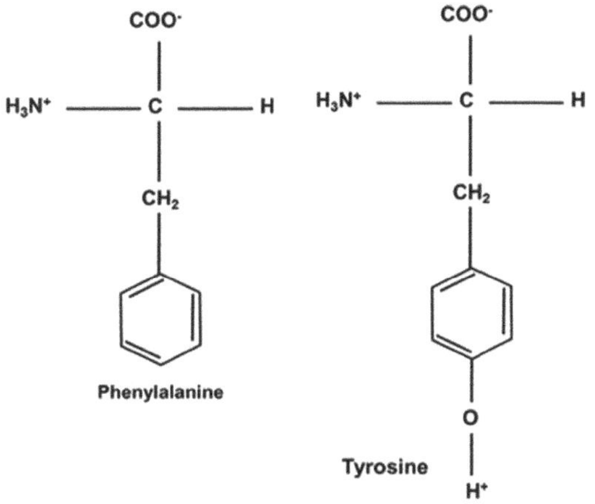

FIGURE 13.2. Phenylalanine and tyrosine; phenylalanine in the blood passes through the liver, where phenylalanine hydroxylase (PAH) is made. PAH transfers one oxygen atom to the carbon ring on the PHE, and a hydrogen atom binds to that oxygen to make tyrosine.

able to recognize the PHE, or works very slowly in converting PHE to tyrosine (Williams *et al.*, 2008). Because PHE is not broken down, it builds up in the blood and higher levels circulate through the body. In the brain, excess PHE builds up and alters function. It is not entirely clear how elevated PHE leads to mental retardation. One hypothesis is that in a high PHE extracellular environment, neurons within the brain do not develop normally, are smaller than normal, and make fewer connections with other neurons. It is hypothesized that these changes lead to the PKU phenotype (Williams *et al.*, 2008). A second hypothesis is that the phenotype is related to low dopamine in the brain, a state found in many people with untreated PKU (Williams *et al.*, 2008). Normally, tyrosine is metabolized into dopamine, a neurotransmitter in the brain that is responsible for reward based behavior, addiction, social behavior, and pain processing. When PHE isn't broken down into tyrosine, the tyrosine deficiency leads to a dopamine deficiency that has been implicated in the PKU phenotype (Williams *et al.*, 2008). Although the mechanism isn't clear, people with PKU have less white matter (myelination) in central brain regions (Williams *et al.*, 2008).

Individuals with PKU are often fair-haired, light-eyed, and light-skinned because melanin, the enzyme responsible for pigment, is a derivative of tyrosine. The typical PKU phenotype in individuals who receive absolutely no treatment is one of normal development for the first 3 to 6 months after birth. As the child grows, developmental milestones are not met and progress to the severe and profound mental retardation that was common before newborn screening and low-PHE diets were introduced. Children with untreated PKU have intellectual disability, delayed mental functioning, delayed speech, delayed social skill development, smaller head sizes, extrapyramidal symptoms, and have a distinct musty odor (Cederbaum, 2002). The odor is caused by the excess PHE in the skin cells. Hyperactivity and attention deficit hyperactivity disorder are common in children with PKU, but are much more severe in those without good PHE control. Without treatment seizures, light sensitivity, eczema, pyogenic infections, keratosis pilaris, and hair loss are common symptoms.

PKU was first described by Dr. Asbjörn Fölling in 1934 with the enzymatic deficiency first identified in 1937 (BioMarin Pharmaceutical Incorporated, 2009). The first trial of newborn screening in the U.S. was initiated in 196;1 however, it was not until 1967 that this practice was implemented across the nation. In most developed countries, newborns are screened for PKU shortly after birth. In the U.S., PKU screening quantifies the PHE protein in the blood with Guthrie Bacterial Inhibition Assay, fluorometric analysis, or tandem mass spectrometry (U.S. Preventive Service Task Force, 2009). Screening is performed at birth with a follow up test at 7 to 10 days of age. For infants who were not screened in that time period, a blood test using the methods outlined above or urine test screening for phenylketones can be performed. PKU is universally included in newborn screening in the U.S. (U.S. Preventative Task Force, 2009) and Canada (Canadian Organization for Rare Disorders, 2012). Additional information on newborn screening can be found in Chapter 6. Routine screening has resulted in early identification of nearly all infants with PKU and has permitted early treatment.

Before 1960, children born with PKU appeared normal at birth and then had a progressive decline in function until they were profoundly retarded, usually before the teen years. In the 1950s, the PKU diet was developed with the first formula for infants being introduced in

1958. It was not until the mid-1960s that children were systematically identified and referred to specialized PKU clinics for management and care. This led to standardized dietary restrictions and routine monitoring for the majority of infants and children with PKU. Maintaining PHE levels within a normal range, generally < 10 milligrams (mg)/milliliter (mL), but often < 6 mg/mL, promotes normal development. This is achieved through strict dietary modification with frequent monitoring of blood PHE levels. The diet lacks protein, so amino acid supplementation is necessary.

The PKU diet significantly restricts PHE intake by avoiding nearly all foods with protein. It is of particular importance that PHE levels be managed in sexually active women of child bearing age if not using effective birth control. During pregnancy, maternal PHE crosses the placental barrier into the intrauterine environment .and high levels of PHE have a teratogenic effect on the developing fetus. Irrespective of the genotype of the fetus, poor maternal PHE control contributes to microcephaly, mental retardation, slow growth and heart defects or disease (MacDonald, Evans, Cochrane, & Wildgoose, 2012; National Institute of Child Health and Human Development, 2006). Advanced practice nurses (APNs) working with women of this age-group need to provide education reinforcing the importance of PHE management and the potential risks to the unborn fetus. Additionally, the mother may be referred to an educational program specifically for women of child-bearing age with PKU (MacDonald et al., 2012; National Institute of Child Health and Human Development, 2006).

For the infant, breast milk may be provided; however, quantity must be monitored and supplementation with special formulas containing amino acids and other nutrients is required. There are formulas available to replace breast milk in part or entirely. The APN caring for the infant and family must consider the most recent PHE level in determining whether it is possible for the mother to provide breast milk to the infant with PKU. It may be required for the mother to express breast milk and feed the infant via bottle to control PHE quantity ingested by the infant (MacDonald et al., 2012). The APN should be familiar with replacement formulas and the specific dose required for the individual infant. It is also important to consider maternal child bonding that often takes place during breast feeding and the overall psychological impact of bottle feeding (MacDonald et al., 2012). Breast feeding and breast milk have many benefits for the infant. Mothers of infants with PKU may experience psychological distress by not being able to provide breast milk to or breast-feed their infant.

For children and adults with PKU, there are multiple resources available to assist in dietary management including books and web sites that list foods and their PHE content. Table 13.1 shows categorization of PHE in high, moderate, low, and free common foods. All infants with PKU should be referred to a PKU clinic that has physicians, nurses, and dieticians with specialized knowledge and skills in managing PKU. Management by this team will continue throughout childhood and often throughout adulthood. There are a number of commercially generated foods that have little to no PHE and web sites of companies marketing these are provided at the end of this chapter. It is also important for children and adults with PKU to supplement the low PHE diet with amino acids and other nutrients that are primarily available in high protein foods (National Institute of Child Health and Development, 2006). The formula designed originally for infants serves as an excellent supplement for children and adults as well. The nutritional supplementation is also available as a pill and nutrition bar.

Current recommendations are that the diet and supplements should be continued throughout the life span. With proper management, children with PKU develop normally, perform normally in school, go to college, and have long, productive lives. Most adults who maintain the diet and dietary supplements have a normal, functioning life and have a normal life span. There are significant challenges in maintaining this diet. It is very restrictive, and adult signs and symptoms are not immediately felt. Many individuals will stop the diet and develop cognitive and behavioral issues as previously noted. Frequent reinforcement of the importance of maintaining the dietary restrictions and supplements for optimal function, despite the lack of immediate symptoms, is an important health education need provided to the adult PKU population by advanced practice nurses.

TABLE 13.1. **Examples of Phenylalanine (PHE) Content in Common Foods.**

Foods with High PHE Content	Foods with Moderate PHE Content	Foods with Low PHE Content	PHE Free Foods
Meats, Poultry, Fish	Potatoes, peas, broccoli,	Most vegetables:	Sugar
Eggs, Dairy	Select fruits:	asparagus, carrots,	Snow cones,
Legumes: soy (including soy sauce),	avocado, bananas	eggplant, lettuce,	sweetened/sugary
tofu.		mushrooms, pumpkin,	drinks and sodas
Nuts and seeds (including peanut		radishes, sweet peppers,	
butter)		tomatoes, zucchini	
Select vegetables:		Fruits/fruit juices: apples,	
Spinach, cabbage, chard, corn,		grapes, plums, pears	
chard, turnip greens, avocado		Low protein breads and	
Flour, grains, yeast. Includes breads		pastas	
and pastas			
Aspartame			
Included in many sugar-free			
products such as gum, soda, etc.			

NIH Consensus Statement, 2006; Schutte, 2010; MacLeod & Ney, 2010.

In the late 1990s, pharmaceutical research and development yielded an additional treatment for PKU. Sapropterin dihydrochloride, a form of tetrahydrobipterin, is used to increase oxidation of phenylalanine, which results in its breakdown into tyrosine (Burton *et al.*, 2007). The drug, marketed as Kuvan™, was the first pill to aid PKU patients in PHE breakdown and was approved by the U.S. Federal Drug Administration in 2007. Sapropterin dihydrochloride administration lowers PHE levels and allows patients with PKU to eat more protein. Although this drug has improved quality of life in many patients, it is only effective in about 50% of the population with specific genetic mutations (Burton *et al.*, 2007). Research is ongoing to develop a similar product for all PKU patients.

13.2.2. Friedreich's Ataxia

Nancy and Walter have a twelve year old daughter, Betsy. Betsy has always been clumsy, but has been tripping a lot for 6 months and has fallen three times in the past 2 weeks. Nancy has brought Betsy to her pediatrician to determine if there is something causing these falls. During her physical examination, the nurse practitioner notes some weakness in her legs and, to a lesser extent, her hand grip-strength. Reflexes in Betsy's ankles and knees are minimal, and there is a decrease in sensation below the knee in both lower extremities. A mild scoliosis is also noted. This examination is suspicious for Friedreich's

ataxia and Betsy is referred to a neurologist who has a geneticist on staff. After the initial visit and several diagnostic tests including magnetic resonance imaging (MRI), lumbar puncture, electromyogram, electrocardiogram, and an echocardiogram, she is diagnosed with Friedreich's ataxia,

Friedreich's ataxia (FRDA) is a neurodegenerative disease of the spinal cord and peripheral nerves with an autosomal recessive inheritance pattern. FRDA is caused by an expansion of trinucleotide repeats in the frataxin (*FXN*) gene, whose gene product is the frataxin protein. Most often symptoms of FRDA first present before age 15 years, although adult onset cases have been identified. Ataxia is the most common presenting symptom with loss of sensation, coordination, and reflexes; dysarthria; and cardiac dysfunction developing as the disease progresses (National Institute of Neurological Disorders and Stroke [NINDS], 2011; Schulz *et al.*, 2009).

Worldwide, FRDA prevalence in Caucasians is 2-4:100,000, and in the U.S., it is about 1:50,000 people (NINDS, 2011; Schulz *et al.*, 2009). Although it is the most common inherited ataxia in Europe, India, the Middle East, North Africa, and North America, it is far less common in Mexico and has not been documented in Southeast Asia and sub-Saharan Africa and in Native Americans (Schulz *et al.*, 2009).

Although the FXN gene is in nuclear DNA, frataxin resides in the mitochondria of cells and promotes iron binding to sulphur within the mitochondria. Without the iron-sulphur complex oxidative phosphorylation is impaired and cellular energy failure ensues (Adinolfi, *et al.*, 2002). In addition to energy failure as a result of inadequate frataxin availability, FRDA is also hallmarked by iron accumulation within affected cells (Adinolfi *et al.*, 2002; Seznec *et al.*, 2005). It is hypothesized that frataxin also detoxifies iron in the mitochondria, but that has not yet been proven (Seznec *et al.*, 2005). The *FXN* gene normally has 7 to 22 guanine-adenine-adenine (GAA) repeats (Campuzano *et al.*, 1996; Durr *et al.*, 1996). Individuals with 55 to 200 GAA repeats have a premutation allele (Durr *et al.*, 1996; Montermini *et al.*, 1997). It is thought that these individuals, while not presenting with FRDA can pass on the disease to their children through expansion of the GAA repeats in germ cell lines (Montermini *et al.*, 1997; NINDS, 2011). Individuals with 200 to 1700 GAA repeats have FRDA, although the vast majority have 600 to 1200 repeats (NINDS, 2011). These repeats are in intron 1 and result in reduced frataxin production (Campuzano *et al.*, 1996). The more repeats there are, the earlier the age at onset, and the more rapid the disease progression (Durr *et al.*, 1996; Schulz *et al.*, 2009).

It is important to note that in a very small number of people with FRDA there is a point mutation rather than an expanded number of repeats (Durr *et al.*, 1996; Schulz *et al.*, 2009). These mutations lead to silencing of the gene, with no frataxin being produced. Individuals with FRDA, who have a point mutation on one allele, often have a trinucleotide repeat within the disease causing range on the other allele (Schulz *et al.*, 2009).

The end result of FRDA induced energy failure is neuronal damage and progressive degeneration. Neurons of the dorsal root ganglia, spinocerebellar tracts, lateral corticospinal tracts, and the posterior columns degenerate. Destruction of the dorsal root ganglia significantly contributes to the destruction of other tracts, in particular, the spinocerebellar tracts and posterior columns, which do not receive the normal amount of stimulation. Gait instability is usually the presenting symptom, progressing to ataxia of arm and ultimately trunk movement. Limb movement in general is not coordinated, and writing and activities of daily living are difficult for patients with FRDA (Pandolfo, 2009). Reflexes are decreased and then lost. Proprioception, vibration sense, and other sensation is lost. Tremors frequently develop as the disease progresses (Pandolfo, 2009). Generalized progressive muscle weakness occurs in the legs and progresses to the arms and the neck in advanced stages. Problems with speech formation and dysarthria, swallowing, hearing loss up to deafness, nystagmus, and visual impairment are common as the disease progresses (Pandolfo, 2009).

FRDA is also associated with dysfunction of other systems. Scoliosis develops in the vast majority of patients because there is not muscle strength to maintain posture (Pandolfo, 2009). Hypertrophic cardiomyopathy develops in over half and diabetes mellitus develops in about 10% of these patients, with a young age of onset. Most patients require a wheelchair and assistance with activities of daily living 10 years after diagnosis. The average life expectancy is significantly reduced; the median age of death is 35 years. Females with FRDA have a longer life expectancy than males, although the rationale for this finding is not clear (Pandolfo, 2009).

FRDA is diagnosed primarily through clinical examination (Schulz *et al.*, 2009). Signs and symptoms, as noted above, in combination with radiographic imaging (e.g., MRI, computed tomography (CT) scan, electromyogram, and/or nerve conduction studies) showing atrophy of the cervical spinal cord and minimal evidence of cerebellar atrophy provide accurate diagnosis (NINDS, 2011; Schulz *et al.*, 2009). Genetic testing is available and utilized in reproductive counseling for couples with one affected child (NINDS, 2011), but not helpful in clinical management.

While there is no cure for FRDA, there are several treatments to support function and limit disability (NINDS, 2011; Powers, 2007). Physical and occupational therapists may provide services to maintain function for as long as possible (Powers, 2007). Ambulation aids facilitate walking and in severe states, surgical insertion of rods may slow the progression of the scoliosis and the need for a wheelchair. Cardiac problems should be monitored and treated accordingly, although there are no recommendations specific to this population (NINDS, 2011). Recent research in cellular models has shown that vitamin B3 inhibits oxidative stress, suggesting that histone deacytylase inhibitors may reduce symptoms of FRDA (Chan *et al.*, 2013).

13.2.3. Fragile X Syndrome

Linda is now 23-years-old and graduating from nursing school with her baccalaureate degree. She is especially proud to have reached this milestone, because she has struggled academically since she was a child. At 8-years-old, she was failing math and evaluated for a learning disability. She went through a series of tests and ultimately was diagnosed with Fragile X syndrome. Although she is a carrier and grateful not to have a more severe phenotype, she has been challenged by her symptoms. During visits to see the specialists managing her symptoms, she has seen many others who are not so fortunate and have more severe disability, autism, and mental retardation.

Fragile X syndrome is a disorder with an X-linked dominant inheritance pattern with variable expression and reduced penetrance caused by multiple CGG repeats in the Fragile X mental retardation gene (*FMR1*) (Garber, Visootsak, & Warren, 2008). It is the most common cause of inherited intellectual disability, and the most common single gene cause of autism in males. The intellectual impairment ranges from moderate learning disabilities to severe mental retardation and memory problems, as well as a characteristic physical appearance.

Some form of *FMR1* mutation is found in 1:200 males and 1:259 females (Peprah, 2012). The incidence of the Fragile X disorder (phenotype) is 1:3600 males and 1:4000–6000 females (Turner, Webb, Wake, & Robinson, 1996). Although these statistics represent the U.S. population, they are similar to the incidence found in the United Kingdom and Australia. Differences in research methodology have made it difficult to compare incidence across populations. The estimated prevalence of Fragile X syndrome varies from 1:2,466 to 1:24,446 (Peprah, 2012). Estimates suggest the worldwide incidence of premutation carriers is 1:800 males and 1:259 females (Seltzer *et al.*, 2012).

The vast majority of cases of Fragile X syndrome are due to multiple CGG repeats in the 5′ untranslated region of the *FMR1* gene (Santoro, Bray, & Warren, 2012). In normal individuals, there are 5 to 44 CGG repeats within this region of the *FMR1* gene. In individuals with Fragile X syndrome, the CGG repeat occurs over 200 times, and some of these individuals have over 1,000 CGG repeats (Peprah, 2012; Santoro *et al.*, 2012). Individuals with 45 to 54 CGG repeats are considered to be at increased risk of passing on Fragile X syndrome to offspring. Individuals with 55 to 200 CGG repeats are considered to have a premutation (Peprah, 2012; Santoro *et al.* 2012). The increased number of CGG repeats results in methylation of this region and, therefore, silences the *FMR1* gene (Santoro *et al.*, 2012). A very small number of Fragile X cases are due to a point mutation within the *FMR1* gene (Santoro *et al.*, 2012). The FMR protein (FMRP) produced by *FMR1* transcription and translation is important in normal brain development. The specific mechanisms through which FMRP promotes neuronal development are not fully understood. Current evidence suggests the FMRP facilitates messenger ribonucleic acid (mRNA) transport from the nucleus to the cytoplasm, mRNA localization in the neuronal dendrites, and synaptic protein synthesis (McLennan, Polussa, Tassone, & Hagerman, 2011). FMRP appears to be involved in synaptic plasticity, or the local protein synthesis response to synaptic stimulus. FMRP is an RNA-binding protein that inhibits ribosomal translation of a large group of mRNAs particularly at the synaptic region (McLennan et al, 2011). These changes have been noted in animal models of Fragile X, result in altered synaptic connections, and are hypothesized to result in the Fragile X phenotype (Bassell & Warren, 2008; McLennan *et al.*, 2011).

There are differences in inheritance of the *FMR1* mutation based on parental characteristics. Typically, females with full *FMR1* mutation (> 200 repeats) pass this on to their children 50% of the time. In female premutation carriers (55 to 200 repeats), CGG repeat expansion occurs during meiosis and offspring inherit the full mutation. Premutation expansion does not occur during male meiosis (sperm formation), so the female offspring of male premutation carriers inherit the premutation intact (Peprah, 2012; Santoro *et al.*, 2012).

Mental impairment is hallmarked by low intelligence quotient; deficits in working memory, short-term memory, visual memory, executive function, and math and visual-spatial relationship impairment (Garber *et al.*, 2008). The physical characteristics of Fragile X syndrome do not present in all affected individuals, but frequently include a long face, large forehead, large ears, prominent jaw, large body size, flat feet, a high palate, hyper-flexible joints, hyper-extendable finger joints and thumbs, a single palm crease, low muscle tone, strabismus, soft skin, and large testicles (Garber *et al.*, 2008). Behavioral disorders are common in people with Fragile X syndrome and include attention deficit disorder (ADD), attention deficit hyperactivity disorder (ADHD), autism spectrum, delayed speech development, sensory disorders, and aggression. Language delays and deficits typically appear in those individuals with other autistic behaviors (Garber *et al.*, 2008). These behavioral disorders do not all present in all males with Fragile X syndrome. People with Fragile X syndrome are also at increased risk for seizures (Garber *et al.*, 2008).

In up to 50% of males over age 50 years with Fragile X syndrome premutations (55 to 200 CGG repeats), Fragile X-associated tremor ataxia syndrome (FXTAS) develops. FXTAS signs and symptoms include urinary incontinence, impotence, cerebellar ataxia, intention tremor, peripheral neuropathy, autonomic nervous system dysfunction, brain atrophy, memory loss progressing to dementia, depression, irritability, and anxiety (Garber *et al.*, 2008). Each individual presents a range of these mental, behavioral, and physical symptoms.

Females with the *FMR1* mutation typically have a less severe phenotype due to random inactivation of the X chromosomes. (Peprah, 2012; Santoro *et al.*, 2012). Females frequently have mild to moderate learning disabilities, anxiety disorders, and emotional and mental health issues. Females may have physical characteristics similar to males with Fragile X syndrome, including a long thin face, large ears hyper-flexible joints, and flat feet. Females additionally have difficulties with infertility and premature menopause due to Fragile X-related primary ovarian insufficiency (FXPOI) (Peprah, 2012; Santoro *et al.*, 2012). Twenty percent of females inheriting premutations will also have FXPOI (Peprah, 2012; Santoro *et al.*, 2012). Signs and symptoms of FXPOI include irregular menses, premature ovarian failure, infertility, elevated follicular stimulating hormone, and other symptoms of ovarian insufficiency. A small percentage (5% to

8%) of females with the premutation will develop FXTAS (Peprah, 2012; Santoro et al, 2012). Although some females inheriting the *FMR1* mutation have these symptoms, about one-third carrying the full mutation will have no signs or symptoms (Peprah, 2012; Santoro *et al.*, 2012).

Although *FMR1* screening is not part of the newborn screening panel in most states in the U.S., many states are considering adding this to the panel because of research showing its efficacy and reliability (Tasson *et al.*, 2012). Prenatal diagnosis is based on CGG expansion detection via polymerase chain reaction, and Southern blot analyses (Garber *et al.*, 2008). It is important to note that this method does not detect point mutations in the *FMR1* gene.

Diagnosis most often occurs in preschool-aged children with developmental delays or elementary school-age children experiencing learning difficulties. CGG repeat analysis, methylation status or complete sequencing of the *FMR1* gene can be used to detect genetic mutations and confirm suspected diagnosis based on clinical examination. Molecular genetic testing is recommended for individuals with the following: (1) intellectual disability, developmental delay or autism especially if accompanied by physical or behavioral characteristics of Fragile X syndrome, a family history of Fragile X syndrome or relatives with undiagnosed intellectual disability (mental retardation); (2) confirmed cytogenetic diagnosis that does not match phenotype; or (3) suspicion of Fragile X–associated disorder (FXTAS or FXPOI) (Garber *et al.*, 2008).

There is no cure or treatment for Fragile X syndrome. Treatment plans are focused on limiting behavioral disturbances and psychological effects. Traditional pharmaceutical and behavioral treatments for autistic spectrum behaviors, ADD, ADHD, depression, aggression, injurious behaviors, seizure prevention, and sleep disorders should be instituted (Eunice Kennedy Shriver National Institute of Child Health [NICHD], 2013). When ADHD is treated with stimulants in this population, additional treatment for increased anxiety and/or depressive symptoms may need to be added. Speech therapy, behavioral therapy, and sensory integration occupational therapy are helpful in maximizing function. Educational curriculum modifications can be implemented to maximize learning. Proponents of this plan may include maintaining a consistent schedule with preparation for variations, visual signs to present materials, functional and educational goals, computers, interactive software, focus on the child's individual learning style, access to a quiet place for retreat and regrouping, and inclusion of time for movement and/or physical activity (NICHD, 2013).

13.2.4. Neurofibromatosis

Marcus is a 9-year old who was recently diagnosed with ADHD. He has had small, light brown spots on his chest since birth and his mother, Patsy, has noticed he has freckling across his chest and armpits since he was a small child. Marcus has always been a small child, but his height and weight have remained in the lower end of the normal range. When his pediatrician provided a diagnosis of ADHD, because of the café-au-lait spots on his chest and freckling of the armpits, he referred the family to a genetic clinic for some testing to rule out neurofibromatosis as a precautionary measure. The genetic testing came back positive, and Patsy has been searching the internet for more information on this disease. The results have made her fearful, because she learns the disease results in tumor formation that can cause hearing problems, balance problems, and other more significant problems. She doesn't remember if the geneticist told her what type of neurofibromatosis Marcus had when she called with the results, so she is preparing a long list of questions to be addressed when she next visits the pediatrician.

Neurofibromatosis is a disease hallmarked by excessive tumor formation originating from nervous tissue. There are three forms: Type 1, Type 2, and schwannomatosis. Each are associated with a different gene. Neurofibromatosis Type 1 (NF1) is the most common form and makes up 90% of neurofibromatosis (Ferner, 2007; NINDS, 2012; Rasmussen & Friedman, 2000). It is inherited in an autosomal dominant pattern and has complete penetrance. Variable expression can confound research and clinical translation of findings. NF1 is caused by a mutation of the *NF1* gene. Neurofibromatosis Type 2 (NF2) is inherited in an autosomal dominant pattern with complete penetrance (Asthagiri *et al.*, 2009; Evans, 2009; Ferner, 2007; NINDS, 2012). The causative mu-

tation is in the *NF2* gene. Schwannomatosis is a very rare type of neurofibromatosis with reduced penetrance and hallmarked by encapsulated, benign tumors of myelinating Schwann cell origin (schwannomas), but without other symptoms of neurofibromatosis (Koontz *et al.*, 2013; NINDS, 2012).

NF1 affects 1:3000 to 1:4000 people worldwide, including people of all races and ethnicities. In the U.S., the frequency is 1:3000 (Friedman, 1999; Rasmussen & Friedman, 2000). NF2 is rarer than NF1, occurring in about 1:60,000 worldwide, although other work has suggested it is far more common, with an incidence of 1:25,000 (Evans, 2009). NF2 affects people of different racial, ethnic, and geographic regions equally. The incidence of schwannomatosis is 1:40,000 (Melean, Sestini, Ammannati, & Papi, 2004). The rarity of this condition, as well as the variability in symptom presentation, has slowed down research to fully define incidence and identify responsible mutations.

The neurofibromin 1 gene is a tumor suppressor gene that produces neurofibromin. Neurofibromin inhibits the p21 ras oncoprotein and without this inhibition, cell proliferation is uncontrolled, promoting tumor formation primarily in the peripheral nervous system (Brooks, 2004; Ferner, 2007; Schnur, 2012). NF2 is caused by a gene with the protein product called merlin, or schwannomin. Merlin functions as a tumor suppressor gene and inhibits cellular division (Brooks, 2004; Evans, 2009; Ferner, 2007). The *NF1* gene is large and contains regions similar to sequences within other genes that promote non-allelic homologous recombination. These two factors increase the likelihood of mutations. NF1 and NF2 are autosomal dominant, with spontaneous de novo mutations accounting for about 50% of all cases (Evans, 2009; Rasmussen & Friedman, 2000). Mosaic forms of NF1 and NF2 do occur and generally have a milder phenotype. There are a large number of possible mutations within these genes, any one of which can contribute to NF1 and NF2 phenotype (Ferner, 2007; Rasmussen & Friedman, 2000; Sestini *et al.*, 2008). It is of interest that NF2 patients with a frameshift mutation have been found to have better prognosis than those with missense or nonsense mutations (Ferner, 2007).

Regardless of the *NF1* mutation, the end result

is either complete absence of neurofibromin or faulty neurofibromin. A specific domain of the gene contains guanesine-triphosphate-activating protein (GAP) that results in neurofibromin function to regulate activation of the Ras cellular activation pathway. The Ras pathway controls cell growth, division, and survival. Neurofibromin specifically modulates the conversion of Ras-guanosine triphosphate to Ras-guanosine diphosphate, which is implicated in tumor formation. Mutations within the NF1 gene result in a lack of or improperly functioning neurofibromin, so this conversion does not occur (Rasmussen & Friedman, 2000). The conversion of Ras-guanosine triphosphate to Ras-guanosine diphosphate inactivates the Ras and the resultant growth signaling; as such, it is vital for proper control of cell growth and division. Without the conversion, Ras-guanosine triphosphate is the active form and thus promotes cellular growth and division. Specifically, cells begin rapid proliferation and hyperplasia occurs. Additional downstream effects of Ras activation and recruitment of additional cells to the developing tumor site are being explored for their contribution to neurofibroma formation and NF1 (Trovó-Marqui & Tajara, 2006). Schwann cells, endoneurofibroblasts, and melanocytes, are particularly affected cell types, which leads to the phenotype of nerve sheath tumors of the peripheral nervous system, Lisch nodules, café-au-lait spots, freckling, and small tumor development in the basal layer of the epidermis.

Mutation of the NF2 gene leads to deficient merlin protein resulting in lack of cell contact-mediated growth inhibition and uninhibited cell cycling (LaJeunesse, McCartney, & Fehon, 1998; McClatchey & Giovanni, 2005). The increase in number of cells and uncontrolled cell growth present as vestibular schwannomas, also known as acoustic neuromas, and other nervous tissue tumors. Merlin protein is highly expressed in nervous tissue; hence, these tissues are at increased risk to form tumors when there is a defect in the protein (McClatchey & Giovanni, 2005).

The specific mutations causing schwannomatosis are not clear. Inherited forms of schwannomatosis only account for 15% of the disease with the vast majority being caused by spontaneous de novo mutations (Koontz et al., 2013; Plot-kin et al., 2013). Duplications in the SMARCB1 gene have been identified as the causative genetic agent in some families (van den Munckhof, Christiaans, Kenter, Baas, & Hulsebos, 2012). The gene product is believed to act as a tumor suppressor (van den Munckhof et al., 2012). Mutation within the SMARCB1 gene has been associated with other tumor types, supporting its role as a tumor suppressor gene (van den Munckhof et al., 2012). Additional work in other families suggests mutation near, but not within, the NF2 gene associated with this disease (Plotkin et al., 2013; Sestini et al., 2008). Research is ongoing to identify the gene specific to this region and to define additional genetic variance that contributes to schwannomatosis. Although other specific genes have not been identified, it appears that this condition requires multiple genetic mutations to develop (Sestini et al., 2008; van den Munckhof et al., 2012). The schwannomas that develop frequently recur if removed. Multiple schwannomas within a region or throughout the body frequently develop. These factors suggest a polygenic nature, and further descriptive work is required to elucidate the pathways promoting such a condition (van den Munckhof et al., 2012).

Symptoms of NF1 include café-au-lait spots present at birth that grow as the child ages, freckling in nontraditional areas such as the armpits and groin and Lisch nodules (hamartomas creating a dome-shaped mound over the iris). In adolescence through adulthood, tumors develop under the skin and peripheral nerve sheath. Although these tumors are usually benign, malignancies develop more frequently in people with NF1 compared with the general population. Brain tumors, optic gliomas, and leukemias are common. Hypertension, short stature, macrocephaly, headaches, epilepsy, scoliosis, other skeletal abnormalities, learning disabilities, and ADHD are common in people with NF1 (Costa & Silva, 2002; Brooks, 2004; Ferner, 2007; Haslam, 2007; NINDS, 2012; Schnur, 2012).

Tumors associated with NF2 are generally benign; include schwannomas, meningiomas, and ependymomas; and most frequently develop bilaterally in the region of cranial nerve VIII, the vestibulocochlear nerve, resulting in hearing loss and balance disturbance. As with NF1, tumors also develop in other nervous tissue, including other cranial nerves, meninges (meningiomas), spinal cord (astrocytomas and ependymomas), and neurofibromas. Adolescent cataracts are a frequent symptom in NF2. NF2 symptoms present in the late teens or early 20s and most often include gradual hearing loss, tinnitus, loss of balance, headaches, facial numbness, and/or weakness. Abnormal corneal reflexes and nystagmus are common manifestations. Symptoms of NF2 in people who develop tumors of the spinal, visual, or peripheral nerves include pain, numbness of arms or legs, weakness of arms or legs, and difficulties with balance. Tumors develop along nerves traveling close to the skin and cause lesions or bumps on the skin or may present as dark rough areas less than one inch with hair. Symptoms are the result of tumor compression of nearby tissue and loss of function of the affected nerve(s). Not all patients develop all symptoms, and tumor location is extremely influential on symptom development (Asthagiri *et al.*, 2009; Brooks, 2004; Ferner, 2007; NINDS, 2012).

Schwannomatosis presents with benign tumors developing on cranial nerves, spinal nerves, peripheral nerves, and in many areas of the body at ages 20 to 40 years. About 30% of patients have tumors limited to one region, such as an arm, a leg, or one section of the spine. Symptoms are related to tumor location and caused by compression of nearby tissue. Chronic pain is by far the most frequent presenting symptom. There is variability in the severity of the pain in different individuals with schwannomatosis. For some, the pain is so mild that treatment is never sought and a diagnosis is not made, whereas for others, the pain is so severe it is debilitating. Most people with schwannomatosis have severe chronic pain that falls in between these two extremes and requires chronic treatment. Numbness, tingling, and weakness of the toes and fingers are common symptoms in schwannomatosis. The eighth cranial nerve is not frequently affected by schwannoma, and hearing is usually spared. Vestibular schwannomas occur but are typically unilateral in schwannomatosis (Koontz *et al.*, 2013; Plotkin *et al.*, 2013; van den Munckhof *et al.*, 2012).

There are differences and similarities in the presentation of NF2 as compared to NF1. While skin bumps appear in NF2, the café-au-lait spots

so prevalent in NF1 do not (Brooks, 2004; Ferner, 2007). Cataracts develop at an earlier age in patients with NF2 compared to the general population (Asthagiri *et al.*, 2009). People with NF2 are also at higher risk of developing other types of nervous system tumors, including ependymomas, gliomas, and meningiomas (Asthagiri *et al.*, 2009; Brooks, 2004; Evans, 2009; Ferner, 2007; NINDS, 2012).

The symptom profile of schwannomatosis is different from other forms of neurofibromatosis. Neurofibromas do not develop as they do in NF1. The acoustic nerve is not involved as it is in NF2, and bilateral vestibular schwannomas are not seen in schwannomatosis (Koontz *et al.*, 2013; Plotkin *et al.*, 2013).

Prenatal testing is available for NF1 and NF2, but not schwannomatosis (NINDS, 2012; Upadhyaya *et al.*, 1992). For postnatal NF1 diagnosis, the U.S. National Institutes of Health has generated a list of diagnostic criteria, including two or more of the following (Stumpf, Alksne, & Annegers, 1988; NINDS, 2012):

(1) Six or more café-au-lait spots (see Figure 8.1) > 5 mm before puberty or > 15 mm after puberty.

(2) Freckling of the axilla or groin regions.

(3) Two or more neurofibromas (see Figure 8.3) of any type or 1 plexiform neurofibroma.

(4) Optic glioma.

(5) Two or more Lisch nodules (See Figure 8.2).

(6) Distinct osseous lesion (kyphoscoliosis, sphenoid dysplasia, and others).

(7) One first degree relative with NF1 diagnosis based on the above criteria.

(8) Positive genetic testing for mutation of the *NF1* gene when performed because of suspicion of NF1 or family history of NF1.

Postnatal diagnosis of NF2 is typically made by the following (Stumpf, Alksne, & Annegers, 1988; NINDS, 2012):

(1) The presence of bilateral acoustic neuromas.

(2) A first-degree relative with NF2 and a unilateral vestibular schwannoma developing before age 30 years.

(3) A first-degree relative with NF2 diagnosis

and the occurrence of neurofibroma, meningioma, glioma, schwannoma, or juvenile posterior subcapsular cataract.

(4) Presence of two of the following:

(a) Glioma

(b) Meningioma

(c) Schwannoma

(d) Juvenile posterior cataract or juvenile cortical cataract

Diagnosis of schwannomatosis is typically based on the presence of one or two of the following criteria: (1) two or more nonintradermal schwannomas without evidence of vestibular tumor or NF2 or (2) diagnosis of nonvestibular schwannoma with a first-degree relative meeting criteria (1) (MacCollin *et al.*, 2005).

There is no cure for NF1, NF2, or schwannomatosis (NINDS, 2012). Treatment is focused on frequent monitoring with regular physical and radiographic examination, alleviation of symptoms, and prevention of complications. Tumors may exert pressure on nearby tissues, causing symptoms. Surgical removal of tumors relieves the symptoms. Surgical removal is also warranted for tumors that may be malignant. Monitoring for malignancies is vital to early identification and initiation of treatment for maximum outcome. Surgery, chemotherapy, and/or radiation therapy is used for malignant neurofibromas and for optic gliomas affecting or potentially affecting vision. Scoliosis and other bone malformations are surgically repaired to maximize function. Cochlear implants or penetrating auditory brain stem implants restore hearing for many patients with NF2. Recent research has shown some pharmaceuticals may alleviate symptoms of NF2. Bevacizumab, an angiogenesis inhibitor, improved hearing in some patients in two small studies (Mautner *et al.*, 2010; Plotkin *et al.*, 2009). More severe cases of NF1 cause disability, disfigurement, and resultant psychological issues. Overall, people with NF1 have a normal life span (NINDS, 2012).

Because of the rarity of NF2, the prognostic profile is difficult to determine. It has been suggested that individuals with NF2 may have a decreased life span. People with a young age of onset who subsequently develop meningiomas appear to be at risk for early mortality. Subsequent generations appear to have shorter life spans based on the natural progression of the disease. Advances in health care, including frequent monitoring and treatment of cardiac dysfunction, have led to an increased life span for individuals with NF2 although the average life span is still shorter than national U.S. averages (NINDS, 2012). Schwannomatosis does not decrease life span (Kluwe, 2006).

13.2.5. Huntington Disease

Imagine Janie, a 23-year-old Caucasian female. From the age of 10 she watched her mother Eileen, only 42 at the time, develop bizarre involuntary muscular twitching and writhing. Eileen was diagnosed with Huntington disease. Eileen was not aware that Huntington Disease ran in her family because her parents were killed in a car accident at age 45. Eileen's condition worsened over the following years. Her muscles became more rigid, and her facial expression became tight. She began to have difficulties with speech at age 45. She stopped going out with her friends because she was too embarrassed by the uncontrollable movements. She stopped knitting for the same reason, but Janie noticed that she wasn't watching her favorite soap opera either. Eileen constantly felt tired but couldn't sleep, and she wouldn't eat. Eileen became sad and depressed, with a very flat affect. Sometime in her late 40s, she began to fall frequently. When she was 50-years-old, she couldn't walk anymore and couldn't balance well enough to stand for more than a few seconds. She also started to have noticeable difficulties thinking at this point. She would start to make dinner, but couldn't plan it right, and things were never ready at the same time or they would burn. When Janie came home for holiday breaks from college it was difficult to even talk to her mother, because she became distracted so easily. Janie noticed that Eileen wasn't going out at all now, wasn't doing anything she used to enjoy doing, and just watched television all day long. When Eileen turned 54, Janie graduate college and moved home to help her father care for her mother. She watched her mother carefully. Eileen was irritable most of the time but didn't seem to care what was happening around her. Janie made her favorite cookies, but Eileen wouldn't eat them. One evening, she nearly choked eating mashed potatoes. Eileen developed a severe aspiration pneumonia and died at 55-years-old. Janie felt as if she needed to know if she had the gene for Huntington disease, so she was tested at age 25. When she found out she was positive, she decided she just wouldn't have children. She didn't want someone to watch her decline the way she had watched her mother decline. When she met her future husband, she had to have some difficult conversations to explain the situation to him. Knowing what the future held for her, she and her husband put her retirement savings into a bank account that they used to travel the world.

Huntington disease (HD), previously known as Huntington's chorea, is an adult-onset neurodegenerative disease of the brain with an autosomal dominant inheritance pattern (Walker, 2007). Symptoms of HD include severe movement disability due to chorea and rigidity, as well as cognitive and psychiatric symptoms. It is caused by an expansion of trinucleotide repeats in the Huntington gene (*HTT*).

HD incidence is difficult to determine because of the adult onset nature of the disease, meaning an unknown number of mutation carriers will eventually develop the disease. There is a juvenile form that affects people under age 20 years (Walker, 2007). The prevalence of HD worldwide is estimated at 5–10/100,000. In the U.S., it is estimated that 1:10,000 people have HD (Driver-Dunckley & Caviness, 2007; Walker, 2007). HD is more common in people of western European descent but does occur in people of all ethnic backgrounds (Walker, 2007).

HD is caused by a mutation, specifically a pathogenic expansion of a trinucleotide repeat, within the *HTT* gene (Walker, 2007). Within the normal *HTT* gene, there is a series of 10 to 26 trinucleotide repeats. The trinucleotide is always cytosine-adenine-guanine (CAG), which is transcribed and translated into the amino acid glutamine. There are two other variants within the *HTT* gene that appear to have clinical implications. Adjacent to the CAG repeats there are either 7 or 10 CCG repeats. At residue 2642 of the gene, some individuals have a GAG codon. Individuals without the GAG codon at residue 2642, and with 7 CCG repeats adjacent to the CAG repeats, have a higher number of CAG repeats compared with those with the GAG codon

at residue 2642 and with 10 CCG repeats. This suggests that these variants may contribute to the expansion of the CAG repeats contributing to HD (Almqvist *et al.*, 1995; Hećimović *et al.*, 2002; Rubinsztein, Leggo, Goodburn, Barton, & Ferguson-Smith, 1995). The Huntingtin protein (Htt), the *HTT* gene product, normally has a chain of glutamines termed a polyglutamine tract. Htt is a cytoplasmic (intracellular) protein produced by all cells of the body, but at higher rates in the brain and testes (Sharp *et al.*, 1995). The Htt protein impacts many cellular processes including transcription, cell signaling, and intracellular transport (Boutell *et al.*, 1999; Gunawardena *et al.*, 2003; Kegel *et al.*, 2002; Li *et al.*, 2002; Peel, *et al.* 2001; Trushina *et al.*, 2004) through interactions with many other proteins. Htt decreases apoptosis and promotes neuronal development and neuronal survival after injury by stimulating Brain Derived Neurotrophic Factor (BDNF) release (Gauthier *et al.*, 2004; Goldberg *et al.*, 1996; Hermel *et al.*, 2004; Zuccato *et al.*, 2001). The mutant Htt protein is known to be toxic and kills cells, particularly those with higher energy needs. It misfolds and aggregates, drawing in other proteins, within the cytosol and nuclei of neurons, and other cells (Dyer & McMurray, 2001).

The number of CAG repeats is directly correlated with age of onset; more repeats result in earlier onset and a faster progression (Walker, 2007). Additionally, with each generation the number of CAG repeats can expand. There are at least 40 CAG repeats in the fully mutated *HTT* gene (Walker, 2007). When there are 36 to 39 CAG repeats, reduced penetrance is exhibited, with some individuals not developing HD and others developing HD later and with slower progression compared with those having more repeats (Walker, 2007). Individuals with 27 to 35 repeats are not affected but at increased risk for passing on the disease to their offspring through expansion (Walker, 2007).

The cells of the striatum, an area of the brain responsible for coordinated modulation of motor activity, produce high amounts of Htt in normal physiology (Graveland, Williams, & DiFiglia, 1985; Heinsen *et al.*, 1994). The mutant Htt is expressed at high levels in this region, killing off cells early (Graveland *et al.*, 1985) and leading to the first symptoms of HD: jerky, random, and uncontrollable movements prior to chorea, and tics. It is quite likely that restlessness, coordination deficit, and slowed saccadic eye movements are evident before the typical chorea symptoms, but because they are less intrusive, they go unnoticed. As more neurons in the striatum and additive effects from loss of neurons of the basal ganglia are affected, muscle rigidity, writhing, and inability to maintain normal posture develop. Neuronal cell death occurs in other areas of the brain as well, causing atrophy to the substantia nigra, cerebral cortex, hippocampus, and the cerebellum (Heinsen et al., 1994; Paulsen et al., 2006). This generalized cell loss leads to the progression of motor symptoms and the cognitive and psychological symptoms of HD.

Motor symptoms of HD include chorea like movements, muscle rigidity, abnormal posturing, writhing, slow and uncontrolled motor movement, abnormal facial expression, and swallowing and speech problems (Walker, 2007). Cognitive symptoms of HD include loss of executive function, short-term memory deficits progressing to long-term memory deficits, word-finding difficulty, loss of impulse control, poor judgment, and, ultimately, dementia (Walker, 2007). Psychological or neuropsychological symptoms of HD include sleep disturbances, personality changes, irritability or moodiness, apathy, sexual inhibition or inappropriate sexual behavior, anxiety, depression, blunted affect, egocentricity, aggression, hallucinations, paranoia, and compulsive or obsessive-compulsive behaviors (Walker, 2007). A small proportion of people with HD have psychoses. Suicidal ideation and suicide attempts are much more common in people with HD compared with the general population (Di Maio et al., 1993; Crauford & Snowden, 2002). It is important to note that people with HD have expression of mutant Htt in all of their tissues, which can result in additional malfunction outside the CNS. Testicular atrophy, muscle atrophy, osteoporosis, impaired glucose tolerance, weight loss, and cardiac failure are also common disorders for HD patients (Walker, 2007).

Juvenile HD is a less common early-onset form of HD. People with juvenile HD have similar symptom profiles to that of the non-juvenile form of HD. In addition to the above listed symptoms, those with juvenile HD may have loss of academic knowledge and skills, a sudden and significant decrease in academic performance, behavioral problems, and fine motor skill impairment, leading to difficulties in writing, tremors, or seizures. Symptoms and the underlying pathology of HD are progressive (Walker, 2007).

Most people with HD are aware that this gene is carried within their family, because they have seen a parent succumb to the disease. Some choose to undergo genetic testing and require significant genetic and psychological/psychiatric counseling before, during, and after the testing (Burson & Markey, 2001; Erwin et al., 2010). Pretesting counseling should occur in multiple sessions (Smith, Michie, Stephenson, & Quarrell, 2002). People who get tested but are determined to be noncarriers may experience a sense of relief, anxiety, survivor guilt, and a host of other concerns depending upon their specific situation. HD is 100% penetrant, so inheritance of the gene means one will develop the disease and thus, a positive test has grave implications. The Huntington Disease Society of America has extensive resources available for patients, families, and health care providers. Their model for genetic testing counseling stresses the importance of informed decision making and individual preference. Specific guidelines for HD include the following (Hersch, Jones, Koroshetz, & Quaid, 1994):

- Minors should not undergo genetic testing unless there is a compelling medical necessity.
- The decision to undergo or not undergo genetic testing for HD should be well informed and carefully considered. At least 1 month should pass between the pretesting sessions and the final decision to have or not have genetic testing performed.
- The individual should be accompanied by a companion for all visits.
- A precounseling interview should occur via telephone or in person.
- At least three pretesting visits for genetic counseling and a neurologic and psychologic examination should occur before genetic testing occurs.
- A fourth in-person visit should be scheduled for disclosure of results. Results should always be given in person and should be disclosed only to the individual being tested unless he or she has given permission for results to be shared with others.

- Post-test counseling is recommended.
- Couples at risk for HD should ideally receive genetic counseling before conception.

Clinical examination is a common tool to diagnose HD in people expressing symptoms but with no known genetic risk. An individual who was adopted or whose parents died at an early age may not be aware that they are at risk for this disease. Physical assessment in combination with psychological and neuropsychological assessments may identify symptoms of HD. Radiographic tests (CT scan or MRI) may reveal atrophy suggestive of HD. Genetic testing may be employed to confirm the diagnosis.

There is no cure for HD. Treatment is focused on limiting the severity of the symptoms and their intrusiveness on everyday life. There is a lack of evidence-based protocols for the treatment of HD; however, a series of publications address symptom management through algorithms based on expert opinion/survey results. Tetrabenazene, antipsychotics (haloperidol, clozapine, or clonazepam), dopamine blockers, or amantadine alleviate chorea symptoms. For patients with psychosis, depression, or aggressive behaviors, antipsychotics are frequently used as first-line treatment (Burgunder *et al.*, 2011). The guidelines for obsessive-compulsive behavior treatment recommend cognitive-behavioral therapy only for patients with mild cognitive impairment. Selective serotonin reuptake inhibitors (SSRI) are the first-line pharmacologic treatment of choice followed by clomipramine, antipsychotics, or antiepileptic mood stabilizers (Andersen *et al.*, 2011). The third set of guidelines addresses treatment of irritability in HD and identifies SSRIs or antipsychotics as the most commonly used first line of therapy, followed by antiepileptics and mirtazapine (Groves *et al.*, 2011). Early evidence suggests physical therapy, occupational therapy, and speech therapy may be beneficial (Quinn & Busee, 2012; Walker, 2007). These resources can provide assistive devices to improve mobility and retain function as long as possible.

13.2.6. Deafness

Angelina has lived in a world without sound for all of her 16 years. Her parents and friends all live in a world without sound. She goes to a deaf school where all of her classmates have grown up in a world without sound. She communicates using sign language. She has an iPad that she can write on and show hearing people when she goes out. Angelina doesn't have a problem with being deaf, but Dr. Breck, her audiologist, has a problem with it. When she went for her routine visit today, he started talking about cochlear implants again. They've had this conversation since she was 12 or 13 years old, and she isn't interested. He keeps bringing up what he considers to be positive things that will happen. For example, she can go to the movie theater in the city and talk on the phone. She doesn't agree. Who wants to go to the movies by themselves? Who would she even talk to on the phone? Her parents, sister, and brother are all deaf. Most of her friends are deaf. She knows some people who aren't deaf, but they use sign language anyway, so what is the sense in hearing? In her community, most everyone is deaf. She can't be sure that her friends would still be her friends if she got implants, and her boyfriend Jeffrey definitely wouldn't approve. Angelina remembers when a girl named Kelly got implants two years ago. Nobody wanted to be her friend anymore and she moved away. Angelina doesn't want to move or lose her friends. She doesn't want to hear. So why does Dr. Breck keep talking about this procedure?

Deafness is the partial or complete inability to hear. There are many causes of deafness, including environmental, traumatic, illness, increasing age, and genetic factors. Congenital deafness is commonly due to genetic causes but can also be caused by toxin exposure resulting in utero developmental deficits, such as Mondini malformation. Deafness at birth can also be part of a syndrome, such as Waardenburg syndrome, NF2, Usher syndrome, Alport syndrome, and Mitochondrial Encephalomyelopathy, Lactic acidosis, and Stroke-like episodes (MELAS). Hearing loss up to the complete inability to hear also occurs as people age in response to persistent loud noise, illness (e.g., measles, meningitis, and syphilis), neurologic disorders (e.g., multiple sclerosis and strokes), medications (e.g., aminoglycosides, diuretics, and nonsteroidal anti-inflammatory drugs), chemical exposure (e.g., solvents, pesticides, and metals), trauma (e.g., ear and brain trauma), or genetic variance (e.g., hereditary progressive hearing loss). The focus of this section is on genetic factors and congenital deafness. There are multiple inheritance patterns of nonsyndromic congenital deafness, including mitochondrial (< 1%), X-linked (1% to 2%; termed DFN), and autosomal dominant (20% to 25%; termed DFNA). However, autosomal recessive (75% to 80%; termed DFNB) is the most common inheritance pattern (Friedman & Griffith, 2003; Gürtler & Lalwani, 2002; Willems, 2000).

Deafness is typically classified by source of abnormality and results in four categories: conductive, sensorineural, mixed hearing loss with components of conductive and sensorineural loss, and central auditory dysfunction. Congenital deafness is classified as syndromic, indicating it is part of a larger syndrome with other organ/system involvement or nonsyndromic, an isolated finding. Additional classification by temporal presentation, specifically before or after the development of speech, is also used.

Congenital deafness affects people of all ethnic and racial backgrounds, as well as both sexes. It presents in 1–2:1,000 live births worldwide. Specifically in the U.S., 1:1,000 children are born without the ability to hear while 2–3:1,000 children are born with significant hearing impairment (National Center for Biotechnology Information, 2011).

Twenty to thirty percent of congenital hearing impairment is syndromic hearing impairment (Table 13.2). The remaining 70% to 80% is due primarily to genetic sources without other symptoms. Genetic nonsyndromic deafness is caused by a mutation in one of many genes. Over 35 genes have been associated with congenital, nonsyndromic deafness. The rarity of inherited deafness and the vast number of genes and possible mutations have resulted in slow progress in identifying genetic mutations and their mechanisms resulting in deafness. Genetic mutations generally result in stereocilia dysfunction, improper cell-to-cell communication, abnormal inner ear development, excessive apoptosis of inner ear cells, and altered neuronal transmission.

The most common genetic cause of congenital, nonsyndromic deafness is mutation of one of the genes producing connexin (Friedman & Griffith, 2003). Connexins are a component of gap channels, a connection between two neighboring cells that permits passage of ions and small molecules back and forth. These gap channels facilitate intracellular ionic balance and in particular potassium balance. Mutations of the gap protein junction beta 2 (*GJB2*) gene, which encodes connexin 26, produces ineffective gap channels. Elevated intracellular potassium results in apoptosis. Over 90 mutations in the *GJB2* gene associate with congenital, nonsyndromic deafness, including point mutations, deletions, and insertions. The connexin 26 protein produced by the mutated gene is unstable, leading to low amounts of protein, abnormally small or misshapen proteins that don't form functional gap channels, or altered protein that forms dysfunctional gap channels. The missing or dysfunctional gap channels inhibit proper intracellular potassium maintenance and result in death of specific cells within the inner ear cells, resulting in deafness (Kenneson, Van Naarden Braun, & Boyle, 2002). This type of deafness, termed DFNB1, is inherited in an autosomal recessive manner.

There are also several point mutations within the *GJB2* gene that result in deafness, termed DFNA3, which is inherited in an autosomal dominant pattern. Additionally *GJB2* mutation carriers who also have mutation of gap protein junction beta 6 (*GJB6*), which encodes connexin 30, have deafness (Kenneson et al., 2002). The loci of *GJB2* mutations appear to be important for function, which results in these different inheritance patterns. There are 12 missense mutations that result in DFNA3 deafness, six related to prelingual hearing loss, three related to postlingual hearing loss, and three not well described at this time. Some different mutations within the *GJB2* gene result in syndromic deafness, specifically palmoplantar keratoderma with deafness and Vohwinkel syndrome (Kenneson et al., 2002).

Nonsyndromic deafness can also have an Xlinked inheritance pattern. Mutations of the POU class 3 homeobox 4 (POU3F4) gene result in a nonsyndromic deafness characterized by prelingual hearing loss that gets progressively worse over time and frequently results in total deafness. The *POU3F* gene encodes a transcription factor vital for neural stem cell proliferation and normal development. Point mutations, deletions, and duplications in the gene and regulatory sequences result in abnormal transcription factor quantity or quality (that leads to early degradation). This

TABLE 13.2. Select Syndromic Causes of Hearing Loss, Inheritance Pattern and Associated Findings.

Syndrome	Hearing Loss Type	Inheritance Pattern	Associated Findings
Alström syndrome	Sensorineural	Autosomal recessive	Short stature, retinitis pigmentosa, diabetes mellitus, obesity, cardiomyopathy, and progressive hearing loss (Marshall, Beck, Maffei, & Naggert, 2007).
Alport syndrome	Sensorineural	Autosomal dominant, autosomal recessive and X-linked forms exist	Corneal dystrophy, dislocation of the lens, posterior cataracts, hematuria, nephritis, and bilateral hearing loss (McCarthy & Maino, 2000).
Branchio-oto-renal syndrome	Conductive, Sensorineural or mixed	Autosomal dominant, variable expressivity	Branchial fistulas, renal anomalies, and external, middle and inner ear anomalies (Kochhar, Fischer, Kimberling, & Smith, 2007).
Jervall and Lange-Nielson	Sensorineural	Autosomal recessive	Prolonged QT syndrome, syncopal attacks, congenital bilateral hearing loss and sudden death (Schwartz *et al.*, 2007).
Mitochondrial Encephalomyelopathy, Lactic acidosis, and Stroke-like episodes (MELAS)	Sensorineural	Mitochondrial	Lactic acidosis, muscle weakness, pain, recurrent headaches, anorexia, vomiting, seizures. and stroke-like episodes (Matsumoto, Saver, Brennan & Ringman, 2005).
Neurofibromatosis Type 2	Sensorineural	Autosomal dominant	Multiple nervous system tumors (Asthagiri *et al.*, 2009).
Osteogenesis imperfect Types 1, 3, and 4	Conductive and/or sensorineural hearing loss	Autosomal dominant	Bone and connective tissue abnormalities. *Type 1*: frequent bone fractures, blue sclera, discolored teeth, teenage to adult onset hearing impairment. *Type 2*: frequent bone fractures, blue sclera, curvature of the spine, poor bone growth, teenage to adult onset hearing impairment. *Type 3*: frequent bone fractures, discolored teeth, teenage to adult onset hearing impairment that is less severe than in Types 1 and 3. (Martin & Shapiro, 2007).
Stickler	Sensorineural	Autosomal dominant	Cleft palate, eye problems, vertebral abnormalities, osteoarthritis, heart problems, and progressive hearing loss (Acke, Dhooge, Malfait & De Leenheer, 2012).
Usher syndrome	Sensorineural	Autosomal recessive	Hearing loss to complete inability to hear, gradual loss of vision progressing to blindness (Ahmed, Riazuddin, Riazuddin, & Wilcox, 2003).
Waardenburg syndrome	Sensorineural	Autosomal dominant with variable penetrance	Dystopia canthorum, hyperplastic high nasal root, hyperplasia of the medial eyebrows, heterochromia irides, circumscribed albinism of frontal hear hair/white forelock, unilateral or bilateral deafness (Pardono *et al.*, 2003).

leads to abnormal cochlear development, often with stapedial fixation, and a phenotype of sensorineural hearing loss or deafness with or without conductive dysfunction. There is considerable variability in the amount of hearing loss and the rate of progression. Males are affected more severely than female carriers (Bitner-Glindzicz *et al.*, 1995).

Mutations within the mitochondrial DNA also result in nonsyndromic deafness. Mutation of the mitochondrial encoded 12S RNA (*MTRNR-1*) gene is inherited in an mtDNA inheritance pattern. *MTRNR-1* gene produces 12S RNA, which facilitates translation of oxidative phosphorylation proteins (Zhao *et al.*, 2005). Without adequate quality and quantity of 12S RNA, inadequate oxidative phosphorylation proteins are made, oxidative phosphorylation is slowed or stopped, and energy failure ensues (Ding, Leng, Fan, Xia, & Xu, 2013), initiating apoptosis. A small number of *MTRNR-1* mutation carriers develop deafness early in life. The mechanism that results in only some carriers developing deafness while others do not is unclear. More commonly, *MTRNR-1* mutation carriers develop hearing loss and deafness after taking aminoglycosides. The *MTRNR-1* mutation leads to a slightly different structure of the 12S RNA, which is similar to bacterial ribosomal RNA (Ding *et al.*, 2013). Aminoglycosides attack bacterial ribosomal RNA but also the 12S RNA, which results in energy failure, oxidative stress toxicity, and apoptosis (Ding *et al.*, 2013; Zhao *et al.*, 2005).

Newborn hearing screening is required in 43 states in the U.S. and all states have an Early Hearing Detection and Intervention program (NIH Research Portfolio Online Tools [RePORT], 2013). Ninety-five percent of newborns are screened within a few weeks of age (NIH RePORT, 2013). Delay in speech development or other development warrants testing of hearing. Older children or adults who complain of hearing problems should also be tested. It is important to differentiate cause of deafness in order to determine functional status and determine potential therapeutic avenues when appropriate (NIH RePORT, 2013) and to assess reproductive risk later in life. Family history, physical examination, otologic evaluation, and audiologic testing should be performed to rule out other disorders and quantify hearing difficulty (Smith, Shearer, Hildebrand, & Van Kamp, 2013). In children or others where inner ear malformations are suspected radiographic testing (CT scan or MRI) is used. Radiographic testing can facilitate focused molecular genetic testing, because temporal bone anomalies are common in people with *SLC26A4* mutations or *POU3F4* gene mutations (Smith *et al.*, 2013). Molecular genetic testing is a final step in diagnosis and can provide direction for genetic counseling (Smith *et al.*, 2013). Genetic

testing may be especially helpful in first-degree relatives of *MTRNR-1* mutation carriers so aminoglycosides can be avoided as a way to prevent deafness (Smith *et al.*, 2013).

Most types of deafness are not amenable to treatment. Treatment consists of maximizing function with hearing aids, vibrotactile devices, and cochlear implants for some eligible and willing people (Smith *et al.*, 2013). A neurologist, audiologist, pediatrician (if appropriate), and nurse practitioner specializing in these areas should coordinate care of these people (Smith *et al.*, 2013). For children in particular, a deaf education specialist should be employed, because hard of hearing or deaf children can often experience delays in reading, speech, and communication skills (Smith *et al.*, 2013). Research has shown that much of the cognitive impairment seen in deaf individuals is not caused by a biological or pathological factor, but rather the result of auditory deprivation. Early intervention to improve or preserve auditory function and to improve early language acquisition is effective in correcting some of these issues (Smith *et al.*, 2013).

The values of the deaf community can have considerable impact on their member's views about genetic services and treatment to restore hearing. The Deaf community (with a capital D) is a community using sign language as the primary method of communication. It includes some, but not all, people who are hard of hearing or deaf, their family members, and sign language interpreters. The Deaf community views deafness as a different way of life, but not a disability. Areas with a concentration of deaf people, including schools for the deaf and social clubs, often develop a Deaf culture. The primary differences in Deaf culture are the use of sign language as the method of communication, focus around a shared institution(s), a unique value system, different cultural norms, reliance on technology for some communication within the hearing community, and distinct art and history. There is a strong sense of pride surrounding their deafness and the support and sense of belonging within their community. Deaf adults have been hesitant to seek genetic services, although a recent study has found a strong interest among deaf young adults in genetic testing to learn why they are deaf. However, this study found little interest in genetic testing for reproductive decision-making

(Boudreault *et al.*, 2010). Discussion of genetic services should be provided with sensitivity toward the values of the individual deaf individual.

For nearly all who have lived a life without hearing, cochlear implants to restore hearing is a life-changing procedure, but the deaf individual may not see this as a benefit. Concerns relate specifically to separating from the Deaf community and a significant change in personal identity. For this reason, restoration of hearing is not always the "best" treatment option. Available treatments, expected results, and the positive and negative impacts on lifestyle should be discussed and thoughtfully considered (National Association of Deaf [NAD] Cochlear Implant Committee, 2000). Resources for more information about Deaf culture are provided at the end of this chapter.

13.3. COMMON COMPLEX DISORDERS OF THE CENTRAL NERVOUS SYSTEM

13.3.1. Multiple Sclerosis

Mike is very familiar with Multiple Sclerosis (MS) and the variability with which it affects people. His maternal grandmother has had the disease since his mother was a child and she walked with support for most of that time, but now is mostly in a wheel chair. His maternal uncle, who married into the family, was diagnosed with MS about fifteen years ago, though he is just now starting to experience significant symptoms. His paternal aunt was also diagnosed with MS about 10 years ago and now drives a van equipped with a lift for her motorized cart so she can maintain a part-time teaching job at a local university.

Mike understands that his uncle's disease has no implications for him, but he is worried about the existence of the disease in maternal and paternal relatives and the risk that may present to him and his siblings. Five years ago, Mike saw a genetic counselor who explained that there was a genetic component to the disease, but not enough was known to do any testing to help quantify his risk. Mike self-monitors for symptoms that might be related to MS without obsessing about it. He also tries to stay up to date with the research, so that he can have testing when it is offered.

MS is an autoimmune disorder of the nervous system in which the myelin covering axons of neurons is attacked by the body's immune system. Symptoms commonly include dysfunction in autonomic nervous system, motor function, vision, and sensation, with a significant decrease in quality of life and shortened life span.

Approximately 2 to 2.5 million people have MS worldwide (World Health Organization [WHO], 2008). MS is more common in women than men (Milo & Kahana, 2010). It is less common in populations living near the equator (Alonzo & Hernan, 2002; Compston & Coles, 2008), although exceptions exist (Pugliatti, Sotgin, & Rosati, 2002), and is more common in Northern European regions (Milo & Kahana, 2010). MS rates vary worldwide and by region, but the general range is 0.5/100,000 in Africa (WHO 2008) to 200/100,000 in Northern Europe (Milo & Kahana, 2010). Individuals moving from one region to another before age 15 years frequently have the new region's MS risk, suggesting a significant environmental contribution (Compston & Coles, 2008). Despite this finding, a number of genetic mutations have been implicated and are discussed in the next section.

The major pathophysiologic mechanism associated with MS is inflammation, autoimmune attack, and demyelination of the axons of neurons. The autoimmune attack on myelin, driven by T cells, initiates inflammation that produces scarring. Oligodendrocytes perform remyelination early in the MS process, but repeat autoimmune attacks and the resultant inflammation produces scarring and axonal/neuronal loss. Scarring induces a block in neuronal transmission, resulting in symptoms (Litzinger & Litzinger, 2009).

The optic nerve, brain stem, basal ganglia, and spinal tracts of the CNS can all be affected in MS, although different patients will have different regions of damage.

It is likely that there are both genetic and environmental influences on MS development and progression. Environmental factors include infectious agents (Compston & Coles, 2008; Gilden, 2005). Cigarette smoking (Ascherio & Munger, 2007), occupational toxin (solvents) exposure, vaccination (Marrie, 2004), diet, and hormone intake (Ascherio & Munger, 2007) have also been explored as causative agents of MS with mixed or insignificant results.

Genes implicated in MS pathology include

TABLE 13.3. Select Genes in Multiple Sclerosis Risk, their Protein Product and Mechanism of Action.

Gene	Protein Product	Mechanism
Major histocompatability complex, class II, DR beta 1 (*HLA-DRB1*)	Human leukocyte antigen complex (Class II)	HLA presents on cell surfaces and presents proteins to immune cells. When bound to a "foreign" protein, it initiates an immune response. Specific mechanism through which mutation leads to autoimmune attack in MS is not clear (Alcina *et al.* 2012; Nischwitz *et al.*, 2010).
Interleukin-7 receptor (*IL7R*)	Interleukin 7 receptor and thymic stromal lymphopoeitin receptor	Receptors are present on immune cells and, when bound, activate cell growth, proliferation and survival pathways. The interleukin 7 receptor is maintained within the cells (rather than presenting on the membrane) in patients with mutations. (Gregory *et al.*, 2007).
Major histocompatability complex, class II, DQ beta 1 (*HLA DQB1*)	Human leukocyte antigen complex (Class II)	HLA presents on cell surfaces and presents proteins to immune cells. When bound to a 'foreign' protein, it initiates an immune response. Specific mechanism through which mutation leads to autoimmune attack in MS is not clear (McElroy *et al.*, 2010; Nischwitz, *et al.*, 2010).
Major histocompatability complex, class II, DQ alpha 1 (*HLA DQA1*)	Human leukocyte antigen complex (Class II)	HLA presents on cell surfaces and presents proteins to immune cells. When bound to a "foreign" protein, it initiates an immune response. Specific mechanism through which mutation leads to autoimmune attack in MS is not clear. The HLA- A*02 allele is protective (Nischwitz *et al.*, 2010).
Major histocompatability complex, class I, A (*HLA-A*)	HLA Class 1 histocompatibility antigen, A-1 alpha chain	HLA presents on cell surfaces and presents proteins to immune cells. When bound to a "foreign" protein, it initiates an immune response (Briggs *et al.*, 2011).
Major histocompatability complex, class I, B (*HLA-B*)	HLA B protein	HLA presents on cell surfaces and presents proteins to immune cells. When bound to a "foreign" protein, it initiates an immune response. Specific mechanism through which mutation leads to autoimmune attack in MS is not clear. The HLA-B*44 allele is protective independently and in combination with the HLA-Cw*5 allele (Healy *et al.*, 2010).
Major histocompatability complex, class I, C (*HLA-C*)	HLA C protein	HLA presents on cell surfaces and presents proteins to immune cells. When bound to a "foreign" protein, it initiates an immune response. Specific mechanism through which mutation leads to autoimmune attack in multiple sclerosis (MS) is not clear. The HLA-Cw*5 allele is protective independently and in combination with the HLA-B*44 allele (Yeo *et al.*, 2007).
Major histocompatability complex, class I, G (*HLA-G*)	HLA G protein	HLA presents on cell surfaces and presents proteins to immune cells. When bound to a "foreign" protein, it initiates an immune response. Provides fetal protection from maternal immune attack. Specific mechanism through which mutation leads to autoimmune attack in MS is not clear (Cree *et al.*, 2010).

(continued)

TABLE 13.3 (continued). Select Genes in Multiple Sclerosis Risk, their Protein Product and Mechanism of Action.

Gene	Protein Product	Mechanism
Vitamin D (1,25- dihydroxyvitamin D3) receptor gene (VDR)	Vitamin D (1,25-dihydroxyvitamin D3) receptor, a nuclear hormone receptor	Regulates several metabolic pathways, including vitamin D & immune function (Tajouri *et al.*, 2005).
Cytochrome P450, family 24, subfamily A, polypeptide 1 (*CYP24A1*)	CYP24A1	Metabolizes vitamin D, thereby modifying calcium homeostasis. Specific role in MS is unclear (Sawcer *et al.*, 2011).
Interleukin 12 (*IL12*)	Interleukin 12	Cytokine that induces T helper cell development. Genetic variants increasing risk for MS cause overexpression of IL12 (Shokrgozar *et al.*, 2009; Sawcer *et al.*, 2011).
Interferon gamma (*IFNG, IFN* gamma)	Interferon gamma	Interferon gamma is a proinflammatory cytokine with antiviral, immunoregulatory, and antitumor properties. Specific mechanism for the association with MS is unclear (Shokrgozar, *et al.*, 2009).
Interleukin 2 (*IL2*)	IL2	IL2 is a proinflammatory cytokine promoting B and T cell proliferation. Specific mechanism for association with MS is unclear (Shokrgozar *et al.*, 2009).
Cytochrome P450, family 27, subfamily B, polypeptide 1 (*CYP27B1*)	CYP27B1	Modulates Vitamin D metabolism. Vitamin D regulates many of the other genes implicated in MS (Ramagopalan *et al.*, 2010).
Interleukin 2 receptor alpha (*IL2RA*)	IL2 receptor alpha	A component of IL2 receptors. IL2 is a growth factor and when bound to IL2 receptors it promotes proliferation of T and B cells (Sawcer *et al.*, 2011).

the human leukocyte antigen (HLA) genes *DR15* and *DQ6*. Other variants within the *HLA* genes, including *HLA-C554* and *HLA-DRB1*11*, appear to provide protection from MS (Compston & Coles, 2008). Many of these genes influence MS risk only in select populations. More recently genome wide association studies (GWASs) have implicated over 50 genes in MS risk (Table 13.3).

Symptoms of MS present any time between ages 20 and 50 years (Milo & Kahana, 2010). Symptoms vary between individuals, because they are driven by location and size of the lesion. There are often bouts of severe symptoms and then remission in MS patients. Initial presentation usually has one of two patterns: sudden onset of severe symptoms lasting days to months followed by bouts of improvements (and later repeats of this pattern) or a gradual progression of dysfunction. Some MS patients will present with the relapse-remission pattern and then convert to a gradual progression pattern, whereas others may have mixed periods of the two patterns. Pat-

terns of MS are classified as follows: "relapsing remitting," "primary progressive" (lacks remission periods), "secondary progressive" (presents as relapsing remitting MS but changes to progressive decline without remission), and "progressive relapsing" (progressive MS but with attacks of increased severity) (Lubin & Reingold, 1996). Relapse is not generally predictable; however, viral infections (Compston & Coles, 2008) and stress (Heesen *et al.*, 2007) increase risk of relapse. Pregnancy is associated with decreased relapse; however, relapse risk is high in the first few months following childbirth (Compston & Coles, 2008).

Symptoms vary widely but frequently include changes in sensation (tingling; pins & needles; numbness; pronounced reflexes; acute or chronic pain; and *Lhermitte's sign*, electrical sensation moving down the back upon neck movement), motor problems (muscle weakness; muscle spasms; difficult movements), ataxia, dysarthria, dysphagia, visual problems (double vision, nystagmus; optic neuritis), bowel and bladder difficulties, and feeling tired (Compston & Coles, 2008). Problems with cognitive processing and mood disorders are also common. Symptoms are often more severe during exposure to high temperature (*Uhthoff's phenomenon*) (Compston & Coles, 2008). Overall, life expectancy is shortened 10 to 15 years as a consequence of MS (Compston & Coles, 2008).

MS is most often diagnosed by symptom presentation in combination with radiographic image findings and laboratory results. For patients presenting after having repeat episodes (two or more) of symptoms with remission characteristic of MS, diagnosis may be made based on that clinical presentation alone. Many patients present during or after a single episode of symptoms and remission. In these cases, diagnosis requires additional testing. MRI, particularly with administration of gadolinium, will show areas of demyelination. Cerebrospinal fluid analysis will show oligoclonal immunoglobulin G (IgG) bands. Visual and somatosensory evoked potentials will show slowed response to stimuli (Compston & Coles, 2008).

There is no cure for MS. Treatment is focused on returning function after an attack, preventing attacks, and preventing disability. During an acute attack, high doses of corticosteroids decrease inflammation and ease the symptoms, although they do not have long term effects. Plasmapheresis is used in severe acute attacks that are not responsive to corticosteroid therapy. Several immunomodulator drugs have shown efficacy in preventing attacks in relapsing-remitting MS, including interferon beta-1a (Tsang & MacDonell, 2011), interferon beta-1b (Tsang & MacDonell, 2011), glatiramer acetate (Freedman, 2011; Quizilbash, Mendez, & Sanchez-de la Rosa, 2012; Tsang & MacDonell, 2011), mitoxantrone (Tsang & MacDonell, 2011), natalizumab (Haasan-Smith & Douglas, 2011; Tsang & MacDonell, 2011), fingolimod, teriflunomide (He *et al.*, 2012), and dimethyl fumarate (Venci, & Gandhi, 2013).

13.3.2. Parkinson Disease

Agnes is 80-years-old and describes herself as having a long, active, happy life up until 12 years ago. She began having problems with balance several years before she went to the doctor. She noticed some leg weakness about 3 years before that, but assumed it was just a consequence of growing older and tried to walk more. When she started having tremors of her left arm, she knew it was time to see the doctor. At 68-years-old, she was diagnosed with Parkinson's disease and started on medication to reduce the symptoms. Despite the medications, the disease progressed. She developed tremors in her other arm and her legs. Her muscles became rigid and her face lost expression. Her movements got slower, and then last year, she began having difficulties walking. She continues to participate in therapy, takes her medications despite the troublesome side effects, and enjoys spending more time with her family, because she knows this is a progressive disease that will likely render her completely disabled and lead to her death.

Parkinson's disease (PD) is the second most common neurodegenerative disease worldwide. It is hallmarked by loss of inhibitory dopaminergic neurons of the substantia nigra in the midbrain region and results in significant motor symptoms that impair quality and quantity of life.

Overall prevalence of PD is very well studied and estimated globally at 3:1000 people, but increases with age; 3% of people over age 60 years and 4% of people over age 80 years have PD (de Lau & Breteler, 2006). There is variability across populations, with prevalence estimates ranging from 2:100,000 in China to 970:100,000 in the Amish Community (primarily in northeastern U.S.) (Ma *et al.*, 2013; Muangpaisan, Hori, & Brayne, 2009; Muangpaisan, Mathews, Hori, & Seidel, 2011; von Campenhausen *et al.*, 2005). Although there is no clearly identified factor for the increased rates in select areas, exposures to various chemicals, life expectancy, and cultural practice differences have been suggested to result in this variation (deLau & Breteler, 2006; Institute of Medicine [IOM], 2009; Friere, & Koifman, 2012; Noyce *et al.*, 2012; Tanner *et al.*, 2011; Van Maele-Fabry, Hoet, Vilain, & Lison, 2012). PD presents in people of all races, although some evidence suggests there may be uneven distribution with Caucasians being at higher risk (Wills, Evanoff, Lian, Criswell, & Racette, 2010). Although there may be differences in prevalence in the sexes in different countries and regions, it does present frequently in both sexes. Worldwide slightly more men than women have

PD (IOM, 2009; Ma *et al.*, 2013; Muangpaisan *et al.*, 2009; von Campenhausen *et al.* 2005; Wills *et al.*, 2011).

Currently there is no single factor identified to result in PD in all patients. It is likely that genetic background places some people at increased risk, and when they are then exposed to some currently unknown factor(s), the disease pathology is initiated. In normal physiologic states, there is a constant inhibitory action from neurons in the pars compact region of the substantia nigra. The neurons produce and release dopamine onto motor neurons (and others), inhibiting transmission of motor impulses down the spinal cord and ultimately motor movement. When movement is initiated, the activity of these neurons is decreased to facilitate motor movement. In PD, these inhibitory dopaminergic neurons die off. As more cells die, there is a dopamine deficiency, inhibition is reduced, and more inappropriate motor impulses are able to travel down the spine causing tremors. The actual cause of neuronal death is unclear. It is hypothesized that abnormal protein degradation and aggregation, lysosomal dysfunction, or mitochondrial dysfunction cause neuronal cell death in PD (Obeso *et al.*, 2010). Of interest, these neurons also contain high amounts of melanin, which provides a dark appearance and this darkness is lost when the cells die.

Although not historically considered a "genetic disease," PD frequently presents in multiple family members, and recent evidence has implicated several genetic mutations that contribute to the PD pathology. The most well-studied gene is the alpha-synuclein gene (*SNCA*), which produces alpha-synuclein, a protein that is widely expressed in CNS tissue but has, as of yet, unidentified functions. Alpha-synuclein is thought to serve as a molecular chaperone within the cell, carrying proteins about the cell and particularly near the synapse. It likely promotes adequate neurotransmitter release and dopamine, in particular, into the synapse. When alpha-synuclein folds improperly, it forms aggregates forming insoluble fragments that accumulate within cells and can be found in patients with PD on autopsy (Davie, 2008; Lesage & Brice, 2009). Mutations of the *SNCA* gene associated with PD most often include duplication and triplication mutations and, rarely, missense mutations (Davie, 2008; Lesage & Brice, 2009).

Mutations in the leucine-rich repeat kinase 2 (*LRRK2*) gene, which codes for the protein dardarin, have been identified in patients with an autosomal dominant form of familial PD. Dardarin regulates protein synthesis via microRNA (miRNA) inhibition. Mutations are most often point mutations and result in abnormal protein degradation and aggregation, decreased dendrites of neurons, and perhaps promote apoptosis of neurons (Davie, 2008; Lesage & Brice, 2009).

Another gene implicated in PD pathology is the parkinson protein 2, E3 ubiquitin protein ligase (*PARK2*) gene. The *PARK2* gene produces parkin, a protein with an unknown function, but is thought to target proteins for degradation. *PARK2* mutations are commonly found in individuals with autosomal recessive, early onset/juvenile PD (Poorkaj *et al.*, 2004). Many mutations of various types (e.g., frameshift, missense, etc.) have been found in patients with PD, with most resulting in qualitative or quantitative parkin deficiency (Lohmann *et al.*, 2003; Poorkaj *et al.*, 2004).

Other genetic variants have been implicated as well. Mutations in the phosphatidylinositol-3, 4, 5-triphophate-3-phosphatase (*PTEN*) induced putative kinase (*PINK1*) gene has been associated with autosomal recessive, early onset PD (Hilker *et al.*, 2012). The *PINK1* gene encodes the PINK1 protein, which inhibits apoptosis promoting cell survival (Arena *et al.*, 2013). The *DJ-1* gene, also known as *PARK7* gene, is a source of genetic variability in individuals with autosomal recessive early onset PD, with point mutations and deletions being most common (Bonifati *et al.*, 2003). It encodes the DJ-1 protein, which is a transcription regulator and may protect cells against oxidative stress and resultant apoptosis (Heutink, 2006). The probable cation-transporting ATPase 13A2 (*ATP13A2*) gene produces the ATP13A2 protein, which transports cations and other substrates across cell membranes. Single point mutations, insertions, and deletions resulting in frameshift, nonsense mutations in this gene have been associated with an autosomal recessive juvenile onset form of PD with dementia (Davie, 2008; Lesage & Brice, 2009).

Symptoms of PD include resting tremor, rigidity, mask-like facial expression, speech and swallowing problems, bradykinesia, gait disruption, and postural instability (Caballol, Martí,

& Tolosa, 2007; Jankovic, 2008). Because the substantia nigra moderates nonmotor impulses as well, additional symptoms develop as the disease progresses and additional neurons are lost. Nonmotor symptoms include autonomic nervous system dysfunction (i.e., orthostatic hypotension, urinary incontinence, excess sweating, oily skin, sexual dysfunction, constipation, and gastric problems), neuropsychiatric dysfunction (i.e., cognitive impairment, dementia, mood disorders and especially depression, behavioral disorders, and psychotic features including hallucinations and delusions), eye/visual dysfunction (i.e., dry eyes, decreased blinking, saccadic eye movements, blurry vision, double vision, upward gaze impairment), sensory dysfunction (i.e., impaired smell, impaired pain sensation, and paresthesias), and sleep impairment (Caballol et al., 2007; Jankovic, 2008). Symptoms typically present in the seventh decade of life, although some forms present much earlier or later (Caballol et al., 2007; Jankovic, 2008). PD is a progressive disease and ultimately results in death, usually due to aspiration pneumonia (Poewe, 2006). Age of PD onset is correlated with survival, with people having an onset at age 25 to 39 years have a 38-year average life expectancy. Those with an onset at age 40 to 64 years have a 21-year life expectancy, and those with an onset at age 65 years or older have a 5-year life expectancy (Poewe, 2006).

Diagnosis of PD is based upon medical history and clinical examination findings (Jankovic, 2008). Diagnostic criteria typically include (1) bradykinesia with (2) rigidity, resting tremor or postural instability and (3) three or more of the following: unilateral onset, tremor at rest, progression of symptoms, motor symptom asymmetry, 5-year response to levodopa, clinical course of 10 years or more, and dyskinesias induced by levodopa. A full differential diagnostic examination is performed to rule out other causes of symptoms. In patients with history and physical examination suggestive of PD, dopamine may be administered. If symptoms are relieved, the diagnosis is considered confirmed. There is no laboratory test used, and no genetic test is available for the general population. Some individuals may seek genetic testing for PD. Genetic testing is available for the parkin, *PARK7, SNCA, LRRK2,* and *PINK1* genes. These genes are not

100% sensitive or specific and, therefore, are not used clinically to diagnose PD, but results may inform diagnosis or future risk.

There is no cure for PD. Treatment eases the symptom burden, and as such, likely promotes both quality and quantity of life. Given that dopamine is too large to cross the blood brain barrier, levodopa (L-Dopa) is administered. L-Dopa crosses the blood brain barrier and is converted to dopamine by the dopaminergic neurons alleviating motor symptoms (National Collaborating Centre for Chronic Conditions [NCCCC], 2006a). Only a small portion of the L-Dopa crosses the blood brain barrier, and a significant amount is converted to dopamine in other tissues generating side effects. Although nausea and joint stiffness are common symptoms, dyskinesias are of particular concern, and patients on L-Dopa should be monitored regularly and the dose adjusted accordingly. Many L-Dopa formulations contain dopa decarboxylase inhibitors, which slow levodopa metabolism, reducing side effects and increasing bioavailability in the CNS. Dopamine agonists are used early in the disease process to delay motor system complications (NCCCC, 2006a). Monoamine oxidase inhibitors, anticholinergics, and amantadine are used less frequently but are useful for some people (NCCCC, 2006a). Deep brain stimulation and purposeful lesion formation via surgery were once commonplace treatments but are now rarely used due to nonsurgical therapeutic development (NCCCC, 2006b). Speech therapy, physical therapy, and occupational therapy may limit disability and maintain function (Goodwin, Richards, Taylor, Taylor, & Campbell. 2008; NCCCC, 2006c). Gene therapy has been used in recent clinical trials of PD (Lewitt et al., 2011). The procedure has been determined to be safe (Obeso et al., 2010), and initial reports of clinical efficacy are promising (Lewitt et al., 2011).

13.3.3. Amyotrophic Lateral Sclerosis (ALS)

Carolyn, a 40-year-old Caucasian mother of three, remembers reading *Tuesdays with Morrie* about 10 years ago when working as a nurse in a rehabilitation setting. The book was especially relevant to her, because she had taken care of a few patients with amyotrophic lateral sclerosis (ALS), the disease inflicting one of the main characters in the book, and it helped her better understand their journey. About 3 months ago, she noticed her right foot was dragging while she was walking, and then last week she started having slurred speech. She went immediately to the emergency room, and it was determined that she was not having a stroke; she was referred to the neurologist. The neurologist ordered some tests to rule out ALS, which were done over the past few days. Today she sits in the neurologist's office waiting for a diagnosis that will surely seal her fate. As a nurse, she has more knowledge than the general public about ALS. She knows it will take her body while preserving her mind. She is very worried about this diagnosis, because she knows if she has ALS, she'll have a progressive

decline in movement and function over the next 3 to 5 years before she dies. She doesn't know who will care for her 7-, 10-, and 12-year-old children in the coming years. As she waits to go in to hear her fate, she begins to pray.

Amyotrophic lateral sclerosis (ALS), or Lou Gehrig's disease, is an adult-onset, progressive degenerative disorder of the spinal cord. Symptoms progress, leading to decreased independence and a shortened life span.

Worldwide prevalence of ALS is 4–5:100,000 (Worms, 2001). ALS affects people of all racial and ethnic backgrounds (Worms, 2001). There may be a higher prevalence in Caucasians, but this is questionable, because most research has focused on Caucasian populations (Cronin, Har-

TABLE 13.4. Amyotrophic Lateral Sclerosis Genes, Protein Product and Protein Function.

Gene	Protein Product	Protein Function
SOD1 (ALS1)	Superoxide dismutase 1	Binds copper and zinc, eliminates free radicals. Poor free radical elimination or SOD1 aggregate build up may result in ALS (Andersen, 2006).
ALS2	Alsin	Binds TPase RAB5, guanine nucleotide exchange factor, intracellular endosomal trafficking (Gros-Louis, Gaspar, & Roleau, 2006).
SMN1	Survival motor neuron protein	Unknown. Potentially involved in small ribonucleoprotein formation. Genetic variants associated with ALS (Blauw et al.; 2012).
UBQLN2	Ubiquilin 2	Modulates in protein degradation (Deng et al., 2011).
SETX	Probable helicase senataxin	DNA/RNA processing, specific function not well known (Blair et al., 2000).
FUS	Fused in sarcoma (FUS)	DNA repair, transcription regulation, RNA splicing, RNA transport (Vance et al., 2009).
VAPB	Vesicle-associated membrane protein-associated protein B/C	Vesicle membrane component, prevents unfolded protein accumulation in the endoplasmic reticulum (Kanekura, Nishimoto, Aiso, & Matsuoka, 2006).
ANG	Aniogenin	tRNA ribonuclease stimulates angiogenesis (Greenway et al., 2006).
TARDBP	Tar DNA-binding protein	Binds DNA and RNA, regulates gene expression, transcription, splicing, and translation (Ferraiuolo et al., 2011).
FIG4	SAC domain-containing protein 3	Signaling molecule, vesicle trafficking (Chow et al., 2011).
OPTN	Optineurin	Mediates apoptosis, inflammation, and others. Specific mechanism unknown (Maruyama et al., 2010).
ATXN2	Ataxin 2	Unknown function (Van Damme et al., 2011).
PRPH	Periphen	Forms microfilaments, regulate cell growth and development, axonal repair (Corrado et al., 2011).
NEFH	Neurofilament heavy polypeptide	Subunit of neurofilaments, contribute to neuronal axon structure (Al-Chalabi et al., 1999).
C9orf72	Chromosome 9 open reading frame 72	Unknown (Chiò et al., 2012).

diman, & Traynor, 2007; Worms, 2001). There are slightly more men than women with ALS; however, presentation may be different in men versus women (McCombe & Henderson, 2010).

The cause of ALS is unknown (National Institute of Neurological Disorders and Stroke [NINDS], 2013a). It has been suggested that overactivation of glutamate receptors, autoimmune response targeting calcium channels, oxidative stress response, or cytoskeletal dysfunction result in an excitotoxic state of the motor neurons (Carunchio et al., 2011; Cleveland & Rothstein, 2001; Cluskey & Ramsden, 2001; Johnson, 2000; Sutedja et al., 2009). Mitochondrial dysfunction, protein aggregation, free radical generation, excitotoxicity, inflammation, and apoptotic cell death occur (Cluskey & Ramsden, 2001). Regardless of cause of death, individual motor neurons in the lateral spinal cord die. As the lateral horn cell dies, associated neurons also die due to Wallerian degeneration. Schwann cells catabolize the myelin sheath and engulf the axon, breaking it into smaller pieces maintained within myelin ovoids, which are engulfed by macrophages. The local lower motor neurons die initially, and subsequently, upper motor neurons die off. As the disease progresses, associated neurons in the brainstem and cortex also die off. The neuronal cell death is specific to the motor neuron system, and for unknown reasons, sensory neurons are spared (Cluskey & Ramsden, 2001).

The majority of ALS cases are sporadic, with up to 10% exhibiting an autosomal dominant inheritance pattern (NINDS, 2013a). As with most nervous system disorders, familial cases typically present earlier than sporadic cases. Although 18 genes have been identified as causative agents in familial ALS (see Table 13.4), few have been implicated in sporadic ALS as well.

The symptoms of ALS include muscle weakness, muscle atrophy, and degeneration of lower and then upper motor neurons. ALS presents in people ages 40 to 70 years (Sabatelli et al., 2008; Chio et al., 2011). The most common presenting symptom is muscle weakness, but excessive muscle twitching, cramping or stiffness, and slurred or nasal speech are common. Specific limb(s) affected at the onset of ALS vary by specific region of the spinal cord that is degenerating first. As more neuronal degeneration occurs, additional symptoms develop. Muscle weakness

and atrophy become bilateral and more noticeable, making movement difficult. Spasticity, hyperreflexia, dysphagia, and dysarthria develop. When muscles of the neck are involved, it is difficult to hold up the head. As movement becomes more difficult, people with ALS are not able to use their hands, arms, and legs. They require assistance with activities of daily living and will be wheelchair bound. A number of the ALS population develop pseudobulbar affect, a condition of inappropriate and uncontrollable laughing, crying, or smiling. Cognitive function, bowel and bladder function, and eye movements are usually maintained (Sabatelli et al., 2008; Chio et al., 2011). The neurons innervating muscles required for breathing and airway maintenance eventually die off, and these patients will require mechanical ventilation in late stage disease. Respiratory failure is the most common cause of death in people with ALS. Average life expectancy is 3 to 5 years after diagnosis, with a very small percent of the population surviving beyond 10 years (Sabatelli et al., 2008).

Prenatal screening is possible if there is a known mutation involved. Prenatal and postnatal genetic testing is typically done for the SOD1, TDP43, FUS, C9ORF72, or UBQLN2 genes for individuals with a first-degree relative with ALS if the specific mutation has been identified. The diagnosis of ALS is based on clinical examination, with loss of upper and motor neuron function in a single limb being highly suggestive of ALS. Testing to rule out other neuromuscular disorders must occur, and the diagnosis of ALS is assigned after the exclusion of all others (NINDS, 2013a). There is not a diagnostic test, genetic or otherwise, for diagnosis of most forms of ALS. Further, for familial ALS, genetic testing does not modify treatment and is generally not carried out.

There is no cure for ALS. Treatment of ALS is primarily focused on alleviating symptoms, maximizing function, and supportive services (NINDS, 2013a). Riluzole, a glutamate antagonist, is the only medication with proven efficacy in treating ALS (Carlesi et al., 2011), delaying the need for ventilator support and extending life by several months. Pharmaceutical intervention, physical therapy, occupational therapy, and speech therapy can all be used to decrease symptom burden for ALS patients (NINDS, 2013a). Noninvasive ventilation for respiratory support

TABLE 13.5. Resources for Genetics/Genomics and Neurological Disorders.

Genetics Home Reference	http://ghr.nlm.nih.gov/	Provides consumer-friendly information about the effects of genetic variations on human health
National Institute of Neurological Disorders and Stroke	http://www.ninds.nih.gov/index.htm	Mission is to reduce the burden of neurological disease, a burden borne by every age group, by every segment of society, by people all over the world; includes funding information; neurological disorders
Phenylketonuria	http://www.pkunews.org/index.htm	National PKU News: Nonprofit organization located in Seattle, Washington. It is dedicated to providing up-to-date, accurate news and information to families and professionals dealing with phenylketonuria.
	http://www.npkua.org/	National PKU Alliance: The National PKU Alliance works to improve the lives of families and individuals associated with PKU through research, support, education, and advocacy, while ultimately seeking a cure.
	http://www.canpku.org/about-pku	The Canadian PKU and Allied Disorders-© non-profit association dedicated to providing accurate news, information and support to families and professionals dealing with PKU
	http://depts.washington.edu/pku/index/html	University of Washington (2008); The Christine M. Trahms Program for Phenylketonuria is an online resource center for parents, family members and healthcare providers of children with PKU.
Fragile X	http://www.fragilex.org/	National Fragile X Foundations: Includes information on Fragile X disorders; treatment & intervention; research; resources; advocacy; support.
	http://www.fragilex.org.uk/	Fragile X Society: Formed in 1990 by families whose children had just been diagnosed with Fragile X Syndrome. Aims: Provide support and information to fragile X families from those who share and understand their concerns and needs; educate and inform the public and professionals about fragile X in order to raise awareness and understanding of the syndrome and improve the care of all people affected by fragile X; ncourage research into all aspects of fragile X and publicize the results.
Friedreich's ataxia	http://www.curefa.org/whatis.html	Friedreich's Ataxia Research Alliance–ational, public, 501(c)(3), nonprofit, tax-exempt organization dedicated to curing Friedreich's ataxia (FA) through research. FARA grants and activities provide support for basic and translational FA research, pharmaceutical/ biotech drug development, clinical trials, and scientific conferences. FARA also serves as a catalyst, between the public and scientific community, to create worldwide exchanges of information that drive medical advances.
Neurofibromatosis	http://www.nfnetwork.org/	Neurofibromatosis Network: Leading national organization advocating for federal funding for NF research and the development of local NF organizations.
	http://www.ctf.org/	Children's Tumor Foundation: Comprehensive approach to improving the lives of individuals and families affected by NF.

(continued)

TABLE 13.5 (continued). Resources for Genetics/Genomics and Neurological Disorders.

Neurofibromatosis	http://www.nfnetwork.org/	Neurofibromatosis Network: Leading national organization advocating for federal funding for NF research and the development of local NF organizations.
	http://www.ctf.org/	Children's Tumor Foundation: Comprehensive approach to improving the lives of individuals and families affected by NF.
Huntington's Disease	http://www.hdsa.org/	Huntington's Disease Society of America: National, voluntary health organization dedicated to improving the lives of people with Huntington's disease and their families. • To promote and support research and medical efforts to eradicate Huntington's disease • To assist people and families affected by Huntington's Ddsease to cope with the problems presented by the disease • To educate the public and health professionals about Huntington's disease
	http://hda.org.uk/	Huntington's Disease Association: UK registered charity which supports people affected by HD. Also provide information and advice to families, friends and healthcare professionals who support Huntington's disease families.
Multiple Sclerosis (MS)	http://www.mymsaa.org/	Multiple Sclerosis Association of America: Resource for the entire MS community, improving lives today through vital services and support.
	http://www.nationalmssociety.org/	National Multiple Sclerosis Society: Mission is to mobilize people and resources to drive research for a cure and to address the challenges of everyone affected by MS.
Parkinson's Disease	http://www.pdf.org/	Parkinson's Disease Foundation: Committed to finding a cure for Parkinson's, while ensuring that those who live with the disease are able to enjoy the best possible quality of life.
	http://viartis.net/parkinsons.disease/	Viartis Parkinson's Disease: Independent and entirely self-funded medical researchers specializing in Parkinson's disease; based in London, England.
Amyotrophic Lateral Sclerosis (ALS)	http://www.alsa.org/	ALS AssociationEstablished in 1985, the ALS Association is the only national non-profit organization fighting Lou Gehrig's Disease on every front, leading the way in global research, providing assistance for people with ALS through a nationwide network of chapters, coordinating multidisciplinary care through certified clinical care centers, and fostering government partnerships. The Association builds hope and enhances quality of life while aggressively searching for new treatments and a cure.

(continued)

TABLE 13.5 (continued). Resources for Genetics/Genomics and Neurological Disorders.

Deafness	http://www.deaf-culture-online.com/	Deaf Culture Online : Web site was created to bring as many perspectives on the deaf and hard of hearing experience as possible. Although the primary focus of this web site is to promote awareness of Deaf culture, it is all-inclusive and covers a wide range of topics such as the following: American Sign Language Parent resources Deaf topics Hard of hearing topics Baby sign language Current trends Communication preferences Stress management/wellness
	http://www.nidcd.nih.gov/health/hearing/pages/coch.aspx	National Institute on Deafness and Other Communication Disorders, Cochlear Implants: Health Information; funding; research; news and events. Part of the National Institutes of Health (NIH); conducts and supports research in the normal and disordered processes of hearing, balance, taste, smell, voice, speech, and language.
	http://www.deafculture.com/	Welcome to Deaf Culture©—What is deaf culture? Toriella, H.V. & Smith, S.D, (2013). Hereditary Hearing Loss and its Syndromes, 3rd Ed. New York: Oxford University Press.

and percutaneous endoscopic gastrostomy for nutrition administration may help prolong life.

13.4. CONCLUSION

There are numerous genetic and genomic disorders associated with the neurologic system. This chapter has only provided a brief overview of some common single gene and complex genomic neurologic disorders. Table 13.5 provides resources on the topic of neurologic disorders overall, as well as specific genetic diseases that may be useful to the reader to further enhance learning.

13.5. REFERENCES

Acke, F. R., Dhooge, I. J., Malfait, F., & De Leenheer, E. M. (2012). Hearing impairment in Stickler syndrome: a systematic review. *Orphanet Journal of Rare Diseases, 7*(84), doi: 0.1186/1750-1172-7-84

Adinolfi, S., Trifuoggi, M., Politou, A. S., Martin, S., & Pastore, A. (2002). A structural approach to understanding the iron-binding properties of phylogenetically different rataxins. *Human Molecular Genetics, 11*(16), 1865–77.

Ahmed, Z. M., Riazuddin, S., Riazuddin, S., & Wil-

cox, E. R. (2003). The molecular genetics of Usher syndrome. *Clinical Genetics, 63*(6), 431–434.

Al-Chalabi, A., Andersen, P. M., Nilsson, P., Chioza, B., Andersson, J. L., Russ, C., . . . & Leigh, P. N. (1999). Deletions of the heavy neurofilament subunit tail in amyotrophic lateral sclerosis. *Human Molecular Genetics, 8*(2), 157–164.

Alcina, A., Abad-Grau Mdel, M., Fedetz, M., Izquierdo, G., Lucas, M., Fernández, O., . . . & Matesanz F. (2012). Multiple sclerosis risk variant HLA-DRB1*1501 associates with high expression of DRB1 gene in different human populations. *PLoS One, 7*(1), e29819. doi: 10.1371/journal.pone.0029819.

Almqvist, E., Spence, N., Nichol, K., Andrew, S. E., Vesa, J., Peltonen, L., . . . & Hayden, M. R. (1995). Ancestral differences in the distribution of the delta 2642 glutamic acid polymorphism is associated with varying CAG repeat lengths on normal chromosomes: Insights into the genetic evolution of Huntington disease. *Human Molecular Genetics, 4*(2), 207–14.

Alonzo, A., & Hernan, M. (2002). Temporal trends in the incidence of multiple sclerosis. *Neurology, 71*(2), 129–135.

Andersen, K., Craufurd, D., Edmondson, M. C., Goodman, N., Groves, M., van Duijn, E., . . . & Goodman, L. (2011). An international survey-based algorithm for the pharmacologic treatment of Obsessive-Compulsive behaviors in Huntington's disease. *PLoS Currents Huntington Disease*. Retrieved from http://currents.plos.org/hd?s=anderson

Andersen, P. M. (2006). Amyotrophic lateral sclerosis associated with mutations in the CuZn superoxide dismutase gene. *Current Neurology and Neuroscience Reports, 6*(1), 37–46.

Arena, G., Gelmetti, V., Torosantucci, L., Vignone, D., Lamorte, G., De Rosa, P., . . . & Valente, E. M. (2013). PINK1 protects against cell death induced by mitochondrial depolarization, by phosphorylating Bcl-xL and impairing its pro-apoptotic cleavage. *Cell Death and Differentiation, 20*(7), 920–930.

Ascherio, A., & Munger, K. L. (2007). Environmental risk factors for multiple sclerosis Part II: Noninfectious factors. *Annals of Neurology, 61*(6), 504–513.

Asthagiri A. R., Parry D. M., Butman J. A., Kim H. J., Tsilou E. T., Zhuang Z., & Lonser R. R. (2009). Neurofibromatosis type 2. *Lancet, 373*(9679), 1974–1986.

Bassell, G. J., & Warren, S. T. (2008). Fragile X syndrome: Loss of local mRNA regulation alters synaptic development and function. *Neuron, 60*(2), 201–14.

Bickel, H., Bachmann, C., Beckers, R., Brandt, N. J., Clayton, B. E., Corrado, G., . . . & Schonberg, D. (1981). Neonatal mass screening for metabolic disorders. *European Journal of Pediatrics, 137*(2), 133–139.

BioMarin Pharmaceutical Incorporated. (2009). *History of PKU (Phenylketonuria)*. Retrieved from http://www.pku.com/What-is-PKU/history-of-phenylketonuria.php

Bitner-Glindzicz, M., Turnpenny, P., Höglund, P., Kääriäinen, H., Sankila, E.M., van der Maarel, S.M., . . . & Pembrey, M. (1995). Further mutations in Brain 4 (POU3F4) clarify the phenotype in the X-linked deafness, DFN3. *Human Molecular Genetics, 4*(8), 14671469.

Blair, I. P., Bennett, C. L., Abel, A., Rabin, B. A., Griffin, J. W., Fischbeck, K. H., . . . & Chance, P.F. (2000). A gene for autosomal dominant juvenile amyotrophic lateral sclerosis (ALS4) localizes to a 500-kb interval on chromosome 9q34. *Neurogenetics, 3*(1), 1–6.

Blauw, H. M., Barnes, C. P., van Vught, P. W., van Rheenen, W., Verheul, M., Cuppen, E., . . . & van den Berg, L.H. (2012). SMN1 gene duplications are associated with sporadic ALS. *Neurology, 78*(11)776–780.

Bonifati, V., Rizzu, P., van Baren, M. J., Schaap, O., Breedveld, G. J., Krieger, E., . . . & Heutink, P. (2003). Mutations in the DJ-1 gene associated with autosomal recessive early-onset parkinsonism. *Science, 299*(5604), 256–259.

Boudreault, P., Baldwin. E. E., Fox, M., Dutton, L. Tullis, L. E., Linden, J., . . . & Palmer, C. G. (2010). Deaf adults' reasons for genetic testing depend on cultural affiliation: results from a prospective, longitudinal genetic counseling and testing study.

Journal of Deaf Studies and Deaf Education, 15 (3), 209–227.

Boutell, J. M., Thomas, P., Neal, J. W., Weston, V. J., Duce, J., Harper, P. S., & Jones, A. L. (1999). Aberrant interactions of transcriptional repressor proteins with the Huntington's disease gene product, huntingtin. *Human Molecular Genetics, 8*(9), 1647–55.

Briggs, F. B., Shao, X., Goldstein, B. A., Oksenberg, J. R., Barcellos, L. F., & De Jager, P. L. (2011). Genome-wide association study of severity in multiple sclerosis. *Genes and Immunity 12*(8), 615–625.

Brooks, D. G. (2004). The neurofibromatosis: Hereditary predisposition to multiple peripheral nerve umors. *Neurosurgery Clinics of North America, 15*(2), 145–55.

Burgunder, J. M., Guttman, M., Perlman, S., Goodman, N., van Kammen, D. P., & Goodman, L. (2011). An international survey-based algorithm for the pharmacologic treatment of chorea in Huntington's disease. *PloS Currents Huntington Disease*, Retrieved from http://currents.plos.org/hd?s=burgunder

Burson, C. M., & Markey, K. R. (2001). Genetic counseling issues in predictive genetic testing for familial adult-onset neurologic diseases. *Seminar Pediatric Neurology, 8*(3), 177–86.

Burton, B. K., Grange, D. K., Milanowski, A., Vockley, G., Fellet, F., Crombez, E. A., . . . & Dorenbaum, A. (2007). The response of patients with phenylketonuria and elevated serum phenylalanine to treatment with oral sapropterin dihydrochloride (6R-tetrahydrobiopterin): a phase II, multicenter, open-label, screening study. *Journal of Inherited Metabolic Disease, 30*(5), 700–707.

Caballol, N., Martí, M. J., & Tolosa, E. (2007). Cognitive dysfunction and dementia in Parkinson disease. *Movement Disorders, 22*(Suppl 17), S358–S366.

Campuzano, V., Montermini, L., Moltò, M.D., Pianese, L., Cossée, M., Cavalcanti, F., . . . Pandolfo, M. (1996). Friedreich's ataxia: Autosomal recessive disease caused by an intronic GAA triplet repeat expansion. *Science, 271*(5254), 1423–7.

Canadian Organization for Rare Disorders. (2012). Newborn Screening in Canada Status Report. Retrieved from http://raredisorders.ca/documents/CanadaNBSstatusupdatedJan.132012.pdf

Carlesi, C., Pasquali, L., Piazza, S., Lo Gerfo, A., Caldarazzo Ienco, E., Alessi, R., . . . Siciliano, G. (2011). Strategies for clinical approach to neurodegeneration in amyotrophic lateral sclerosis. *Archinves Italiennes de Biologie, 149*(1), 151–67.

Carunchio, I., Curcio, L., Pieri, M., Pica, F., Caioli, S., Viscomi, M. T., . . . Zona, C. (2010). Increased levels of p70S6 phosphorylation in the G93A mouse model of amyotrophic lateral sclerosis and in valine-exposed cortical neurons in culture. *Experimental Neurology, 226*(1), 218–230.

Cederbaum, S. (2002). Phenylketonuria: an Update. *Current Opinions in Pediatrics, 14*(6), 702706.

Chan, P.K., Torres, R., Yandim, C., Law, P., Khadayate, S., Mauri, M., . . . Festenstein, R. (2013). Heterochromatinization induced by GAA-repeat hyperexpansion in Friedreich's ataxia can be reduced upon HDAC inhibition by Vitamin B3. *Human Molecular Genetics, 22*(13), 2662–2675.

Chio, A., Calvo, A., Moglia, C., Mazzini, L., Mora, G., & Parals Study Group. (2011). Phenotypic heterogeneity of amyotrophic lateral sclerosis: A population based study. *Journal of Neurology, Neurosurgery & Psychiatry, 82*(7), 740–746.

Chiò, A., Borghero, G., Restagno, G., Mora, G., Drepper, C., Traynor, B.J., . . . Sabatelli, M. (2012). Clinical characteristics of patients with familial amyotrophic lateral sclerosis carrying the pathogenic GGGGCC hexanucleotide repeat expansion of C9ORF72. *Brain, 135*(Pt 3), 784–793.

Chow, C.Y., Landers, J.E., Bergren, S.K., Sapp, P.C., Grant, A.E., Jones, J.M., . . . Meisler, M.H. (2011). Deleterious variants of FIG4, a phosphoinositide phosphatase, in patients with ALS. *American Journal of Human Genetics, 84*(1), 85–88.

Cleveland, D.W. & Rothstein, J.D. (2001). Review from Charcot to Lou Gehrig: Deciphering selective motor neuron death in ALS. *Nature Reviews: Neuroscience, 2*(11), 806–19.

Cluskey, S. & Ramsden, D.B. (2001). Mechanisms of neurodegeneration in amyotrophic lateral sclerosis. *Molecular Pathology, 54*(6), 386–392.

Compston, A., & Coles, A. (2008). Multiple Sclerosis. *Lancet, 372*(9648), 1502–1517.

Corrado, L., Carlomagno, Y., Falasco, L., Mellone, S., Godi, M., Cova, E., . . . D'Alfonso, S. (2011). A novel peripherin gene (PRPH) mutation identified in one sporadic amyotrophic lateral sclerosis patient. *Neurobiology of Aging, 32*(3), 552 e1-6.

Costa, R.M., & Silva, A.J. (2002). Molecular and cellular mechanisms underlying the cognitive deficits associated with neurofibromatosis 1. *Journal of Child Neurology, 17*(8), 622-626.

Crauford, D., & Snowden, J. (2002). Neuropyschological and Neuropsychiatric aspects of Huntington's disease. In Bates G, Harper P, and Jones L. (Eds.) Huntington's Disease—Third Edition. Oxford: Oxford University Press. pp. 62–87.

Cree, B.A., Rioux, J.D., McCauley, J.L., Gourraud, P.A., Goyette, P., McElroy, J., . . . Hauser, S.L. (2010). A major histocompatibility Class I locus contributes to multiple sclerosis susceptibility independently from HLA-DRB1*15:01. *PLoS One, 5*(6), e11296.

Cronin, S., Hardiman, O., & Traynor, B.J. (2007). Ethnic variation in the incidence of ALS: A systematic review. *Neurology, 68,*1002–1007.

Davie, C.A. (2008). A review of Parkinson's disease. *British Medical Bulletin, 86*(1): 109–27.

de Lau L.M. & Breteler, M.M. (2006). Epidemiology of Parkinson's disease. *Lancet Neurology, 5*(6), 525–535.

Deng, H.-X., Chen, W., Hong, S.-T., Boycott, K. M., Gorrie, G. H., Siddique, N., . . . Sidduque, T. (2011). Mutations in UBQLN2 cause dominant X-linked juvenile and adult-onset ALS and ALS/dementia. *Nature 477*, 211–215.

Di Maio, L., Squitieri, F., Napolitano, G., Campanella, G, Trofatter, J.A., & Conneally, P.M. (1993). Suicide risk in Huntington's disease. *Journal of Medical Genetics, 30*(4): 293–5.

Ding, Y., Leng, J., Fan, F., Xia, B., & Xu, P. (2013). The role of mitochondrial DNA mutations in hearing loss. *Biochemical Genetics, 51*(7-8), 588–602.

Driver-Dunckley, E., & Caviness, J.N. (2007). Huntington's disease. In Schapira AHV. (Ed.) *Neurology and Clinical Neuroscience.* Mosby Elsevier. pp. 879–885.

Durr, A., Cossee, M., Agid, Y., Campuzano, V., Mignard, C., Penet, C....Koenig, M. (1996). Clinical and genetic abnormalities in patients with Friedreich's ataxia. *New England Journal of Medicine, 335*(16), 1169–75.

Dyer, R.B., & McMurray, C.T. (2001). Mutant protein in Huntington disease is resistant to proteolysis in affected brain. *Nature Genetics, 29*(3), 270–278.

Erwin, C., Williams, J., Juhl, A., Mengeling, M., Mills, J., Bombard, Y....Paulson, J. (2010). Perception, experience, and response to genetic discrimination in Huntington disease: The international RESPOND-HD study. *American Journal of Medical Genetics Part B: Neuropsychiatric Genetics 153B*, 1081–1093.

Evans, D.G. (2009). Neurofibromatosis type 2 (NF2) a clinical and molecular review. *Orphanet Journal of Rare Diseases, 4*(16), doi:10.1186/1750-1172-4-16.

Ferner, N.E. (2007). Neurofibromatosis 1 and neurofibromatosis 2: A twenty first century perspective. *Lancet Neurology, 6*(4), 340–351.

Ferraiuolo, L., Kirby, J., Grierson, A.J., Sendtner, M., & Shaw, P.J. (2011). Molecular pathways of motor neuron injury in amyotrophic lateral sclerosis. *Nature Reviews Neurology, 7*(11), 16–30.

Freedman, M.S. (2011). Long-term follow-up of clinical trials of multiple sclerosis therapies. *Neurology, 76*(1), S26–34.

Freire, C, & Koifman, S. (2012). Pesticide exposure and Parkinson's disease: Epidemiological evidence of association. *Neurotoxicology, 33*(5), 947–71.

Friedman, J.M. (1999). Epidemiology of Neurofibromatosis Type 1. *American Journal of Medical Genetics, 89*(1), 1–6.

Friedman, T.B, & Griffith, A.J. (2003). Human non-syndromic sensorineural deafness. *Annual Review of Genomics and Human Genetics, 4*, 341–402.

Garber, K.B., Visootsak, J., & Warren, S.T. (2008). Fragile X syndrome. *European Journal of Human Genetics, 16*(6), 666–672.

Gauthier, L.R., Charrin, B.C., Borrell-Pagès, M., Dompierre, J.P., Rangone, H., Cordelières, F.P., . . .

Saudou, F. (2004). Huntingtin controls neurotrophic support and survival of neurons by enhancing BDNF vesicular transport along microtubules. *Cell, 118*(1), 127–138.

Gilden, D.H. (2005). Infectious causes of multiple sclerosis. *Lancet Neurology, 4*(3), 195–202.

Goldberg, Y.P., Nicholson, D.W., Rasper, D.M., Kalchman, M.A., Koide, H.B., Graham, R.K., . . . Hayden MR. (1996). Cleavage of huntingtin by apopain, a proapoptotic cysteine protease, is modulated by the polyglutamine tract. *Nature Genetics, 13*(4), 442–449.

Goodwin, V.A., Richards, S.H., Taylor, R.S., Taylor, A.H., & Campbell, J.L. (2008). The effectiveness of exercise interventions for people with Parkinson's disease: a systematic review and meta-analysis. *Movement Disorders, 23*(5), 631–640.

Graveland, G.A., Williams, R.S., & DiFiglia, M. (1985) Evidence for degenerative and regenerative changes in neostriatal spiny neurons in Huntington's Disease. *Science, 227*(4688), 770–773.

Greenway, M.J., Andersen, P.M., Russ, C., Ennis, S., Cashman, S., Donaghy, C., . . . Hardiman, O. (2006). ANG mutations segregate with familial and 'sporadic' amyotrophic lateral sclerosis. *Nature Genetics, 38*(4), 411–413.

Gregory, S.G., Schmidt, S., Seth, P., Oksenberg, J.R., Hart, J., Prokop, A., . . . Multiple Sclerosis Genetics Group. (2007). Interleukin 7 receptor alpha chain (IL7R) shows allelic and functional association with multiple sclerosis. *Nature Genetics, 39*(9), 1083–1091.

Gros-Louis, F., Gaspar, C., & Rouleau, G.A. (2006). Genetics of familial and sporadic amyotrophic lateral sclerosis. *Biochimica et Biophysica Acta (BBA)—Molecular Basis of Disease, 1762*(11-12), 956–972.

Groves, M., van Duijn, E., Anderson, K., Craufurd, D., Edmondson, M.C., Goodman, N., . . . Goodman L. (2011). An international survey-based algorithm for the pharmacologic treatment of irritability in Huntington's disease. *PLoS Current Huntington Disease*. Retrieved from http://currents.plos.org/hd?s=groves

Gunawardena, S., Her, L.S., Brusch, R.G., Laymon, R.A., Niesman, I.R., Gordesky-Gold, B. . . . Goldstein, L.S. (2003). Disruption of axonal transport by loss of huntingtin or expression of pathogenic polyQ proteins in Drosophila. *Neuron, 40*(1), 25–40.

Gürtler, N., & Lalwani, A.K. (2002). Etiology of syndromic and nonsyndromic sensorineural hearing loss. *Otolaryngolic Clinics of North America, 35*(4), 891–908.

Haasan-Smith, G., & Douglas, M.R. (2011). Management and prognosis of multiple sclerosis. *British Journal of Hospital Medicine, 72*(11), M174–176.

Haslam, R.H.A. (2007). Neurocutaneous syndromes.

In: Kliegman RM, Behrman RE, Jenson HB, Stanton BF (Eds), Nelson Textbook of Pediatrics. 18th ed. Philadelphia PA: Saunders Elsevier.

He, D., Xu, Z., Dong, S., Zhang, H., Zhou, H., Wang, L., & Zhang, S. (2012). Teriflunomide for multiple sclerosis. In Zhou, Hongyu. Cochrane database of systematic reviews (Online) 12: CD009882.

Healy, B.C., Liguori, M., Tran, D., Chitnis, T., Glanz, B., Wolfish, C., . . . De Jager, P.L. (2010). HLA B*44: protective effects in MS susceptibility and MRI outcome measures. *Neurology 75*(7), 634–640.

Hećimović, S., Klepac, N., Vlasić, J., Vojta, A., Janko, D., Skarpa-Prpić, I., . . . Pavelić, K. (2002). Genetic background of Huntington's disease in Croatia: Molecular analysis of CAG, CCG, and Δ2642 (E2642del) Polymorphisms. *Human Mutations, 20*(3), 233.

Heesen, C., Mohr, D.C., Huitinga, I., Bergh, F.T., Gaab, J., Otte, C., & Gold, S.M. (2007). Stress regulation in multiple sclerosis: current issues and concepts. *Multiple Sclerosis, 13*(2), 143–148.

Heinsen, H., Strik, M., Bauer, M., Luther, K., Ulmas, G., . . . Götz, M. (1994). Cortical and striatal neurone number in Huntington's disease. *Acta Neuropathologica, 88*, 320–333.

Hermel, E., Gafni, J., Propp, S.S., Leavitt, B.R., Wellington, C.L., Young, J.E., . . . Ellerby, LM. (2004). Specific caspase interactions and amplification are involved in selective neuronal vulnerability in Huntington's disease. *Cell Death Differentiation, 11*(4), 424–438.

Hersch, S., Jones, R., Koroshetz, W., & Quaid, K. (1994). The Neurogenetics Genie: Testing for the HD Mutation. *Neurology, 44*(8).

Heutink, P. (2006). PINK-1 and DJ-1—new genes for autosomal recessive Parkinson's disease. *Journal of Neural Transmission. Supplement, 70*(70), 215–9.

Hilker, R., Pilatus, U., Eggers, C., Hagenah, J., Roggendorf, J., Baudrexel, S., . . . Hattingen, E. (2012). The bioenergetic status relates to dopamine neuron loss in familial PD with PINK1 mutations. *PLos One, 7*(12), e51308, Retrieved From: http://www.plosone.org/article/info%3Adoi%2F10.1371%2Fjournal.pone.0051308

Hofman, K. J., Steel, G., Kazazian, H. H. & Valle, D. (1991). Phenylketonuria in U.S. blacks: molecular analysis of the phenylalanine hydroxylase gene. *American Journal of Human Genetics, 48*(4), 791–798. Retrieved from: www.ncbi.nlm.nih.gov/pmc/articles/PMC1682942/

Institute of Medicine (IOM) (2009). *Neurologic disorders. Veterans and Agent Orange: Update 2008.* Washington D.C.: The National Academies Press. pp. 510–545. ISBN 0-309-13884-1.

Jankovic, J. (2008). Parkinson's disease: clinical features and diagnosis. *Journal of Neurology, Neurosurgery, and Psychiatry, 79*(4), 368–376.

Johnson, W.G. (2000). Review Late-onset neurodegenerative diseases--the role of protein insolubility. *Journal of Anatomy, 196*(Pt 4), 609–16.

Kanekura, K., Nishimoto, I., Aiso, S., & Matsuoka, M. (2006). Characterization of amyotrophic lateral sclerosis-linked P56S mutation of vesicle-associated membrane protein-associated protein B (VAPB/ALS8). *Journal of Biological Chemistry, 281*(40), 30223–33.

Kegel, K.B., Meloni, A.R., Yi, Y., Kim, Y.J., Doyle, E., Cuiffo, B.G.... DiFiglia, M. (2002). Huntingtin is present in the nucleus, interacts with the transcriptional corepressor C-terminal binding protein, and represses transcription. *Journal of Biological Chemistry, 277*(9), 7466–76.

Kenneson, A., Van Naarden Braun, K., & Boyle, C. (2002). GJB2 (Connexin 26) Variants and Nonsyndromic sensorineural hearing loss: a HuGE review. *Genetic Medicine, 4*(4), 258–274.

Kluwe L. (2006) Schwannomatosis. Atlas of Genetics and Cytogenetics in Oncology and Hematology. Retrieved from: http://AtlasGeneticsOncology.org/Kprones/SchwannomatID10122.html.

Kochhar, A., Fischer, S.M., Kimberling, W.J., & Smith, R.J. (2007). Branchio-oto-renal syndrome. *American Journal of Medical Genetics A, 143A*(14), 1671–1678.

Koontz, N.A., Wiens, A.L., Agarwal, A., Hingtgen, C.M., Emerson, R.E., & Mosier, K.M. (2013) Schwannomatosis: The overlooked neurofibromatosis? *American Journal of Roentgenology, 200*(6), W646–653.

LaJeunesse, D.R., McCartney, B.M., & Fehon, R.G. (1998). Structural analysis of Drosophila Merlin reveals functional domains important for growth control and subcellular localization. *Journal of Cell Biology, 141*(7), 1589–99.

Lesage, S. & Brice, A. (2009). Parkinson's disease: From monogenic forms to genetic susceptibility factors. *Human Molecular Genetics 18*(R1): R48–859.

Lewitt, P.A., Rezai, A.R., Leehey, M.A., Ojeman, S.G., Flaherty, A.W., . . . Feigin, A. (2011). AAV2-GAD gene therapy for advanced Parkinson's disease: a double-blind, sham-surgery controlled, randomised trial. *Lancet Neurology, 10*(4): 309–319.

Li, S.H., Cheng, A.L., Zhou, H., Lam, S., Rao, M., Li, H., & Li, X.J. (2002). Interaction of Huntington disease protein with transcriptional activator Sp1. *Molecular Cell Biology, 22*(5), 1277–1287.

Litzinger, M.H. & Litzinger, M. (2009). Multiple Sclerosis: A Therapeutic Overview. *US Pharmacist, 34*(1), HS3-HS9.

Lohmann, E., Periquet, M., Bonifati, V., Wood, N.W., De Michele, G., Bonnet, A.M., . . . Brice, A. (2003). How much phenotypic variation can be attributed to parkin genotype? *Annals of Neurology, 54*(2), 176–185.

Lubin, F.D., & Reingold, S.C. (1996). Defining the clinical course of multiple sclerosis: results of an international survey. *Neurology, 46*(4), 907–911.

Ma, C.L., Su, L., Xie, J.J., Long, J.X., Wu, P., & Gu, L. (2014). The prevalence and incidence of Parkinson's disease in China: a systematic review and meta-analysis. *Journal of Neural Transmission, 121* (2), 123–134.

MacCollin, M., Chiocca, E.A., Evans, D.G., Friedman, J.M., Horvitz, R., Jaramillo, D., . . . Roach, E.S. (2005). Diagnostic criteria for schwannomatosis. *Neurology, 64*(11), 1838–1845.

MacDonald, A., Evans, S., Cochrane, B., & Wildgoose, J. (2012). Weaning infants with phenylketonuria: a review. *Journal of Human Nutrition and Diet, 25*(2), 103–110.

Marrie, R.A. (2004). Environmental risk factors in multiple sclerosis aetiology. *Lancet Neurology, 3*(12), 709.

Marshall, J.D., Beck, S., Maffei, P., & Naggert, J.K. (2007). Alström syndrome. *European Journal of Human Genetics, 15*(12):1193–202.

Martin, E., & Shapiro, J.R. (2007). Osteogenesis imperfecta:epidemiology and pathophysiology. *Current Osteoporosis Reports, 5*(3), 91–97.

Maruyama, H., Morino, H., Ito, H., Izumi, Y., Kato, H., Watanabe, Y., Kinoshita, Y., . . . Kawakami, H. (2010). Mutations of optineurin in amyotrophic lateral sclerosis. *Nature, 465*, 223–226.

Matsumoto, J., Saver, J.L., Brennan, K.C., & Ringman, J.M. (2005). Mitochondrial encephalomyopathy with lactic acidosis and stroke (MELAS). *Reviews in Neurologic Diseases, 2*(1), 30–34.

Mautner, V. F., Nguyen, R., Kutta, H., Fuensterer, C., Bokemeyer, C., Hagel, C., . . . Panse, J. (2010). Bevacizumab induces regression of vestibular schwannomas in patients with neurofibromatosis type 2. *Neuro-Oncology, 12*(1), 14–18.

McCarthy, P.A. & Maino, D.M. (2000). Alport syndrome: a review. *Clinical Eye and Vision Care, 12*(3-4), 139–150.

McClatchey, A.I., & Giovannini, M. (2005). Membrane organization and tumorigenesis—the NF2 tumor suppressor, Merlin. Genes Development, 19(19), 2265–77.

McCombe, P.A., & Henderson, R.D. (2010). Effects of gender in amyotrophic lateral sclerosis. *Gender Medicine, 7*(6), 557–570.

McElroy, J.P., Cree, B.A., Caillier, S.J., Gregersen, P.K., Herbert, J., Khan, O.A., . . . Gourraud, P.A. (2010). Refining the association of MHC with multiple sclerosis in African Americans. *Human Molecular Genetics, 19*(15), 3080–3088.

McLennan, Y., Polussa, J., Tassone, F., & Hagerman, R. (2011). Fragile X syndrome. *Current Genomics, 12*(3): 216–224.

Melean, G., Sestini, R., Ammannati, F., & Papi, L. (2004). Genetic insights into familial tumors of the nervous system. *American Journal of Medical Genetics, 129C* (1), 74–84.

Milo, R., & Kahana, E. (2010). Multiple sclerosis: Geopeidemiology, genetics and the environment. *Autoimmune Reviews, 9*(5), A387–394.

Montermini, L., Andermann, E., Labuda, M., Richter, A., Pandolfo, M., Cavalcanti, F., . . . Cocozza, S. (1997). The Friedreich ataxia GAA triplet repeat: premutation and normal lleles. *Human Molecular Genetics, 6*(8), 1261–1266.

Muangpaisan, W., Hori, H., & Brayne, C. (2009). Systematic review of the prevalence and incidence of Parkinson's disease in Asia. *Journal of Epidemiology, 19*(6), 281–293.

Muangpaisan, W., Mathews, A., Hori, H., & Seidel, D. (2011). A systematic review of the worldwide prevalence and incidence of Parkinson's disease. *Journal of the Medical Association of Thailand, 94*(6), 749–55.

National Association of Deaf (NAD) Cochlear Implant Committee. (2000) *NAD Position Statement on Cochlear Implants (2000).* Retrieved from http://www.nad.org/issues/technology/assistive-listening/cochlear-implants.

National Center for Biotechnology Information (US) (Updated 2011, January 31). Deafness. *Genes and Disease* [Internet]. Bethesda (MD): National Center for Biotechnology Information (US); 1998. Retrieved from http://www.ncbi.nlm.nih.gov/books/NBK22204/

National Collaboration Centre for Chronic Conditions (UK). (2006a). Symptomatic pharmacological therapy in Parkinson's disease (Chapter 7) (NICE Clinical Guidelines, No. 35). In *Parkinson's Disease: National Clinical Guideline for Diagnosis and Management in Primary and Secondary Care.* London: Royal College of Physicians (UK). Retrieved from http://www.ncbi.nlm.nih.gov/books/NBK48523/

National Collaboration Centre for Chronic Conditions (UK). (2006b). Surgery for Parkinson's disease (Chapter 8) (NICE Clinical Guidelines, No. 35). In *Parkinson's Disease: National Clinical Guideline for Diagnosis and Management in Primary and Secondary Care.* London: Royal College of Physicians (UK). Retrieved from http://www.ncbi.nlm.nih.gov/books/NBK48525/

National Collaborating Centre for Chronic Conditions (UK) (2006c). Other key interventions. (NICE Clinical Guidelines, No. 35). In *Parkinson's Disease: National Clinical Guideline for Diagnosis and Management in Primary and Secondary Care.* Chapter 10, pp. 135–46. London: Royal College of Physicians (UK). Retrieved from http://www.ncbi.nlm.nih.gov/books/NBK48517/

National Institute of Child Health and Human Development [NICHD]. (2006). National Institutes of Health Consensus Development Conference Statement: Phenylketonuria: Screening and Management October 16-18, 2000. Retrieved from http://www.nichd.nih.gov/publications/pubs/pku/Pages/sub3.aspx.

National Institute of Child Health and Human Development [NICHD]. (2013). Fragile X syndrome: overview. Retrieved from http://www.nichd.nih.gov/health/topics/fragilex/Pages/default.aspx

National Institute of Neurological Disorders and Stroke (NINDS). (2011). *Friedreich's Ataxia Fact Sheet.* Retrieved from www.ninds.nih.gov/disorders/friedreichs_ataxia/detail_friedreichs_ataxia.htm

National Institute of Neurological Disorders and Stroke (NINDS). (2012). *Neurofibromatosis Fact Sheet.* Retrieved from http://www.ninds.nih.gov/disorders/neurofibromatosis/detail_neurofibromatosis.htm

National Institute of Neurological Disorders and Stroke (NINDS). (2013a). *Amyotrophic Lateral Sclerosis (ALS) Fact Sheet.* Retrieved from http://www.ninds.nih.gov/disorders/amyotrophiclateralsclerosis/detail_ALS.htm

National Institutes of Health Research Portfolio Online Reporting Tools (2013). *Newborn Hearing Screening.* Retrieved from http://report.nih.gov/nihfactsheets/ViewFactSheet.aspx?csid=104

National PKU News. (2000-2013). Retrieved from http://www.pkunews.org/

Nischwitz, S., Cepok, S., Kroner, A., Wolf, C., Knop, M., Müller-Sarnowski, F., . . . Weber, F. (2010). Evidence for VAV2 and ZNF433 as susceptibility genes for multiple sclerosis. *Journal of Neuroimmunology, 227*(1-2), 162-166.

Noyce, A.J., Bestwick, J.P., Silveira-Moriyama, L., Hawkes, C.H., Giovanonni, G., Lees, A.L., Schragg, A. (2012). Meta-analysis of early nonmotor features and risk factors for Parkinson disease. *Annals of Neurology, 72*(6), 893–901.

Obeso, J.A., Rodriguez-Oroz, M.C., Goetz, C.G., Marin, C., Kordower, J.H., Rodriguez, M....Halliday, G. (2010). Missing pieces in the Parkinson's disease puzzle. *Nature Medicine, 16*(6), 653–661.

Pandolfo, M. (2009). Friedreich ataxia: The clinical picture. *Journal of Neurology, 256* (1 Suppl), 3–8.

Pardono, E., van Bever, Y., van den Ende, J., Havrenne, P.C., Iughetti, P., Maestrelli, S.R., . . . Otto PA. (2003). Waardenburg syndrome: clinical differentiation between types I and II. *American Journal of Medical Genetics A, 117a*(3) 223–235.

Paulsen, J.S., Magnotta, V.A., Mikos, A.E., Paulson, H.L., Penziner, E., Andreasen, N.C., & Nopoulos, P.C. (2006). Brain structure in preclinical Huntington's disease. *Biological Psychiatry, 59*(1), 57–63.

Peel, A.L., Rao, R.V., Cottrell, B.A., Hayden, M.R., Ellerby, L.M., & Bredesen, D.E. (2001). Double-stranded RNA-dependent protein kinase, PKR, binds preferentially to Huntington's disease (HD) transcripts and is activated in HD tissue. *Human Molecular Genetics, 10*(15), 1531–1538.

Peprah, E. (2012). Fragile X syndrome: the FMR1 CGG repeat distribution among world populations. *Annals of Human Genetics, 76*(2), 178–191.

Plotkin, S.R., Stemmer-Rachamimov, A.O., Barker, F.G., Halpin, C., Padera, T.P., Tyrrell, A., . . . di Tomaso, E. (2009). Hearing improvement after bevacizumab in patients with neurofibromatosis type 2. *New England Journal of Medicine, 361*(4), 358–367.

Plotkin, S.R., Blakeley, J.O., Evans, D.G., Hanemann, C.O., Hulsebos, T.J., Hunter-Schaedle, K. . . . Giovannini, M. (2013). Update from the 2011 International Schwannomatosis Workship: from genetics to diagnostic criteria. *American Journal of Medical Genetics. Part A, 16*(3), 405–416.

Poewe, W. (2006). The natural history of Parkinson's disease. *Journal of Neurology, 253*(Suppl 7), V112–V116.

Poorkaj, P., Nutt, J.G., James, D., Gancher, S., Bird, T.D., Steinbart, E., . . . Payami, H. (2004). Parkin mutation analysis in clinic patients with early-onset Parkinson disease. *American Journal of Medical Genetics, A129*(1), 44–50.

Powers, W. (2007). Holding steady: How physical therapy can help patients with Friedreich's Ataxia. *Advance, 18*(1), 26.

Pugliatti, M., Sotgin, S., & Rosati, G. (2002). The worldwide prevalence of multiple sclerosis. *Clinical Neurology & Neurosurgery, 104*(3), 182–191.

Quinn, L., & Busee, M. (2012). Development of physiotherapy guidance and treatment-based classifications for people with Huntington's disease. *Neurodegenerative Disease Management 2* (1): 21–31. doi:10.2217/nmt.11.86.

Quizilbash, N., Mendez, I., & Sanchez-de la Rosa, R. (2012). Benefit-risk analysis of glatiramer acetate for relapsing-remitting and clinically isolated syndrome multiple sclerosis. *Clinical Therapeutics, 34*(1), 159–176.

Ramagopalan, S.V., Heger, A., Berlanga, A.J., Maugeri, N.J., Lincoln, M.R., Burrell, A., . . . Knight, J.C. (2010). A ChIP-seq defined genome-wide map of vitamin D receptor binding: associations with disease and evolution. *Genome Research 20,* 1352–1360.

Rasmussen, S.A., & Friedman, J.M. (2000). NF1 gene and neurofibromatosis 1. *American Journal of Epidemiology, 151*(1), 33–40.

Rubinsztein, D. C., Leggo, J., Goodburn, S., Barton, D. E. & Ferguson-Smith, M. A. (1995). Haplotype analysis of the delta 2642 and (CAG)n polymorphisms in the Huntington's disease (HD) gene provides an explanation for an apparent 'founder' HD haplotype. *Human Molecular Genetics, 4,* 203–206.

Sabatelli, M., Madia, F., Conte, A., Luigetti, M., Zollino, M., Mancuso, I., & Tonali, P. (2008). Natural history of young-adult amyotrophic lateral sclerosis. *Neurology, 71*(12): 876–881.

Santoro, M.R., Bray, S.M., & Warren, S.T. (2012). Molecular mechanisms of Fragile X syndrome: a twenty-year perspective. *Annual Review of Pathology: Mechanisms of Disease, 7,* 219–45.

Sawcer, S., Hellenthal, G., Pirinen, M., Spencer, C.C., Patsopoulos, N.A., Moutsianas, L., . . . Compston, A. (2011). Genetic risk and a primary role for cell-mediated immune mechanisms in multiple sclerosis. *Nature, 476*(7359), 214–219.

Schnur, R.E. (2012). Type 1 Neurofibromatosis: a geno-oculodermatolig update. *Current Opinion in Opthalmology, 23*(5), 364–372.

Schulz, J.B., Boesch, S., Burk, K., Dürr, A., Giunti, P., Mariotti, C....Pandolfo, M. (2009). Diagnosis and treatment of Friedreich ataxia: a European perspective. *Nature Reviews Neurology, 10,* 2222–2234.

Schwartz, P.J., Spazzolini, C., Crotti, L., Bathen, J., Amlie, J.P., Timothy, K., . . . Denjoy, I. (2007). The Jervell and Lange-Nielsen syndrome: natural history, molecular basis, and clinical outcome. *Circulation, 113*(6), 783–790.

Seltzer, S.M., Baker, M.W., Hong, J., Maenner, M., Greenberg, J., & Mandel, D. (2012). Prevalence of CGG expansions of the FMR1 gene in a US population-based sample. *American Journal of Medical Genetics Part B, Neuropsychiatric Genetics, 159B*(5), 589–597.

Sestini, R., Bacci, C., Provenzano, A., Genuardi, M., & Papi, L. (2008) Evidence of a four-hit mechanism involving SMARCB1 and NF2 in Schwannomatosis-Associated Schwannomas. *Human Mutation, 29,* 227–231.

Seznec, H., Simon, D., Bouton, C., Reutenauer, L., Hertzog, A., Golik, P., . . . Puccio H. (2005) Friedreich ataxia: the oxidative stress paradox. *Human Molecular Genetics, 14*(4), 463–474.

Sharp, A.H., Loev, S.J., Schilling, G., Li, S.H., Li, X.J., Bao, J., . . . Lo, A. (1995). Widespread expression of Huntington's disease gene (IT15) protein product. *Neuron, 14*(5), 1065–74.

Shokrgozar, M.A., Sarial, S., Amirzargar, A., Shokri, F., Rezaei, N., Arjang, Z., . . . Lotfi, J. (2009). IL-2, IFN-gamma, and IL-12 gene polymorphisms and susceptibility to multiple sclerosis. *Journal of Clinical Immunology, 29*(6), 747–751.

Smith, J. A., Michie, S., Stephenson, M., & Quarrell, O. (2002). Risk perception and decision-making processes in candidates for genetic testing for Huntington's disease: An interpretive phenomenological analysis. *Journal of Health Psychology 7*(2), 131–144.

Smith, R.J., Shearer, A.E., Hildebrand, M.S., & Van Kamp, G. Deafness and Hereditary Hearing Loss Overview. 1999 Feb 14 [Updated 2013 Jan 3]. In: Pagon RA, Adam MP, Bird TD, *et al.,* (Eds.) GeneReviews™ [Internet]. Seattle (WA): University of Washington, Seattle; 1993-2013. Retrieved from: http://www.ncbi.nlm.nih.gov/books/NBK1434/

Stumpf, D.A., Alksne, J.F., & Annegers, J.F. (1988). Neurofibromatosis. Conference statement. National

Institutes of Health Consensus Development Conference. *Archives of Neurology, 45*, 575–578.

Sutedja, N.A., Fischer, K., Veldink, J.H., van der Heijden, G.J., Kromhout, H., Heederik, D., . . . van den Berg, A.H. (2009). What we truly know about occupation as a risk factor for ALS: a critical and systematic review. *Amyotrophic Lateral Sclerosis, 10*(5–6): 295–301.

Tajouri, L., Ovcaric, M., Curtain, R., Johnson, M.P., Griffiths, L.R., Csurhes, P., . . . Lea, R.A. (2005). Variation in the vitamin D receptor gene is associated with multiple sclerosis in an Australian population. *Journal of Neurogenetics, 19*(1), 25–38.

Tanner, C.M., Kamel, F., Ross, G.W., Hoppin, J.N., Goldman, S.M., Korrell, M., . . . Langston, J.W. (2011). Rotenone, Paraquat and Parkinson's Disease. *Environmental Health Perspectives, 119*(6), 866–872.

Tassone, F., Iong, K.P., Tong, T.H., Lo, J., Gane, L.W., Berry-Kravis, E., . . . Hagerman, R.J. (2012). FMR1 CGG allele size and prevalence ascertained through newborn screening in the United States. *Genome Medicine, 4*(12), 100. doi:10.1186/gm401.

Trovó-Marqui, A.B., & Tajara, E.H. (2006). Neurofibromin: a general outlook. *Clinical Genetics, 70*(1), 1–13.

Trushina, E., Dyer, R.B., Badger, J.D., Ure, D., Eide, L., Tran, D.D., . . . McMurray, C.T. (2004). Mutant huntingtin impairs axonal trafficking in mammalian neurons in vivo and *in vitro*. *Molecular Cell Biology, 24*(18), 8195–209.

Tsang, B.K., & Macdonell, R. (2011). Multiple sclerosis- diagnosis, management and prognosis. *Australian Family Physician, 40*(12), 948–955.

Turner, G., Webb, T., Wake, S., & Robinson, H. (1996). Prevalence of fragile X syndrome. *American Journal of Medical Genetics, 64*(1), 196–197.

Upadhyaya, M., Fryer, A., MacMillan, J., Broadhead, J., Huson, S.M., & Harper, P.S. (1992). Prenatal diagnosis and presymptomatic detection of neurofibromatosis Type 1. *Journal of Medical Genetics, 29*(3), 180–183.

United States National Library of Medicine (2013). PAH. In *Genetics Home Reference* [online]. Retrieved from ghr.nlm.nih.go/gene/PAH

United States Preventive Services Task Force. (2009). Screening for Phenylketonuria: Reaffirmation recommendation Statement. *American Family Physician, 80*(12), 1466–1467.

Van Damme, P., Veldink, J. H., van Blitterswijk, M., Corveleyn, A., van Vught, P. W. J., Thijs, V., . . . Robberecht, W. (2011). Expanded ATXN2 CAG repeat size in ALS identifies genetic overlap between ALS and SCA2. *Neurology, 76*, 2066–2072.

van den Munckhof, P., Christiaans, I., Kenter, S.B., Baas, F., & Hulsebos, R.J.M. (2012). Germline SMARCB1 mutation predisposes to multiple meningiomas and schwannomas with preferential lo-cation of cranial meningiomas at the falx cerebri. *Neurogenetics, 13*, 1–7.

Van Maele-Fabry, G., Hoet, P., Vilain, F., & Lison, D. (2012). Occupational exposure to pesticides and Parkinson's disease: a systematic review and meta-analysis of cohort studies. *Environment International 46*, 30–43.

Vance, C., Rogelj, B., Hortobágyi, T., De Vos, K.J., Nishimura, A.L., Sreedharan, J., . . . Shaw, C.E. (2009). Mutations in FUS, an RNA processing protein, cause familial amyotrophic lateral sclerosis type 6. *Science, 323*(5918), 1208–1211.

Venci, J.V., & Gandhi, M.A. (2013). Dimethyl Fumarate (Tecfidera): A new oral agent for multiple sclerosis. *The Annals of Pharmacotherapy, 47*(12), 1697–1702.

von Campenhausen, S., Bornschein, B., Wick, R., Bötzel, K., Sampaio, C., Poewe, W., ... Dodel, R. (2005). Prevalence and incidence of Parkinson's disease in Europe. *European Neuropsychopharmacology, 15*(4), 473–490.

Walker, F.O. (2007). Huntington's disease. *Lancet, 369*(9557), 218–228.

Willems, P.J. (2000). Genetic causes of hearing loss. *New England Journal of Medicine, 342*(15), 1101–1119.

Williams, R.A., Mamotte, C.D., & Burnette, J.R. (2008). Phenylketonuria: an inborn error of phenylalanine metabolism. *Clinical Biochemistry Reviews, 29*(1), 31–41.

Wills, W.A., Evanoff, B.A., Lian, M., Criswell, S.R., & Racette, B.A. (2010) Geographic and ethnic variation in Parkinson disease: a population-based study of US Medicare beneficiaries. *Neuroepidemiology, 34*, 143–151.

World Health Organization. (2008). Atlas: *Multiple Sclerosis Resources in the World*. Retrieved from: http://www.who.int/mental_health/neurology/Atlas_MS_WEB.pdf

Worms, P.M. (2001). The epidemiology of motor neuron diseases: a review of recent studies. *Journal of Neurological Science, 191*, 3–9.

Yasuno, K., Bilguvar, K., Bijlenga, P., Low, S.K., Krischek, B., Auburger, G., . . . Günel, M. (2010). Genome-wide association study of intracranial aneurysm identifies three new risk loci. *Nature Genetics, 42*(5), 420–425.

Yaday, S., Hasan, N., Marjot, T., Khan, M.S., Prasad, K., Bentley, P., . . . Sharma, P. (2013). Detailed analysis of gene polymorphisms associate with ischemic stroke in South Asians. *PLoS One, 8*(3), e57305.

Yeo, T.W., De Jager, P.L., Gregory, S.G., Barcellos, L.F., Walton, A., Goris, A., . . . Sawcer, S. (2007). A second major histocompatibility complex susceptibility locus for multiple sclerosis. *Annals of Neurology, 61*(3), 228–236.

Zhao, H., Young, W.Y., Yan, Q., Li, R., Cao, J., Wang,

Q., . . . Guan, M.X. (2005). Functional characterization of the mitochondrial 12S rRNA C1494T mutation associated with aminoglycoside-induced and non-syndromic hearing loss. *Nucleic Acids Research, 33*(3), 1132–1139.

Zuccato, C., Ciammola, A., Rigamonti, D., Leavitt, B.R., Goffredo, D., Conti, L., . . . Cattaneo, E. (2001). Loss of huntingtin-mediated BDNF gene transcription in Huntington's disease. *Science, 293*(5529), 493–498.

Chapter 14

Endocrine Disorders

CATHERINE LING, Ph.D, FNP-BC, FAANP

LUCIA NOVAK, MSN, ANP-BC, BC-ADM

Objectives:

- Recognize the genetic inheritance patterns of complex endocrine disorders.
- Describe the genetic etiology of complex metabolic diseases like T2D and obesity.
- Discuss the genomics of complex metabolic diseases.
- Identify the ethical implications to be considered when offering genomic testing of endocrine disorders.

14.1. INTRODUCTION

This chapter addresses genetic inheritance patterns, risk assessment, genetic counseling concepts, and ethical issues salient for advanced practice nurses working with individuals, and families with endocrine disorders. The chapter opens by briefly discussing some of the more common single gene endocrine disorders. Because the most commonly encountered endocrine disorders are not caused by single-gene mutations, most of this chapter is devoted to describing what is known and understood about the genetics of complex endocrine disorders. The bulk of this chapter will focus on discussing endocrine disorders caused by multiple genes, or by gene-environment interactions; the relationship between genes involved in immune regulation and those involved in maintenance and normal function of endocrine systems will be highlighted. In addition, most of the content in the chapter is dedicated to discussing endocrine disorders most commonly encountered in clinical practice: Type I Diabetes Mellitus (T1D), Grave's disease (GD), Hashimoto's thyroiditis (HT), and Addison's disease (AD). Because obesity and Type 2 Diabetes Mellitus (T2D) are both significant health concerns that are approaching epidemic proportions in the United States (U.S.), this chapter will also review what is known about the genetic and environmental influences of T2D and obesity. At the end of the chapter, some of the important current and future ethical, legal, and social issues will be highlighted. The issues are not just relevant to advanced practice nurses working in direct patient care, but also are applicable to all nurses prepared at the graduate level, regardless of practice setting. There are implications for nurses working in direct patient care, education, research, and leadership roles.

14.2. INHERITANCE PATTERNS

Although some single-gene endocrine disorders are quite rare (1:30,000 babies are born with multiple endocrine neoplasia Type 1 [MEN1]), others are more common (1:2370 Americans born without a functional thyroid gland, and 1:15,000 born with Congenital Adrenal Hyperplasia). Because all nurses, regardless of specialty, may encounter individuals with these disorders, a brief review of the important genetic concepts underlying single gene and complex endocrine disorders organized by inheritance pathway is provided. For more detailed descriptions of these inheritance patterns, please see Chapter 1 in this book.

14.2.1. Selected Single-Gene Disorders

14.2.1.1. Monogenic Diabetes Types 1-6

Also known as maturity-onset diabetes of the young (MODY), this is a rare form of diabetes that manifests in childhood. The type of MODY is determined by the specific genetic mutation, with each type manifesting in a different way. In general, the genes associated with MODY play key roles in beta-cell function, and lead to altered patterns of glucose-stimulated insulin secretion or premature apoptosis (cell death). Both of these result in hyperglycemia (Table 15.1).

14.2.1.2. Multiple Endocrine Neoplasia Type 1 (MEN1)

MEN1 is caused by a loss-of-function mutation in the MEN1 gene, which is a tumor suppressor gene located on chromosome 11. These patients are at a very high risk for developing tumors that involve a number of different endocrine glands (i.e. the pituitary, parathyroid, and pancreas). Pancreatic tumors that are more common in patients with MEN1 include both insulinomas and gastrinomas.

14.2.1.3. Multiple Endocrine Neoplasia Type 2 (MEN2) A/B

MEN2 is caused by a gain-of-function mutation of the RET oncogene (tyrosine kinase receptor) on chromosome 10. Patients with MEN2 Type A commonly develop medullary thyroid cancer, pheochromocytoma, hyperparathyroidism, and lichen amyloidosis. Patients with MEN2 Type B develop medullary thyroid cancer, ganglioneuromas, pheochromocytoma, and may have characteristic physical features similar to patients with Marfan syndrome (i.e., long limbs, arachnodactyly, and hyperlaxity). For more information, an excellent review by Moline and Eng (2013) is available at http://www.ncbi.nlm.nih.gov/books/NBK1257/.

14.2.1.4. Congenital Adrenal Hyperplasia (CAH)

Almost 90% of cases of congenital adrenal hyperplasia (CAH) are caused by mutations or deletions in the CYP21A gene, causing a deficiency in 21-hydroxylase. Mutations or partial deletions in this gene are common, particularly in Ashkenazi Jews (as high as 1 in 3) and Northern Europeans (as high as 1 in 60); CAH is an autosomal recessive disorder, and only 1 in 15,000 live-born infants have classic CAH symptoms (Wilson, 2012, Nimkarn, & New 2013). 21-OHD muta-

tions cause enzyme deficiencies that culminate in decreased cortisol production, adrenal hyperplasia, and increased androgen production. Classic CAH manifestations begin in utero. Female infants with CAH are often born with ambiguous genitalia and pseudohermaphroditism. Males may have normal external genitalia in infancy, because fetal androgens are produced in the testes, but they develop precocious puberty in infancy and early childhood. Metabolic symptoms include saltwasting and chronic adrenal insufficiency. Nonclassic CAH is typically caused by partial enzyme deficiency, and affected individuals manifest milder symptoms of hyperandrogenism, which occurs later in life. CAH is included in newborn screening programs in the United States.

14.2.1.5. Autoimmune Polyendocrine Syndrome Type 1 (APS 1)

APS 1 is the rarest form of the autoimmune polyendocrine syndromes (APS) and also the only one of the three APS types that is both Autosomal Recessive (AR) and an autoimmune disorder. APS 1 is linked to a mutation in the autoimmune regulator gene (AIRE gene), which, as its name implies, helps to regulate autoimmune function. The AIRE gene is located on the long (q) arm of chromosome 21. Although there does not appear to be an association between APS and HLA Class 2 alleles, the specific type of HLA alleles an individual has may help to determine what other autoimmune disease(s), such as T1D, vitiligo, autoimmune hepatitis, and pernicious anemia, an individual might be predisposed to developing (Barker & Eisenbarth, 2012). The AIRE gene expresses a transcription factor in the medulla of the thymus and controls the mechanism (negative selection) that prevents the immune system from attacking and destroying itself. Negative selection is the process where T cells that bind strongly to self-antigens are eliminated in the thymus. Unlike most autoimmune disorders, APS1 symptoms manifest very early in life and males and females are equally affected. The initial presentation is chronic mucocutaneous candidiasis, which presents in infancy, followed most often by autoimmune hypoparathyroidism and AD. Over half of the affected individuals will have all three conditions, and lifelong surveillance is required, because decades may separate the development of the different associated disorders. In addition to the classic three disorders, up to 60% of affected women and 14% of affected men will experience gonadal failure, and some (14%) will develop T1D before age 21.

14.2.1.6. Immune Dysregulation, Polyendocrinopathy, Enteropathy, X-linked (IPEX) Syndrome

IPEX Syndrome is a very rare disorder (fewer than 150 people diagnosed world-wide) caused by a mutation of Foxp3 gene which controls the regulatory function of CD4, CD25, and regulatory T-cells. The disease commonly presents in neonates with fatal autoimmunity, and affected children (usually males) often die in infancy, many in the first days of life. Symptoms in infants include severe watery diarrhea, T1D, thyroiditis, and dermatitis in males younger than age 6 months. Although a few children with a milder phenotype survive two to three decades, most (up to 80%) will develop T1D early in childhood and autoimmune thyroid disease has been reported (Barker & Eisenbarth, 2012; Hannibal & Torgerson, 2011).

14.2.1.7. Nephrogenic Diabetes Insipidus (NDI)

NDI is very rare (8.8/1 million), and approximately 90% are caused by mutations in the *AVPR2* gene, inherited in an X-linked recessive fashion, and 10% by mutations in the *AQP2* gene inherited in an AR manner. Both genes are involved in regulating the amount of water excreted in the urine, and mutations impair the kidneys' ability to respond to antidiuretic hormone (ADH); therefore, the kidneys do not reabsorb water properly. The disease is usually diagnosed within the first few months of life, and affected infants manifest with symptoms of failure to thrive, polyuria, polydipsia, and dehydration, particularly when the weather is hot or during illness (Knoers, 2012; U.S. National Library of Medicine [USNLM], 2013).

14.2.2. Complex Disorders

14.2.2.1. Autoimmune Disorders Associated with Endocrine Disease

HLA Mutations. The human leukocyte antigen (HLA) complex on chromosome 6p21.3, contains several hundred genes that are divided into one of two classes; HLA class I (A, B, and C) and HLA class II (DR, DM, DOA, DOB, DQ, and DP), which are associated with immune response and function. HLA mutations have been associated with virtually all autoimmune disorders and may be more deleterious than mutations that directly impact the function of the downstream organ or tissue (Skinningsrud *et al.*, 2011). Class II HLA mutations are most strongly associated with autoimmune diseases, because class II genes encode for cell-surface antigen-presenting proteins that introduce antigens from outside of the cell to T-lymphocytes, starting a cascade of events that culminate in the production of a specific antibody to that antigen. If a foreign antigen is present, antigen-presenting proteins present [TG3] the antigen to T-lymphocytes; activated T-lymphocytes stimulate T-helper cells, which in turn stimulate B-cells to create an antibody to eliminate the antigen. Regulatory T-cells (formerly called suppressor T-cells), balance the activation process and maintain tolerance to self-antigens by suppressing immune system activation and autoantibody formation. This complex process is complicated even further by the enormous diversity in the HLA genes; more than a dozen different alleles have been reported in each of the nine different Class I and II loci, and this area of genome is one of the most rapidly evolving coding regions in the human genome (Parham & Ohta, 1996). Some HLA mutations increase the risk for developing autoimmune diseases, whereas others provide protection against them. As these HLA mutations are passed down, affected family members may develop a number of different autoimmune disorders, three of which (T1D, AD, and autoimmune thyroiditis) will be discussed here.

Several HLA alleles are associated with an increased risk for T1D, most notably DQ (DQ2 and DQ8) and DR (DR3 and DR4). More than 90% of people with T1D are heterozygous for HLA DR3-DQ2 or DR4-DQ8, with the *highest risk* found in homozygous individuals. People with DR2 very rarely develop T1D, however, so mutations in DR2 may be protective (Baker, 1997; Cooper et al, 2008). Several risk alleles for the development of AD have been identified, particularly mutations in B8 (Class I) and DR3 or

DR4 (Class II) (Skinningsrud *et al.*, 2011). Autoimmune thyroid disease does not seem to be strongly associated with HLA mutations; class II genes are thought to contribute to less than 5% of the genetic risk for the development of GD or HT. The HLA mutations most consistently linked to thyroid disease are DR3 and DR4 chains and overlap with T1D (Hasham & Tomer, 2012; Tomer, 2010).

Non-HLA Complex Disorders of Autoimmune System. Several genes (CTLA-4 g, a t-cell activation suppressor; PTPN22 a T-cell receptor signaling/activation regulator; CD25 a and c controlling IL-2 receptors on regulator T-cells) located on chromosome 6 but not associated with the HLA genes have also been strongly associated with an increased risk for developing T1D and autoimmune thyroiditis (Hasham & Tomer, 2012; Huber, Menconi, Corathers, Jacobson, & Tomer, 2008; Tomer, 2010). Other non-HLA mutations have also been shown to increase the risk for developing GD, including CD40 (a B-cell antigen-presenting gene) and FOXP3 (which differentiates T-cells into regulator T-cells and affects tolerance to selfantigens). As with the HLA genes, some of the variants appear to be protective as well. For example, individuals with CTLA-4 a and t variants, and CD25 g and t variants, appear to be somewhat resistant to developing T1D, GD, and HD.

14.2.2.2. Autoantigens Associated with Endocrine Disease

Antigens stimulate the immune system to manufacture antibodies to destroy bacterial or viral invaders. Autoantigens are antigens that stimulate the immune system to manufacture antibodies that destroy normal tissue (they no longer recognize "self"), and are commonly found in autoimmune diseases. Several genes are associated with an increased risk for developing autoantigens.

Type 1 Diabetes Mellitus (T1D). Several autoantibodies are associated with T1D: Glutamic-acid decarboxylase 65 (GAD65), insulinoma-associated protein 2 (IA-2), insulin variable number tandem repeats (INS VNTR), and zinc transporter (ZnT8). One gene, INS class III (also located on chromosome 6), appears to be protective (Pietropaolo, 2013).

Hashimoto's Thyroiditis. Autoantibodies for thyroglobulin (Tg), thyroid peroxidase (TPO), and thyrotropin receptor (TSHR) blocking gene. Almost all patients with HT have high serum concentrations of antibodies to Tg and/or TPO (Davies, 2012b).

Grave's Disease (GD). Almost 100% of patients with GD are found to have thyroid-stimulating autoantibodies (THSR-Ab). These autoantibodies activate the receptor and stimulate thyroid hormone synthesis and secretion. This in turn causes thyroid growth and leads to development of a diffuse goiter that is a common characteristic of this disease (Davies, 2012a).

Congenital Adrenal Hyperplasia (CAH). Several autoantibodies are associated with CAH, most commonly CYP21A2, 21-? hydroxylase (most often); CYP11A1, 11?hydroxylase; and CYP17, 17-a-hydroxylase, all of which produce steroids (Nieman, 2013).

Autoimmune Polyglandular Syndromes (APS) Type 1, 2, and 3. There is significant overlap of both HLA class 2 genes and the non-HLA immune regulatory genes associated with T1D, GD, HT, and AD; therefore, it is quite common to see more than one autoimmune endocrine disorder (and nonendocrine autoimmune disorders) in the same individual; the disorders also tend to cluster in families (Barker & Eisenbarth, 2012). Individuals diagnosed with more than one autoimmune endocrine disease should be tested for APS, and if they are found to have it, the type (1, 2, or 3) will be determined by the specific endocrine disorders they have developed.

- *APS 1* is not HLA associated and was described earlier in this chapter under autosomal recessive pattern of inheritance.
- *APS 2* is the most common type of APS and 70% of APS 2 patients will have both AD and one of the autoimmune thyroid disorders (most often HT). Less commonly, individuals with APS 2 may have AD and T1D. APS 2 is associated with multiple HLA genes (A1, B8, DR3, DR4, and DQ) and clusters in families, but to date no identifiable inheritance pattern has emerged. As is the tendency for most autoimmune disorders, APS 2 occurs more often in young women (3:1) in their 20s and 30s. Primary hypogonadism, myasthenia gravis, and celiac disease have also been observed in this syndrome.

- *APS 3* is the co-occurrence of autoimmune thyroid disease (most often HT), with at least two other autoimmune disorders, such as T1D, celiac disease, pernicious anemia, rheumatoid arthritis, but not AD.

14.2.2.3. Obesity and Type 2 Diabetes Mellitus

Type 2 Diabetes Mellitus (T2D) and obesity can be attributed to a number of different etiologies, but the genetic underpinnings of both diseases share similar characteristics. In the broadest sense, obesity is an imbalance between energy intake and expenditure resulting in excess energy storage and T2D is impaired glucose equilibrium. When viewed from an epidemiologic perspective, clusters of cases are seen in families, communities, and racial or ethnic groups, which could easily lead an observer to believe that this is because of genetic inheritance patterns. However, familial aggregation is not the same as heritability, and very little of the total manifestation of T2D and obesity has been directly attributed to specific genetic mutations. Unlike some of the conditions noted earlier in this section, T2D and obesity can have any one of three genetic etiologies (Table 15.2.) (Mutch & Clément, 2006; Sabin, Werther, & Kiess, 2011):

Monogenetic. Rare and severe forms of obesity and T2D have been associated with nonsyndromic monogenetic changes. As noted earlier in the chapter, mutations at seven different genes have been associated with MODY. In the case of obesity, severe and early onset has been associated with alterations in genes that affect brain-derived neurotrophic factor (BDNP) and leptin (Styrkarsdottir, 2009).

Obesity can be a hallmark feature of a number of genetic syndromes, some of which may cluster within families. Prader-Willi syndrome (PWS), was the first human disorder attributed to a genomic imprinting defect, in which genes are "imprinted" (turned off or on) depending on which parent contributed the gene. PWS is a relatively common (1/15,000-1/30,000), occurs equally in males and females and most cases are sporadic and not inherited. Children normally inherit two copies of chromosome 15: one from each parent, and the section of chromosome 15 that came from the mother is turned off (methylated), so the only

functioning genes come from the baby's father. In PWS, the father's genes do not work. Three different types of genetic errors are associated with PWS; a paternal deletion (70% of cases), maternal uniparental disomy (25% of cases) or an imprinting defect (< 5% of cases). In paternal deletion, a section of paternal chromosome 15 has been deleted (or rarely that section of chromosome 15 has been involved in a translocation error). In the case of maternal uniparental disomy, the baby inherits two copies of chromosome 15 from their mother (none from their father), and both of the mother's chromosomes are silenced. While genomic imprinting defects are rare, microdeletions or other small defects in the imprinting center located close to the PWS genes on the Father's chromosome 15 may cause the gene to remain silenced (methylated), resulting in PWS. Characteristic features of PWS include neonatal failure to thrive, poor muscle tone, poor eye coordination, short stature, incomplete sexual development, and learning disabilities. One of the most prominent features of PWS is insatiable appetite contributing to the development of severe obesity, which may be life threatening (Sabin *et al.*, 2011, Driscoll, Miller, Schwartz, *et al.* 2014). Obesity is also a major feature in other genetic syndromes, including Bardet-Biedl syndrome (obesity with extra digits, degenerative ophthalmic, and renal conditions with impaired sexual and intellectual development), Cohen syndrome (later childhoodonset of obesity with impaired intellectual development, ophthalmic disorders, and poor muscle tone), Ayazi syndrome (obesity with ophthalmic and hearing disorders), and MOMO [Macrosomia, Obesity, Macrocephaly, and Ocular abnormalities] syndrome causing fetal and childhood obesity, ophthalmic disorders, and macrocephaly. A genetic syndrome should be considered when people develop early-onset severe obesity (onset < age 10 years and body mass index > 3 standard deviations above normal) (Walley, Asher, & Froguel, 2009).

Multifactorial. The most common etiology for both T2D and obesity is the interplay between genomic and environmental factors. Assessing the impact of individual genes is most difficult to isolate for several reasons: (1) the phenotype is not necessarily altered in the presence of pathologic genotype, (2) correlations between phenotype and genotype are not necessarily causal, (3) small changes in genes that contribute to obesity or T2D do not necessarily combine to create a severe form of the disease (gene effects are not additive), (4) T2D and obesity comorbidities may be related to the proximity of genes or to similar sensitivity to environmental factors, (5) current methods for isolating polygenetic-phenotypic relationships only account for 10% to 15% of T2D and < 2% of obesity, (6) genes associated with monogenetic and syndromic etiologies have also been found to play a part in polygenetic phenotypes, and (7) the relationship between environmental exposures and epigenetic changes are still very poorly understood.

T2D is a multifactorial disease; over 50 different gene loci have been associated with its development and more than 90 chromosomal regions containing single nucleotide polymorphisms (SNPs) have been linked to insulin secretion and pancreatic beta cell function genes. These have been shown to influence the development of T2D (Rosengren et al., 2012). But even these large gene regions are not homogeneous among individuals with T2D (Cornelis & Hu, 2012; Taneera et al., 2012). Given the lack of consistent causal components, it is hypothesized that several genes contribute to T2D pathology through aggregate pathways (Chen et al, 2012; de Lorenzo, Greco, Fiorentino, Mannino, & Hribal, 2013; Prokopenko, McCarthy, & Lindgren, 2008). Until more is known about the genes that contribute to T2D, diagnosis and monitoring of disease progression will continue to be based upon clinically discernible characteristics, such as elevated fasting glucose and hemoglobin A1c levels.

Obesity is very similar to T2D in that genetic, neurologic, behavioral, and endocrine pathways are all involved. The alarming global rate of obesity has often been vilified as a result of sedentary and high stress lifestyle, coupled with an overabundance of readily available, calorically dense, but nutritionally poor foods (Gluckman & Hanson, 2008; Prentice, Hennig, & Fulford, 2008). Traditional obesity treatment has focused on reducing mass and body fat through adjustment of energy balance by decreasing energy intake while simultaneously increasing energy expenditure. These approaches oversimplify the cause, effects, and treatment of obesity, however, because they do not include the genetics of metabolic metabolism. Genes regulate hunger, satiety, and inflammation, as well as energy storage and expenditure, all of which are major contributors to the pathophysiology of obesity (Chaput, Doucet, & Tremblay, 2012; Mutch & Clément, 2006; Sabin et al., 2011). To date, over 50 distinct gene loci have been associated with increased body mass (Bradfield et al., 2012; Herrera, Keildson, & Lindgren, 2011). Alteration in the FTO (Fat mass and Obesity-Associated) gene, for example, has been found in many population groups, but the gene only appears to account for approximately 1% of obesity (Herrera et al., 2011; Walley et al., 2009). Many environmental factors that will be reviewed in the epigenetics section, appear to strongly influence gene regulation, co-creating the obesity phenotype (Figure 15.1).

Like T2D, obesity is strongly associated with an increased risk for morbidity and early mortality. Obesity has been related to insulin resistance. The increasing BMI is the stressor that brings forth variance in genetic expression leading to precursors of insulin resistance which in turn can lead to other conditions such as T2D (Manning et al., 2012). There are some significant differences between the two disorders as well. The progression from risk to T2D is well defined clinically and metabolically, but the degree to which body mass is linked to disease is questionable (Chaput et al., 2012; McAuley & Blair, 2011). For example, although many obese individuals eventually receive a diagnosis of T2D, many obese individuals never have metabolic impairment (Stephens, 2012).

Although epidemiologic data have consistently shown that obesity and T2D clusters within both families and ethnic groups, no single "obesity" or "T2D" gene has been identified. There are several theories for why a putative gene (or genes) has (have) not been found: (1) redundant genetic pathways contribute to the various pathologies so that changes in different areas create the same pathologic outcome (Morris et al., 2012), (2) similar diabetes risk alleles and SNPs have been found in multiple ethnic populations though at differing prevalence rates (Haiman et al., 2012; Parchwani, Murthy, Upadhyah, & Patel, 2013; Yang et al., 2010; Zia, 2013), (3) high risk gene mutations occur infrequently or only manifest when present in combination with other high risk genes (Manolio et al., 2009) and "net-

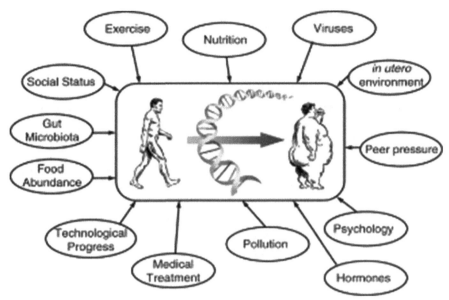

FIGURE 14.1. Figure and figure title originally found in and is attributed to Mutch, D. M., & Clément, K. (2006). Unraveling the Genetics of Human Obesity. PLoS Genetics, 2(12), e188. doi:10.1371/journal.pgen.0020188 This is an open-access article distributed under the terms of the Creative Commons Attribution License, which permits unrestricted use, distribution, and reproduction in any medium, provided the original author and source are credited.

work" etiology makes causal distinctions difficult (Meng, Mäkinen, Luk, & Yang, 2013), and 4) the answer may lie in epigenetic expression resulting from gene-environment interaction (Chen *et al.*, 2012).

Epigenetics, discussed in detail in Chapter 1, is a change in gene expression that occurs without changing the genetic code itself; the "spelling" of the gene is normal, but the gene cannot be accessed to transform it into an appropriate "downstream" product (Drong, Lindgren, & McCarthy, 2012). Epigenetic changes can cause the gene to be silenced ("turned off") or over expressed ("turned on"). In T2D, environmental factors such as stress and starvation can trigger the creation of microRNAs (miRNA), which have been shown to impair B cell function (Guay, Roggli, Nesca, Jacovetti, & Regazzi, 2011), causing short-term (immediate), latent, and/or long term (heritable) responses (Campión, Milagro, & Martínez, 2009; Haemer, Huang, & Daniels, 2009; Herrera *et al.*, 2011; Hochberg *et al.*, 2010) or reversible changes (Drong *et al.*, 2012; Slomko, Heo, & Einstein, 2012). The constant interaction between genes, epigenetics, and the environment all appear to influence the risk for the development of autoimmune disorders, T2D, and/or the obese phenotype.

14.3. ASSESSING RISK

Autoimmune disorders affect approximately 8% of the population, most (78%) of whom are women (National Institutes of Health [NIH], 2005). Autoimmune disorders are highly complex because causative factors, interaction between causal factors, and the underlying complexity of the immune system itself make the diseases difficult to understand and often just as difficult to treat. One thing that does seem to be clear is that individuals who develop autoimmune diseases are genetically predisposed to developing them. These disorders run in families, often affecting multiple generations. *Familial* predisposition alone, however, is insufficient to explain the development of disease, because the concordance rate in monozygotic twins is not 100%. Therefore, it is believed that epigenetic and environmental factors play a significant, often determinant, role in the development of autoimmune disorders. These nongenetic forces are believed to act as either initiators or accelerators of autoimmunity or they may precipitate overt symptoms in those who already have a degree of glandular dysfunction. Environmental influences can modulate gene expression even during the prenatal period, as described in Chapter 5 (Prenatal chapter) of this book, and it is likely that even our susceptibility to environmental modifiers is determined by genes. Risk assessment is both necessary and complicated. Determining who is at risk, when they are at risk, what increases their risk, and how to modify that risk are critical pieces of information necessary to assess and understand the etiology of complex diseases.

14.3.1. Family History

Arguably the most important aspect of a patient's assessment is the collection of a family health history. Families share many things: genes, environments, and lifestyles, which together can provide important clues about medical conditions that tend to run in families and guide surveillance for individuals and their families. A complete health history should include health information from three generations of relatives, including children, parents, siblings, grandparents, aunts, uncles, and first-degree cousins. Because endocrine disorders almost always have a genetic component, the family history usually sheds light on the heritability of these disorders and may assist in identifying family members who may be at increased risk.

14.3.2. Environmental Risks

The list of potential environmental exposures linked to autoimmune disease is growing longer as scientists continue to identify and attempt to explain the differences within populations, ethnic groups, and families. Although it is clear that the environment is certainly involved in the etiology of autoimmune and nonautoimmune endocrine disease, the specific mechanisms remains unclear. It is nearly impossible to determine the true impact of environmental exposures have in causing disease because of differences in geographical distributions/locations, duration of exposures, combinations of exposures, and individual genetic susceptibility to these exposures. In addition, other factors such as socioeconomic status, hygiene practices, and vaccination status may play a role in the development of endocrine diseases, which is yet to be fully understood. Although these environmental exposures may not directly cause disease, the fact that they are so strongly correlated with disease suggests that

they are somehow involved in triggering a cascade of events that lead to overt autoimmune or complex metabolic disease. This is often expressed as Gene × Environment or G×E in the literature.

14.3.3. Antenatal Environment

An individuals' biologic response to nutrition begins at conception, and appears to be modified continually throughout life. The timing of maternal exposures to nutritional excesses and/ or deficits "preprograms" a baby to respond to nutrition in very specific ways later in life. The 2-year famine (1944–1945) in Holland during the World War II provides an unfortunate example of how the timing of maternal starvation can have a life-long effect on a developing fetus. Several sibling studies explored the nutritional status of adults exposed/not exposed in utero to maternal undernutrition during the famine (Roseboom, de Rooij, & Painter, 2006; Roseboom, Painter, van Abeelen, Veenendaal, & de Rooij, 2011). The studies showed that intrauterine undernutrition at any time during gestation was associated with a higher risk for glucose intolerance later in life, but infants exposed during the first trimester had a much higher risk for obesity, cardiovascular disease, and cancer in adulthood compared to their adult siblings. These findings also have been seen in other populations, and appear to persist regardless of birth weight (Bouchard *et al.*, 2012; Heerwagen, Miller, Barbour, & Friedman, 2010; Kaati, Bygren, & Edvinsson, 2002). Other factors have been associated with an increased risk for diabetes and obesity; including poor intrauterine growth (Fernandez-Twinn & Ozanne, 2006; Yazbek, Spiezio, Nadeau, & Buchner, 2010) and maternal and/or paternal prenatal obesity (Fernandez-Twinn & Ozanne, 2006; Soubry *et al.*, 2013). The underlying mechanisms driving these life-long effects are thought to be a combination of fetal epigenetic responses to availability of nutrients, intrauterine stress, and genetic predisposition (Hochberg *et al.*, 2010).

14.3.4. Microbiome

Many functions of the human body do not appear to be controlled by human genes, but rather are regulated by the genes of the thousands of different microbes that live in the gut and vagina and on the skin. Collectively, these microbial organisms and their genes comprise the human "microbiome." This human/microbial interaction is both protective and synergistic. The organisms have a rich environment in which to live, and in turn, protect their human hosts from more lethal microorganisms, produce essential nutrients (i.e., vitamin K), and play a major role in digestion and nutrient absorption (Grice & Segre, 2012). The gastrointestinal (GI) tract alone contains over 5,000 different classes of organisms, which vary between individuals and throughout life (Grice & Segre, 2012). Although sterile at birth, microorganisms begin colonizing the GI tract almost immediately, but the types and numbers of organisms that predominate are greatly influenced by the environment from the very beginning. Environmental influences, the route of delivery (vaginal or caesarean), antibiotic use, breastfeeding, and the presence of older siblings can shift the GI flora in ways that can have an impact on health many years later (Penders *et al.*, 2006). As a child comes into contact with other people and environments, the GI flora continues to evolve, changing with diet, geography, age, medications (particularly antibiotics and probiotics), and stress (Bäckhed *et al.*, 2012). Human microbial partners are not inert however, and have been shown to enhance nutrient extraction and energy storage, alter energy expenditure and glucose homeostasis, and influence inflammation, potentially contributing to the development of both obesity and T2D (Cani, Osto, Geurts, & Everard, 2012; Greenblum, Turnbaugh, & Borenstein, 2011; Musso, Gambino, & Cassader, 2010). Distinct patterns of microbial colonization have been associated with both obesity and T2D. The GI tracts of obese adults are colonized with fewer *Bacteroidetes* and more *Firmicutes* species than leaner adults, but as they lost weight (regardless of the weight loss method) their GI flora shifted: the number of *Bacteroidetes* colonies rose and *Firmicutes* colonies decreased (Ley, Turnbaugh, Klein, & Gordon, 2006; Cani *et al.*, 2012). Probiotics, although usually taken to support immune function and decrease inflammation, appear to prevent weight gain (Poutahidis *et al.*, 2013). Patients with T2D also have altered gut flora, producing more butyrate bacteria, which may contribute to the rise opportunistic GI

pathogens (e.g., *Escherichia coli* and *Clostridium*) and alterations in the function of other GI microbes (e.g., decreasing sulfates and protecting against oxidative stress) (Qin *et al.*, 2012). Potentially useful future applications of GI flora analysis include screening highrisk patients for T2D, using stool samples to diagnose, or stratify T2D into classes.

The microbes a baby is exposed to at birth (skin [via caesarean] vs. vaginal) appear to be as important for the development of a healthy immune system, because they are for regulation of nutrition later in life. Babies born by cesarean section appear to have a 20% increased risk for developing T1D compared to babies delivered vaginally (Vehik & Dabelea, 2012; Cardwell *et al.*, 2008). The theory is that an abdominal delivery in a sterile operating room environment may lead to a poorly developed immune system and an increased risk for developing autoimmune disorders such as T1D (Vehik & Dabelea, 2012; Cardwell *et al.*, 2008).

In addition to the GI tract's microbial contribution to nutrition and nutrition disorders, such as T2D and obesity, the GI tract appears to be very much involved in regulating immunity. Perhaps the most intriguing theory involves the GI "zonulin pathway." The GI epithelium normally consists of epithelial cells that are very tightly pressed together. Zonulin, first described in 2000 (Sapone, *et al.*, 2006) is a protein that modulates the gaps between the normally tight intercellular junctions. This pathway, along with the lymphatic and neuroendocrine systems, regulates the body's tolerance/immunity response to non–self- antigens. Although it is not yet known what causes dysregulation of the zonulin pathway, most hypotheses point to an environmental exposure, such as early introduction of cow's milk (bovine, serum, albumin, and/or beta-casein) or to wheat protein (gliadin) (Merriman, 2009). These environmental insults may cause the normally tight epithelial junctions to "leak," triggering an immune response, which may be particularly damaging in a child genetically predisposed to developing immune disorders. The role of the zonulin pathway in the development of several autoimmune and allergic disorders, including T1D, celiac disease, rheumatoid arthritis, atopic dermatitis, and asthma, is being closely examined, and may help explain why T1D and celiac disease often occur together (Fasano, 2012; Patelarou *et al.*, 2012; Vaarala *et al.*, 2012). Breastfeeding may be particularly important for babies at increased risk for autoimmune disorders, because it appears to offer some protection from autoimmune diseases. Breast milk is easy to digest, highly nutritious, and loaded with antimicrobial proteins, such as lactoferrin, secretory IgA, lysozyme, and bifidus factor, which help stimulate the immune system. This could possibly explain the lower incidence of T1D in children and adolescents exclusively breastfed for at least 6 months during infancy (Patelarou *et al.*, 2012).

14.3.5. Physical Activity

Regular physical activity has been shown to modify epigenetic expression, decreasing the risk for both obesity and T2D (American College of Sports Medicine [ACSM] & American Diabetes Association [ADA], 2010). The ongoing *Human Gene Map for Performance and Health-Related Fitness Phenotypes* has identified 214 unique genes linked to athleticism and participation in physical activities (Bray *et al.*, 2009). What is not yet known is the degree to which these linkages are causal, nor if everyone will benefit equally from adjusting physical activity levels (Bouchard *et al.*, 2012; Bray *et al.*, 2009). There is some encouraging evidence that fat mass and obesity-associated (*FTO*) genes are expressed in the hypothalamus, altering overall metabolic response to physical activity (Sailors & Bray, 2011). Several studies have found a difference in weight loss response to physical activity with different *FTO* genotypes (Franks & Brito, 2011; Mitchell *et al.*, 2009; Sailors & Bray, 2011). Physical activity has been shown to alter the expression of genes involved in inflammation, insulin resistance, and adipocyte activity, but more research is needed before this research becomes actionable in a clinical setting (Bouchard *et al.*, 2012; Franks & Brito, 2011; Sailors & Bray, 2011).

14.3.6. Infections

Viruses and other infectious agents have garnered attention as etiologic candidates for autoimmune disorders because of their ability to penetrate host cells and alter the way in which these cells are then recognized by the immune system.

Unraveling when and how these environmental exposures occur is problematic, however, because exposure can occur in-utero, but not manifest for years or even decades, a causal relationship is difficult to establish.

Many clinicians are aware that viruses have been linked to the development of T1D, but the details have only recently begun to be understood. Two common viruses, Coxsackie virus B (CVB) and rotavirus RV-VP7, have been implicated in the development of autoimmune diseases. Each of these viruses have gene sequences that are virtually identical to human sequences found in pancreatic islet autoantigens (Christen, Bender, & von Herrath, 2012). The theory is that immunogenic viral peptide genes can "mimic" human peptides, activating autoreactive T or B cells and triggering or exacerbating the development of T1D (Honeyman *et al.*, 2010).

A few other infections are associated with endocrine disorders. Tuberculosis and disseminated fungal infections are associated with adrenal insufficiency, and human T-cell lymphotrophic virus type 1, hepatitis C, and *Yersina enterocolitica* have all been associated with autoimmune thyroid disease (Hasham & Tomer, 2012; Nieman, 2013).

14.3.7. Nutritional

Micronutrients and macronutrients can influence the development of endocrine disorder; however, regardless of the condition or risk, a healthy diet is associated with better outcomes (Nettleton *et al.*, 2012). Vegetarian diets are associated with marked reduction in the methylation of DNA (Campión *et al.*, 2009), and very low calorie diets alter leptin triggers for appetite (Bray *et al.*, 2009). A low glycemic index diet has been shown to reduce the risk for the development of T2D in people with a mutation in transcription factor 7-like 2 (TCF7L2), the gene marker that to date is most significantly associated with the development of T2D (Cornelis & Hu, 2012). Four of the five Circadian Locomotor Output Cycles Kaput (CLOCK) genes that regulate circadian rhythms have been associated with obesity. Compared to people with the "wild type" (normal) version of the *CLOCK* gene, individuals with the *rs1801260 CLOCK* "G" variant have greater difficulty losing weight and lose less weight over time. Interestingly, individuals with the G variant also sleep fewer hours at night, and have higher cholesterol levels after dieting than do those people with "wild type" *CLOCK* genes. These circadian rhythm differences may explain some of the recent studies associating less sleep with weight gain and lipid disorders (Garaulet *et al.*, 2010).

Adequate levels of micronutrients are important to endocrine function. Vitamin D deficiency has recently received much attention from researchers and the media and has been associated with many disorders, including autoimmune dysfunction, cancer, and cardiovascular disease (Holick, 2004). Vitamin D appears to play a key role in the preservation of glucose tolerance, insulin secretion, and insulin binding action. Low vitamin D levels have been shown to increase the risk for developing both obesity and T2D (Alvarez & Ashraf, 2010). Because vitamin D is fat soluble, it is quickly stored; although total body stores are high in obese people, serum levels are low, because the vitamin is biologically unavailable. This becomes a vicious cycle: low vitamin D levels increase adipocyte intracellular calcium (CA) levels, intracellular CA stimulates lipogenesis, and lipopgenesis increases body weight (Takiishi, Gysemans, Bouillon, & Mathieu, 2010). Low levels of Vitamin D3 (25OHD) in utero and early childhood have also been shown to increase the risk for the development of T1D, because Vitamin D3 is an immunosuppressant, decreasing lymphocyte proliferation and cytokine production (Zipitis & Akobeng, 2008). Normal Vitamin D3 levels appear to be particularly important in infancy and early childhood. Studies have shown that cod liver oil supplementation is inversely associated with T1D, whereas signs of rickets during the first year of life is positively associated with T1D (Hypponen, Laara,

Reunanen, Jarvelin, & Virtanen, 2001; Stene, Ulriksen, Magnus, & Joner, 2000). Because Vitamin D3 is fat soluble, it is found in relatively few foods, all of which contain fat, such as fish, fish oil, egg yolks, and cheese. It is also found in milk and orange juice that has been fortified with Vitamin D3. However, the most important source of Vitamin D for most people is sunlight. When the skin is exposed to sunlight, ultraviolet rays trigger the first step in a series of biochemical actions culminating in the synthesis of Vitamin D3. The amount of ultraviolet (UV) light reaching bare skin varies widely, however, and depends on geographical location, latitude, season, and sunscreen use. Reduced exposure to UV rays may help to explain the increased incidence of T1D the further away one lives from the equator (Hagenau *et al.*, 2009; Mohr, Garland, Gorham, & Garland, 2008). Although the exact mechanisms are still unclear, birth month may also be associated with the development of T1D (Kahn *et al.*, 2009). Some researchers are exploring the relationship between maternal/early childhood exposure to sunlight on immune system dysfunction. Their studies examining the relationship between sun exposure and the development of T1D have shown an increased risk for babies born in northern latitudes (> 49′) during the late spring and early summer months (peaking in May) compared with those born south of that latitude, where there is no apparent birth-month affect (Webb, Kline, & Holick, 1988). The possible mechanisms they describe include the effect of maternal sunlight exposure during periods where fetal pancreatic cells are developing and the exposure to sunlight during critical periods of pancreatic development during infancy or early childhood (Webb *et al.*, 1988).

TABLE 14.1. Some Online Resources Useful in Understanding Genetic/genomic Endocrine Disorders.

The Human Genome Project Information	www.ornl.gov/sci/techresources/Human_Genome/elsi/elsi.shtml
American Board of Medical Genetics	www.abmg.org/pages/searchmem.shtml
GeneTests/Gene Reviews	www.genetests.org
Online Mendelian Inheritance in Man	www.OMIM.org
US Surgeon General—My Family Health Portrait	https://familyhistory.hhs.gov/fhh-web/home.action
CDC's Office of Public Health Genomics—Using Family History to Promote Health	www.cdc.gov/genomics/famhistory/famhist.htm
National Human Genome Research Institute	www.genome.gov/11510372

TABLE 14.2. MODY-related Genes and the Clinical Phenotypes Associated with Mutations[a].

MODY Type	Gene	Clinical Features (Heterozygotes)	Clinical Features (Homozygotes)	Management (Heterozygote)	Mechanism
1	HNF 4α	DM, microvascular complications; Low serum triglycerides, apolipoproteins AII and CIII, and Lp(a)		Oral hypoglycemic agent, insulin	Abnormal regulation of gene transcription in beta cells, causing defective metabolic signaling of insulin secretion, beta-cell mass, or both
2	Glucokinase	Impaired fasting glucose, impaired glucose tolerance, DM, normal proinsulin-to-insulin ratio in serum	Neonatal DM, requiring insulin	Diet and exercise	Defect in sensitivity of beta cells to glucose caused by reduced glucose phosphorylation; defect in hepatic storage of glucose as glycogen
3	HNF-1α	DM, microvascular complications, renal glycosuria, increased sensitivity to sulfonylureas, increased serum proinsulin-to-insulin ratio		Oral hypoglycemic agent, insulin	Abnormal beta cell gene transcription, leading to a defective signaling of insulin secretion, betacell mass, or both
4	IPF-1	DM	Pancreatic agenesis; neonatal DM, requiring insulin	Oral hypoglycemic agent, insulin	Abnormal transcriptional regulation of beta-cell development and function
5	NHF-1β	DM; renal abnormalities; progressive renal dysfunction, chronic renal insufficiency and failure; internal genital abnormalities (female carriers)		Insulin	Abnormal beta cell gene transcription, leading to a defective signaling of insulin secretion, beta-cell mass, or both
6	NeuroD1, or BETA2	DM		Insulin	Abnormal transcriptional regulation of beta-cell development and function

[a]Diabetes is characterized by a plasma glucose concentration > 126 mg per deciliter (7.0 mmol per liter) during fasting or > 200 mg per deciliter (11.1 mmol per liter) 2 hours after glucose administration; impaired fasting glucose by a plasma glucose concentration »110 mg per deciliter (6.1 mmol per liter) and < 126 mg per deciliter during fasting; and impaired glucose tolerance by a plasma glucose concentration »140 mg per deciliter (7.8 mmol per liter) and < 200 mg per deciliter two hours after glucose administration. MODY denotes maturity-onset diabetes of the young; HNF hepatocyte nuclear factor, IPF insulin promoter factor, NeuroD1 neurogenic differentiation factor 1, and BETA2 beta-cell E-box transactivator 2.

[†]Studies of proinsulin-to-insulin ratios in serum have been carried out only in persons with MODY 2 or MODY 3. Increased sensitivity to sulfonylurea drugs has been reported in some patients with mutations in the gene encoding HNF-1a1,2

From "Molecular Mechanisms and Clinical Pathophysiology of Maturity-Onset Diabetes of the Young," by S. S. Fajans, G. I. Bell, and K. S. Polonsky, 2001, *New England Journal of Medicine*, 345, p. 972. Reprinted with permission.

TABLE 14.3. Obesity Comparison Table.

	Monogenetic	Syndromic	Polygenetic
T2DM	MODY	Possibly gestational DM	Common etiology
Obesity	Congenital leptin deficiency	Prader-Willi syndrome Bardet-Biedl Cohen syndrome Ayazi syndrome MOMO	Common etiology

(Drong, Lindgren, & McCarthy, 2012; Hinney, Vogel, & Hebebrand, 2010; O'Rahilly & Farooqi, 2006; Watanabe *et al.*, 2007).

14.3.8. Others

Many substances have been implicated in triggering or accelerating endocrine disorders/disease, particularly abnormalities of the thyroid gland, which appears to be particularly sensitive to environmental exposures. Therapeutic agents such as amiodorone and immunomodulation therapies such as INF-alpha used to treat cancer and hepatitis C increase the risk for developing GD or HT (Brent, 2010; Kong, Wei, & Tomer, 2010). Pollutants and toxins such as cigarette smoke accelerate the production of pro-inflammatory cytokines, reduce the levels of anti-inflammatory cytokines, cause DNA damage, and promote genetic mutations leading to autoimmune disease, especially GD (Arnson, Shoenfeld, & Amital, 2010). Excess or inadequate iodine intake increases the risk for developing HT and GD. Ionizing radiation significantly increases the risk for thyroid disease, particularly thyroid cancer, as evidenced by the high incidence of thyroid cancer in people exposed to radiation during detonation of the atomic bombs in Hiroshima and Nagasaki and the nuclear power plant accident in Chernobyl (Brent, 2010; Brenner *et al.*, 2011). Finally, pregnancy itself appears to be an independent risk factor for developing HT through a mechanism called fetal microchimerism. Fetal cells present in maternal circulation can migrate to the maternal thyroid gland and initiate a graft-versus-host reaction, triggering autoimmune HT (Davies, 2012b).

14.4. PHARMACOGENOMICS

There is no cure for most endocrine disorders at the present time, and treatment is focused primarily on managing hormone imbalances (most often deficiencies) caused by a nonfunctioning/damaged gland. Treatments are available for a few endocrine disorders, however, such as the management of MODY. Identifying the specific type of MODY a patient has inherited is important, because the disease is very heterogeneous. Patients with MODY2 (the most common type), usually have mild hyperglycemia from birth, but rarely develop microvascular disease. Oral agents are very effective if patients need pharmacologic support. Patients with MODY1 or MODY3, however, develop severe hyperglycemia during/after puberty, and they are at increased risk for developing diabetic retinopathy and nephropathy, but not for cardiovascular disease. Although patients with MODY3 remain sensitive to sulfonylureas, most will require insulin therapy. Patients with MODY5 require additional screening, because this form of MODY is associated with pancreatic atrophy, morphologic and functional abnormalities of the kidneys, and genital and liver abnormalities. Genotyping patients suspected of having MODY helps clinicians select the most appropriate pharmacologic therapies, helps predict whether insulin may be required, and facilitates targeted screening (Timsit, Bellanné-Chantelot, Dubois-Laforgue, & Velho, 2005). Table 14.1 provides a concise summary of the above.

T2D, on the other hand, is a complex polygenetic disease comprised of a multitude of pathophysiologic factors (e.g., insulin resistance, increased glucagon secretion, inappropriate hepatic glucose release, etc.) and genetic miscues. The explosion of pharmacologic agents targeting various pathways in T2D management is testament to the complexity of the disease. Future research will be most be focused on identifying who will respond or not respond to certain medications and who will be most likely to develop adverse side effects (Scott, Mohlke, & Boehnke, 2007).

14.5. GENETIC TESTING, COUNSELING, ETHICAL IMPLICATIONS

An excellent review was recently published regarding the role and applicability of genetic testing in patients with endocrine disorders (Kirmani, 2012). The utility and appropriateness of genetic testing and counseling are fairly clear when a Mendelian disorder is suspected, because the results can clarify disease risk, justify surveillance testing, direct counseling of presymptomatic family members, and guide couples considering a pregnancy. Ordering genetic tests presents a series of unique challenges (see Chapter 2), including concerns about sensitivity and specificity, financial and psychosocial costs, controlling access, and whether or not genomic information can be used to improve health outcomes (Kirmani, 2012). The key to making accurate disease predictions and diagnoses may lie in understanding the interactions between multiple genes (Huber *et al.*, 2008).

14.6. ACKNOWLEDGMENTS

The authors gratefully acknowledge the following individuals' contributions of expertise, insight and support: Diane C. Seibert, PhD, ARNP; Robert A. Vigersky, MD; Babbette C. Glister, MD; and Scott Urquhart, PA-C.

14.7. REFERENCES

Alvarez, J. A. & Ashraf, A. (2010). Role of vitamin D in insulin secretion and insulin sensitivity for glucose homeostasis. *International Journal of Endocrinology, 2010*(2010). Retrieved from http://www.ncbi.nlm.nih.gov/pmc/articles/PMC2778451/?tool=pubmed

American College of Obstetricians and Gynecologists. (2011). Update on carrier screening for cystic fibrosis. Committee Opinion No. 486. *Obstet Gynecol, 177*, 1028-1031. Retrieved from http://www.acog.org/Resources_And_Publications/Committee_Opinions/Committee_on_Genetics/Update_on_Carrier_Screening_for_Cystic_Fibrosis

American College of Sports Medicine, & American Diabetes Association. (2010). Exercise and type 2 diabetes: American College of Sports Medicine and the American Diabetes Association. *Medicine & Science in Sports & Exercise, 42*(12), 2282-2303. doi: 10.1249/MSS.0b013e3181eeb61c

Arnson, Y., Shoenfeld, Y., & Amital, H. (2010). Effects of tobacco smoke on immunity, inflammation and autoimmunity. *Journal of Autoimmunity, 34*(3), J258-J265.

Bäckhed, F., Fraser, C. M., Ringel, Y., Sanders, M. E., Sartor, R. B., Sherman, P. M., . . . & Finlay, B. B. (2012). Defining a healthy human gut microbiome: Current concepts, future directions, and clinical applications. *Cell Host & Microbe, 12*(5), 611–622. doi: 10.1016/j.chom.2012.10.012

Baker, J. R. (1997). Autoimmune endocrine disease. *Journal of the American Medical Association, 278*(22), 1931–1937.

Barker, J. M. & Eisenbarth, G. S. (2012). Autoimmune polyendocrine syndromes. In: G. S. Eisenbarth (Ed.), *Type 1 diabetes: Cellular, molecular & clinical immunology.* Retrieved from http://www.ucdenver.edu/academics/colleges/medicalschool/centers/BarbaraDavis/OnlineBooks/Pages/Type1Diabetes.aspx

Bouchard, C., Blair, S. N., Church, T. S., Earnest, C. P., Hagberg, J. M., Häkkinen, K., . . . Rankinen, T. (2012). Adverse metabolic response to regular exercise: Is it a rare or common occurrence? *PLoS ONE, 7*(5), e37887. doi:10.1371/journal.pone.0037887

Bouchard, L., Hivert, M.-F., Guay, S.-P., St-Pierre, J., Perron, P., & Brisson, D. (2012). Placental adiponectin gene DNA methylation levels are associated with mothers' blood glucose concentration. *Diabetes, 61*(5), 1272–1280. doi:10.2337/db11-1160

Bradfield, J. P., Taal, H. R., Timpson, N. J., Scherag, A., Lecoeur, C., Warrington, N. M., . . . Thiering, E. (2012). A genome-wide association meta-analysis identifies new childhood obesity loci. *Nature Genetics, 44*(5), 526–531. doi:10.1038/ng.2247

Bray, M. S., Hagberg, J. M., PéRusse, L., Rankinen, T., Roth, S. M., Wolfarth, B., & Bouchard, C. (2009). The human gene map for performance and health-related fitness phenotypes: The 2006–2007 update. *Medicine & Science in Sports & Exercise, 41*(1), 35–73. doi:10.1249/MSS.0b013e3181844179

Brenner, A. V., Tronko, M. D., Hatch, M., Bogdanova, T. I., Oliynik, V. A., Lubin, J. H. . . . Ron, E. (2011). I-131 dose-response for incident thyroid cancers in Ukraine related to the Chornobyl accident. *Environmental Health Perspectives, 119*(7), 933–939.

Brent, G. A. (2010). Environmental exposures and autoimmune thyroid disease. *Thyroid, 20*(7), 755–761.

Campión, J., Milagro, F. I., & Martínez, J. A. (2009). Individuality and epigenetics in obesity. *Obesity Reviews, 10*(4), 383–392. doi:10.1111/j.1467-789X.2009.00595.x

Cani, P. D., Osto, M., Geurts, L., & Everard, A. (2012). Involvement of gut microbiota in the development of low-grade inflammation and type 2 diabetes associated with obesity. *Gut Microbes, 3*(4), 279–288. doi:10.4161/gmic.19625

Cardwell, C. R., Stene, L. C., Joner, G., Cinek, O., Svensson, J., Goldacre, M. J., . . . Patterson, C. C. (2008). Caesarean section is associated with an increased risk of childhood-onset type 1 diabetes mellitus: A meta-analysis of observational studies. *Diabetologia, 51*(5), 726–735.

Chaput, J.-P., Doucet, E., & Tremblay, A. (2012). Obesity: A disease or a biological adaptation? An update. *Obesity Reviews: An Official Journal of the International Association for the Study of Obesity, 13*(8), 681–691. doi:10.1111/j.1467-789X.2012.00992.x

Chen, R., Corona, E., Sikora, M., Dudley, J. T., Morgan, A. A., Moreno-Estrada, A., ... Butte, A. J. (2012). Type 2 diabetes risk alleles demonstrate extreme directional differentiation among human populations, compared to other diseases. *PLoS Genetics, 8*(4), e1002621. doi:10.1371/journal.pgen.1002621

Christen, U., Bender, C., & von Herrath, M. G. (2012). Infection as a cause of type 1 diabetes? *Current Opinion in Rheumatology, 24*(4), 417–423.

Cooper, J.D., Smyth, D.J., Smiles, A.M., Plagnol, V., Walker, N.M., Allen, J.E., Downes, K., Barrett, J.C., Healy, B.C., Mychaleckyj, J.C., Warram, J.H., Todd, J.A. (2008). Meta-analysis of genome-wide association study data identifies additional type 1 diabetes risk loci. *Nature Genetics; 40*(12):1399.

Cornelis, M. C., & Hu, F. B. (2012). Gene-environment interactions in the development of type 2 diabetes: Recent progress and continuing challenges. *Annual Review of Nutrition, 32*(1), 245-259. doi:10.1146/annurev-nutr-071811-150648

Davies, T. F. (2012a). Pathogenesis of Graves' disease. In: D. S. Basow (Ed.), *UpToDate*. Retrieved from http://www.uptodate.com/home/index.html

Davies, T. F. (2012b). Pathogenesis of Hashimoto's thyroiditis (chronic autoimmune thyroiditis). In: D. S. Basow (Ed.), *UpToDate*. Retrieved from http://www.uptodate.com/home/index.html

De Lorenzo, C., Greco, A., Fiorentino, T. V., Mannino, G. C., & Hribal, M. L. (2013). Variants of insulin-signaling inhibitor genes in type 2 diabetes and related metabolic abnormalities. *International Journal of Genomics, 2013*, 1–13. doi:10.1155/2013/376454

Driscoll DJ, Miller JL, Schwartz S, et al. Prader-Willi Syndrome. 1998 Oct 6 [Updated 2014 Jan 23]. In: Pagon RA, Adam MP, Ardinger HH, *et al.*, editors. *GeneReviews®* [Internet]. Seattle (WA): University of Washington, Seattle; 1993-2015. Available from: http://www.ncbi.nlm.nih.gov/books/NBK1330/

Drong, A. W., Lindgren, C. M., & McCarthy, M. I. (2012). The genetic and epigenetic basis of type 2 diabetes and obesity. *Clinical Pharmacology & Therapeutics, 92*(6), 707–715. doi:10.1038/clpt.2012.149

Fajans, S. S., Bell, G. I., & Polonsky, K. S. (2001). Molecular mechanisms and clinical pathophysiology of maturity-onset diabetes of the young. *New England Journal of Medicine, 345*(13), 971–980.

Fasano, A. (2012). Leaky gut and autoimmune diseases. *Clinical Reviews in Allergy and Immunology, 42*(1), 71–78.

Fernandez-Twinn, D. S., & Ozanne, S. E. (2006).

Mechanisms by which poor early growth programs type-2 diabetes, obesity and the metabolic syndrome. *Physiology & Behavior, 88*(3), 234–243. doi:10.1016/j.physbeh.2006.05.039

Franks, P. W., & Brito, E. (2011). Interaction between exercise and genetics in type 2 diabetes mellitus: An epidemiological perspective. In L. Pescatello & S. M. Roth (Eds.), *Exercise Genomics*. New York: Humana Press.

Garaulet, M., Corbalán, M. D., Madrid, J. A., Morales, E., Baraza, J. C., Lee, Y. C., & Ordovas, J. M. (2010). CLOCK gene is implicated in weight reduction in obese patients participating in a dietary programme based on the Mediterranean diet. *International Journal of Obesity, 34*(3), 516–523. doi:10.1038/ijo.2009.255

Gluckman, P. D. , & Hanson, M. A. (2008). Developmental and epigenetic pathways to obesity: An evolutionary-developmental perspective. *International Journal of Obesity, 32*, S62–S71.doi:10.1038/ijo.2008.240

Greenblum, S., Turnbaugh, P. J., & Borenstein, E. (2011). Metagenomic systems biology of the human gut microbiome reveals topological shifts associated with obesity and inflammatory bowel disease. *Proceedings of the National Academy of Sciences, 109*(2), 594–599. doi:10.1073/pnas.1116053109

Grice, E. A., & Segre, J. A. (2012). The human microbiome: Our second genome. *Annual Review of Genomics and Human Genetics, 13*(1), 151–170. doi:10.1146/annurev-genom-090711-163814

Guay, C., Roggli, E., Nesca, V., Jacovetti, C., & Regazzi, R. (2011). Diabetes mellitus, a microRNA-related disease? *Translational Research, 157*(4), 253–264. doi:10.1016/j.trsl.2011.01.009

Haemer, M. A., Huang, T., & Daniels, S. (2009). The effect of neurohormonal factors, epigenetic factors and gut microbiota on risk of obesity. *Preventing Chronic Disease: Public Health Research, Practice and Policy, 6*(3), 1–8.

Hagenau, T., Vest, R., Gissel, T. N., Poulsen, C. S., Erlandsen, M., Mosekilde, L. & Vestergaard, P. (2009). Global vitamin D levels in relation to age, gender, skin pigmentation and latitutde: An ecologic meta-regression analysis. *Osteoporosis International, 20*(1), 133–140.

Haiman, C. A., Fesinmeyer, M. D., Spencer, K. L., Buzkova, P., Voruganti, V. S., Wan, P., . . . Pankow, J. S. (2012). Consistent directions of effect for established type 2 diabetes risk variants across populations: The Population Architecture using Genomics and Epidemiology (PAGE) Consortium. *Diabetes, 61*(6), 1642–1647. doi:10.2337/db11-1296

Hannibal M. C., & Torgerson, T. (2011). IPEX syndrome. In: R. A. Pagon, M. P. Adam, T. D. Bird, C. R. Dolan, C. Fong, & K. Stephens (Eds.), *GeneReviews™* Retrieved from http://www.ncbi.nlm.nih.gov/books/NBK1116/

Hasham, A., & Tomer, Y. (2012). Genetic and epigenetic mechanisms in thyroid autoimmunity. *Immunologic Research, 1-3*(54), 204–213.

Heerwagen, M. J. R., Miller, M. R., Barbour, L. A., & Friedman, J. E. (2010). Maternal obesity and fetal metabolic programming: A fertile epigenetic soil. *AJP: Regulatory, Integrative and Comparative Physiology, 299*(3), R711–R722. doi:10.1152/ajpregu.00310.2010

Herrera, B. M., Keildson, S., & Lindgren, C. M. (2011). Genetics and epigenetics of obesity. *Maturitas, 69*(1), 41–49. doi:10.1016/j.maturitas.2011.02.018

Hinney, A., Vogel, C. I. G., & Hebebrand, J. (2010). From monogenic to polygenic obesity: Recent advances. *European Child & Adolescent Psychiatry, 19*(3), 297–310. doi:10.1007/s00787-010-0096-6

Hochberg, Z., Feil, R., Constancia, M., Fraga, M., Junien, C., Carel, J.-C., . . . Albertsson-Wikland, K. (2010). Child health, developmental plasticity, and epigenetic programming. *Endocrine Reviews, 32*(2), 159–224. doi:10.1210/er.2009-0039

Holick, M. F. (2004). Vitamin D: importance in the prevention of cancers, type 1 diabetes, heart disease, and osteoporosis. *American Journal of Clinical Nutrition, 79*(3), 362–371.

Honeyman, M.C., Stone, N.L., Falk, B.A., Nepom, G., & Harrison, L.C. (2010). Evidence for molecular mimicry between human T cell epitopes in rotavirus and pancreatic islet autoantigens. *Journal of Immunology, 184*, 2204–2210.

Huber, A., Menconi, F., Corathers, S., Jacobson, E., & Tomer, Y. (2008). Joint genetic susceptibility to type 1 diabetes and autoimmune thyroiditis: From epidemiology to mechanisms. *Endocrine Reviews, 29*(6), 697–725.

Hypponen, E., Laara, E., Reunanen, A., Jarvelin, M.-J., & Virtanen, S. M. (2001). Intake of vitamin D and risk of type 1 diabetes: A birth-cohort study. *The Lancet, 358*(9292), 1500–1503.

Kaati, G., Bygren, L. O., & Edvinsson, S. (2002). Cardiovascular and diabetes mortality determined by nutrition during parents' and grandparents' slow growth period. *European Journal of Human Genetics, 10*(11), 682–688. doi:10.1038/sj.ejhg.5200859

Kahn, H.S., Morgan, T.M., Case, L.D., Dabelea, D., Mayer-Davis, E.J., Lawrence, J.M., . . . Imperatore, G. (2009). Association of type 1 diabetes with month of birth among U.S. youth: The SEARCH for Diabetes in Youth Study. *Diabetes Care, 32*(11), 2010–15.

Kirmani, S. (2012). Molecular genetic testing in endocrinology-a practical guide. *Endocrine Practice, 18*(1), 85–89.

Klehm, M., & Korson, M. (2008). *A clinician's guide to the management of mitochondrial disease: A manual for primary care providers.* Retrieved from http://www.mitoaction.org/guide

Knoers, N. (2012). Nephrogenic diabetes insipidus. In: R. A. Pagon, M. P. Adam, T.D. Bird, C. R. Dolan,

C. Fong, & K. Stephens (Eds.), *GeneReviews™* Retrieved from http://www.ncbi.nlm.nih.gov/books/NBK1177/

Kong, Y. M., Wei, W. Z., & Tomer, Y. (2010). Opportunistic autoimmune disorders: From immunotherapy to immune dysregulation. *Annals of the New York Academy of Sciences, 1183*(1), 222–236.

Ley, R. E., Turnbaugh, P. J., Klein, S., & Gordon, J. I. (2006). Human gut microbes associated with obesity. *Nature, 444*(21), 1022–1023. doi:10.1038/nature4441022a

Lillycrop, K. A., & Burdge, G. C. (2010). Epigenetic changes in early life and future risk of obesity. *International Journal of Obesity, 35*(1), 72–83. doi:10.1038/ijo.2010.122

Lowell, B. B., & Shulman, G. I., (2005). Mitochondrial dysfunction and type 2 diabetes. *Science, 307*, 384–387.

Manning, A. K., Hivert, M.-F., Scott, R. A., Grimsby, J. L., Bouatia-Naji, N., Chen, H., . . . Prokopenko, I. (2012). A genome-wide approach accounting for body mass index identifies genetic variants influencing fasting glycemic traits and insulin resistance. *Nature Genetics, 44*(6), 659–669. doi:10.1038/ng.2274

Manolio, T. A., Collins, F. S., Cox, N. J., Goldstein, D. B., Hindorff, L. A., Hunter, D. J., . . . Visscher, P. M. (2009). Finding the missing heritability of complex diseases. *Nature, 461*(7265), 747–753. doi:10.1038/nature08494

Moline J, Eng C. (2013) Multiple Endocrine Neoplasia Type 2. In: Pagon RA, Adam MP, Bird TD, et al., editors. *GeneReviews™* [Internet]. Seattle (WA): University of Washington, Seattle; 1993–2013. Available from: http://www.ncbi.nlm.nih.gov/books/NBK1257/

McAuley, P. A., & Blair, S. N. (2011). Obesity paradoxes. *Journal of Sports Sciences, 29*(8), 773–782. doi:10.1080/02640414.2011.553965

Meng, Q., Mäkinen, V.-P., Luk, H., & Yang, X. (2013). Systems biology approaches and applications in obesity, diabetes, and cardiovascular diseases. *Current Cardiovascular Risk Reports, 7*(1), 73–83. doi:10.1007/s12170-012-0280-y

Merriman, T. R. (2009). Type 1 diabetes, the A1 milk hypothesis and vitamin D deficiency. *Diabetes Research and Clinical Practice, 83*(2), 149–156.

Mitchell, J. A., Church, T. S., Rankinen, T., Earnest, C. P., Sui, X., & Blair, S. N. (2009). FTO genotype and the weight loss benefits of moderate intensity exercise. *Obesity, 18*(3), 641–643. doi:10.1038/oby.2009.311

Mohr, S. B., Garland, C. F., Gorham, E. D., & Garland, F. C. (2008). The association between ultraviolet B irradiance, vitamin D status and incidence rates of type 1 diabetes in 51 regions worldwide. *Diabetologia, 51*(8), 1391–1398.

Morris, A. P., Voight, B. F., Teslovich, T. M., Ferreira, T., Segrè, A. V., Steinthorsdottir, V., . . . Mahajan, A.

(2012). Large-scale association analysis provides insights into the genetic architecture and pathophysiology of type 2 diabetes. *Nature Genetics, 44*(9), 981–990. doi:10.1038/ng.2383

Musso, G., Gambino, R., & Cassader, M. (2010). Obesity, diabetes, and gut microbiota: The hygiene hypothesis expanded? *Diabetes Care, 33*(10), 2277–2284. doi:10.2337/dc10-0556

Mutch, D. M., & Clément, K. (2006). Unraveling the genetics of human obesity. *PLoS Genetics, 2*(12), e188. doi:10.1371/journal.pgen.0020188

National Heart, Lung, and Blood Institute. (2009). Sickle cell anemia: Who is at risk? Retrieved from http://www.nhlbi.nih.gov/health/dci/Diseases/Sca/SCA_WhoIsAtRisk.html

National Human Genome Research Institute. (2011). Learning about Tay-Sachs disease. Retrieved from http://www.genome.gov/10001220

National Institutes of Health, The Autoimmune Diseases Committee. (2005). Progress in autoimmune diseases research: Report to Congress. Retrieved from http://www.niaid.nih.gov/topics/autoimmune/documents/adccfinal.pdf

Nettleton, J. A., Hivert, M.-F., Lemaitre, R. N., McKeown, N. M., Mozaffarian, D., Tanaka, T., ... Ngwa, J. S. (2012). Meta-analysis investigating associations between healthy diet and fasting glucose and insulin levels and modification by loci associated with glucose homeostasis in data from 15 cohorts. *American Journal of Epidemiology, 177*(2), 103–115. doi:10.1093/aje/kws297

Nimkarn S, New MI. (2013). 21-Hydroxylase-Deficient Congenital Adrenal Hyperplasia. In: Pagon RA, Adam MP, Bird TD, et al., editors. *GeneReviews®* [Internet]. Seattle (WA): University of Washington, Seattle; 1993-2014. Available from: http://www.ncbi.nlm.nih.gov/books/NBK1171/

O'Rahilly, S., & Farooqi, I. S. (2006). Genetics of obesity. *Philosophical Transactions of the Royal Society B: Biological Sciences, 361*(1471), 1095–1105. doi:10.1098/rstb.2006.1850

Parchwani, D., Murthy, S., Upadhyah, A., & Patel, D. (2013). Genetic factors in the etiology of type 2 diabetes: Linkage analyses, candidate gene association, and genome-wide association—Still a long way to go! *National Journal of Physiology, Pharmacy and Pharmacology, 3*(1), 57. doi:10.5455/njppp.2013.3.57-68

Parham, P. and Ohta, T. (1996). Population Biology of Antigen Presentation by MHC class I Molecules". *Science 272* (5258): 67–74. doi:10.1126/science.272.5258.67.

Patelarou, E., Girvalaki, C., Brokalaki, H., Patelarou, A., Androulaki, Z., & Vardavas, C. (2012). Current evidence on the associations of breastfeeding, infant formula, and cow's milk introduction with type 1 diabetes mellitus: A systemic review. *Nutrition Reviews, 70*(9), 509–519.

Penders, J., Thijs, C., Vink, C., Stelma, F.F., Snijders, B., Kummeling, I., ... & Stobberingh, E.E. (2006) Factors influencing the composition of the intestinal microbiota in early infancy. *Pediatrics, 118*, 511–521.

Phillips, T. (2008). The role of methylation in gene expression. *Nature Education, 1*(1), 127. Retrieved from http://staging-www.nature.com/scitable/topicpage/the-role-of-methylation-in-gene-expression-the-role-of-methylation-in-gene-expression-The-Role-of-Methylation-in-Gene-Expression-1070

Poutahidis, T., Kleinewietfeld, M., Smillie, C., Levkovich, T., Perrotta, A., Bhela, S., ... Erdman, S. E. (2013). Microbial reprogramming inhibits western diet-associated obesity. *PLoS ONE, 8*(7), e68596. doi:10.1371/journal.pone.0068596

Prentice, A. M., Hennig, B. J., & Fulford, A. J. (2008). Evolutionary origins of the obesity epidemic: Natural selection of thrifty genes or genetic drift following predation release? *International Journal of Obesity, 32*(11), 1607–1610. doi:10.1038/ijo.2008.147

Prokopenko, I., McCarthy, M. I., & Lindgren, C. M. (2008). Type 2 diabetes: New genes, new understanding. *Trends in Genetics, 24*(12), 613–621. doi:10.1016/j.tig.2008.09.004

Qin, J., Li, Y., Cai, Z., Li, S., Zhu, J., Zhang, F., ... Shen, D. (2012). A metagenome-wide association study of gut microbiota in type 2 diabetes. *Nature, 490*(7418), 55–60. doi:10.1038/nature11450

Roseboom, T., de Rooij, S., & Painter, R. (2006). The Dutch famine and its long-term consequences for adult health. *Early Human Development, 82*(8), 485–491. doi:10.1016/j.earlhumdev.2006.07.001

Roseboom, T. J., Painter, R. C., van Abeelen, A. F. M., Veenendaal, M. V. E., & de Rooij, S. R. (2011). Hungry in the womb: What are the consequences? Lessons from the Dutch famine. *Maturitas, 70*(2), 141–145. doi:10.1016/j.maturitas.2011.06.017

Rosengren, A. H., Braun, M., Mahdi, T., Andersson, S. A., Travers, M. E., Shigeto, M., ... Eliasson, L. (2012). Reduced insulin exocytosis in human pancreatic-cells with gene variants linked to type 2 diabetes. *Diabetes, 61*(7), 1726–1733. doi:10.2337/db11-1516

Sabin, M. A., Werther, G. A., & Kiess, W. (2011). Genetics of obesity and overgrowth syndromes. *Best Practice & Research Clinical Endocrinology & Metabolism, 25*(1), 207–220. doi:10.1016/j.beem.2010.09.010

Sailors, M., & Bray, M. S. (2011). The interaction between genetic variation and exercise and physical activity in the determination of body composition and obesity status. In L. Pescatello & S. M. Roth (Eds.), *Exercise Genomics.* New York: Humana Press.

Sapone, A., De Magistris, L., Pietzak, M., Clemente, M. G., Tripathi, A., Cucca, F., ... Fasano, A. (2006). Zonulin upregulation is associated with increased gut permeability in subjects with type 1 diabetes and their relatives. *Diabetes, 55*(5): 1443–1449. doi:10.2337/db05-1593

Scott, L. J., Mohlke, K. L, & Boehnke, M. (2007), A genome-wide association study of type 2 diabetes in Finns detects multiple susceptibility variants, *Science, 316*(5829); 1341–45.

Slomko, H., Heo, H. J., & Einstein, F. H. (2012). Mini-review: Epigenetics of obesity and diabetes in humans. *Endocrinology, 153*(3), 1025–1030.

Skinningsrud, B., Lie, B.A, Lavant, E., Carlson, J.A., Erlich, H., Akselsen, H.E., Gervin, K., Wolff, A.G., Erichsen, M.M., Lovas, K., Husebye, E. and Undlien, D.E. (2011) Multiple Loci in the HLA Complex Are Associated with Addison's Disease, *J Clinical Endocrinologic Metabolism, 96,* E1703–E1708.

Soubry, A., Schildkraut, J. M., Murtha, A., Wang, F., Huang, Z., Bernal, A., . . . Hoyo, C. (2013). Paternal obesity is associated with IGF2 hypomethylation in newborns: Results from a Newborn Epigenetics Study (NEST) cohort. *BMC Medicine, 11*(1), 29. doi:10.1186/1741-7015-11-29.

Stene, L. C., Ulriksen, J., Magnus, P., & Joner, G. (2000). Use of cod liver oil during pregnancy associated with lower risk of type 1 diabetes in the offspring. *Diabetologia, 43*(9), 1093–1098.

Stephens, J. M. (2012). The fat controller: Adipocyte development. *PLoS Biology, 10*(11), e1001436. doi:10.1371/journal.pbio.1001436

Takiishi, T., Gysemans, C., Bouillon, R., & Mathieu, C. (2010). Vitamin D and diabetes. *Endocrinology and Metabolism Clinics of North America, 39*(2), 419–446.

Taneera, J., Lang, S., Sharma, A., Fadista, J., Zhou, Y., Ahlqvist, E., ... Groop, L. (2012). A systems genetics approach identifies genes and pathways for type 2 diabetes in human islets. *Cell Metabolism, 16*(1), 122–134. doi:10.1016/j.cmet.2012.06.006

Thorleifsson, G., Walters G.B., Gudbjartsson, D.F., Steinthorsdottir, V., Sulem, P., Helgadottir, A., Styrkarsdottir, U., Gretarsdottir, S., Thorlacius, S., Jonsdottir, I., Jonsdottir, T., Olafsdottir, E.J., Olafsdottir, G.H., Jonsson, T., Jonsson, F., Borch-Johnsen, K., Hansen, T., Andersen, G., Jorgensen, T., Lauritzen, T., Aben, K.K., Verbeek, A.L., Roeleveld, N., Kampman, E., Yanek, L.R., Becker, L.C., Tryggvadottir, L., Rafnar, T., Becker, D.M., Gulcher, J., Kiemeney, L.A., Pedersen, O., Kong, A., Thorsteinsdottir, U., Stefansson, K. (2009) Genome-wide association yields new sequence variants at seven loci that associate with measures of obesity. *Nature Genetics 41*(1):18-24. doi: 10.1038/ng.274.

Timsit, J., Bellanné-Chantelot, C., Dubois-Laforgue, D., & Velho, G. (2005). Diagnosis and management of maturity-onset diabetes of the young. *Treatments in Endocrinology, 4*(1), 9–18.

Tomer, Y. (2010). Genetic susceptibility to autoimmune thyroid disease: Past, present, and future. *Thyroid, 20*(7), 715-725.

U.S. National Library of Medicine. (2013, September 9). Nephrogenic diabetes insipidus. *Genetics Home Reference.* Retrieved from http://ghr.nlm.nih.gov/condition/nephrogenic-diabetes-insipidus

Vaarala, O., Ilonen, J., Ruohtula, T., Pesola, J., Virtanen, S. M., Harkonen, T., . . . Knip, M. (2012). Removal of bovine insulin from cow's milk formula and early initiation of beta-cell autoimmunity in the Finnish Dietary Intervention Trial for the Prevention of Type 1 Diabetes (FINDIA) Pilot Study. (2012). *Archives of Pediatric & Adolescent Medicine, 166*(7), 608–614.

Vehik, K. & Dabelea, D. (2012). Why are c-section deliveries linked to childhood type 1 diabetes? *Diabetes, 61*(1), 36–37.

Walley, A. J., Asher, J. E., & Froguel, P. (2009). The genetic contribution to non-syndromic human obesity. *Nature Reviews Genetics, 10*(7), 431–442. doi:10.1038/nrg2594

Watanabe, R. M., Black, M. H., Xiang, A. H., Allayee, H., Lawrence, J. M., & Buchanan, T. A. (2007). Genetics of gestational diabetes mellitus and type 2 diabetes. *Diabetes Care, 30*(Supplement_2), S134–S140. doi:10.2337/dc07-s205

Webb, A. R., Kline, L., & Holick, M. F. (1988). Influence of season and latitude on the cutaneous synthesis of vitamin D3: Exposure to winter sunlight in Boston and Edmonton will not promote vitamin D3 synthesis in human skin. *The Journal of Clinical Endocrinology and Metabolism, 67*(2), 373–378.

Wilson, T. A. (2012). Congenital adrenal hyperplasia. In: S. Kemp (Ed.), *Medscape Reference.* Retrieved from http://emedicine.medscape.com/article/919218-overview#a0199

Yang, Q., Liu, T., Shrader, P., Yesupriya, A., Chang, M. -h., Dowling, N. F., . . . & the MAGIC Investigators. (2010). Racial/ethnic differences in association of fasting glucose-associated genomic loci with fasting glucose, HOMA-B, and impaired fasting glucose in the U.S. adult population. *Diabetes Care, 33*(11), 2370–2377. doi:10.2337/dc10-0898

Yazbek, S. N., Spiezio, S. H., Nadeau, J. H., & Buchner, D. A. (2010). Ancestral paternal genotype controls body weight and food intake for multiple generations. *Human Molecular Genetics, 19*(21), 4134–4144. doi:10.1093/hmg/ddq332

Zia, A. (2013). Genetic susceptibility to type 2 diabetes and implications for therapy. *Journal of Diabetes & Metabolism, 04*(03). doi:10.4172/2155-6156.1000248

Zipitis, C. S. & Akobeng, A. K., (2008). Vitamin D supplementation in early childhood and risk of type 1 diabetes: A systematic review and meta-analysis. *Archives of Disease in Childhood, 93*(6), 512–517.

Chapter 15

Cancer Genomics: Current and Future Concepts to Define Health Care Practices and Personalized Care

QUANNETTA T. EDWARDS, Ph.D, FNP-BC, WHNP-BC, AGN-BC, FAANP
ANN H. MARADIEGUE, Ph.D, FNP-BC, FAANP
KORY W. JASPERSON, MS, CGC

Objectives:

- Distinguish between sporadic, familial, and hereditary types of cancer.
- Discuss the significance of the cell cycle in carcinogenesis.
- Describe different type of genes (e.g. oncogenes, tumor suppressor, and repair genes) and how they influence cancer initiation.
- Explain epigenetic factors and their impact on cancer development.
- Differentiate between personal, familial, and environmental factors that could be considered red flags for hereditary cancer syndromes.
- Summarize the role of future genomic technologies and how they affect cancer personalized care.
- Explain and provide examples of how pharmacogenomics can be applied to the care of a cancer patient in clinical settings.
- Analyze selected cases for hereditary cancer syndromes and discuss the role of the advanced practice nurse.

15.1. DEFINITION OF TERMS ASSOCIATED WITH CANCER GENETICS AND USED IN THIS CHAPTER

Allele   Variant forms of a gene.

Apoptosis   Normal series of programmed cellular death necessary and critical for ensuring unwanted cells and tumor formation.

Differentiated Cells   Mature cells that are specialized to perform a specific function while maintaining the same genome.

Epigenetics   Events other than mutations in the DNA sequence that during cell development and proliferation influence gene functioning and protein expression.

Familial Cancer   Same type of cancer occurring in 2 or more family members that is not a result of a known inherited gene mutation found in the germ line, but is attributed to the combination of genomic influences shared by relatives, as well as environmental factors.

Hereditary Cancer   Mutations in the germ line and transmitted to the infant at time of conception, increasing the risk of cancer.

Methylation   Form of epigenetics involving the addition of a methyl group in the promoter region of the gene.

microRNA   Class of noncoding RNAs that regulate gene expression posttranscription.

Mutation   Genetic changes due to alterations from its normal state.

Oncogenes   Conversion of a proto-oncogene into a cancer-causing gene.

Phosphorylation   Addition of a phosphate group post–translation of the cell cycle that can activate or inactivate a protein.

Progenitor Cells   Early descendants of stem

cells that are partly differentiated cells present in fetal and adult tissues that divide to produce mature cells.

Proto-Oncogenes   Normal gene that codes proteins to regulate cell cycle, including growth and differentiation that, if mutated, can affect the structure and function of the protein, resulting in an oncogene that is able to form cancer.

Sporadic Cancer   Cancer that is not due to a germ line mutation (hereditary).

Stem Cells   Undifferentiated cells that can divide and self-renew, producing copies of itself with the ability to differentiate into mature cell types through the cell cycle and division.

Ubiquitin   Small, regulatory protein found in cells that influences cell cycle control, DNA repair, cell growth, and signaling through regulated protein degradation.

15.2. INTRODUCTION

Over the past 3 decades since 1975, trend data regarding the overall age-adjusted cancer incidence rates (per 100,000) for men and women and for all racial and ethnic groups in the United States (U.S.) have declined (Eheman *et al.*, 2012). Data for the years 2004 to 2008 revealed that cancer incidence declined by an average of 0.6% for men and 0.5% for women from 2004 to 2006, then leveled off thereafter (Eheman *et al.*, 2012) (see Figure 15.1).

Relative survival rates for the disease have also been improving. Relative survival rates compare survival among cancer patients to that of individuals without the disease of similar race, age, and ethnicity and represent individuals who are alive for a specified period of time (usually 5 years) relative to those without cancer (American Cancer Society [ACS], 2012). Although sur-

All Cancer (invasive) Age-adjusted SEER Cancer Incidence Rates by Year, Race and Sex (1975-2010)

FIGURE 15.1. Surveillance, Epidemiology and End Results (SEER) data for all cancer sites (invasive), ageadjusted incidence rates by year, race and sex. SEER 9 areas (San Francisco, Connecticut, Detroit, Hawaii, Iowa, New Mexico, Seattle, Utah, and Atlanta). Rates are per 100,000 and are age-adjusted to the 2000 US Standard Population (19 age groups - Census P25-1130). Retrieved from National Cancer Institute http://seer.cancer.gov/csr/1975_2010/browse_csr.php?section=2&page=sect_02_table.05.html

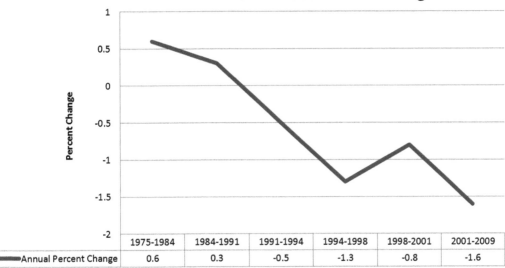

FIGURE 15.2. Historical trends indicating mortality rates during the years 1975-2009 in the United States (U.S.) for all cancer sites, all ages, races (including Hispanics), and both sexes. Data on the figure reveals rates rising from 1975–1985 and 1984–1991; stable during 1991–1994; and falling during the periods of 1994–1998, 1998–2001, and 2001–2009. Obtained from the National Cancer Institute, Surveillance Epidemiology and End Results with Source: Death data provided by the National Vital Statistics System (http://www.cdc.gov/nchs/nvss.htm) public use data file. Death rates calculated by the National Cancer Institute (NCI) using SEER*Stat. Death rates per 100,000 population per year ageadjusted to the 2000 U.S. Census populations as modified by NCI. The U.S. populations included with the data release have been adjusted for the population shifts due to hurricanes Katrina and Rita for 62 counties and parishes in Alabama, Mississippi, Louisiana, and Texas. The 1969-2009 U.S. population file is used with mortality data.

vival statistics of cancer differ by diagnosis, the relative 5-year survival rate for all cancers during the years 2004 to 2010 was 68.0%, up significantly from that of 49.0% during the years 1975 to 1977 (ACS, 2015). Further, the overall cancer mortality rates per 100,000 declined in the past decade for both men and women in the U.S., with a slightly larger decline among males (1.8% per year) compared with females (1.4% per year) (Edwards *et al.*, 2014; National Cancer Institute [NCI], Surveillance Epidemiology and End Results [SEER], 2013a.). Figure 15.2 depicts the annual percent of change data based upon the overall observed mortality rates for cancer in the U.S. reported over a 35-year time period.

Despite these declining changes in overall cancer trends, including incidence, mortality, and survival rates, cancer continues to be a major health problem in the U.S., with lifetime disease probability estimated at slightly less than 1 in 2 for men and slightly more than 1 in 3 for women; over 1,658,370 cases predicted to occur in 2015

(ACS, 2015). Cancer is the second most common cause of death, with 1 out of 4 individuals dying from a cancer causing illness and mortality rates exceeded only by that of heart disease (ACS, 2015). In 2015, approximately 589,430 Americans are expected to die from cancer (ACS, 2015).

The genomic era is expected to have a significant impact on cancer. The genomic era has led to significant advancements in cancer screening, diagnostics, prognostics, risk assessment, and therapeutic management to provide *personalized* healthcare in prevention, early recognition, and management of the disease (NCI, nd; Weitzel *et al.*, 2011). *Personalized cancer management* focuses on a wide range of measures to prevent, diagnose, and treat the disease based upon the individual's *molecular genomic* makeup, which influence and impact disease occurrence, prognosis, and therapeutic management (De Abreu *et al.*, 2014). For example, in the last several decades, past discoveries of numerous genetic tests focusing on single gene disorders (e.g., hereditary breast cancer and ovarian cancer [HBOC], *BRCA 1* and *BRCA 2*; hereditary colon cancer, Lynch syndrome and familial adenomatous polyposis [*FAP*]) have resulted in enhanced surveillance, chemoprevention, risk-reduction surgery, and targeted therapies (National Comprehensive Cancer Network [NCCN], 2015a; NCCN, 2015) geared to improving outcomes and quality of life for *at high-risk* cancer patients. The insurgence of targeted therapies that focus on the *genomic* profile of cancer tumors and biomarkers is also resulting in novel measures to treat or combat cancer (Garnett *et al.*, 2012), as well as determining disease prognosis (Jeschke *et al.*, 2012). Current and future applications of pharmacogenomics furthers the potential to enhance the optimization of cancer therapeutics by impacting drug action and efficacy and reducing adverse drug effects, including toxicity. Thus, advancements in *cancer genomics* have and will continue to play a major role in contributing to the diagnosis, prognosis, and treatment of the disease, resulting in improved cancer survival rates in the U.S. as well as worldwide. These advances also have social issues that will have ethical considerations, impact health services and costs, and have significant policy implications.

Precision medicine is a newer term often used to reflect a more accurate image of diagnosis that is person-centered and multifaceted. Precision medicine reflects the use of genomic, epigenomic, prognostic and predictive markers, exposure, and other information to define individual patterns of disease, potentially leading to better individual treatment in patients with cancer (Duffy & Crown, 2014; Insel, 2011). To gain better insights into the biology of diseases, an initiative focusing on precision medicine that takes into account individual variability in genes, environment, and lifestyle for each person is underway (NCI, 2015a). The *Precision Medicine Initiative*, sponsored by the National Institutes of Health (NIH), is aimed to expand efforts in cancer genomics to create prevention and treatment successes for more cancers. Immediate goals of this initiative include "supporting clinical trials to test combinations of targeted therapies that are based on a tumor's molecular signature; developing solutions to drug resistance that commonly limit the effectiveness of targeted therapies; developing approaches that can assess response to therapy, and possible development of resistance; and developing new tumor cell models to predict response to drug combinations and to define mechanisms of resistance" (NCI, 2015a, para 2).

This chapter centers on current and evolving practices in oncology for the advanced practice registered nurse (APRN), nurse leader, researcher or academician and focuses on genomics and personalized/precision management of care. It begins with a definition and overview of carcinogenesis to familiarize the reader on the importance and implications that genomics, epigenetics, and environmental factors have on the occurrence, reoccurrence, progression, and therapeutic management of cancer. The 3 common types of cancer, *sporadic, familial*, and *inherited/hereditary* forms, are also discussed, as well as disease etiology related to extrinsic factors and environmental agents. An overview of inherited cancer syndromes is also presented in this chapter, including a special section on hereditary breast and colorectal cancer (CRC) syndromes. Advances in genomic care emphasizing personalized/precision management and practice implications are presented and explained, with focus on tumor profiling, genomic markers, single nucleotide polymorphisms (SNPs), protein expression studies, next generation sequencing, and selected pharmacogenomic agents that may impact cancer management. Ethical, legal, and social implications of genomics are also discussed, as well as the implications of genomics in healthcare for nursing. The chapter concludes with application of the material presented herein, using several case studies relative to clinical practice and the genomic core competencies for APRNs.

15.3. CARCINOGENESIS—A PRIMER

Cancer is a genomic disease, of which the initiation of cancer cell development, maintenance, and progression requires knowledge and understanding of the cell cycle, including genes, cell cycle control systems (e.g., cyclin-dependent kinases), regulators, and other epigenetic factors related to cell synthesis, division, control, and normal programmed cell death (apoptosis). (Note: Chapter 1 of this textbook provides a basic review of genomics and the cell cycle). Cancer can be described as a genetically unstable process that occurs at a molecular level, resulting in *unregulated abnormal cellular growth* and apoptosis leading to uncontrolled cellular proliferation and tumor formation (neoplasm). This process evades the rules that control normal cellular division. Cancer evolution is based upon several theories, including theory of *clonal evolution* and *stem cell theory*, both involving genetic mutations. In the clonal evolution model proposed in the 1970s, genetic mutations occur in a single cell, giving it a selective growth advantage and outnumbering other cells, which results in additional mutations and proliferation into a large clone or clonal expansion (Chandar & Viselli, 2010; Greaves & Maley, 2012). According to this theory, cancer cells over time acquire various combinations of mutations and, with clonal expansion, results in a growth advantage over normal cells, leading to tumor development. The process is one of the complex mutations involving key genes that transform a single cell to that of a tumor. As the tumor progresses, genetic instability and uncontrolled proliferation allow the production of cells, with additional mutations and new characteristics (Clark *et al.*, 2006). In contrast, the stem cell theory of cancer suggests that cancer arises from *cancer stem cells* with indefinite proliferation, progression, and self-renewal similar to adult stem cells (Han, Shi, Gong, Zhang, & Sun, 2013). According to the *American Association of Cancer Research Workshop on Cancer Stem Cells*, the consensus definition of a cancer stem cell is a "cell within a tumor that possesses the capacity to self-renew and to cause the heterogeneous lineages of cancer cells that comprise the tumor" (Campbell & Pollack, 2007). The development of *cancer stem cells* (original clone of neoplastic cells serving as a reservoir of genetically unstable cells (Nussbaum, McInnes, & Willard 2007) is hypothesized to result in mutations derived from a stem cell (cells that can continuously divide or self-renew with the ability to differentiate into mature cells) or progenitor cell (descendants of stem cells that can differentiate to form 1 or more cells) or from differentiated cells that have undergone mutations (Alberts *et al.*, 2008a; Goldthwaite, 2011) (See Figure 15.3). Cancer stem cells not only have the ability to self-renew, but also are distinguishable from other cells by their ability to differentiate into other types of cells, generating

tumor heterogeneity (Campbell & Pollack, 2007; Goldthwaite, 2011). Thus, cancer stem cells have characteristics of self-renewal, heterogeneity, and potential for multidirectional differentiation and are resistant to apoptosis (Gil, Stembalska, Pesz, & Sasiadek, 2008). The cancer stem cells are a result of accumulation of key genes and epigenetic alterations. This behavior of cancer stem cells is different when compared to those from clonal expansion, because tumors derived from cancer stem cells are felt to be more resistant to treatment, less likely to respond to treatment, and more likely to have disease recurrence after successful treatment (Chandar & Viselli, 2010; Gil *et al.*, 2008). These differences have implications for molecular targeting and therapeutic strategies.

Regardless of the theoretical basis of the disease in malignant neoplasm or cancer, aberrant cells continue with uncontrolled growth, failure to undergo cellular death (*apoptosis*), invade or infiltrate leading to disease, and if left unabated or untreated, spread to distant sites including the blood stream and lymphatic system (*metastasis*) (Frank, 2007; Nussbaum, McInnes, & Willard, 2007; Warshawsky, 2006). This process of transformation from the normal cell to invasive cancer is referred as *carcinogenesis* (Alberts *et al.*, 2008b). The hallmark of cancer, therefore, is uncontrolled cell proliferation and tumors with gene alterations that directly relate to the normal cell cycle. The process is complex, involving heterogeneous cell populations, with similarities occurring in individuals diagnosed with the same type of cancer, as well as differences based upon one's personal biological and genomic make-up (Goldthwaite, 2011). Thus, this shows the importance of understanding the implications of personalized/precision medicine for the disease, including therapeutic management.

Cancer cells are the result of uncontrolled cell proliferation occurring from aberrations in the normal cell cycle. There are checkpoints in the normal cell cycle that protect the fidelity of the cell, guarding critical cell cycle transitions and checking that the cells are free of errors to continue to cell cycle completion. Major checkpoint control processes occur during the following cycles: (1) *Gap1* (G_1) *cell-cycle entry*, whereby cells are responding to extracellular signals and cyclin dependent protein kinases (CDKs)

How Do Cancer Stem Cells Arise?

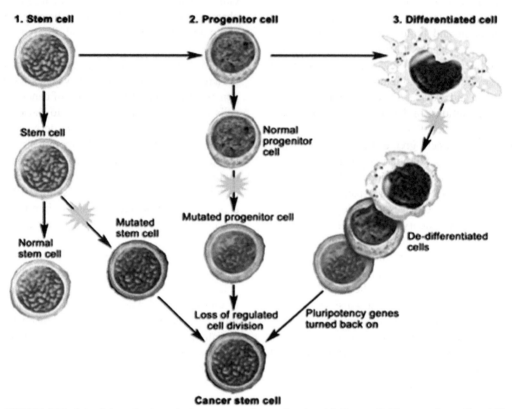

FIGURE 15.3. Potential mechanisms for how cancer stem cells arise; (1) Stem cell; (2) progenitor cell; or (differentiated cell) denoting mutations and development of cancer (Goldwaithe, 2011). Approval to use figure from Terese Winslow.

or withdrawing from the cycle into Go or resting state; (2) *late G_1* or the restriction phase, in which the cells become refractory to extracellular growth regulatory signals to progress through the cell cycle; (3) G_1 transition and entry into "S" (synthesis phase) controlled by CDKs dependent on positive and negative phosphorylation, certain genes and genetic pathways (e.g., retinoblastoma [RB] and *p53* pathways) that can act as surveillance points to repair damaged genes or stop the cycle protection again aberrant cells, including apoptosis; (4) G_2/M phase further regulated by specific CDKs and genes (Alberts *et al.* 2008c; Sherr, 1996) preventing cell cycle progression of damaged or nonproperly replicated DNA, including apoptosis; corrects chromosome alignment (Smits & Medema, 2001); and (5) *metaphase to anaphase* of the cell cycle completing *mitosis,* including *ubiquitin*-dependent proteolysis of key regulatory proteins involved in protein deg-

radation of some cyclins, as well as chromatid separation and cytokinesis (Hochstrasser,1996; Smits & Medema, 2001). Cell cycle progression from one phase to the next is controlled by a complex of CDKs (see Figure 15.4), important mechanisms that rise and fall throughout the cycle, leading to changes in phosphorylation of intracellular proteins that initiate and regulate the cell cycle from entry to mitosis (Alberts *et al.*, 2008c). Cell cycle kinases regulate the cell cycle, DNA synthesis, and mitosis integral to normal cellular development and when altered, impact carcinogenesis (Malumbres & Barbacid, 2007).

Because cancer development is a complex process, there are numerous genetic and epigenetic factors that can alter normal cellular development. Aberrant cell development due to cancer is a consequence of genetic changes because of alterations (*mutations*) in the DNA sequence or because of *epigenetic changes,* events other than mutations in the DNA sequence, which during cell development and proliferation, influence gene functioning and protein expression (You & Jones 2012). Genetic disruptions and alterations can also be from alterations in DNA sequence due to chromosomal abnormalities, including rearrangements or translocations (Zarbl, 2006) that effect normal protein expression important to normal cellular development. Cancer development from either genetic or epigenetic alteration results in abnormal gene expression and thus cancer cells are considered genetically unstable (*genetic instability*) (Alberts *et al.*, 2008b; You & Jones, 2012). A further discussion of each of these mechanisms is briefly explained later in this chapter.

15.3.1. Genetic Mutations and Cancer Development

Mutations in DNA sequencing can result in cancer development. The alterations can be defined as *sporadic*, resulting in cancer that initially occurred from a single somatic cell mutation, or *hereditary*, resulting in mutations due to a single gene found in the germ line with the mutation

found in every cell of the body at birth (Nussbaum, McInnes, & Willard 2007). The majority of cancers in humans are sporadic (approximately 75%) and attributed to somatic mutations. Somatic mutations resulting in abnormal genetic expression are due to multifactorial events, a consequence acquired through genetic and environmental interactions. Individuals with sporadic cancers usually develop disease occurrence at an age of onset expected for the specific type of cancer (e.g., woman diagnosed with breast cancer at age 59). It is estimated that approximately 10% to15% of cancers are *familial*, referred to as the same type of cancer occurring in 2 or more family members, that is not a result of a known inherited gene mutation found in the germ line but is attributed to the combination of genomic influences shared by relatives, as well as environmental factors. Individuals with familial cancer have an above average risk for cancer. For example, a 2- to 3-fold increased risk of cancer development has been found in first-degree relatives with multiple forms of the disease (ACS, 2015; Nussbaum, McInnes, &Willard, 2007). Hereditary cancers compromise the remaining type of cancer. Hereditary cancers occur because

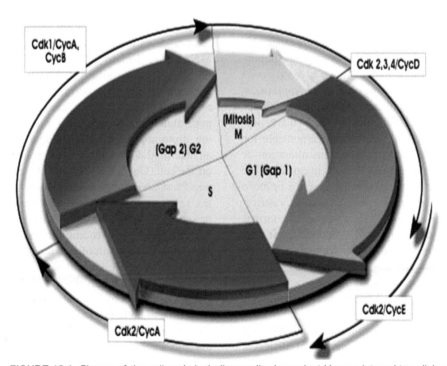

FIGURE 15.4. Phases of the cell cycle including cyclin dependent kinases integral to cellular development. Figure obtained with permission from Terese Winslow.

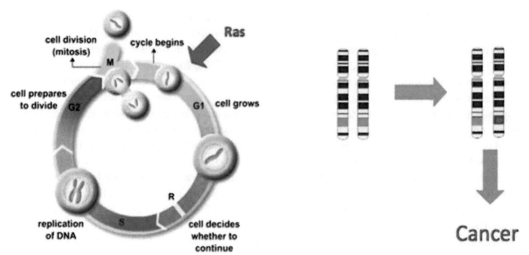

FIGURE 15.5. Proto-oncogenes normally function to promote cell growth and division in a controlled manner. A mutation in 1 copy of the gene (noted here as the RAS gene marked in red) can be enough to drive cancer. Ras gene products are involved in kinase signaling pathways controlling gene transcription. Figure courtesy of the Wellcome Trust Sanger Institute Communication and Public Engagement team.

of mutations in the germ line (ovary or sperm), transmitted to the infant at time of conception, and with the mutated gene present in every cell in the body. Further discussion of hereditary cancers is presented later in this chapter.

15.3.2. Proto-Oncogenes, Oncogenes, and Carcinogenesis

The genetic mutations resulting in cancer involve 2 major broad categories of genes important in cellular functioning known as *proto-oncogenes* (growth promoting) and *tumor suppressor genes* (growth inhibiting) (Alberts *et al.*, 2008b; Chow, 2010). These genes are particularly important in encoding for proteins responsible for cell growth and proliferation, thus alteration or inactivation of these genes results in cancer. Most cancers have inactivating mutations in 1 or more proteins of these major gene categories, restricting progression through the stages of the normal cell cycle (see Figure 15.5). Abnormal gene proteins that can lead to cancer formation include those proteins affecting growth factors, growth factor receptors, signal transducer, transcription factors, apoptosis, cell cycle control, and DNA repair (Lodish *et al.*, 2000).

Proto-oncogenes are important in promoting cell growth, division, and survival at all levels of the cell cycle (Chow, 2010). In normal cells, proto-oncogenes code for the proteins that send

a signal to the nucleus to stimulate cell division. These signaling proteins act in a series of steps called signal transduction cascades or pathways. Proto-oncogenes encode a variety of important functions, including extracellular growth factors, major cellular growth factor receptors (e.g., protein tyrosine kinases), molecules involved in signaling cascades and pathways, transcriptional regulators, cell cycle control intracellular proteins, and apoptosis (Chial, 2008a; Nussbaum, McInnes, & Willard 2007; Zarbl, 2006). Proto-oncogenes can be inactivated as a result of genetic point mutations or chromosomal breaks, rearrangements, or translocations that impact gene functioning, converting normal functioning proto-oncogenes into *oncogenes* that have an abnormal dominant, growth-promoting effect on the cell. Oncogenes can also be activated by *amplification* in the gene or increase in gene copies, resulting from chromosomal nondisjunction or tandem gene replication (Zarbl, 2006). Oncogenes are genes encoding for proteins that induce cancer as a result of interference of cellular growth pathways (Lodish *et al.*, 2000). They can alter normal signaling pathways of the cell at all levels (Zarbl, 2006) affecting cell proliferation, apoptosis, or both. Regardless of the mechanism, conversion of proto-oncogenes to oncogenes leads to a *gain of function* or dominant activity requiring only one of two alleles of the gene to deregulate cell proliferation and induce cancer

(Ashworth, Lord, & Reis-Filho, 2011; Lodish *et al.*, 2000). Oncogenes work by increasing the abnormal activity of the cell cycle, accelerating the stages of the normal cell cycle, which results in DNA duplication and contributes to cancerous cell growth (Chow, 2010; Zarbl, 2006). Oncogenes increase production of proteins that stimulate cell division and cell differentiation while also inhibiting apoptosis characteristics of cancer cells and enabling them to continue without a programmed death. Oncogenes due to chromosomal translocation, such as that of *BCR/ABL*, also cause abnormal unregulated cell cycling (Chow, 2010; Nussbaum, McInnes, & Willard, 2007). In *BCR/ABL* translocation, the *ABL* proto-oncogene is fused to the *BCR* gene, encoding an oncogenic ABL fusion protein that influences and accelerates the tyrosine kinase activity and results in chronic myelogenous leukemia (Croce, 2008). This chromosome is often referred to as the Philadelphia chromosome (Figure 15.6).

A useful analogy for comparing proto-oncogenes to that of oncogenes can be made by considering these genes as part of the cell cycle controlled by that of a *gas pedal*. For example, different proto-oncogenes control the movement of the cell cycle with the proper acceleration of the gas pedal via functioning genes for growth

factor receptors, signal transducers, transcription factors, protein tyronines, enzymes, and apoptosis. In contrast, oncogenes pushes the gas pedal to the floor or have a gas pedal that is "stuck," resulting in constant uncontrolled high rates of activity for the cell cycle and uncontrolled cell proliferation. Cancers associated with oncogenes can be sporadic or hereditary. Knowledge of oncogenes has significant implication to clinical practice, because they provide a means for molecular targeted therapy to combat cancer cells (Chial, 2008a). Table 15.1 provides examples of oncogenes and the cancer site often associated with the genes.

15.3.2.1. Tumor Suppressor Genes and Carcinogenesis

Tumor suppressor genes are another major category of genes resulting in carcinogenesis. Similar to proto-oncogenes, tumor suppressor genes influence the cell cycle. In contrast to proto-oncogenes, which are associated with a cellular gain of function, tumor suppressor genes code for proteins that restrict cellular growth and proliferation while promoting apoptosis and are associated with a *loss of function* (Ashworth, Lord, & Reis-Filho, 2011; Chow, 2010). Tumor sup-

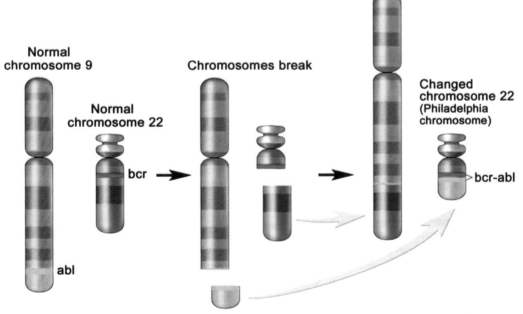

FIGURE 15.6. Philadelphia chromosome depicting translocation. Permission to use figure obtained from Terese Winslow.

**TABLE 15.1. Example of Oncogenes Associated with
Cancer including Function and Site of Cancer(s).**

Gene	Function	Common Sites Associated with Cancer
BCL2	Apoptosis; stimulates angiogenesis	Leukemia; Lymphoma
HER2/neu	Tyrosine Kinase, Growth Factor Receptor	Breast; Ovarian
Myc	Transcription Protein-protein interactions with cells	Burkitt's Lymphoma
RAS	Signal transduction cascade	Pancreatic; Colorectal; Bladder; Breast; Kidney; Lung; Leukemia; Melanoma
SIS	Growth Factor	Glioma
BRAF	Serine-threonine kinases Activation of signaling pathways	Colon
RET	Tyronine kinase receptor	Papillary thyroid; Multiple endocrine Neoplasia (MEN 2)*

*Type of hereditary cancer syndrome.

pressor genes impact cell cycle control, cellular structure, transcriptional regulation, signal transduction, DNA replication and repair, and protein degradation (Agarwal, Kabir, DeInnocentes, & Bird, 2012; Weissman, 2006). Mechanisms resulting in inactivation of tumor suppressor genes include gene mutations, chromosomal deletions, and epigenetic factors (Oliveira, Ross, & Fletcher, 2005). Inactivation of tumor suppressor genes inhibits the progression into the synthesis (S) phase of the cell cycle, stopping cell proliferation (Chow, 2010) (see Figure 15.7).

For example, the *p53* gene, located on chromosome 17p13 and the most commonly mutated tumor suppressor gene in human tumors, plays an important critical role as an apoptotic gene that prevent cells with damaged DNA from dividing and passing on the DNA damage to daughter cells. It also targets other genes involved in growth regulation to halt the cell cycle, playing a major regulatory role in G1 phase (growth phase) for cellular repair, to take place due to DNA damage to preserve the integrity of the genome and to prevent tumor formation or cancer (see Figure 15.7). The purpose of *p53* is to regulate genes involved in cell cycle control, apoptosis, DNA repair, and angiogenesis. The gene is very important and has been known as the "guardian of the genome." The *p53* gene is the most frequently altered gene in human cancers (Vogelstein, Sur, & Prives, 2010) and has been associated with more than 50% of human tumors due to mutations in the gene.

Unlike that of oncogenes, tumor suppressor gene inactivation requires that both genes are nonfunctional (maternal and paternal) as a result of a germ line mutation in 1 allele and a somatic event (e.g., mutation, *loss of heterozygosity*, hypermethylation, etc.) in the other allele, as seen in many hereditary cancer syndromes, or 2 somatic events (e.g., deletion of both alleles of a gene [*loss of* homozygosity]) (Alberts *et al.*, 2008b; Chow, 2010; Weissman, 2006). The first reported tumor suppressor gene resulting in cancer is that of the hereditary form of retinoblastoma (RB), which is associated with a rare form of retinal cancer occurring in childhood (Alberts, 2008b; Weissman, 2006). This disease can be attributed to either somatic mutations or hereditary disease. Knudson's *two-hit hypothesis* aids in explaining why certain tumors, such as retinoblastoma, occur in both hereditary and sporadic cancers. For example, in hereditary retinoblastoma based upon the two-hit hypothesis, cancer cells develop when a heterozygous cell due to a germ line mutation in a tumor-suppressor gene called *RB1* undergoes a second somatic event that inactivates the other allele (new mutation), resulting in *loss of function* of both genes. This combination of the first hit (inherited) and the second somatic hit eliminates the protein of the *RB1*, resulting in disease (Knudson, 2001). In the sporadic form of diseases using the two-hit hypothesis, both alleles are inactivated because of 2 somatic events occurring in the same cells (Nussbaum, McInnes, & Willard, 2007). This 2-hit hypothesis holds true for most tumor suppressor genes. Although both alleles of tumor suppressor genes must be nonfunctional for disease to occur, individuals with a *germ line mutation* (inherited disease) have a 50% chance of passing the mutation on to each offspring (autosomal dominant [AD]). Further, because the mutation is present at birth and thus in every cell of the body, individuals are predisposed to multiple cancer occurrences, including more than one type of cancer (syndrome) and cancers occurring at early ages. In either case, tumor suppressor genes facilitate cancer development by slowing cellular proliferation via a loss of function of both alleles and a cellular recessive effect. This is unlike that of oncogenes, which facilitate cancer development by a dominant function with only 1 allele loss of function required for growth promoting oncogenes and cellular proliferation.

There are different subtypes of tumor suppressor genes. Certain tumor suppressor genes are considered *gatekeepers* (e.g., *RB1*, *p53*; adenomatous polyposis coli [APC] genes), because they directly regulate cell growth by inhibiting growth or promoting death (Ashworth, Lord, & Reis-Filho, 2011; Deininger,1999) or are considered caretakers (e.g., *BRCA1*; *BRCA2*) genes when functioning to repair DNA damage or chromosome breaks (Ashworth, Lord, & Reis-Filho, 2011; Deininger, 1999; Nussbaum, McInnes, & Willard, 2007) for genomic maintenance.

The gatekeeper genes control or inhibit cellular growth and work by blocking tumor development via the regulation and transition of cells through the checkpoints of cell division commonly referred as the gates (Ashworth, Lord, & Reis-Filho, 2011; Deininger, 1999; Nussbaum, McInnes, & Willard 2007; Oliveira, Ross, & Fletcher, 2005). The role of gatekeeper in tumor suppressor genes also includes promoting/mediating programmed cell death and, thus, controlling cell division and survival (Ashworth, Lord, & Reis-Filho, 2011; Campisi, 2005; Deininger, 1999; Oliveira, Ross, & Fletcher, 2005; Nussbaum, McInnes, & Willard, 2007). Each cell has one or a few gatekeeper gene(s), and inhibiting or inactivating these important genes results in cancer. Caretaker tumor suppressor genes, in contrast, do not directly affect cell proliferation, but act by protecting the integrity of the genome through repairing DNA, chromosomal disruptions, or apoptosis (Campisi, 2005; Levitt & Hickson, 2002; Nussbaum, McInnes, & Willard, 2007).

A useful analogy for tumor suppressor genes can be made by considering these genes as part of the cell cycle controlled by that of a *brake pedal* from the G1 (growth) to the S (synthesis) phase of the cell cycle—putting the brake on cellular proliferation to ensure repair of damaged DNA or apoptosis for irreparable DNA. In mutated or nonfunctioning tumor suppressor genes,

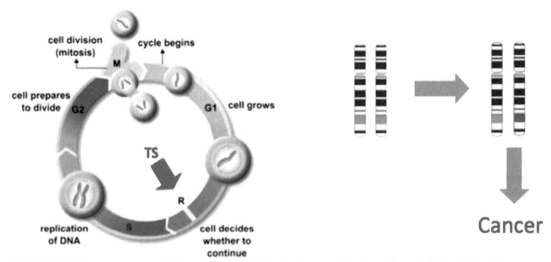

FIGURE 15.7. Tumor suppressor(TS) genes normally function to prevent cell growth and division. To lead to cancer, both copies of the gene would have to be mutated. Figure courtesy of Wellcome Trust Sanger Institute Communication and Public Engagement team.

TABLE 15.2. Examples of Tumor Suppressor Genes Associated with Cancer including Function and Site of Cancer(s).

Gene	Function	Common Sites Associated with Cancer
APC	Transcription of target genes	Colorectal; Familial adenomatous polyposis (FAP)*
BRCA1	Cell cycle control	Breast; ovarian, prostate
BRCA2	DNA repair	Breast; pancreatic; leukemia
p16	Cyclin dependent kinase inhibitor	Leukemia; melanoma; pancreatic; multiple myeloma
p21	Cyclin dependent kinase inhibitor	Colon; ovarian; breast
p53	Apoptosis; Transcription factor	Colorectal; breast; ovarian; bladder, cervical, esophageal, skin lung; gliobastoma,; osteogenic sarcoma; hepatocellular; Li Fraumeni*
RB	Regulation of cell cycle	Retinoblastoma;* small cell lung carcinoma; breast cancer
VHL	Cell division; apoptosis; cell differentiation response to cell stress	Kidney
WT1, WT2	Cell division; transcriptional regulation	Wilm's tumor

Nussbaum, McInnes, & Willard, 2007.
*Type of hereditary cancer syndrome.

the brake pedal is "released," and cells move into the S phase of the cycle unrestrained, which results in a proliferating state of damaged DNA facilitating cancerous changes. Mutations in tumor suppressor genes, as stated previously, can result in sporadic or hereditary cancer syndromes. Table 15.2 provides examples of tumor suppressor genes, their function, and associated carcinogenesis development.

15.3.3. DNA Repair Genes

Alterations in the DNA repair genes have also been associated with carcinogenesis. The DNA repair systems function through diverse cellular pathways and are essential to the maintenance of the integrity of the human genome (Ronen & Glickman, 2001). Over 150 human DNA repair genes have been described in the literature (Milanowska, Rother & Bujnicki, 2011; Wood, Mitchell, & Lindahl, 2005). These genes code for proteins whose function is to correct errors during cellular duplication during cell division. Examples include genes that affect pathways for base excision repair, conserved DNA damage response, direct reversal of DNA damage, nucleotide excision repair, homologous recombination, nonhomologous end joining, DNA polymerases, Fanconi anemia, chromatin structure, editing and processing nucleases, mismatch excision repair, and other genes identified or suspected for DNA

repair function (Milanowska et al., 2011; Wood, Mitchell, & Lindahl, 2005). Alterations in DNA repair genes have been associated with hereditary (e.g., Muir-Torre sydrome, Fanconi anemia) and sporadic cancers (e.g., breast, colorectal, gastric cancers) (Milanowska et al., 2011).

15.3.4. Epigenetics and Carcinogenesis

Not all cancers develop from DNA sequence alterations. Epigenetic mechanisms also play an important role in carcinogenesis. Epigenetic changes result in *silencing* of gene expression without alterations found in the DNA sequence through inappropriate inactivation or inhibition of various cellular signaling pathways (You & Jones, 2012). Epigenetic changes include modification of DNA bases, through addition or removal of simple chemicals, such as a methyl group, and similar changes of the proteins that are closely entwined with DNA to form chromatin, the functional form of the genome (see Figure 1.18 [Chapter 1]).

DNA methylation is a complex mechanism and a common form of epigenetics involving the addition of a methyl group in the promoter region of the gene. The addition of this methyl group serves as an important regulator of gene transcription (Das & Singal, 2004). Transcriptional repression takes place when increased or hypermethylation expression occurs in tumor suppressor genes, leading to silencing of the gene and the potential for carcinogenesis (Das & Singal, 2004; You & Jones, 2012; Zhu, 2006). Also, *microsatellites*, repeated sequences of DNA, have been known to be affected by hypermethylation, resulting in lengthening or shortening of the sequence leading to genomic instability (Simmons, 2008). Epigenetic events, such as hypermethylation, have been observed in many forms of

cancer including, but not limited to, colorectal (Al-Sohaily *et al.*, 2012; Pancione, Remo, & Colantuoni, 2012); hepatocellular (Zhu, 2006); ovarian (Chen, Hardy, & Tollefsbol, 2011); renal (Maher, 2013); prostate, breast, liver, and head and neck (Das & Singal, 2004; and gastric (Gigek *et al.*, 2012) cancers.

Histones can also be impacted by epigenetics. Histones consist of 8 proteins that bind to the

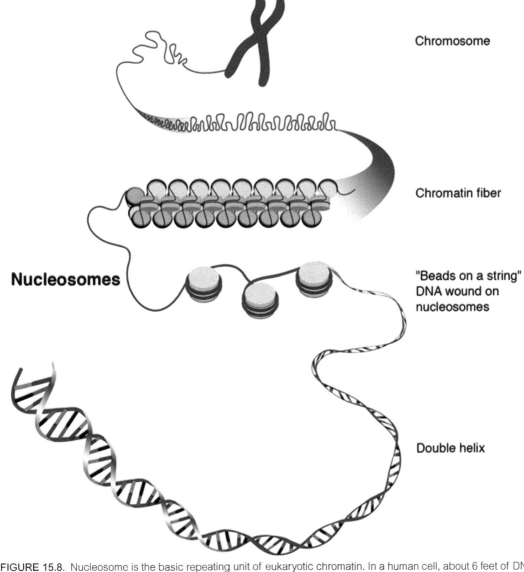

FIGURE 15.8. Nucleosome is the basic repeating unit of eukaryotic chromatin. In a human cell, about 6 feet of DNA must be packaged into a nucleus with a diameter less than a human hair. A single nucleosome consists of about 150 base pairs of DNA sequence wrapped around a core of histone proteins. The nucleosomes are arranged like beads on a string. They are repeatedly folded in on themselves to form a chromosome. Courtesy of the National Human Genome Research Institute (NHGRI), Darryl Leja, NHGRI. Retrieved from: http://www.genome.gov/dmd/img.cfm?node=Photos/Graphics&id=85212

double-stranded DNA and are packaged as *nucleosomes* (see Figures 15.8 and 1.18 [Chapter 1]) regulating gene expression. This arrangement is further packaged into higher order structures through coils and loops, forming chromatin that consists of the double-stranded DNA, histones, as well as other nonhistone proteins and small quantities of ribonucleic acid (RNA). During metaphase of the cell cycle, this structure can be observed as paired chromosomes (Chandar & Viselli, 2010). DNA is wrapped around in histones that are the targets for post-translational modification by acetylation, enzymatic modification of the amino-terminal tails, and decreases in acetylation (hypoacetylation), resulting in transcriptional inactive regions of the genome or gene silencing (Plass, 2002; You & Jones, 2012). Decreased histone acetylation leads to downregulation of proteins involved in cellular apoptosis, resulting in carcinogenesis (Spannhoff, Sippl, & Jung, 2009).

15.3.5. MicroRNAs

MicroRNAs were first discovered in 1993 and are considered a major player in tumorigenesis and carcinogenesis. MicroRNAs (miRNA) are a class of noncoding RNAs that regulate gene expression post-transcription. These small RNAs are approximately 17–25 nucleotides in length and are estimated to regulate over 30% of protein coding genes affecting cytokines, transcription growth, and other factors impacting regulation of the cell cycle, cell proliferation, differentiation, and apoptosis (Garzon, Calin, & Croce, 2009). MicroRNAs are transcribed from a DNA sequence; however, these molecules are not translated into protein but referred as an RNA gene. The biogenesis of miRNAs goes through various mechanisms in a multistep process (see Figure 15.9). The process begins with the transcription of miRNA genes to generate pri-miRNA by RNA polymerase located in the nucleus of the cell to cleavage to pre-miRNA via various ribonuclease enzymes (Drosh and Dicer) and processes generating a double-stranded miRNA. These small RNA base-pairs are then bound to a protein (Argonaut 2) and unwound and undergo processing to form *RNA induced silencing complex* (*RISC*) with the other strand degraded. The RISC then attaches to complementary nucleotide sequences

targeted for messenger RNA (mRNA), leading to RNA interference and resulting in rapid degradation, mRNA cleavage of the targeted mRNA, and repression of protein translation (Alberts *et al.*, 2008d; Zhang, Dahlberg, & Tam, 2007). This translational repression of important proteins can lead to tumorigenesis and cancer development. Currently, it is estimated that there are over 2,000 identified human miRNAs (Friedländer *et al.*, 2014) and genomic alterations of miRNA have been associated with diseases, including initiation and progression of cancer, many of which act as oncogenes or tumor suppressor genes.

15.3.6. Cancer, a Multistage Genetic and Genomic Process

Cancer involves a multistage process arising from genetic mutations and subsequent mutations initiating tumorigenesis and tumor progression (Frank, 2007). Genetic and epigenetic events can generate multiple genetic pathways in cancer progression with disease development dependent on sequential stages of morphologic and genetic changes rather than one single or individual gene. For example, approximately 85% of CRC occurs because of accumulation of mutations in tumor suppressor genes and oncogenes that control cell growth and apoptosis, as well as epigenetic factors such as DNA hypermethylation or hypomethylation resulting in genomic instability (Rodriguez-Bigas, Lin, & Crane, 2003). Genomic instability is a major factor in tumor development and can be a result of 3 distinct pathways in colorectal cancer including chromosomal instability, microsatellite instability and CpG island methylator phenotype pathways (Armaghany, Wilson, Chu, & Mills, 2012; Pino & Chung, 2010). This pathway is referred as the *chromosomal instability pathway* (adenoma—carcinoma sequence). Examples of these mutated genes involved in the pathway include the following:

- *Adenomatous polyposis coli* (*APC*)— tumor suppressor pathway affecting Wnt signaling and responsible for most colon adenomas and cancer involved in the regulation of β-catenin in cytoskeleton organization, apoptosis, cell cycle control, and cell adhesion
- *Kirsten rat sarcoma* (*K-RAS*)—oncogene

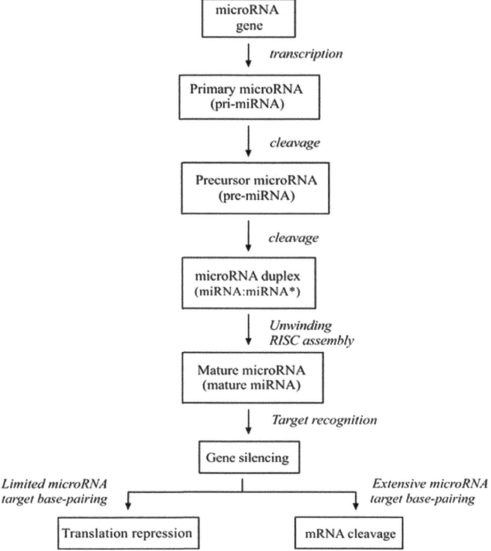

FIGURE 15.9. MicroRNA complex process involving mRNA degradation or translational repression. The miRNA gene is transcribed to generate a primary microRNA (pri-miRNA) precursor molecule that undergoes nuclear cleavage to form a precursor microRNA (pre-miRNA). The pre-miRNA is cleaved in the cytoplasm to create a microRNA duplex (miRNA:miRNA*, passenger strand designated with asterisk) containing the mature miRNA. The duplex unwinds and the mature miRNA assembles into RISC. The miRNA base-pairs with target mRNA to direct gene silencing via mRNA cleavage or translation repression based on the level of complementarity between the miRNA and the mRNA target. Figure and citation from McFarlane & Murphy (2010) MicroRNA: Biogenesis, Function and Role in Cancer in Current Genomic, 11(7), 536–561. Retrieved from http://www.ncbi.nlm.nih.gov/pmc/articles/PMC3048316/figure/F1/

involved in signal transduction and cell proliferation

- *Tumor protein p53* (*p53*)—transcription factor for genes associated with cell cycle progression, apoptosis, and angiogenesis inhibition; deleted in colon cancer gene
- *Deleted in Colorectal Carcinoma* (*DCC*) or DCC netrin 1 receptor-tumor suppressor

- Mothers Against Decapentaplegic Homolog 4, 2 (*SMAD4, SMAD2*)—genes that interacts with transforming growth factor beta (TGFβ) that suppresses normal cellular growth (Frank 2007; Rodriguez-Bigas, Lin, & Crane, 2003).

This multistage process usually is slow growing and characterized by adenoma development prior to cancer development, with predictable genetic and histologic changes and loss of heterozogosity of the long arm of chromosome 18 (Armaghany *et al.*, 2012). Additional genes and alternative pathways are also associated with some hereditary CRC through defects in mismatch repair (MMR) genes such as that found in Lynch syndrome (Armaghany *et al.*, 2012).

The diversity in genetic mutations observed in many tumor cells of the same tissue origin may have a similar phenotypic effect or different histologic features or clinical behavior. The importance of understanding these genomic differences has implications for treatment and clinical prognosis.

15.3.7. Characteristics of Cancer Cells

Cancer cells have altered genomes that have phenotypic characteristics due to self-sufficiency in growth signals and insensitivity to growth inhibition, resulting in deregulated cell proliferation, failure to differentiate, loss of apoptosis, genetic instability, increased/sustained angiogenesis, invasion, and metastasis. There are numerous morphologic and functional changes of the cancer cell (Baba & Câtoi, 2007). Cancer cells typically have large nuclei and because of the altered cell cycles, the chromosomes in some cancer cells are often assorted improperly during mitosis, resulting in *aneuploidy* (abnormal number of chromosomes, gain or loss). The characteristics of cancer cells and morphologic changes provide a means for histologic grading and staging of the disease for diagnosis, prognosis, disease recurrence, and therapeutic management. Histologic grading of cancer tumors provides a means to differentiate cancer cells from that of normal cells and to assess the *aggressiveness* of the tumor. It includes nuclear grading that assesses the size and shape of the nucleus in tumor cells and the percentage of dividing tumor cells activity or tumor mitotic activity. The grading system differs depending on the type of cancer but usually is based on a numerical system, with lower scores often indicating well-differentiated tumors and higher scores representing high grade, poorly differentiated or undifferentiated tumors that are typically more aggressive. Aggressive features that are common to all cancer grading systems are the number of cells in mitosis (cell division) per high power mi-

croscope field of view, the adherence of the cells to the original cells of organ origin from which they derived the homogeneity of the cellular pattern, and the adoption of structures similar to that of the original organ. The Gleason score, one example of a grading system, is used as an important predictor for prostate cancer and is integral in prognosis and therapeutic decision-making of the disease.

Because cancer cells have loss of apoptosis, increased and sustained angiogenesis, invasion, and metastasis, *staging* is also important in diagnosis, prognosis, and management of the disease. Staging in cancer is the extent that the disease has spread. An international system is used for cancer staging and includes 3 systems to designate the extent of the disease (TNM): (1) size and extent of primary tumor (T); (2) presence and extent of lymph node metastasis (N); and (3) presence of distant metastasis (M) (Edge & Compton, 2010; NCI, 2015b). The classification system is based upon the site of the disease and usually includes information on the grading of the tumor.

Tumor profiling of cancer tumors can also be used in many types of the disease to predict outcomes and determine appropriate disease management for target anticancer therapy. Tumor profiling serves as a measure for personalized/precision care for individuals with specific genetic or genomic alteration. Tumor markers may be used to help diagnose cancer, predict a patient's response to certain cancer therapies, check a patient's response to treatment, or determine disease recurrence. Molecular profiles of cancer tumors can be used to identify the multiplicity of alterations that can occur in the tumors, and the use of these profiles can play an important role in targeted therapy and personalized/precision cancer care (Ashfaq, 2012). Additional information regarding tumor profiling may be found in this chapter under Section 15.3, Genomics of Cancer-New and Future Advances and Technologies.

15.3.8. Cancer Types and Causes

There are more than 100 different types of cancer (NCI, 2015c). Cancer is classified based upon the tissue and cell from which the disease originates (histologic classification) or the origin or location of the disease (e.g., breast; colon).

TABLE 15.3. Examples of Behavioral, Chemical, Physical and Infectious Agents Considered Carcinongens and Associated Cancers.

Category	Carcinongen	Associated Cancers
Behavioral	Nicotine	Lung; laryngeal; oropharynx; esophageal; renal; bladder; penile; pancreatic
	Alcohol	Liver; oropharynx; breast; laryngeal
Environmental	Benzenes	Acute leukemias
	Asbestos	Mesothelioma
Radiation	Non-ionizing (sun exposure)	Skin cancers (basal cell; squamous; melanoma)
	Ionizing	Lymphoma; thyroid; leukemia; sarcomas; breast; lung
Infectious	Hepatitis B and C	Liver
	Human Papillomavirus HPV	Cervix; anogenital; oropharyngeal
	Epstein Barr Virus	Lymphoma
	Helicobacteria pylori	Gastric
	Human T cell leukemia virus (*HTLV*)	Leukemia
	Human immunodeficiency virus (*HIV*)	Kaposi's sarcoma
Overweight/Obesity Physical Activity		Esophageal; pancreas postmenopausal breast; endometrial; colon; kidney

Major categories of cancer using histologic classification by cells and tissue types include carcinoma, sarcoma, myeloma, leukemia, lymphoma, and mixed types. *Carcinomas* are the most common form of cancer, accounting for 80% to 90% of the disease and referring to those cancers that originate in the *epithelial* tissue, including skin or tissues that line or cover internal organs or cell linings (e.g., intestine, bronchi, or mammary duct). *Sarcomas*, another major form of cancer, arises from the mesenchymal tissue that begins in bone (osteosarcoma), cartilage (chondrosarcoma), fat (liposarcoma), muscle connective tissue, or supportive tissue (e.g., leiomyosarcoma, rhabdomyosarcoma). Cancers of the *central nervous system* are another major category and include such cancers as gliomas and meningiomas and nerve sheath tumors. Carcinomas not compromising these forms include hematopoietic and lymphoid, originating in the bone marrow, *leukemia*; plasma cells of the bone marrow, *myeloma*; glands or nodes of the immune or lymphatic system, *lymphoma*; or a *mixture of types* (e.g. adenosquamous) (Alberts *et al.*, 2008b; NCI, 2015c; Nussbaum, McInnes, & Willard, 2007).

A number of physical, chemical, and biological agents and a combination of agents have been considered carcinogens damaging DNA or generating mutations. It is estimated that 75% to 80% of cancers are associated with agents that are due to environmental and lifestyle factors (ACS, 2012) that interact negatively with the genome. Many of these external factors are based upon behaviors that are preventable or are associated with other external factors that are controllable. For example, approximately 30% to 35% of cancers are attributable to behaviors associated with diet, and approximately one-third of all cancers are due to tobacco products (ACS, 2012; Anand *et al.*, 2008). Overweight, obesity, and physical inactivity have also been associated with more than a third of all cancers (ACS, 2012). Significant increase in the relative risk (RR) associated with excess weight and lack of sufficient physical activity for example has been found in endometrial (RR 1.60), kidney (RR 1.31), and colorectal (RR 1.18) cancers (Eheman *et al.*, 2012). Chronic alcoholism, another modifiable behavior, has also been associated with increased risk for many different types of cancer (ACS, 2012; Anand *et al.*, 2008). Radiation exposures, environmental pollutants, occupational hazards, and infectious agents also contribute to a significant number of cancers. Table 15.3 provides examples of common carcinogens and cancers associated with these agents.

15.4. HEREDITARY CANCER SYNDROMES

Although the majority of cancer is sporadic, approximately 5.0% to 10.0% of all cancer is hereditary (Garber & Offit, 2005; Nagy, Sweet, & Eng, 2004; Warshawsky, 2006). Inherited cancer syndromes are a result of *highly penetrant genes* (risk of cancer increased approximately 5 to 50-fold) (Stadler *et al.*, 2010) that are present at birth and significantly increase an individual's risk for 1 or more malignancies. A germ line mutation can occur from the sperm or ovum, resulting in the genetic makeup of every cell in the individual with that mutation (Frank, 2001) and, thus, leading in a limited number or a broad spectrum of cancers and other symptoms depending on the gene involved (Bignon, 2004; Nagy *et al.*, 2004). This is in contrast to sporadic cancers in which cancer tumors develop from normal cells that acquire somatic mutations during cell division, with the cancer developing at a specific site.

There are currently over 200 known hereditary cancer syndromes (Nagy *et al.*, 2004). Most of the genes involved in hereditary cancer syndromes are AD, transmitted from either parent, resulting in a 50% chance of inheritance to each offspring. Examples of hereditary cancer syndromes can be found in Tables 15.4 to 15.7. Online Inheritance in Man (OMIM), an online database that provides a comprehensive compendium of human genes and genetic phenotypes including genes resulting in hereditary cancer syndromes, is an important resource for health professionals to use to learn about genetic disorders (OMIM, 2015). This authoritative database was initiated in the 1960s by Dr. Victor A. McKusick and is updated daily (OMIM, 2015). As of March 28, 2015, OMIM contained information regarding gene descriptions for autosomal, X linked, Y linked, and mitochondrial disorders for 14,866 genes, with additional numbers found regarding gene and phenotype combined; phenotype description, molecular basis known; phenotype description or locus, molecular basis unknown; and other, mainly phenotypes with suspected Mendelian basis, totaling 22,847 entries (OMIM, 2015). The reader is recommended to access this free online set for review of specific genes resulting in hereditary cancer syndromes not present in

TABLE 15.4. Examples of Hereditary Cancer Syndromes Associated with Breast Cancer Including Gene, Gene Function, Chromosome, Online Inheritance and Man (OMIM) Entry Number, Associated Cancers and Inheritance Patterns.

Hereditary Cancer Syndromes	Gene	Gene Function	Chromosome	OMIM	Associated Cancers	Inheritance Pattern
Hereditary Breast and Ovarian Cancer	BRCA1; BRCA2	DNA repair; Cell cycle checkpoint control; Maintenance of genomic stability	17q21.31 13q13.1	113705 660185	Breast; ovary; prostate; pancreas; fallopian tube; peritoneal; melanoma	AD
Li Fraumeni	p53	Tumor suppressor	17p13.1	151623	Soft tissue sarcomas; osteosarcoma, breast; brain, leukemia; adrenocortical	AD
Cowden's syndrome; Bannayan-Riley-Ruvalcaba syndrome (BBRS)	PTEN	Tumor suppressor	10q23.31	158350 153480	Breast; thyroid; endometrial	AD
Peutz Jeghers	STK11	Tumor suppressor	19p13.3	175200	Colon, small bowel; breast ovarian; lung; pancreatic	AD
Hereditary Diffuse Gastric Cancer	CDH1	Tumor suppressor; Cell adhesion and differentiation	16q22.1	137215	Diffuse gastric; lobular breast; colorectal	AD

PTEN = Phosphatase and Tensin Homolog; CDH = E-cadherin; STK11 = serine/theorine kinase gene; AD = Autosomal Dominant; AR = Autosomal.

TABLE 15.5. Examples of Hereditary Cancer Syndromes Associated with Colon Cancer Including Gene, Gene Function, Chromosome, Online Inheritance and Man (OMIM) Entry Number, Associated Cancers and Inheritance Patterns.

Hereditary Cancer Syndromes/Polyps	Gene(s)	Gene Function	Chromosome	OMIM Gene #	Associated Cancers	Inheritance Pattern
Lynch Syndrome formerly referred as Hereditary non-polyposis colorectal cancer-HNPCC Few to no adenomatous polyps	MLH1 MSH2 MSH6 PMS EpCAM	Mismatch Repair MSH2 hyper-methylation	3p22.2 2p21 2p16.3 7p22.1 2p21	120436 609309 600678 600259 151623	Colon; endometrial; ovarian; CNS* stomach; hepatobiliary renal pelvis; small bowel; pancreatic; skin	AD
Familial Adenomatous Polyposis (FAP) / **Attenuated FAP (AFAP)** Adenomatous Polyps	APC APC	Tumor suppressor	5q22.2	611731	Colon; CNS**; duodenum; peri-ampulla; stomach; liver; pancreas; thyroid; hepatoblastoma	AD 30% de novo
MUTYH-Associated Polyposis (MAP) Adenomatous Polyps	MUTYH	Base-excision Repair	1p34.1	604933	Colon; duodenum	AR
Peutz Jeghers Hamartomatous Polyps	STK11	Tumor Suppressor	19p13.3	175200	Colon, small bowel; breast; ovary; stomach; pancreas; cervix; lung	AD
Juvenile Polyposis Hamartomatous Polyps	BMPRIA SMAD4		10q23.2 18q21.2	174900	Colon; pancreas; stomach; small bowel	AD
Hereditary Diffuse Gastric Cancer	CDH1	Tumor suppressor	16q22.1	137215	Diffuse gastric; lobular breast; colorectal	AD

CDH = E-cadherin; STK11 = serine/theorine kinase gene; AD = autosomal dominant; AR = autosomal recessive;
*central nervous system (gliobastoma)'
**CNS = meduloblastoma

this chapter or for further discussion of a specific syndrome discussed herein. OMIM can be found at http://www.ncbi.nlm.nih.gov/omim.

Hereditary cancer syndromes are often associated with clinical characteristics considered *red flags* for diagnosis. The personal and family history is important in order to have an accurate assessment of individuals and families at risk for hereditary cancer syndromes. Personal history suspect for hereditary cancer syndromes include early-age-onset not typically associated with the cancer; unusual cancer or cancer pathology; multiple primary cancers, history of cancers, or disorders associated with a hereditary cancer syndrome; and/or pathological features suspect for hereditary syndromes.

Family history is also critical to the assessment of genetic risk. A family history of the same cancer or other cancers or disorders associated with the syndrome is a red flag for hereditary

cancer. An analysis of the family history, particularly a minimum of a 3-generation pedigree on both the maternal and paternal lineage, may indicate an AD pattern of inheritance found in many hereditary cancer syndromes. Although most hereditary cancer syndromes are AD, APRNs must also be knowledgeable of those syndromes that are autosomal recessive (AR) or have a high rate of de novo mutations, because some cancer syndromes may not manifest as an AD inheritance pattern. For example, *MUTYH*-associated polyposis (MAP) is a hereditary cancer syndrome that is AR due to a biallelic mutation in the *MUTYH* gene, resulting in an increased risk of multiple adenomatous colon polyps and colon cancer. There is a 25% risk of the offspring inheriting the biallelic mutations if both parents are carriers of a *MUTYH* gene mutation. In contrast, a de novo mutation is a new mutation, present for the first time in the family and thus the pedigree may not reveal a prior familial history of the cancer. De novo mutations are commonly seen in certain types of hereditary cancer syndromes. For example, 50% of individuals diagnosed with multiple endocrine neoplasia type 2B (Moline & Eng, 2013) have de novo mutations without family history of the disease. In addition, approximately 10% to 40% (Aretz, Vasen, & Olschwang, 2011) of patients diagnosed with familial adenomatous polyposis (hereditary colon cancer syndrome) are a result of a de novo *APC* mutation with some reports noting 20% to 25% of individuals diagnosed with an *APC*-associated polyposis condition as a single occurrence in a family (Jasperson & Burt, 2014). Hereditary cancer syndromes

due to de novo and AR genetic mutations may be challenging to diagnose given the limited or lack of family history. In these cases, the astute clinician will need to utilize other resources, such as comprehensive personal history, physical examination, and knowledge of genomics, including use of resources (e.g., OMIM) and referral consultations to make a diagnosis.

Besides the personal and family history, assessment of risk for hereditary cancer syndromes should consist of a physical examination significant for the relative cancer syndrome and the use of laboratory and/or ancillary tests as needed (e.g., mammography and colonoscopy when assessing breast or colon cancer risks, respective-

TABLE 15.6. Examples of Hereditary Cancer Syndromes Associated with Skin with Gene, Gene Function, Chromosome, Online Inheritance and Man (OMIM) Number, Associated Cancers and Inheritance Patterns.

Hereditary Cancer Syndromes	Gene	Gene Function	Chromosome	OMIM	Associated Cancers	Inheritance Pattern
Neurofibromatosis (*NF*) 1 Café-au-lait spots; intertriginous freckling; fibromatous tumors; Lisch nodules in the eye)	*NF1*	Tumor suppressor	17q11.2	613113	Optic pathway gliomas; Astrocytomas; peripheral nerve sheath tumors (neurofibro-sarcoma); pheo–chromocytomas	AD
Neurofibromatosis (*NF*) 2 Café-au-lait spots (fewer than associated with NF1)	*NF2*	Tumor suppressor	2p11.1	607379	Menigiomas; ependymomas; rarely astryomas; Gliomas; non-cancerous bilateral vestibular schwannomas	AD; 50% *de novo*
Hereditary Melanoma Melanoma	*CDKN2A; p14; p16* (Note: CDKN2A produces *p14* and *p16* that are cyclin dependent kinase inhibitors) *CDK4*	Regulates 2 critical cell cycle regulatory pathways: p53 and RB	9p21.3	600160	Malignant melanoma; Pancreatic andenocarcinoma	AD
Birt-Hogg Dubé fibrofolliculomas Hair follicle hamartomas Angiofibromas Acrochordons Trichodiscomas Perifollicular fibromas increased spontaneous pneumothorax	*FLCN*	Tumor suppressor regulates folliculin for cell growth and division	17p11.2	607273	Clear cell renal cancer	AD

AD = Autosomal Dominant.

TABLE 15.7. Examples of Hereditary Cancer Syndromes Changes with Designated Gene, Gene Function, Chromosome, Online Inheritance and Man (OMIM) Entry Number, Associated Cancers and Inheritance Patterns.

Hereditary Cancer Syndromes	Gene(s)	Gene Function	Chromosome	OMIM Gene #	Associated Cancers	Inheritance Pattern
Von Hippel-Lindau	*VHL*	Tumor Suppressor	3p25.3	193300 608537	renal cell carcinoma (RCC), pancreatic; pheo- chromocytoma; hemangioblastoma of the retina, brain, spinal cord;	AD
Multiple endocrine neoplasia (MEN) Type 1 [associated with benign tumors of para-thyroid gland; islet cells of pancreas; anterior pituitary gland	*MEN1*	Tumor Suppressor	11q13.1	131100 613733	islet-cell tumors of pancreas (1/3rd are cancer); mediastinal carcinoid; gastrinomas	AD
MEN Type 2A [associated with pheochromocytoma; parathyroid adenomas]	*RET*	Oncogene	10q11.21	171400 164761	Amyloid producing medullary thyroid	AD
MEN Type 2B [associated with pheochromocytoma; mucosal neuromas of lips and tongue; Marfanoid features]	*RET*	Oncogene	10q11.21	164761 162300	Medullary thyroid	AD; 50% *de novo*

AD = Autosomal Dominant.

ly). Empiric probability models for some hereditary cancer syndromes, such as breast cancers due to *BRCA1* and *BRCA2* mutations, are also available to assist trained health care providers in assessing risk for hereditary breast and ovarian cancer syndrome (see section of hereditary breast cancer syndromes in this chapter).

If a hereditary cancer syndrome is expected, individuals suspect for the syndrome should be provided expert genetic counseling regarding appropriate genetic testing and risk management based upon the genetic findings and personal and family history. To emphasize the importance of counseling, the American Society of Clinical Oncology (ASCO) policy statement regarding genetic testing recommends that testing be done in the setting of pre- and post-test counseling when the individual has "personal or family history features suggestive of a genetic cancer susceptibility condition; the test can be adequately interpreted, and the results will aid in diagnosis or influence the medical or surgical management of the patient or family members at hereditary risk of cancer" (ASCO, 2003, p. 2397; Robson,

Storm, Weitzel, Wollins, & Offit, 2010). Genetic counseling for hereditary cancer syndromes involves collection, evaluation, and validation of the family and medical history, assessment of risk and psychosocial status, genetic education, discussion of genetic testing options, discussion of management and screening recommendations, discussion of insurance and employment issues, post-test results disclosure and interpretation, and discussion of the implications of results for the individual and family members. The impact of genetic testing in individuals at risk for a hereditary cancer syndrome is largely contingent on the implementation of appropriate surveillance and preventive strategies to reduce the risk of cancer development or to diagnose cancer at an early stage.

15.4.1. Hereditary Breast Cancer Syndromes

Breast cancer is the leading form of cancer worldwide and the principle form of cancer deaths globally in women ages 20 to 59 years in high-income countries (World Health Organization [WHO] 2013; WHO, 2009). In the U.S., approximately 1 out of 8 (12.5%) women are expected to develop breast cancer during their lifetime. Excluding skin cancer, breast cancer is the leading form of cancer in the U.S. and the second leading cause of cancer deaths in women (ACS, 2013–2014). Most (approximately 75%) breast cancers among women in the U.S. are sporadic with approximately 79.0% of new cases occurring in women age 50 years and over (ACS, 2013–2014). It is estimated however that 5.0% to 10.0% of all breast cancers result from an inherited mutation predisposing individuals with the mutation at increased risk for breast cancer and other cancers and disorders. Although there are many hereditary syndromes that lead to an increased breast cancer risk, 95.0% of hereditary breast cancers are due to mutations in the *BRCA1* and *BRCA2* genes (ACS, 2015) referred to as the *hereditary breast and ovarian cancer* (HBOC) syndrome. Germ line mutations other than *BRCA1* or *BRCA2* have also been attributed to an increased risk of breast cancer, as noted in Table 15.4. However, these rare syndromes account for a small percentage of inherited breast cancers.

15.4.2. Hereditary Breast and Ovarian Cancer (*BRCA1* and *BRCA2*)

The number of individuals with a mutation in *BRCA1* or *BRCA2* account for 1% of the population (ACS 2013–2014), estimated at 1:300 to 1:800 or about 18,000 of the more than 200,000 women diagnosed each year with the disease (Garber & Offit, 2005; Whittemore, Gong, & Itnyre, 1997). However, for certain ethnic groups such as those of Ashkenazi Jewish ancestry/descent, the frequency of *BRCA* mutations are much higher compared with the general population in the U.S. It is estimated that 1 in 40 (2.5%) of individuals of Ashkenazi descent has a founder *BRCA1* mutation (185delAG or 5382insC) or *BRCA2* (6174delT) mutation (Warner *et al.*, 1999), and founder *BRCA* mutations have also been noted in Icelandic, Swedish, and Hungarian populations. In addition, recent data suggest some common mutations in high-risk Hispanic populations (Weitzel *et al.*, 2013; Weitzel *et al.*, 2005).

Mutations in the *BRCA* genes account for most of the hereditary breast and ovarian cancers. The

BRCA1 gene was first localized to chromosome 17q21 in 1990 and later cloned in 1994 (Hall *et al.*, 1992). In 1995, the discovery of the *BRCA2* gene on chromosome 13q12.3 was reported (Wooster *et al.*, 1994), and commercial genetic testing of these 2 genes became clinically available in 1996. The *BRCA* genes have a role in genomic stability, and each has distinct roles in the repair of DNA double-strand breaks and interaction of numerous other proteins to modulate transcription and the cell cycle (Scully, 2000; Venkitaraman, 2001). Both are tumor suppressor genes delaying the cell cycle before or during replication or before cell division for DNA repair (Roy, Chun, & Powell, 2011). Mutations in the *BRCA* genes are transmitted in the germ line through an AD Mendelian inheritance pattern (see Figure 15.10). Individuals with a germ line mutation in *BRCA1* or *BRCA2* are born with a normal functioning gene on 1 chromosome (*wild type*) and a genetic mutation on the other gene. Homozygous *BRCA1* mutations have been found to be embryonically lethal (Evers & Jonkers, 2006; Foulkes, 2008), whereas homozygous *BRCA2* mutations result in Fanconi anemia (rare chromosomal instability disorder). The development of cancer from germ line mutations in the *BRCA* genes fits Knudsen's two-hit hypothesis model of carcinogenesis requiring disease occurrence as a result of a second acquired somatic mutation disabling the 1 wild type *BRCA* allele (Chial, 2008b; Roy *et al.*, 2011). Because the syndrome is AD, offspring of a parent (either maternal or paternal) with a mutation in either the *BRCA1* or *BRCA2* gene has a 50% chance of inheriting the mutation. The AD inheritance pattern associated with *BRCA* mutations will usually show a family history pedigree that depicts a vertical pattern of inheritance (see Figure 15.10). However, few females within the family, surgeries (removal of the ovaries), and early-age onset of death of females, because of noncancerous etiologies (e.g., motor vehicle accidents; heart disease, etc.), may limit this pattern from being observed (see Figure 15.11).

15.4.3. Phenotype/Clinical Characteristics— Deleterious BRCA Mutations

Germ line mutations in *BRCA1* or *BRCA2* genes are associated with a high risk for devel-

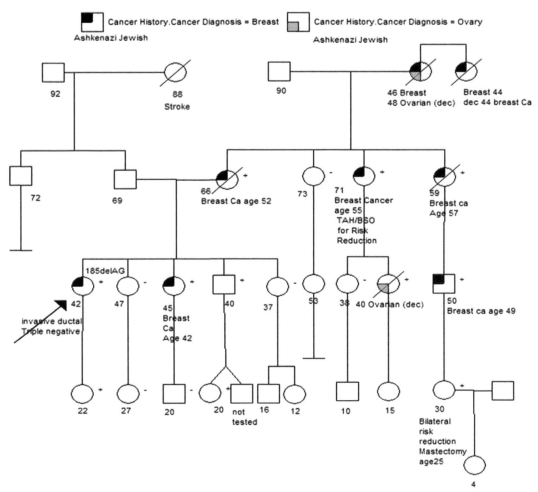

FIGURE 15.10. Fictitious 5-generation pedigree depicting an autosomal dominant pattern of hereditary breast and ovarian cancer syndrome due to a *BRCA1* mutation 185 delAG in an Ashkenazi Jewish family (+ signs indicate mutation positive).

oping breast and/or ovarian cancer. However, mutations in *BRCA1* or *BRCA2* do not mean that individuals who inherit these mutations will develop cancer. Nevertheless, individuals with mutations in either of the 2 genes have a similar high predisposition (*high penetrance*) for developing breast cancer, with a lifetime breast cancer risk for women estimated at 50% to 87% (Antoniou *et al.*, 2005; Ford *et al.*, 1998) and an increased risk of contralateral breast cancer. Cumulative risk for contralateral breast cancer up to 25 years after initial diagnosis has been estimated to be as high as 56% for women with *BRCA1* or *BRCA2* mutations (Graeser *et al.*, 2009). Further, studies have revealed an 11% to 62% lifetime risk of developing ovarian cancer by age 70; the risk varies by genes, with mutation carriers in

BRCA1 reported as having higher ovarian cancer risk compared with carriers with *BRCA2* mutations (Antoniou *et al.*, 2003; King, Marks, Mandell, & New York Breast Cancer Study Group, 2003; Risch *et al.*, 2001). In 1 meta-analysis of 10 studies that assessed *BRCA1* and *BRCA2* penetrance, the resulting cumulative risks by age 70 years for ovarian cancer risk were reported as 39% (95% confidence intervals [CI], 34% to 45%) for *BRCA1* and 17% (95% CI, 13% to 21%) for *BRCA2* mutation carriers (Chen & Parmigiani, 2007). Although neither of the *BRCA* gene mutations is 100% penetrant, the cancer risks are dramatic compared with the 12% to 13% lifetime breast cancer risk for U.S. women in the general population and the 1.48% lifetime risk for ovarian cancer in the same population.

Although *BRCA* mutations have an AD pattern of inheritance with equal transmission occurrence to both male and female offspring, breast cancer risk for men is much lower when compared with women. In men with a *BRCA* mutation, the risk of breast cancer is uncommon and estimated at approximately 7.0%, with most attributed to mutations in the *BRCA2* gene; a higher risk among men, however, has been reported among ethnic groups with founder mutations, such as in Ashkenazi Jewish and Icelandic populations (Liede, Karlan, & Narod, 2004; Mohamad & Apffelstaedt, 2008). Although the 7% risk for breast cancer in men appears low, this breast cancer risk is significantly higher when compared with the approximately 1% of breast cancers that occur among men in the U.S., with incidence rates reported at 1.2 cases per 100,000 men during the years 2005–2010 (ACS 2013–2014).

Early-age onset of breast cancer, particularly at or before age 50, is a *red flag* for risk of an inherited breast cancer syndrome, including germ line mutations due to *BRCA* genes (NCCN, 2015a). The absolute incidence of breast cancer for *BRCA1* carriers is approximately 3% to 4% per year among 40 to 49-year-olds, with a cumulative risk of 38% to 59% by age 50. In *BRCA2* carriers, this risk is approximately 16% to 28% by age 50 year (Ford *et al.*, 1998). These findings are high when compared with less than 2% population risk of developing the disease by age 50 years among women without a known germ line mutation for breast cancer (NCI, 2012).

Adenocarcinoma of ductal type is the most

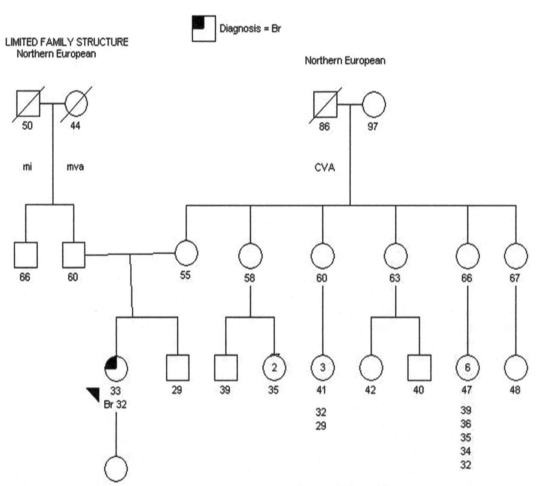

FIGURE 15.11. Three-generation family history with limited family structure on the paternal lineage and a proband (noted by arrowhead) with early-age onset breast cancer found to be *BRCA1*-positive on genetic testing. The family structure is limited by no females on the paternal lineage, except paternal grandmother who died early-age of onset of motor vehicle accident [MVA].

common breast cancer phenotype in women, including those diagnosed with a *BRCA* mutation. Approximately 74% of women with a *BRCA* mutation have tumors that are of the invasive ductal adenocarcinoma type (van der Groep, van der Wall, & van Diest, 2011). In addition, certain histology features of genetic expression, such as *triple negative breast cancer* (estrogen receptor [ER], progesterone receptor [PR], and human epidermal growth factor receptor 2 [*HER/neu2*]), have been reported to occur more frequently in *BRCA* mutation carriers compared with noncarriers, and most were associated with *BRCA1* mutations and early-age onset of breast cancer (Gonzalez-Angulo et al., 2011; Lee et al., 2011; Mavaddat et al., 2012; Young et al., 2009). Among individuals with *BRCA1* mutations, approximately 80% to 90% of breast cancers are ER-negative tumors and predominately PR negative with negative *HER2neu* protein expression (Roy et al., 2011). Triple negative breast cancer is defined by the lack of gene expression of ER, PR, and *HER/neu2* and provides an important tumor marker/molecular subtype for treatment and prognosis. Tumors with these features often occur at younger age, are insensitive/nonresponsive to many breast cancer therapies, result in early metastatic spread, and have poorer prognoses and outcomes when compared with tumors with positive expression or other subtypes. This histopathologic finding is significant given recent professional guidelines recommending *BRCA* genetic testing for triple negative breast cancer patients who are less than age 60 years (NCCN, 2015a). In addition to triple negative tumors, many of the *BRCA1* breast cancer tumors have basal-like subtypes based upon expression of certain cytokeratins, epidermal growth factor receptor, and p-cadherin and are aneuploidy. These tumors also are found to be more aggressive and have a poor prognosis, and many have triple negative phenotype (Rakha, Reis-Filho, & Ellis, 2008) when compared with tumors without these characteristics. In contrast to *BRCA1* breast cancer tumors, the predominance of histopathologic characteristics among those with a *BRCA2* mutation is similar to sporadic cancer tumors regarding ER and PR expression. The majority of *BRCA2* mutations have expression for the PR, with approximately 60% to 65% of these tumors expressed positively for the ER. Low amplification of *HER/2neu* has also been reported (van der Groep et al., 2011) with approximately 15% of *BRCA2* tumors associated with positive amplification of *HER/neu2* (Roy et al., 2011).

Ovarian cancer phenotype due to *BRCA* germ line mutations are most often serous histology (i.e, serous papillary) and frequently are high-grade tumors (Bowtell, 2010; Lynch et al., 2009). Serous histology is a type of epithelial ovarian cancer and the most common type of the disease. Although the majority of ovarian cancers in *BRCA* carriers are of serous histology, low rates of endometroid (Lynch et al., 2009; Mavaddat et al., 2012), mucinous and clear cells histology have also been reported (Mavaddat et al., 2012). Women with *BRCA* mutations are also at increased risk for fallopian tube and peritoneal cancers (Lynch et al., 2009).

Men with *BRCA* mutations, particularly *BRCA2*, have been shown to have high rates of prostate cancer (Agalliu et al., 2009; Liede et al., 2004). Prostate cancer is 3 to 4 times more common among *BRCA* mutation carriers with approximately a 39% risk among *BRCA2* carriers (Liede et al., 2004; van Asperen et al., 2005). Men of Askenazi Jewish ancestry with founder mutations are associated with increased prostate cancer risk, including disease associated with mutations in *BRCA1* (Roy et al., 2011). This is higher when compared with the 17.9% lifetime incidence of prostate cancer among U.S. men. Mutations in the *BRCA* genes have also been found to increase the risk of other cancers, including cancer of the larynx, pancreas, bile duct, gallbladder, and melanoma in both men and women (Easton et al., 1997; Thompson, Easton, & Breast Cancer Linkage Consortium, 2002).

15.4.4. Risk Assessment

Mutations in the *BRCA* gene significantly increase a woman's susceptibility to breast and ovarian cancers. Both men and women with the mutation may also be at increased risk for other cancers previously described. Identification of at-risk individuals and families is important so that counseling, genetic testing if applicable, and appropriate management of care are implemented to reduce risk and improve early detection of cancer. There are numerous red flags to alert the APRN to individuals/families who may be at high risk for a *BRCA* mutation and who warrant referral for genetic counseling and possible genetic testing. Risk assessment involves collection of data including the personal and family history, identification of red flags or elements that increase risk, and determination of risk probability using either quantitative (probability risk assessment tools) or qualitative (e.g., low, moderate, or high-risk) measures based upon the data. The RAPID approach discussed in Chapter 2 can be used as a guide to implement risk assessment (see Figure 15.12). The RAPID approach focuses on 5 important elements of the *Risk Assessment Process*: (1) data collection, (2) identification of red flags, (3) probability of risk, (4) assessment of the data for risk communication, and (5) assessment of the data for risk management.

15.4.5. Data Collection

15.4.5.1 Personal History

Collection of data pertinent to the personal and family history is integral to a thorough and accurate assessment of breast cancer risk, specifically when addressing at-risk individuals who may have a germ line *BRCA* mutation. Personal history should be queried and documented, entailing the following: current age; race, ethnicity; current and past medical histories,particularly history of any cancer(s) including type, age of onset of disease, laterality, treatment, and disease reoccurrence; carcinogen exposure (if applicable); reproductive and obstetrical history; surgical history including age, type of surgery, par-

FIGURE 15.12. RAPID Steps to Risk Assessment for use in breast cancer risk assessment including 5 steps: (1) Data Collection; (2) Identification of Red Flags; (3) Probability; (4) Risk Assessment of data for Risk Communication; and (5) Risk Assessment of Data for Risk Management.

ticularly if a history of salpingo-oophorectomy; history of previous breast biopsies and pathology report; medications including hormonal replacement therapy; and behavioral assessment (e.g., alcohol use and amount). Whenever possible, medical and surgical records should be obtained to confirm findings and to assess reports for any red flags that may be suspect for hereditary breast and ovarian cancer syndrome. For example, a 50-year-old woman of Ashkenazi Jewish ancestry diagnosed with breast cancer at age 45 with a pathology report of ER, PR, *HER2/neu* negative tumor would warrant counseling for *BRCA* genetic testing because of multiple red flags in the personal and medical history, including Ashkenazi Jewish ancestry (high-risk ancestry), early age of onset breast cancer (≤ age 45), and triple negative breast cancer less than age 60.

15.4.5.2. Family History

Family history is a very important part of breast cancer risk assessment and is the strongest single predicator of risk for the disease. A detailed family history should include both the maternal and paternal lineage and ancestry of origin (ethnicity) of each lineage and entail a minimum of 3 generations. The data are best depicted in a pedigree enabling visualization of patterns and traits that clusters around the family and provide a means to determine potential Mendelian patterns of inheritance. The pedigree also depicts visually the number of individuals in the family, gender status, and their vital health status (living/dead), including age and cause of death. This information is important when interpreting the family history for patterns of inheritance that may be masked by limited family size, number of females, or early-age onset deaths because of causes other than cancer. The detailed family history should include the following:

(1) Ancestry of origin on both maternal and paternal lineage

(2) Age of each family member and if deceased, age of death and cause of death

(3) Medical history with particular attention to cancer history, including type and age of diagnosis and bilaterality of disease

(4) Surgical history that may reduce cancer risk (e.g., hysterectomy, oophorectomy) and the reason for the surgery (cancer or noncancerous conditions), including history of chemoprevention and/or risk-reducing surgery

(5) Medical record documentation of pathology reports, including history of breast biopsy(ies) with number and pathology report (e.g., atypical hyperplasia) (NCCN, 2015a)

Pertinent medical findings besides cancers associated with hereditary breast and ovarian cancer should be included on all members when obtaining the family history, because the data may play a role in the differential diagnosis of other inherited breast cancer syndromes or hereditary disorders. For example, examining the patient's medical and family histories may indicate a maternal history of ovarian cancer diagnosed at age 45 years. However, further analysis of the maternal lineage also reveals a history of early-age onset colon and endometrial cancers throughout the pedigree, suggestive of another hereditary cancer syndrome known as Lynch syndrome, rather than *BRCA* mutation. Further, families with early-onset sarcomas, leukemias, or breast, brain, or adrenocortical cancers might be suggestive of Li-Fraumeni syndrome (see Table 15.4), another inherited syndrome associated with an increased risk for breast cancer.

15.4.5.3. Physical Examination

The physical examination is an important means of data collection for early recognition of disease and may aid in the differential diagnosis of other rare hereditary syndromes that increase the risk of breast and/or ovarian cancer other than mutations in the *BRCA* genes. The focused physical examination should be conducted by a qualified clinician and include a measurement of the head circumference, visualization of the skin and oral surfaces for dermatologic manifestations (e.g., gums, lips and tongue) that may be suspect for hereditary cancer syndromes, examination and palpation of the thyroid and breast, and, if clinically applicable, examination of the abdomen and pelvis. This focused examination is useful in conjunction with the personal and family history to differentiate individuals with other hereditary syndromes, such as that of Cowden's syndrome due to mutations in the tumor suppressor *PTEN* (phosphatase and TENsin homolog) gene. Women with mutations in this gene have a 25% to 50% risk of developing breast cancer, with an average age of diagnosis between 38 and 46 years (Eng, 2014). The syndrome is also associated with numerous other cancers including nonmedullary thyroid (usually follicular), endometrial, and renal clear cell (Table 15.4). Clinical features of Cowden's syndrome include macrocephaly (occipital frontal circumference ≥ 97th percentile) and mucocutaneous skin lesions such as trichilemmomas and acral keratoses (Eng 2014). Women with Cowden's syndrome also have as high as a 67% risk for benign breast disease, and uterine fibroids are also common (Eng, 2014). Further, colonic polyposis is a common finding in Cowden's syndrome, and various polyp types may be seen, including ganglioneuromas, juvenile hamartomas, and inflammatory, hyperplastic, and adenomatous polyps. Thus, the physical examination and medical history in conjunction with the family history may be extremely helpful when pertinent clinical findings suggestive of the phenotype for Cowden's syndrome are observed, so that appropriate genetic counseling and testing can be initiated.

15.4.6. Other Data Collection Resources

Additional data important to accurate risk assessment for hereditary breast and ovarian cancer includes personal or family medical records to confirm diagnosis when applicable (e.g., history of prostate cancer in father, unconfirmed with medical reports revealing benign prostatic hypertrophy; mother thought to have endometrial cancer with pathology report revealing cervical cancer) or to evaluate pathology results (e.g., triple negative breast cancer). Procuring death certificates on family members may be warranted when there is an uncertainty of past cancer history (e.g., maternal history of ovarian cancer later confirmed to be benign ovarian cyst). Also, when there is a known genetic mutation in the family, attempts to obtain the results will be useful in confirming the genetic disorder and to determine appropriate testing. However, risk disclosure of information among family members must take into consideration the Health Insurance Portability and Accountability Act of 1996 (HIPAA), confidentiality and privacy of the patient, and

state and federal protections including Genetic Information Nondiscrimination Act of 2008 (Gina) (Pub. L. No. 110-223). Radiographic, ancillary, and/or laboratory tests, including mammography, ultrasonography, and magnetic resonance imaging (MRI), may also be needed to aid in diagnosis and assessment of the client's risk.

15.4.7. Identification of Risk Elements and Red Flags

Once the personal and family history have been obtained, a thorough review of the data should be conducted to identify elements of risks and potential red flags that may be suspect for a hereditary breast cancer syndrome, including *BRCA* germ line mutations. The personal and family history may provide key information for determination of risk and the need for genetic referral and counseling and/or genetic testing. Example of red flags suspect for hereditary breast and ovarian cancer (*BRCA* mutation) include early-age onset breast cancer, triple negative breast cancer, male breast cancer, ovarian cancer, constellation of cancers in 1 or more individuals (e.g., HBOC, breast, ovary, and pancreas), known mutation in the family, Ashkenazi Jewish ancestry, other ethnic populations at risk, and 2 or more breast cancer primaries in the same individual (Bosserman, 2008; NCCN, 2015a). Table 15.8 and Figure 15.13 provide red flags suggestive of individuals suspect for hereditary breast cancer syndromes. Specific guidelines are available from professional organizations regarding genetic evaluation and testing depending on personal and family history (NCCN, 2015a; Robson *et al.*, 2010).

15.4.7. Risk Assessment—Risk Probability

15.4.7.1. Germ Line Mutation Pretest Prediction

Determining risk probability is a component of risk assessment. The history is an essential component of determining risk. Red flags (see Table 15.8) in the personal and/or family history may be cues to action for genetic counseling and possible genetic testing for hereditary breast cancer syndromes. Probability models (e.g., BRCAPRO, BOADICEA, PENN II, and Tyrer-

TABLE 15.8. Red Flags Suspect for Hereditary Cancer Syndromes with Examples.

Red Flags Suspect for Hereditary Cancer Syndromes	Examples
Early Age of Onset of Disease than Expected	Breast cancer age 30 years Colon cancer age 40 years
Family History of Multiple Family Members	Mother, maternal grandmother and sibling with breast cancer
Cancer in the less often affected sex	Male breast cancer
Ethnic predisposition	Ashkenazi Jewish with a personal or familial history of breast or ovarian cancer
Cancers or diseases associated with the syndrome on the same side of the family or within 1 individual	Colon and endometrial cancers; Breast and ovarian cancers Pancreatic and melanomas
Multiple primary cancers	Two or more 'new' cancers developing in same individual particularly if associated with hereditary syndrome (e.g. female with endometrial cancer at age 37 years and colon cancer at age 40 years)
Unusual presentation/phenotype	Polyposis (colon); medullary thyroid cancer
Pathological characteristics	Microsatellite (MSI) high tumors (colon; endometrium)

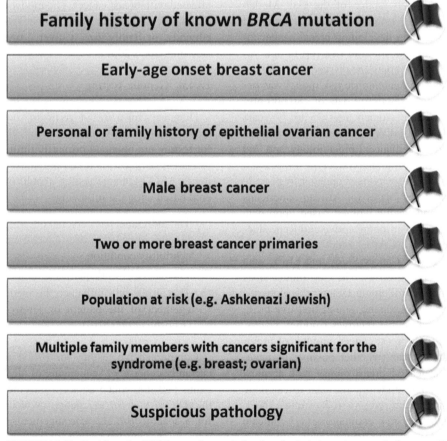

FIGURE 15.13. Red flags for *BRCA* germ line mutation (particularly breast cancer before age 45 years; however, early-age of onset less than age 50 years may be relevant pending on personal and family history and histopathology).

Cuzik) are also available for trained health care providers and counselors to provide a quantitative value using a variety of personal and family risk factors that aid in predicting the likelihood (pretest prediction) of an individual carrying a germ line *BRCA1* or *BRCA2* mutation. The models in conjunction with the personal and family history, including family structure, can be used to determine candidates for testing.

15.4.7.2. Empiric Risk Models

Besides probability models to assess pretest prediction for germ line mutations, empiric risk assessment models (e.g., Gail, Claus, and Tyrer-Cuzik) are also available to estimate the likelihood of developing breast cancer over a period of time for women without a prior history of the disease and who are not suspect or have a history of an hereditary breast cancer syndrome. One of the most commonly used empiric risk assessment models is that of the Gail Model. The Gail Model estimates the probability of unaffected women developing breast cancer including 5-year and lifetime risk (up to age 90) estimates of developing the disease (NCI, 2011). This evidence-based empiric risk model was developed using case-control data of 280,000 predominately white women ages 35 to 79 years from the Breast Cancer Detection Demonstration Project and Surveillance, Epidemiology, and End Results (SEER) Program (Gail *et al.*, 1989; NCI, 2011). The model was later updated to provide more accurate estimates for African-Americans and Asian and Pacific women based upon data from the Women's Contraceptive and Reproductive Experiences (CARE) Study and the Asian American Breast Cancer Study and SEER data respectively (NCI, 2011). The Gail model takes into account the following factors: the woman's age, her age at menarche, age at first live birth, number of 1st degree relatives (mother, sisters, daughters) with breast cancer, number of previous breast biopsies (whether positive or negative), and at least 1 breast biopsy with atypical hyperplasia. These factors are used to calculate a 5-year and lifetime empiric risk estimate (NCI, 2011). Five year risk estimates ≥ 1.7 indicate candidates for chemoprevention with tamoxifen or other agents (e.g., raloxifene) to reduce breast cancer risk. The model, however, does not take

account paternal lineage or 2nd-degree relatives and should not be used in women with a personal history of ductal or lobular carcinoma in situ or breast cancer, if the personal and/or family history are suggestive of high-risk disease, or if a history of a hereditary breast cancer syndrome is confirmed. An interactive Gail model is available online from the NCI via the following link: http://www.cancer.gov/bcrisktool/Default.aspx (NCI, 2011).

The Claus model is another empiric risk estimate tool that provides a quantitative risk value of developing breast cancer for unaffected women based upon family history. The model takes into account both the maternal and paternal lineage and was developed using data from the Cancer and Steroid Hormone Study (CASH), a population-based case-control study of women ages 20 to 54 years (Wingo *et al.*, 1988). The model provides risk estimates in 10-year increments up to age 79 years, incorporating up to 2 relatives affected with breast cancer. The model is limited by its lack of incorporation of other risk factors, ethnicity, or family size (Culver, Lowstuter, & Bowling, 2006-2007).

15.4.8. Genetic Testing

Diagnosis for a *BRCA* germ line mutation is made through DNA genetic testing. Specimens for testing are obtained primarily through blood or buccal samples. As noted previously, according to ASCO, genetic testing should be considered based upon the following:

(1) The individual has personal or family history features suggestive of a genetic cancer susceptibility condition.

(2) The test can be adequately interpreted.

(3) The results will influence the medical management of the patient or family member (Robson *et al.*, 2010).

Comprehensive testing for *BRCA* mutations currently consists of sequencing of all translated exons and immediate adjacent intronic areas of the *BRCA1* and *BRCA2* genes, as well as a test for 5 specific *BRCA1* rearrangements. In addition, comprehensive testing for certain large genomic rearrangements not detectable by primary sequencing assays should also be a part of the assessment analysis (NCCN, 2015a; Palma *et al.*, 2008). Testing strategies for high risk groups such as Ashkenazi Jewish individuals may warrant initial testing using only the analysis for the 3 Ashkenazi Jewish founder mutations (*BRCA1, 187delAG, 5385insC, BRCA1, 6174delT*). Because this test result does not exclude the possibility of other predisposing mutations that have been reported in individuals of Ashkenazi Jewish ancestry, additional comprehensive testing may be needed for this ethnic group depending on personal and family history if test results for the 3 founder mutations are uninformative (e.g., no mutations found). Next generation sequence (NGS) testing using multi-gene testing may also be considered when assessing for hereditary breast cancer syndromes depending on an individual's personal and family history. Further discussion on NGS testing is presented later in this chapter.

The American College of Medical Genetics and Genomics (ACMG) with the Association for Molecular Pathology and the College of American Pathologists have established standards and guidelines in an effort to standardize interpretation and reporting of genomic test results (Richards *et al.*, 2015). These recent guidelines were developed as a measure to describe variants identified in genes that cause Mendelian disorders. Five standard classifications are used: "pathogenic," "likely pathogenic," "uncertain significance," "likely benign," and "benign" (Richards *et al.*, 2015).

Genetic testing involves "interpretation of results," including distinguishing between a true-positive, true-negative, uninformative or indeterminate result, and inconclusive due to variants of unknown significant results (NCCN, 2015a). When a deleterious mutation is found through testing, information regarding the specific gene involved (e.g. *BRCA1* or *BRCA2*), as well as the type of mutation and specific location on the gene, are included as part of the genetic test results. Knowing the specific gene and its location are beneficial to other family members within the lineage warranting testing, because it requires only single-site testing for the known family mutation rather than more costly comprehensive testing of both genes.

Genetic testing for *BRCA* mutation can also result in a finding known as a *variant of uncertain significance* (VUS). VUS findings are challenging because the evidence is lacking to definitely determine whether the variant is causing the increased risk for cancer in a family or if it is a benign polymorphism. When testing reveals no mutation (uninformative), the personal and family history must be taken into account, and consideration for other hereditary breast and/or ovarian cancer syndromes may be warranted, particularly if the history is suspect. Referral to a genetic specialist is also warranted when the history is suspect for an inherited syndrome, but genetic testing is uninformative. Genetic referral and counseling are important when test results reveal a VUS since additional information pertaining to the mutation will be needed before significance of the impact of the gene variant is understood (NCCN, 2015a). Because of the complexity of genetic testing, including interpretation of findings, individuals suspect for an inherited cancer syndrome should be referred to those with training and expertise in the field of cancer genetics (e.g. genetic counselor, advanced genetics nurse [AGN], and geneticist).

15.4.9. Risk Communication/Counseling and Risk Management

Risk counseling and management are important components of risk assessment. Risk assessment involves the following: (1) Data collection; (2) Identification of risk (e.g., red flags) based upon collected data, including personal and family histories as well as significant laboratory and/or ancillary tests; (3) Risk probability; (4) Risk Assessment of data for Risk Communication; and (5) Risk Assessment of data for Risk Management based upon the findings (RAPID Approach). Critical components of risk assessment for individuals suspect for hereditary breast cancer like that of HBOC syndrome, includes assessment of personal medical and family histories, physical examination, determination and communication of cancer risk (risk probability), assessment of the individual's and family's risk perception, education regarding the genetics of the disorder, discussion of molecular testing if appropriate (including benefits, risks, and limitations), and any necessary follow-up (risk management). Risk communication may also consist of appropriate preventive measures to reduce future cancer risk, surveillance for early identification, chemoprevention if applicable, and risk-reduction surgery or other interventions, if applicable, to reduce risk (see Figure 15.12). This process involves interaction between the assessor/risk counselor, patient/client(s), and other significant members. Risk communication should be a mutually inclusive process that focuses on the patient's/client's needs and preferences considering his or her psychosocial, religious/spiritual, and cultural considerations when discussing the risk for disease, medical condition, genetic implications, testing (including genetic tests), risk probability, and management of care strategies. In order to provide insight into the patient's/client's understanding of risk, assessing his or her current perception of risk for disease occurrence is an important part of the process so that personalized strategies can be implemented that are mutually agreed upon to improve outcomes, including risk reduction. Risk management should also consider interprofessional collaboration (keeping in mind ethical considerations and patient privacy), because some clients and patients may require follow-up management of care with a variety of health care professionals. Providing resources for psychosocial support may also be a necessary part of risk communication and risk management, particularly when results disclosure reveals abnormal findings (e.g., abnormal genetic test results). An example of one resource is that of *Facing Our Risk of Cancer Empowered*© (FORCE), which provides supportive measures via newsletters, support groups, webinars, conferences, special events, and help lines for individuals and spouses with hereditary breast cancer syndromes that can be found on their web link: http://www. facingourrisk.org. Fertility counseling and reproductive decision-making may also be needed for some women of childbearing age who are at high breast cancer risk, particularly if diagnosed with HBOC. Results disclosure for *BRCA* mutation carriers is important in ensuring that appropriate family members are informed of their risk of inheriting the mutation as well as provided education and options regarding testing and management of care if applicable. Family results disclosure should be discussed during risk counseling and management. Disclosure of results to family members may be complex and sometimes stressful, often influenced by differences in culture and

family structure, functioning, and dynamics. Providing clear information regarding tests results, family members warranting testing, and reasons for testing including benefits of testing is important in helping the proband communicate findings to family members and to encourage genetic counseling and follow-up for family members.

15.4.9.1. Primary Prevention—Chemoprevention

Chemoprevention may be suitable for some individuals who are *BRCA* positive to reduce their risk for breast and/or ovarian cancer. The use of selective estrogen receptor modulator (SERM) hormones (e.g., tamoxifen, raloxifene) has been shown to reduce the risk of breast cancer. For example, tamoxifen has been shown to reduce breast cancer by as much as much as 62% among individuals who are *BRCA2* mutation positive, but no reduction in the disease is observed among *BRCA1* mutation carriers (King et al., 2001). The lack of benefits in breast cancer reduction among *BRCA1* carriers may be attributed to the high incidence of estrogen receptor negative tumors in these individuals, which are unresponsive to SERMs.

Oral contraceptives (OC) may be a source of chemoprevention to reduce the risk of ovarian cancer. In 1 matched case-control study, use of OCs reduced the risk of ovarian cancer by approximately 45% in carriers of *BRCA1* mutations and approximately 66% in *BRCA2* mutation carriers (McLaughlin et al., 2007). A meta-analysis of 18 studies of *BRCA1* and *BRCA2* mutation carriers reported a reduced risk of ovarian cancer of approximately 50% (summary RR = 0.50) among women who used oral contraceptive and a 36% risk reduction for each additional 10 years of OC use (Iodice et al., 2010). Although studies have shown a reduction in the risk of ovarian cancer with the use of OCs, data regarding breast cancer risk reduction with OC use have been conflicting. In 1 population-based study, neither oral contraceptive use overall nor the use of low dose oral contraceptives was associated with an increased risk of breast cancer among women with *BRCA* mutations (Lee et al., 2008), and no evidence was found overall that use of OCs for at least 1 year was associated with breast cancer risk for *BRCA1* and *BRCA2* mutation carriers before age 50 (Haile et al., 2006). In another population-based study, oral contraceptives were found to decrease breast cancer risk for *BRCA1* mutation carriers but not for *BRCA2* mutation carriers (Milne *et al.*, 2005). In another study of *BRCA1* mutation carriers, a slight increased risk of early onset breast cancer was found, particularly among women who first used oral contraceptives before 1975, who used them before age 30, or who used the medications for 5 or more years. This finding, however, was not observed among *BRCA2* mutation carriers (Narod *et al.*, 2002).

15.4.9.2. Secondary Prevention—Enhanced Surveillance-Early Detection

Professional guidelines are available on the management of care of individuals who are at high risk for breast and/or ovarian cancer, including those who are *BRCA* positive (NCCN, 2015a). Risk-reduction strategies should be based upon individual preferences and mutually agreed upon strategies involving the individual and their health care provider/team. Secondary preventive measures for early detection of breast cancer for individuals who are *BRCA* positive include breast self-examination monthly beginning at age 18 with clinical breast exams every 6 to 12 months at age 25 and mammography alternating with breast MRI based upon earliest age of onset in the family or beginning at age 25 years (NCCN, 2015a). For young women ages 25 to 29 years (or individualized based on family history of breast cancer is diagnosed before age 25 years), an annual breast MRI is preferred unless unavailable, then a mammography should be used (Lowry *et al.*, 2012; NCCN, 2015a). The use of MRI alternating with mammography in *BRCA* mutation carriers has been found to be more effective than mammography alone in detecting early stage breast cancers (Le-Petross *et al.*, 2011) and is an ACS guideline for use in high-risk individuals (Saslow *et al.*, 2007). In 1 study, a reported sensitivity of 86% in detecting breast cancers among women with *BRCA* mutations who screened with MRI was reported compared to a lower 19% sensitivity rate among those who screened with mammography over a 12-year period (Passaperuma *et al.*, 2012). Options for risk-reduction mastectomy should also be part of risk management counseling. Studies have shown that mastectomy reduces the risk of

breast cancer by 50%. For men, NCCN (2015a) guidelines recommend breast self-examination training and education starting at age 35 years, with clinical examinations every 12 months beginning at the same time of initial breast self-examination training.

Risk-reduction salpingo-oophrectomy (RRSO) between ages 35 and 40 years is recommended due to the high risk of ovarian cancer and the poor prognosis of the disease even when screening for ovarian cancer is being performed (NCCN, 2015a). For women who elect to not undergo RRSO, consideration should be made for transvaginal ultrasound starting at ages 30 to 35 years, with serum CA125 as an additional screening test. However, these measures have not shown to be sensitive or specific to support routine ovarian screening (NCCN, 2015a). Various studies have shown that RRSO in *BRCA*-positive women has a significant impact in reducing the risk for high-risk cancers associated with the mutation, thus decreasing the risk of ovarian and fallopian tube cancers by 75% to 96% and breast cancer by approximately 50% (Eisen *et al.*, 2005; Finch *et al.*, 2006; Kauf *et al.*, 2002; Kramer *et al.*, 2005; Rebbeck, 2002; Rebbeck *et al.*, 1999; Rebbeck, Kauf, & Domchek, 2009). However, estrogen deficiency as a consequence of RRSO can result in quality of life issues, including menopausal symptoms (e.g., hot flushes) and sexual discomfort (e.g., vaginal dryness, dyspareunia), as well as loss of bone density, and can increase risk to cardiovascular health (Finch, Evans, & Narod, 2012). Risk management should be individually tailored based upon personal and family history, as well as other factors that can impact women's risks for osteoporosis and cardiovascular disease.

15.4.10. When the Hereditary Breast Cancer Syndrome is Not due to a Deleterious *BRCA* Mutation—Other Inherited Breast Cancers

An accurate risk assessment, including a thorough personal and family history, should be an integral part of identifying individuals who may be at increased risk for hereditary cancers (Berliner, Fay, Cummings, Burnett, & Tillmanns, 2013). Individuals suspect for a mutation in 1 of the 2 *BRCA* genes and who are tested but whose results are uninformative (negative) may warrant further evaluation for other hereditary breast and/

or ovarian cancer syndromes depending upon the personal and family history. Although mutations in the *BRCA* genes account for most hereditary breast or ovarian cancers, numerous other rare hereditary syndromes have also been associated with increased risks for these 2 cancers (see Tables 15.4 and 15.5). Referral for detailed cancer risk assessment and genetic counseling and follow-up to experts in this area (e.g., genetic counselors, geneticists, AGNs) should always be considered for those individuals suspect for an inherited cancer syndrome.

15.5. HEREDITARY COLON CANCER— LYNCH SYNDROME

Colon cancer continues to be a major health problem in the U.S. Although incidence rates for the disease have been declining over the past 2 decades (ACS, 2014) probably a result of early detection of polyps due to screening, it is still the third most common form of cancer in the U.S. According to the ACS (2014), an estimated 96,830 new cases of colon cancer and 40,000 cases of rectal cancer were projected to occur in the U.S. during the year 2014. For the year 2015, it's estimated that 93,090 cases of colon cancer and 39,610 cases of rectal cancer will be diagnosed in the U.S. (ACS, 2015). Most cases of colon cancer are due to sporadic causes; however, approximately 5% are inherited due to germ line mutations. Hereditary colon cancer syndromes are associated with a high propensity for colon as well as other cancers and include Lynch syndrome (previously referred as hereditary nonpolyposis colorectal cancer [HNPCC]), familial adenomatous polyposis, MAP, and some hamartomatous polyposis syndromes (e.g., Peutz-Jeghers and juvenile polyposis [JP]) (Jasperson, Tuohy, Nekalason, & Burt, 2010). Hereditary diffuse gastric cancer and Cowden's and Li Fraumeni syndromes have also been associated with an increased colon cancer risk, although the risk is less defined (see Table 15.5). Of the myriad of hereditary syndromes associated with colon cancer, the most common inherited form is that of Lynch syndrome accounting for 2% to 4% of all colon cancers (Hampel *et al.*, 2008).

Lynch syndrome is an AD genetic syndrome that is caused by a germline mutation in 1 of 4 mismatch repair (MMR) genes: *MLH1, MSH2,*

MSH6, and *PMS2* (Gruber, 2006; Peltomäki, 2005). All of these genes play a major role in maintaining the integrity of the DNA, checking for and correcting errors that if not repaired, have the potential for tumor formation and carcinogenesis (Harfe & Jinks-Robertson, 2000; Peltomäki, 2005). Specifically, MMR genes correct single-base mismatches and insertion-deletions that may occur during replication of DNA, particularly due to DNA damage (Gruber & Kohlmann, 2003; Jasperson *et al.*, 2010). Of the 4 MMR genes associated with Lynch, up to 90% are due to mutations in *MLH1* (approximately 50%) and *MSH2* (approximately 40%), whereas mutations in *MSH6* account for approximately 10% of the Lynch cases and *PMS2* accounts for only a small proportion of those with the syndrome (Peltomäki, 2005). Recent studies have found that deletions in the epithelial cell adhesion molecule (*EpCAM*) gene cause Lynch syndrome through an epigenetic mechanism (hypermethylation), resulting in inactivation of the *MSH2* gene despite no alterations in the *MSH2* gene sequence (Kovacs, Papp, Szentirmay, Otto, & Olah, 2009; Ligtenberget, Kuiper, Geurts van Kessel, & Hoogerbrugge, 2013).

15.5.1. Phenotype and Characteristics of Lynch Syndrome—Colon

Germ line mutations due to Lynch syndrome are highly penetrant. Individuals with the syndrome have a lifetime CRC risk of up to 80% as well as an increased risk of extracolonic cancers, including endometrium, ovary, stomach, small bowel, pancreas, hepatobiliary tract, ureter, renal pelvis, and skin (e.g., sebaceous adenomas, sebaceous carcinomas, and keratocanthomas in a variant form of Lynch syndrome known as Muir-Torre syndrome) (see Table 15.5). Of significance is the early age of onset of colon cancers attributed to Lynch syndrome, with the mean age of onset of the disease occurring at approximately age 45 years compared with age 64 years for the general population (Abdel-Rahman, Mecklin, & Peltomäki, 2006; Kohlmann & Gruber, 2014; Lynch & de la Chappelle, 2003). Colon adenomas may also occur with the syndrome, usually at an early-age onset and without polyposis. In addition, the histologic characteristics of the colon cancer are usually poorly differentiated, with mucinous or signet ring cell morphology and with a large number of infiltrating lymphocytes, Crohn's like lymphocytic reaction, and medullary growth patterns (Abdel-Rahman *et al.*, 2006; Lynch *et al.*, 2009). The location of colon cancer due to Lynch syndrome also has preponderance for right-sided tumors (proximal) compared with left sided tumors (distal) found predominately in sporadic disease (Lynch & de la Chapelle, 2003). The incidence of synchronous (multiple primary cancers occurring simultaneously as well as metachronous [multiple cancers occurring at intervals]) CRCs are often found to occur more frequently among individuals diagnosed with Lynch syndrome, with reports up to 50% occurrence compared with less than 20% risk in individuals with sporadic disease (Lynch *et al.*, 2009; Lynch & Lynch, 2000). Further, the syndrome is often characterized by tumors with a high level of *microsatellite instability* (MSI-H) as a result of the defective MMR genes (Gruber & Kohlmann, 2003; Hampel *et al.*, 2005). Microsatellites are repetitive DNA that should remain constant within an individual's cells (de la Chapelle & Hampel, 2010). When differences in microsatellite repeats occur, MSI is present. Markers are available to assess the stability of certain tumors, such as colon cancers that may be useful in determining individuals suspect for Lynch. Five common microsatellite markers are often used for this testing, and tumors with 2 or more positive loci are determined to be MSI-H (Geiersbach & Samowitz, 2011; Hampel *et al.*, 2005) suspect for Lynch syndrome. Despite the abnormal features associated with MSI-H tumors, individuals diagnosed with this type of CRC have a more favorable prognosis compared with individuals without MSI.

Besides MSI-H features, many cancerous tumors (e.g., colon, endometrium) of individuals diagnosed with Lynch often fail to express proteins associated with the MMR genes. Protein expression can be evaluated through immunohistochemical (IHC) staining, a useful test for individuals suspect for Lynch syndrome (Lynch *et al.*, 2009; Peltomäki, 2005). Knowledge of the characteristic features of colon cancer are important and may be red flags suggestive of Lynch syndrome, including early-age onset of disease than is usually found in the general population, left-sided tumors, metachronous or synchronous tumors, distinguishing pathological features (e.g., presence of tumor infiltrating lymphocytes, signet ring, or medullary growth pattern), MSI-H, and loss of MMR protein expression.

15.5.2. Phenotype and Characteristics of Lynch Syndrome—Extracolonic

Endometrial cancer is the most common extracolonic cancer seen in Lynch syndrome, with a 25% to 60% lifetime risk of the disease compared with a 2.7% population risk for the disease (Aarnio *et al.*, 1999; Kolhmann & Gruber, 2014; Vasen *et al.*, 2001). In addition, the 10 year cumulative risk of endometrial cancer following CRC among women with Lynch syndrome is also increased and in 1 study was found to occur among 23.4% of women with Lynch syndrome compared to a sporadic rate of 1.6% risk for women without the syndrome (Obermair *et al.*, 2010). In women who develop both colon and endometrial cancer, approximately 50% of them are initially diagnosed with cancer of the endometrium (Lu & Broaddus, 2005).

Endometrial cancer among women with Lynch syndrome usually occurs at an earlier age of onset compared with sporadic disease. The median age of onset of endometrial cancer for women with this syndrome is approximately 48 years (approximately 57% occurring before age 50 years), with a reported age range of 27 to 72 years compared with a mean age of 60 years in women from the general population (Kohlmann & Gruber, 2012; Lindor *et al.*, 2006; Meyer, Broaddus, & Lu, 2009; Weissman *et al.*, 2012). Of the 4 MMR genes, *MSH2* and *MSH6* genes are more frequently associated with endometrial cancers due to Lynch syndrome compared with the *MLH1* or *PMS2* gene mutations (Weissman *et al.*, 2012). Similar to that found in colon cancer, endometrial cancers resulting from Lynch syndrome are also more likely to be MSI-high with loss of MMR protein expression (via IHC) compared with sporadic disease, important pathological characteristics when considering individuals suspect for the syndrome (Meyer *et al.*, 2009; Weissman *et al.*, 2012).

Ovarian cancer is another gynecologic cancer associated with Lynch syndrome. The lifetime risk of developing ovarian cancer in women who are diagnosed with the syndrome is estimated at 4% to 12%, much higher than the population 1.6% risk (Aarnio *et al.*, 1999; Kohlmann & Gruber, 2014). Other extracolonic cancers associated with the syndrome and their lifetime and population risks include the following: stomach 6% to 13% lifetime risk (1.6% population risk); hepatobiliary 1.4% to 4% lifetime (< 1% population risk); small bowel 3% to 6% lifetime risk (< 1% population risk); brain, 1% to 3%/lifetime risk (< 3% populations risk); sebaceous neoplasms 1% to 9% lifetime risk (< 1% population risk) (Kohlmann & Gruber, 2014); and uroepithelial cancers 1% to 4% lifetime risk (< 1% population risk) with higher occurrences of this cancer occurring in *MSH2* mutation carriers compared to the other 3 MMR genes (Kolhmann & Gruber, 2014; Aarnio *et al.*, 2012). Early-age onset of these cancers or multiple family members with Lynch syndrome cancers or a personal history of multiple primary Lynch syndrome related cancers are red flags suggestive of Lynch syndrome.

15.5.3. Variants of Lynch Syndrome: Muir-Torre and Turcot

Muir-Torre syndrome and Turcot syndrome are terms that have been used to describe certain families with Lynch syndrome. Both of these terms were coined prior to the availability of genetic testing for Lynch syndrome and are mainly of historical interest given they are both caused by germline mutations in the MMR genes. Muir-Torre syndrome is associated with genodermatoses involving sebaceous neoplasms as well as other Lynch associated cancers (e.g., colon, endometrium). Skin lesions that can be seen in Lynch syndrome and Muir-Torre syndrome include sebaceous adenomas and carcinomas, epitheliomas (sebaceomas), and keratocanthomas (Shalin, Lyle, Calonje, & Lazar, 2010). Genetic referral should be considered when these rare sebaceous gland neoplasias are diagnosed (Abbas and Mahalingam, 2009; Abdel-Rahman *et al.*, 2006). Like that of the colon and endometrium specimens, sebaceous adenomas and carcinomas can be histologically assessed for MSI/IHC to assess for Lynch syndrome (Entius *et al.*, 2000; Roberts *et al.*, 2012). Turcot syndrome is the other variant form of Lynch syndrome. This syndrome is associated with glioblastomas and other Lynch syndrome related cancers (Abdel-Rahman *et al.*, 2006).

15.5.4. Risk Assessment—Identifying Individuals/Families Suspect for Lynch Syndrome

Hereditary colon cancer syndromes including Lynch syndrome are defined based on clinical, pathological, and genetic findings. Assessment of the personal and family history is integral to evaluating the risk for Lynch syndrome. Assessment information should include ethnicity of origin of both paternal and maternal lineage; any history of consanguinity; current age, type of cancer(s), and age at cancer(s) diagnosis; date of last CRC screening; and findings to include presence or absence of colon polyps and the type and number of polyps (e.g., adenomas, hamartomas, juvenile polyps, presence/absence of polyposis); age of death of family members including cause; history of any prior surgeries (e.g., hysterectomy, oophorectomy, colectomy); and detailed medical and surgical history where applicable (e.g., inflammatory bowel disease). History of any other inherited conditions and birth defects should also be documented during the personal and family history intake of syndrome-specific features (e.g., skin changes consistent with sebaceous adenomas) found during the physical examination (NCCN, 2015b). A minimum of a 3-generation family history documenting this assessment information should be conducted on all individuals evaluated for Lynch syndrome. Tissue histopathologic findings of any Lynch-related cancers should also be noted, including if MSI and/or IHC was performed for any of the MMR genes. The results of any genetic tests conducted on family members should be included in the intake of individuals undergoing assessment for Lynch syndrome (NCCN, 2015b).

Diagnosis of Lynch syndrome is made via confirmation of genetic testing for any 1 of the 4 MMR genes (*MLH1, MLSH2, MSH6, PMS2*) or presence of a germ line *EpCAM* gene deletion. There are several resources available to assist health care providers and counselors in determining whether or not genetic testing is warranted based upon the personal and family history. The *Amsterdam criteria II* and *revised Bethesda guidelines* are important and useful tools to use in clinical practice to identify those individuals and families suspect for Lynch syndrome. The Amsterdam II criteria were derived from previously established criteria known as Amsterdam I. In Amsterdam I, the criteria for genetic testing is the same as Amsterdam II, with the exception that cancer cases only entailed individuals and families diagnosed with CRC (Amsterdam I criteria). The criteria were later updated to include colorectal and certain extracolonic Lynch-related cancers (Amsterdam II) (Vasen *et al.*, 1999). Amsterdam II criteria include the following:

(1) Three or more cases in the family of CRC and/or Lynch syndrome–related cancers (e.g., endometrium; ureter or renal pelvis, small bowel, etc)

(2) Two or more generations affected with one affected individual a 1st-degree relative of the other two

(3) One or more cases diagnosed before age 50 years

(4) Exclusion of familial adenomatous polyposis (FAP)

When using these criteria, tumors should be verified by pathological examination and consideration for IHC may also be useful in determining which of the 4 genes to initially test. However, since germ line mutations in *MLH1* and *MSH2* account for the majority of Lynch syndrome cases, genetic testing often begins with these genes (Jasperson *et al.*, 2010). The Amsterdam II is limited by its stringent criteria that may result in failure to test individuals who truly have Lynch syndrome. The following case (see Figure 15.14) is an example of a family meeting Amsterdam II criteria who had a family member who tested positive for Lynch syndrome:

> Mr. G. I. (fictitious case) is a 38-year-old white male of Northern European ancestry on both the maternal and paternal lineage who is recently diagnosed for colon cancer. There was no polyposis on histopathology and diagnosis revealed adenocarcinoma Stage I. He has a father diagnosed with colon cancer at age 49 and died of the disease at age 52; a paternal aunt with endometrial cancer at age 43 and colon cancer at age 52 who died shortly after; and a paternal grandfather with colon cancer diagnosed at age 52 who died 1 year later of a car accident. There are no other family members with cancer history. No prior history of genetic testing in the family.

The 3-generation pedigree of Mr. G.I.'s family reveals that all criteria for Amsterdam II were met, warranting germ line genetic testing. As indicated in the pedigree (see Figure 15.14) there are 3 generations of family members with Lynch syndrome–related cancers (endometrium and colon), with 2 diagnosed before age 50, and at least one affected individual a first-degree relative of the other two. The proband diagnosed with colon cancer did not have a history of polyposis. Mr. G.I.'s tumor was also MSI-H. While hospitalized, his colon cancer tumor was tested with IHC and found to be absent for the MSH6 protein. He underwent genetic counseling and genetic testing for the *MSH6* gene and was found to be mutation positive confirming the diagnosis of Lynch syndrome. The patient has notified family members of the results and is undergoing management of the disease.

The revised Bethesda guidelines are another resource to use for determination of tumor testing (MSI and/or IHC) for individuals diagnosed with colorectal or endometrial cancer who may warrant further need for evaluation of Lynch syndrome with germ line testing (NCCN, 2015b). Unlike the Amsterdam II criteria, the Bethesda guidelines do not have as strict guidelines regarding testing and provide a higher sensitivity in detecting individuals with Lynch syndrome (Umar *et al.*, 2004). The Bethesda guidelines incorporate family history and clinical and pathologic findings to determine individuals suspect for Lynch for tumor testing (MSI/IHC) and include any one of the following criteria:

(1) CRC cancer diagnosed in an individual younger than age 50 years

(2) Multiple primary Lynch syndrome associated tumors (synchronous or metachronous colorectal, or other Lynch-related cancers)

(3) CRC cancer with MSI-H histology diagnosed in individuals younger than age 60 years, with characteristics of Lynch syndrome pathology, including MSI-H (tumor-infiltrating lymphocytes, Crohn's like reactions, signet ring cells, mucinous adenocarcinoma, or medullary growth patterns)

(4) CRC and a 1st-degree relative with a Lynch syndrome associated cancer (one diagnosed before age 50 years)

(5) CRC and 2 close family members (1st or 2nd degree) with Lynch syndrome–associated cancers regardless of age (Umar, 2004)

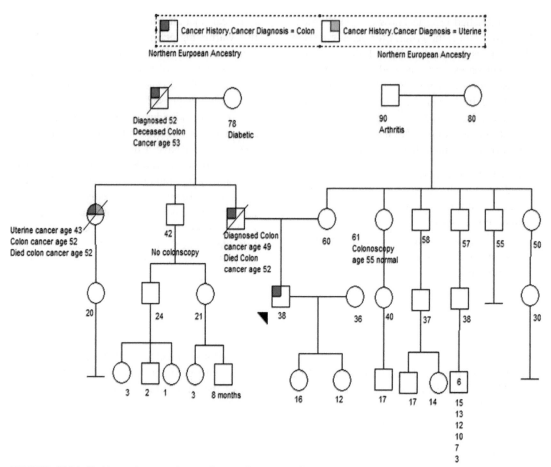

FIGURE 15.14. Fictitious 4-generation pedigree of case #1 G.I., a 38-year-old male (noted by arrowhead) with early-age onset colon cancer depicting 3 generations with Lynch-related cancers (colon and endometrial) meeting Amsterdam II criteria for genetic testing for Lynch syndrome.

The following case of Mrs. I.G. depicts an example of an individual who meets Bethesda guidelines.

Mrs. I. G. (fictitious case) is a 40-year-old white female of British ancestry on both the maternal and paternal lineage who is recently diagnosed with stage I colon cancer after a recent history of rectal bleeding and biopsied confirmed adenocarcinoma. Her medical history is otherwise unremarkable; family history is limited in structure; both parents are deceased: father at age 42 years of cardiovascular disease; paternal lineage has an uneventful cancer history. On the maternal lineage, her mother age 40 died of an automobile accident and her maternal grandmother had uterine cancer. However, age of initial diagnosis is unknown; she died at age 52 years of unknown causes. There are 2 siblings, a sister age 30 years and a brother age 32 years whose medical histories are unremarkable. Tumor testing was performed on I. G. that revealed MSI-H and loss of MLH1 and PMS2 proteins (these proteins are often lost in pairs). She was provided genetic counseling and consented to germ line testing for *MLH1* gene, confirming the diagnosis of Lynch syndrome (see Figure 15.15).

The patient meets one of the Bethesda guidelines (CRC younger than age 50 years) warranting further evaluation for tumor testing with MSI. An MSI-H tumor warrants further evaluation, including assessment of protein expression and possible germ line genetic testing. Analyzing tumor tissue of affected individuals for MSI before germ line testing is a cost effective approach in determining those who might have the syndrome. Approximately 90% of individuals with Lynch syndrome will have MSI-H tumors (Jasperson *et al.*, 2010). Further, tumor testing with IHC assessing for protein expression of the

4 MMR genes *MLH1, MSH2, MLH6*, and *PMS2* provides further evaluation of gene functioning and determines which of the 4 genes to begin germ line testing. Tumor testing using MSI or IHC to aid in the diagnosis of Lynch has been shown to be of value when evaluating CRC and endometrial cancers (NCCN, 2015b; Vasen *et al.*, 2004).

There are some pitfalls in tumor testing, making diagnosis of Lynch syndrome at times complex and challenging. An abnormal IHC and/or MSI are not diagnostic of Lynch syndrome. Although these tumor tests are useful in identifying individuals who are suspect for Lynch syndrome, approximately 10% to 15% of sporadic colon cancers also have MSI-H tumors or loss of protein expression as a result of acquired cellular changes (Boland, 2007; Geiersbach & Samowitz, 2011; Hawkins & Ward, 2001; NCCN, 2015b; Yoon *et al.*, 2011). MSI-H tumors may be a result of somatic events, such as promoter hypermethylation of *MLH1* or *BRAF V600E* mutations, both of which are associated with sporadic CRC and

Lynch syndrome (Kastrinos & Syngal, 2012). In these cases, abnormal IHC staining for MLH1 and PMS2 proteins may be observed, warranting further evaluation of *MLH1* promoter methylation and *BRAF V600E* gene mutation in order to differentiate sporadic disease from Lynch syndrome (Geiersbach & Samowitz, 2011). Other considerations when assessing for Lynch syndrome should include germ line deletions in the *EpCAM* gene and evaluating for other hereditary colon cancer syndromes, if applicable. Because of the complexity of testing, experts (e.g., genetic counselors, AGNs, geneticists) in hereditary colon cancer syndromes should be consulted or referred when considering testing individuals and families for Lynch syndrome.

Additional testing guidelines have been recommended by several organizations and groups. The Evaluation of Genomic Application in Practice and Prevention (EGAPP) working group (2009) recommends "genetic testing to detect Lynch syndrome in all individuals with newly diagnosed CRC as a strategy to reduce

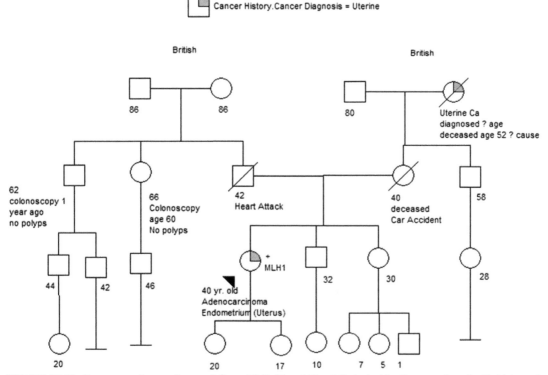

FIGURE 15.15. Four-generation pedigree of Case #2 (fictitious) Mrs. I.G. (noted by the arrowhead) with history of early-age onset endometrial cancer, a Lynch-related cancer (age < 50 years) with microsatellite-high tumor on immunohistochemistry meeting Bethesda II guidelines.

CRC morbidity and mortality in their relatives" (EGAPP Working Group 2009, page 35). Recommended testing from this group includes MSI or IHC tumor testing to patients diagnosed with CRC. Recommendations for clinical use were based upon evidenced-based panels and systematic review of evidence regarding validity and utility (EGAPP, 2009). Studies have found that not only early identification of the syndrome can be obtained through screening, but also cost-effectiveness and quality of life related to year gained can be achieved (Ladabaum *et al.*, 2011; Wang *et al.*, 2012). Revised guidelines for the clinical management of Lynch syndrome by one European expert group recommended "testing all CRC (or individuals with CRC < 70 years) and all endometrial cancers (or individuals with endometrial cancer < 70 years) by IHC or MSI as useful for the identification of patients with Lynch syndrome" (Vasen *et al.*, 2012). Many NCI-Comprehensive Cancer Centers have reported using reflex IHC/MSI to screen for Lynch syndrome; however, this practice is not well adopted by community hospitals (Beamer *et al.*, 2012). "Increasing the proportion of persons with newly diagnosed colorectal cancer who receive genetic testing to identify Lynch syndrome (or familial colorectal cancer syndromes)" is currently cited as 1 of the 10 year genomics objectives in *Healthy People 2020* (U.S. Department of Health and Human Services, 2014).

15.5.5. Management of Lynch Syndrome

Because of the high genetic penetrance of Lynch Syndrome and the multiple cancers associated with the syndrome, professional guidelines have been established regarding secondary preventive health care for early detection and surveillance (NCCN, 2015b). Specific surveillance for *MLH1, MSH2*, and *EPCAM* mutation carriers has been recommended by the NCCN (2015b). For example, surveillance guidelines for individuals with these mutations include CRC screening individualized based upon personal and family history with recommendations of colonoscopy beginning at age 20 to 25 years or 2 to 5 years prior to the earliest colon cancer, with repeated examination performed every 1 to 2 years (NCCN, 2015b). Prophylactic hysterectomy and bilateral salpingo-oophrectomy

is a risk-reducing option for women who have completed childbearing for endometrial and ovarian cancer prevention in women with Lynch syndrome (NCCN, 2015b). Screening for endometrial cancer via biopsy is optional since no data are available to support routine screening. However, for those women of childbearing years, education regarding abnormal vaginal bleeding should be explained, because this condition may warrant evaluation to rule out endometrial cancer. Transvaginal ultrasound may be a consideration at the health care provider's discretion, with serum CA-125 testing for endometrial and ovarian cancer; however, like that of routine endometrial biopsy, these screening regimens have not been found to be highly sensitive for disease recognition (NCCN, 2015b). Surveillance of other extracolonic cancers associated with the syndrome should also be considered (these are based on expert opinion as opposed to evidence-based recommendations) to include annual urinalysis for urothelial cancer beginning at age 25 to 30 years and annual physical examination for evaluation of the central nervous system at age 25 to 30 years (NCCN, 2015b). Selected individuals/families or those of Asian descent should be considered for esophagogastroduodenoscopy (EGD) with extended duodensocopy beginning ages 30–35 years every 3–5 years (NCCN, 2015b). At this time, there is no recommended screening for pancreatic cancer, and although there is some suggestion of increased breast cancer rates among individuals with the syndrome, no specific screening recommendation for breast cancer is recommended currently by the 2015b NCCN professional guidelines (NCCN, 2015b).

Professional guidelines for surveillance for *MSH6* and *PMS2* mutation carriers are also available (NCCN, 2015b), with similar screening for colon, endometrial, and ovarian cancer, as noted for *MLH1, MSH2*, and *EPCAM* gene mutation carriers discussed previously. However, because of the lower risk of other Lynch-related cancers among women with *MSH6* and *PMS2* mutations, there were no screening recommendations for these disorders reported by NCCN 2015b guidelines (NCCN, 2015b) for Lynch syndrome among individuals with these mutations. (*Note*: Caution is made to the reader regarding future research, data, and technology that may warrant change/revisions/modifications in professional guidelines.) Also, because of the complexity of Lynch syndrome, personal and family history must always be taken in consideration regarding management of individuals with this hereditary syndrome. Further, the use of an interprofessional collaborative team experienced in high-risk individuals such as those with Lynch syndrome is integral to disease prevention and management of care.

15.5.6. Hereditary Colon Cancer Syndromes—Differential Diagnoses

When germ line testing for Lynch syndrome fails to show a genetic mutation in individuals suspect for a hereditary colon cancer syndrome and suspicion remains, other hereditary cancer syndromes should be considered based upon the personal and family history. History data should include the type and number of polyps, as well as personal and family medical and cancer history. For example, a woman with a history of hamartomatous colon polyps, increased head circumference, and early-age onset of breast cancer (e.g., age 38 years) is suspect for Cowden's syndrome. Personal and family history of ovarian cancer warrants evaluation for mutations in the *BRCA* genes. Numerous hereditary CRC syndromes may need to be included in the differential diagnoses. A brief explanation is provided on some of these rare hereditary CRC syndromes.

15.5.7. Polyposis Syndromes

Although Lynch syndrome is characterized by few to no adenomatous polyps, some hereditary CRC syndromes manifest with *polyposis* defined as numerous colon polyps as well as other features. FAP is an inherited CRC syndrome associated with mutations in the *APC* gene. The feature is the presence of ≥ 100 to thousands of adenomatous colorectal polyps (fewer in individuals of younger age) (Half, Bercovich, & Rozen, 2009). FAP is the second most common inherited CRC syndrome after that of Lynch syndrome. Age of onset for FAP usually occurs early in life, with a mean age of 16 and age of the disorder ranging from 7 to 36 years (Jasperson & Burt, 2014). The syndrome is highly penetrant with approximately 95% of individuals developing polyps by age 35; penetrance is 100% with subsequent develop-

ment of colon cancer if left untreated with colectomy (Jasperson & Burt, 2014). FAP is inherited in an AD Mendelian pattern; however, the rate of occurrence of de novo mutations is estimated as high as 30% (Bisgaard, Fenger, Bülow, Niebuhr, & Mohr, 1994; Claes *et al.*, 2011). There is also a high risk of developing extracolonic cancers with FAP, particularly when compared with the general population. Specific extracolonic cancers associated with FAP include small bowel, particularly the duodenum and periampulla, pancreas (adenocarcinoma), thyroid, CNS usually meduloblastoma, hepatoblastoma (usually occurring before age 5 years), bile duct, and stomach (Jasperson & Burt, 2014). Other possible associated noncancerous findings of FAP are congenital hypertrophy of the retinal pigment epithelium (CHRPE), an ovoid benign asymptomatic, pigmented fundal lesion of the eye (Chen *et al.*, 2006; Half *et al.*, 2009; NCCN, 2015b) (see Figure 15.16); osteomas, supernumerary teeth, odontomas, desmoids tumors, duodenal and other small bowel adenomas and gastric fundic gland polyps; and sebaceous neoplasms including epidermoid cysts (Jasperson *et al.*, 2010; Jasperson & Burt, 2014; NCCN, 2015b).

Gastric fundic gland polyposis is a common presentation of the syndrome with approximately 50% to 90% of individuals reported with this extra-colonic feature (Burt, 2003; Half *et al.*, 2009). Extracolonic adenomatous polyps also frequently occur in this syndrome, presenting in the 2nd and 3rd part of the duodenum and periampullary region of the duodenum (Half *et al.*, 2009). The presence of osteomas (benign growths mostly on skull and mandible) and dental abnormalities such as unerupted teeth often are usually found during dental examination and may be an additional finding of the syndrome (Half *et al.*, 2009; Jasperson & Burt, 2014; NCCN, 2015b). Desmoid tumors, benign soft tissue tumors usually occurring in the mesentery, abdominal wall, or areas of scars that do not metastasize but may be locally invasive, are found in approximately 10% to 30% of individuals with FAP (Sinha, Tekkis, Gibbons, Phillips, & Clark, 2011; Sturt & Clark, 2006). Desmoids frequently occur in individuals with FAP during ages 20 and 30 years with the majority (80%) occurring by age 40 years (Sinha *et al.*, 2011). Desmoids are the second leading cause of mortality in FAP and are commonly

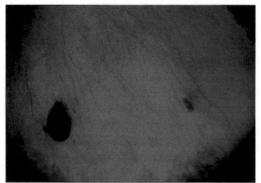

FIGURE 15.16. Congenital hypertrophy of retinal pigment epithelium (CHRPE). E. Half, E. Bercovich, D. & Rozen. P. (2009) Familial adenomatous polyposis Orphanet Journal of Rare Diseases, 4(22). doi:10.1186/1750-1172-4-22. PMID 19822006 Retrieved from http://commons.wikimedia.org/wiki/File:Congenital_hypertrophy_of_the_retinal_pigment_epithelium.jpg with license under the Creative Commons Attribution-Share Alike 2.0 Generic.

found in a variant form of FAP known as Gardner's syndrome.

There are variant forms of FAP, all attributed to mutations in the APC genes, including attenuated familial polyposis (AFAP) characterized with a phenotype that has fewer polyps (< 100 adenomas) known as Gardner's syndrome and Turcot syndrome. Gardner's syndrome is a variant form of FAP phenotypically characterized by colorectal polyposis and cancer in addition to osteomas, desmoids tumors, and epidermoid skin lesions (Cankaya et al., 2012; Sinha et al., 2011). Turcot syndrome also due to a germline APC mutation, is associated with colon polyposis, cancer, and medulloblastoma (Jasperson & Burt, 2014; NCCN, 2015b).

15.5.8. MUTYH-Associated Polyposis (MAP)

Another hereditary CRC syndrome associated with polyposis of the colorectum and increased CRC risk is that attributed to mutations in the MUTYH gene (also known as MYH) and is referred to as MUTYH-associated polyposis (MAP). The gene was discovered in 2002. Unlike most hereditary cancer syndromes, MAP is AR, requiring that both copies of the gene are mutated. Thus, a family pedigree may show a horizontal rather than a vertical transmission pattern, with siblings affected and parents heterozy-

gous for MUTYH mutation without manifestations of the syndrome (see Figure 15.17). MAP has similar characteristics to that of AFAP, including polyposis predominately adenomatous. Polyposis in MAP usually numbers < 100, with a range that can vary from 100 to >1000 (rare instances) (NCCN, 2015b). However, in contrast to FAP, hyperplastic and serrated polyps may also be seen. Colon polyposis in MAP typically occurs at an older age than classical FAP, with mean age of onset of polyposis in the 40s and median age of CRC over age 50 years (Bolocan, Ion, Stoaian, & Serban, 2011; Brand, Nielsen, Lynch, & Infante, 2012; Jasperson et al., 2010; NCCN, 2015b). Like that of other hereditary CRC syndromes, there is an increased lifetime risk of developing CRC, estimated at a 43% risk of developing the disease with some reports as high as 100% in absence of adequate and timely surveillance or colectomy (Brand et al., 2012). Besides CRC risk, MAP is associated with duodenal adenomas (found in approximately 17% to 25%) and cancers (4%) (Brand et al., 2012; Vogt et al., 2009). Increased risks for other malignancies have been reported for ovarian, bladder, and skin cancer, occurring at median ages of onset between ages 51 and 61 years (Vogt et al., 2009).

15.5.9. Other Hereditary Cancer Syndromes Not Associated with Adenomatous Polyps

15.5.9.1. Hamartomatous Polyposis Conditions

Other types of polyposis such as those found in hereditary cancer syndromes attributed to hamartomatous conditions increase the risk of colon and other cancers. Peutz-Jeghers (PJ) is an AD-inherited syndrome due to germ line mutations in the STK11 (LKB1) gene that is associated with increased breast, colon, stomach, pancreas, small bowel, ovary, testes, and lung cancer risks. Females are at risk for gynecologic tumors in ovarian sex cord tumors with annular tubules (SCTATs) that are typically bilateral, multifocal, and benign compared with SCTATs that occur in the general population, which are associated with a 20% cancer risk (Young, 2005). In addition, females with PJ are at risk for mucinous tumors of the ovaries and fallopian tubes and a rare uterine/cervical cancer called adenoma malignum (McGarrity, Amos, Frazier, & Wei, 2013). Males are at risk for a rare form of testicular cancer called Sertoli-Leydig cell tumor. Hamartomatous polyps are frequently observed in this syndrome and are usually found in the small intestines (jejunum, ileum, and duodenum); however, other organs including the stomach and large bowel, and even the nasal passages, have been found to have hamartomatous polyps (McGarrity *et al.*, 2013). Characteristic hyperpigmented mucocutaneous macules (see Figure 15.18) are frequently observed in individuals with PJ and are often present in early infancy, though rarely are observed at birth. These lesions tend to fade in later years, usually by puberty and adulthood (McGarrity *et al.*, 2013). Because of the gastrointestinal polyp involvement associated with PJ, chronic bleeding recurring obstruction and intussusceptions are frequent in individuals with PJ (McGarrity *et al.*, 2013; Wang, Luo, Liu, Huang, Wu, & Wang, 2011.). Clinical diagnosis can be made when the following features are observed:

(a) 2 or more histologic PJ-type hamartomatous polyps; (b) mucocutaneous hyperpigmentation of lips, mouth, nose, eyes, genitalia, or fingers in an individual who has a family history of PJ in a close relative; (c) PJ-type polyps detected in and individual with a family history of PJ; (d) any number of PJ-type polyps in an individual with characteristics of mucocutaneous pigmentation (McGarrity *et al.*, 2013; NCCN, 2015b).

15.5.10. Juvenile Polyposis

Another hereditary cancer syndrome associated with high risk for colon cancer is that of juvenile polyposis (JP), an AD syndrome caused by mutations in the *mothers against decapentaplegic homolog 4* (*SMAD4*) gene or in the gene encoding *bone morphogenetic protein receptor-1A* (*BMPR1A*). *SMAD4* and *BMPR1A* mutations are found in approximately 50% of JP cases. JP is a rare hereditary cancer syndrome that is asso-

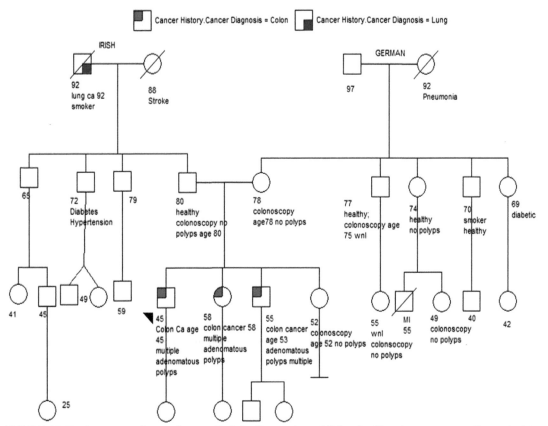

FIGURE 15.17. Four-generation pedigree with 3 family members (siblings) with colon cancer; pedigree depicts horizontal pattern of transmission suspect for autosomal recessive pattern and MUTYH hereditary colon cancer syndrome. Proband is noted by arrowhead.

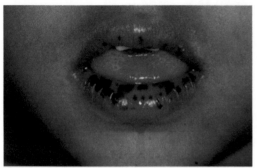

FIGURE 15.18. Peutz-Jeghers syndrome characterized by black spots localized in the perioral area. From Gondak, R., da Silva-Jorge, R., Lopes, M. A., & Vargas, P.A. (2012) Oral pigmented lesions: Clinicopathologic features and review of the literature. Medical Oral, Patologia Oral y Cirugia Bucal 17(6): e919-e924; © 2012 Medicina Oral S. L. Retrieved from: http://www.ncbi. nlm.nih.gov/pmc/articles/PMC3505710/. Open access article distributed under the terms of the Creative Commons Attribution License.

ciated with *juvenile polyps* (type of hamartoma) of the gastrointestinal tract, particularly stomach, small intestines, colon, and rectum (Haidle & Howe, 2014). Lifetime cancer risk associated with JP includes the following: colon (40% to 50%), stomach (21%), and to a lesser undefined cancer risk, the small intestines and pancreas (NCCN, 2015b). Clinical diagnosis is considered based upon any one of the following criteria:

(1) At least 3 to 5 juvenile polyps of the colorectum

(2) Multiple juvenile polyps found throughout the GI tract

(3) Any number of juvenile polyps found in an individual with family history of JP (Haidle & Howe, 2014; NCCN, 2015b)

Because of the myriad of hereditary colon cancer syndromes, it is important that clinicians and APRNs who are providing assessment of individuals and families who are suspect for these syndromes provide genetic referral and consultation. Recommend that clinicians examine one's competency of practice regarding hereditary cancer syndromes and identify strengths as well as weaknesses that may warrant referral to genetic professionals. These strengths should be based upon one's genomic knowledge, skills, and attitudes regarding hereditary cancer syndromes. Working with an interprofessional collaborative

team, including genetic counselors, geneticists, AGNs, oncologists, and other health professionals enables comprehensive, safe, quality, and accessible patient-centered care for high-risk cancer individuals and families.

15.5.11. Ethical, Legal, and Social Implications of Single Gene Testing for Hereditary Cancer Syndromes

When considering genetic testing for individuals suspect for hereditary syndromes, clinicians must consider interpretability of results and practical utility prior to ordering genetic tests. Nurses must ensure that individuals requiring genetic testing have been educated regarding the syndrome, purpose of testing, possible results of testing, and follow-up management of care. Nurses trained in providing risk assessment and predictive genetic testing for cancer genetic and genomic diseases and syndromes should consider the individual's age, culture, and psychosocial status while maintaining privacy and confidentiality based upon HIPAA. Thus, pre- and posttest counseling should be an integral part of genetic testing, focusing on major ethical principles of *do no harm* (*nonmalficence*), providing services that are beneficial to individuals (*beneficence*), and enabling *autonomy* in decision-making through informed consent that is just and fair (*justice*). Age of the individual requiring predictive testing should be considered, because some syndromes such as that due to *BRCA* mutations should be performed when the individual is of age of consent, allowing for informed decision-making. On the other hand, some syndromes manifesting during early childhood warrant testing at an early age (e.g., FAP, JP), requiring parental or guardian consent.

Nurse leaders and administrators should ensure that policies and guidelines regarding ethical, legal, and social implications (ELSI) of genetic testing are available in the clinical setting. Continuing education regarding ELSI and genetic testing should be a part of staff education using an interprofessional team approach to discuss genetic privacy, screening, and other issues that may impact an individual's care management. With advanced technology and changing diagnostic measures (e.g., routine CRC tumor testing for Lynch), ongoing discussions should be conducted in clinical settings in which genetic testing is conducted so that clinician's beliefs and practices are communicated and policies are maintained that emphasize ethical, social, and legal issues that impact individuals, families, and populations.

15.6. GENOMICS OF CANCER— NEW AND FUTURE ADVANCES AND TECHNOLOGIES

Numerous scientific achievements and advances have led to an expansion in the repertoire of genomic approaches that has resulted in significant changes to cancer diagnosis, management, and care. Next generation sequencing (NGS) is one example of the advances in genetics and genomics revolutionizing cancer research, diagnosis, and therapy. NGS includes selected panel, exome, and whole genome sequencing providing comprehensive approaches for multiple genome analysis to enhance personalized management of care. NGS techniques represent the next phase in the evolution of DNA sequencing technology at dramatically reduced cost compared with traditional Sanger single-gene sequencing (Gullapalli, Desai, Santana-Santos, Kant, & Becich, 2012).

Next-generation selected panel sequencing is one advanced technologic measure currently used in clinical settings. NGS panel sequencing analyzes multiple cancer susceptibility genes simultaneously (Fecteau, Vogel, Hanson, & Morrill-Cornnelius, 2014; Rainville & Rana, 2014). Selected panel sequencing provide an advantage over traditional Sanger-based sequencing strategies particularly when single gene sequencing fails to provide an immediate answer to individuals suspect for an inherited cancer syndrome or if the personal and family history is suspect for more than 1 inherited syndrome. In addition, the use of NGS panel testing to assess for inherited cancer syndromes provides testing of many genes at a fraction of what it would cost to test a single gene separately (Fecteau *et al.*, 2014; Gullapalli, Desai, Santana-Satos, Kant, & Becich, 2012).

Selected panel sequencing is currently available from a wide range of laboratories for use in clinical practice to assess for many hereditary cancer syndromes. For example, cancer panel tests are available for individuals suspect for breast, ovarian, colon, endometrial, kidney, pancreatic, parangangliomas, and phenochromocytoma susceptibility genes. Gene panel testing may include multiple high-penetrance genes or a combination of high-penetrance as well as moderate-penetrance and newer-risk genes. Gene panel tests vary regarding the number of genes analyzed. For example, in 1 targeted breast cancer high risk panel, 6-genes that focus on high risk breast cancer susceptibility are analyzed including *BRCA1, BRCA2, CDH1, PTEN, STK11*, and *TP53* genes (GeneDX™, 2014). Another panel that analyzes 21 genes for breast and ovarian cancer includes high-risk genes: *BRCA1, BRCA2, CDH1, EPCAM, MLH1, MSH2, MSH6, PMS2, PTEN, STK11, TP53*; moderate-risk genes: *ATM, CHEK2, PALB2*; and newer-risk genes: *BARD1, BRIP1, FANCC, NBN, RAD51C, RAD51D*, and *XRCC2* (GeneDX™, 2014). An example of a multigene panel test for colon cancer is one that provides a comprehensive analysis of 14 colorectal cancer susceptibility genes including *APC, BMPRIA, SMAD4, CDH1, Chek2, MLH1, MSH2, EPCAM, MSH6, MUTYH, PMS2, PTEN, STK11*, and *TP53* (Ambry Genetics™, 2014–2015; Ambry Genetics, nd)

Genetic panel tests may be beneficial, because genetic heterogeneity of many of the cancer syndromes often results in diagnostic challenges, particularly when families are suspect for specific cancer syndromes, diagnosis is unclear, and single-gene sequencing fails to find the answers. In a study that assessed the contribution of 19 genes associated with breast and ovarian cancer in *BRCA1* and *BRCA2* negative patients, panel testing identified 67 mutations in individuals with a personal history of breast and/or ovarian cancer including mutations in *BRIP, MSH6, CHEK2, ATM*, and *TP53* genes (Minion *et al.*, 2015). In another study, mutations in 19 genes, most frequently *BRCA1, BRCA2, CHEK2, ATM*, and *PALB2* were found in individuals with breast cancer who were referred for *BRCA1/2* genetic testing and who were tested using a 25-gene panel test (Tung *et al.*, 2015). Panel testing can therefore provide an analysis of many genes associated with the cancer, reducing costs as well from frequent clinician visits due to multiple single genetic testing. However, selected panel testing may be challenging and entail results that are difficult to interpret, particularly when findings involve a VUS or multiple genes with a VUS (Fecteau *et al.*, 2014; Rainville & Rana, 2014). Such findings are considered uninformative and carry the risk of being both anxiety provoking and misinterpreted by patients and their clinicians, prompting some experts to express caution about the drawbacks of multiplex panel testing until further data are available. In addition, identification of mutations without clear clinical significance, including mutations in rare pathogenic cancer susceptibility genes may result in some panel tests making risk management strategies unclear (Fecteau *et al.*, 2014; Rainville & Rana, 2014). Therefore it is important when ordering panel testing that selection of the appropriate test should be based upon phenotype (personal & family history and suspect for inherited predisposition to cancer). Pretest counseling and informed consent are important when ordering panel testing particularly to inform individuals of potential VUS results and incidental/unexpected findings (Fecteau *et al.*, 2014). Because of the complexity of testing and the challenges that may occur regarding tests results, panel testing

should be ordered by individuals experienced in genetic counseling, testing, results interpretation, and clinical applicability.

Exome sequencing is another approach to analyzing multiple genes that can be used for discovery and diagnostic purposes. Several exome sequencing approaches are available for use in clinical practice. Exome sequencing involves analysis and interpretation of the coding regions (exons) of the DNA that can be useful in cancer genetics to elucidate the genetic basis of Mendelian disorders as well as used as a diagnostic tool for specific genetic and phenotypic heterogeneity (Ku *et al.*, 2012; Thompson *et al.*, 2012). Although 3 billion nucleotides make up the human genome, only approximately 1% are exomes important in making proteins. Exome sequencing can be targeted for specific exons or can involve coding regions of all genes. The comprehensive mutation analysis of tumors using exome sequencing have led to the identification of a number of genes involved in the etiology of cancers and resulting in tailored management of care and drug therapy for some cancers, such as that

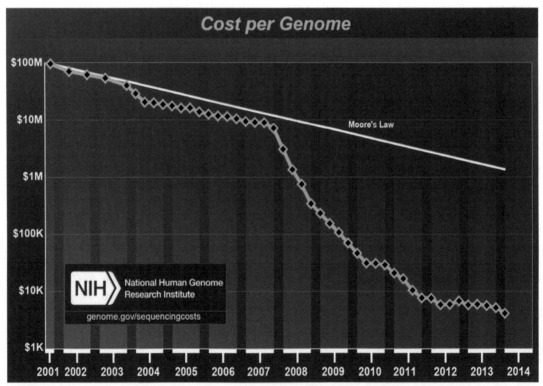

FIGURE 15.19. Costs per genome from 2001 to 2014. Figure from National Institutes of Health, National Human Genome Research Institute (NHGRI) (2014). http://www.genome.gov/sequencingcosts/.

found for *BRAF*-mutation melanomas (Dutton-Regester & Hayward, 2012).

Whole genome sequence is a more comprehensive and more costly analysis of the genome when compared with the other NGS tests previously described. Costs of whole genome sequencing have steadily been declining and have been dramatically reduced from the $100 million dollar cost of performing this procedure in 2001 (National Human Genome, Research Institute [NHHRI], 2014). For example, reported costs of the genome testing was over $95,000 in 2001 compared with a much lower cost of $4,000 for whole genome testing reported in January 2014 by the National Institutes of Health (NIH), NH-GRI (NHGRI, 2014) (see Figure 15.19).

Whole genome sequencing facilitates the discovery of somatic and germline mutations, and identification of the insertions, deletions, and structural rearrangements, including translocations and inversions, in novel disease genes enabling more comprehension of tumor initiation and development (Tuna & Amos, 2012). Whole genome analysis has been used to identify genes and genetic pathways that influence diagnostic management and personalize/precision management of care. Because of novel discovered genes, this approach has also been used to diagnose rare disorders.

Future advancements in NGS will provide further information into understanding cancer, risk assessment, diagnosis, prognosis, and management of care to guide medical decision-making towards personalized medicine. As research increases in the areas of NGS, translation of many of these approaches may become a part of routine clinical care as technologic costs are reduced and scientific findings become more precise. These approaches, however, will not come without some concerns and a need for social and political changes. Regulatory and reimbursement policies, as well as legislative protections for privacy for system-wide adoption (Ginsburg & Willard, 2009), will be required to ensure ethical considerations are being withheld when evaluating genomic information (e.g., beneficence, non-malficence, justice, and dignity). For example, expansive data generated from some of these approaches can lead to complex or unexpected findings, sometimes complicating clinical utility and patient benefit (Ali-Khan, Daar, Shuman, Ray, & Scherer, 2009) that may cause undo harm or have no effective management of care, resulting in emotional distress.

15.6.1. Genome-Wide Association Studies

Genome-wide association (GWAS) studies are important in identifying common genetic factors that influence health and disease by the use of genetic markers and their relationship to the trait of interest. These studies analyze hundreds of thousands of single nucleotide polymorphisms to identify disease susceptibility genes. The National Human Genome Institute GWAS catalog (http://www.genome.gov/gwastudies/) provides published data for 18 categories of disorders, including cancer. This catalog can be used to guide future research of the role of common variants and complex disorders such as cancer (Hindorff *et al.*, 2009). As of February 2015, the catalog included 2,111 publications and 15,396 SNPs (NHGRI, 2015). GWAS has been instrumental in mapping of thousands of genes to traits; it is expected that these numbers will continuously rise, bringing a better understanding of the inter-individual genetic variation and phenotypes (Gao & Edwards, 2011).

15.6.2. Tumor Markers

A major advancement in genomic cancer care is the use of biomarkers and tumor profiling for prognosis and management of care among individuals diagnosed with certain types of cancer. Biomarkers are used to measure and evaluate the normal biological and pathogenic processes, or pharmacologic and pharmacodynamic responses to a therapeutic intervention (Saijo, 2012). Tumor molecular gene assays are currently available to provide individualized prediction of chemotherapy benefit and prognosis regarding disease. For example, OncotypeDX® is 1 assay that can be used for patients with *ER*-positive, *HER2*-negative, and lymph node–negative invasive breast cancer (Stage I or Stage II) for management of care decisions. The assay at present provides a quantitative score based on 21 different genes and gives a "Recurrence Score" between 0 and 100 to determine prediction for chemotherapy and 10-year distant recurrence to inform adjuvant treatment decisions (OncotypeDX, Breast

Cancer Assay®, 2004-2015a; Paik *et al.*, 2006). OncotypeDX® scores of 1 to 17 are considered low recurrence and based upon this finding, individuals are expected to respond well to hormonal treatment with little if any benefit from chemotherapy. Scores between 18 and 30 indicate uncertainty regarding whether chemotherapy is necessary and whether hormonal therapy alone may be sufficient. Scores of 31 or higher indicate a benefit from chemotherapy being added to hormonal therapy (OncotypeDx® Breast Cancer Assay, 20042015b). Other profiles are also currently available as predictive markers for breast cancer, such as MammaPrint™, a prognostic profile that is used to determine distant recurrence and survival of primary breast cancer (Agendia, 2015). This test evaluates 70 prognostic genes to determine individual's recurrence risk for breast cancer (Gullapalli *et al.*, 2012; Slodkowska & Ross, 2009). These and other genetic profiling tests will continue to be an important and emerging technology for identifying genes that impact current and future breast cancer prognosis and therapeutic management to improve outcomes (Győrffy, Hatzis, Sanft, Hofstatter, Aktas, & Pusztai, 2015).

Molecular biomarkers to determine the effectiveness of targeted therapies in cancer treatment have also been used widely in CRC. Oncotype DX® Colon Cancer Assay is a 12-gene assay that provides an individualized score (Recurrent Score) reflective of the risk of colon cancer recurrence for individuals diagnosed with Stage II or Stage III colon cancer (OncotypeDX Colon Cancer Assay, 2004–2015). Assessment of CRC tumors for *KRAS* mutations found in about 30% to 40% of CRC is also important in determining appropriate management of care for individuals diagnosed with this disease (Arrington *et al.*, 2012). *KRAS* mutations have been associated with poor prognosis because of their aggressive metastatic behavior. *KRAS* status needs to be determined in individuals with CRC, because some therapies such as those with antibodies against the epithelial growth factor receptor (e.g., cetuximab) are effective only in tumors bearing the *KRAS* wild-type and not that of cancers with mutations in the *KRAS* gene (Lièvre *et al.*, 2008; NCI, 2013c). Numerous other biomarkers are currently available for a wide range of cancers whose heterogeneity suggests the need for per-

sonalized management of care to improve outcomes.

There are numerous genomic biomarkers currently used for cancer screening, diagnosis, and management; however, improved and novel biomarkers are expected to occur in the future because of rapidly developing technologic advancements in genomics. Current and future studies of miRNAs, the short noncoding RNAs that post-transcriptionally regulate gene expression, are being conducted because these miRNAs may play a role as circulating and tissue expression biomarkers for cancer diagnosis, prognosis, target therapy, and prediction. Recent discoveries in some DNA methylation biomarkers have also shown promise for future studies in CRC (Lange *et al.*, 2012). Because of these evolving and rapidly changing areas, nurses, APRNs, and nurse leaders, including nurse administrators working in oncology, must keep abreast of genomics and how it influences all aspects of cancer health care, including primary, secondary, and tertiary prevention and how these new technologies can be implemented safely and ethically into clinical settings to improve health outcomes.

15.6.3. Pharmacogenomics and Cancer

Pharmacogenomics is important to oncology and personalized medicine, because it focuses on individual's genomic variability that impacts their response to drug therapy. This is important in all aspects of healthcare including oncology because understanding individual differences regarding therapeutic drug response enables clinicians to provide the right drug to the right patient at the right dose. Although there are numerous factors that influence drug responses (e.g., age, disease-state, drug-drug interactions, genetics, administration route), genetic variation plays an important role regarding drug response and toxicity. Genotyping to assess for single-nucleotide polymorphisms (SNPs) and copy number variations (variation in the human genome due to duplications and deletions of DNA sequences that typically range in length from 1,000 base pairs to 5 megabases) have been found to provide useful genetic information to predict drug action and drug responses for a number of medications used in oncology care.

There are a number of medications commonly used in oncology where pharmacogenomics may play a significant role regarding personalized management of care. Tamoxifen is a selective estrogen receptor modulator commonly used in oncology as a chemopreventive measure for individuals at risk for breast cancer. It is also used as an adjuvant chemotherapy drug for certain individuals with ER+ breast cancer tumors. However, individual genetic variation particularly regarding the cytochrome P450 2D6 (CYP2D6) enzyme, have been found to influence metabolism of tamoxifen to endoxifen, an important process for therapeutic success regarding disease-free survival (Trojan, Vergopoulos, Breitenstein, Tausch, Seifert, & Joechle, 2013). Certain variants (SNPs) of this gene have been found to result in poor metabolism of tamoxifen to endoxifen, consequently affecting therapeutic response of the drug in reducing breast cancer recurrence and disease-free survival. Approximately 5% to 7% of European and North American populations are considered to be poor metabolizers of tamoxifen. In addition, the concomitant use of certain medications such as antidepressants (e.g., paroxetine and fluoxetine) also is known to inhibit CYP2D6. Antidepressants are frequently used for antidepression or for hot flushes, a common experience in some women who also may be taking tamoxifen therapy. Because of some inconsistent studies, currently *CYP2D6* genotyping is not currently recommended as a standard of care for individuals with breast cancer treated with tamoxifen. Assessment of concomitant medications such as antidepressants with tamoxifen should be reviewed and alternative medications (e.g., aromatase inhibitors) may be warranted.

Irinotecan is a topoisomerase I inhibitor frequently used to treat colorectal as well as other forms of cancers. It is also combined with other cancer chemotherapeutic agents to include FOLFIRI (leucovorin, 5-flurouracil, irinotecan, and cetuximab or oxaliplatin). Irenotecan has been associated with dose-limiting toxicities, including severe diarrhea and life-threatening neutropenia (grade IV). Irinotecan is metabolized by a crucial drug metabolizer uridine 5′diphosphoglucuronosyl-transferase (UGTIA1) enzyme and certain variations of the *UGTIA1* gene may cause poor metabolism and adverse response to therapy (Ando, Fujita, Sasaki, & Hasegawa,

2007). Specifically, individuals homozygote for the allele *UGTIA1*28* have been associated with poor metabolism and adverse drug response, and currently the Federal Drug Administration has revised the package insert of irinotecan in order to warn of the association between toxicity and *UGTIA1*28* (Ando et al., 2007). Molecular assays are currently available for genotyping *UGTIA1*.

Thiopurines (e.g., azathioprine and 6-mercaptopurine [6-MP]) are also drug agents used in oncology care, primarily for the treatment of hematologic malignancies. ThiopurineS methyltransferase (TPMT) is an enzyme that metabolizes the thiopurines 6-mercaptopurine, 6thioguanine, and azathioprine, drugs that are widely used for treatment of many hematologic cancers such as acute leukemia, as well as certain other medical conditions. The enzyme has been found to be associated with genetic variation in the *TPMT* gene. Certain variations in the gene have led to reduced protein activity and half-life, with the potential for severe toxic or inadequate drug effect (Mladosievicova, Dzurenkova, Sufliarska, & Carter, 2011). Genotyping and phenotyping assays are available to determine the status of TPMT. Genotyping focuses on genetic variation, particularly *TPMT*2*, *3A*, and *3C* variants, whereas phenotyping focuses on TPMT function and status and not genetic variation. Testing has the potential to reduce or eliminate toxicities associated with the use of azathioprine and maximize its safety and efficacy when treating specific disorders, including cancer.

15.6.4. Direct-to-Consumer Testing—and Cancer Genetics

A wide-range of direct-to-consumer (DCT) tests have been available to the public marketed for an individual's personal choice in providing genetic information on a variety of medical, pharmacogenomic, and hereditary issues, including information on ancestry. These tests have been sold directly to consumers via a variety of venues, including television, internet, or other marketing strategies, without consultation of health care professionals (Su, 2013). Many DCT tests involve diverse genetic tests, with some including analyses of certain cancer genes. DCTs have been available, often at low costs and

easy to administer, with most requiring only saliva for testing. Further, the availability of DCT
tests has not warranted a prescription by health
care providers. Although DCT tests can provide
individual *autonomy* in decision-making for
knowledge of one's genetic make-up and disease
risk, the use of these tests can result in pitfalls
and significant challenges, including results interpretation and clinical applicability. Results
interpretation is significant, because DTC tests
do not involve important data collection that is
essential for evaluating appropriate risk assessment, including personal and family history.
Another concern is that many DTC tests examine DNA variants, which typically have a minimal risk impact and account for only a fraction
of the heritable component of cancer (Bellcross,
Page, & Meaney-Delman, 2012). Moreover,
interpretation of these variant findings can be
complex, particularly in asymptomatic patients
in which genetic testing would not be routinely
indicated, resulting in challenges in test interpretation for health care providers. This is significant, because studies have shown that many
patients who personally order DTC tests rely on
their health care providers to interpret DTC test
findings (Darst, Madlensky, Schork, Topol, &
Bloss, 2014).

At present, DTC tests do not meet professional guidelines (e.g., American Society of Clinical
Oncologists) regarding genetic testing, because
these tests are patient prescribed, lacking essential criteria for genetic testing, that of pre- and
post-test counseling, clinical utility and applicability, interpretability of findings, and personal
and/or family history, all important criteria when
suspecting individuals for an inherited cancer
predisposition (Robson et al., 2010). Further,
there are additional concerns for many DTC tests
regarding safety, effectiveness, associated risks,
and clinical utility. In November 2013, the U.S.
Food and Drug Administration (FDA) sent out
warning letters to certain DTC test companies
regarding marketing of these genetic tests (U.S.
Department of Health & Human Services, U.S.
FDA, 2013).

In summary, advanced technology and research discoveries in genomic sequencing methods have led to continuous cost reductions, opening the door to the future era of fully sequencing
the human genome and leading to further break-
throughs in personalized care. Nurses at all
levels of health care working in oncology must
understand genomic science and how it will be
integrated into clinical practice, as well as its impact on the social, ethical, and legal implications
for individuals, families, and communities. This
requires that nurses keep current on this rapidly
changing field and integrate new evidence-based
genetic and genomic information into practice at
all levels of nursing care.

15.6.5. Important Addendum, Direct-to-Consumer Genetic Testing

Since the initial writing of this chapter a new
direct-to-consumer (DTC) test for breast cancer
genes to test to the masses has become available
at reduced costs ($249.00 to date). This test of-
fers testing via saliva for 19 genes known to be
correlated with higher risk of breast and ovarian cancer including mutations in the *BRCA*
genes. It is recommended that the reader become
knowledgeable and keep abreast of this new
DTC testing regarding its acceptability, use in
clinical practice, decision-making, and ethical,
legal and social implications. More information
on this test can be found on the website https://
getcolor.com. Reader is recommended to review
other data and publications pertaining to the test
as needed regarding decision-making.

15.7. UTILIZATION OF THE RAPID APPROACH: SELECTED BREAST CANCER CASE

In-depth assessment and targeted physical examination is integral in the risk assessment process, including evaluating individuals suspect
for hereditary cancer syndromes. This chapter
concludes with the use of the RAPID approach
discussed in Chapter 2 of this text and how it may
be applied to a fictitious case suspect for an inherited cancer syndrome.

Figure 15.20 depicts a 4-generation pedigree
with the proband, a 46-year-old white female of
Italian/Greek and Northern European ancestry
with a 6-month history of diagnosed invasive
breast cancer, Stage I, *ER, PR*, and *Her2neu* positive tumor. She had comprehensive *BRCA* genetic testing with uninformative (negative) results.
She was referred to an advanced practice nurse

practitioner with specialization and training in genetics for further evaluation and genetic counseling. The RAPID approach (see Chapter 2) was conducted focusing on *data collection*, with an in-depth personal and family history, including a 4-generation pedigree (see Figure 15.21). All medical and surgical records were reviewed, and further assessment data were obtained that entailed a circumference of the head and skin and thyroid examination. Besides the early-age onset of breast cancer, the data collection identified additional red flags, including enlarged head circumference (59 centimeters) and mucocutaneous lesions consistent with trichilemmomas on the facial area. The family history also revealed red flags suggestive of a high probability for an inherited cancer syndrome. The proband's mother had a history of 2 primary cancers, including

breast cancer diagnosed at age 50 years and renal cancer at age 56 years; a brother with follicular thyroid cancer at age 33 years; a sister with fibrocystic breast disease and uterine fibroids; a maternal aunt with uterine fibroids and metastatic endometrial cancer diagnosed at age 46 years; and a maternal grandmother with early-age onset breast cancer, diagnosed at age 45 years (see Figure 15.20). These diagnoses were confirmed with pathology reports and death certificates. Based upon *identified red flags*, the proband had pretest counseling for Cowden's syndrome, including recommendation for *PTEN* genetic testing. The identified red flags based upon assessment data included the following: (1) Three generations of early-age onset breast cancer on the maternal lineage (AD pattern); (2) history of 2 primary cancers on the maternal lineage in the mother; (3)

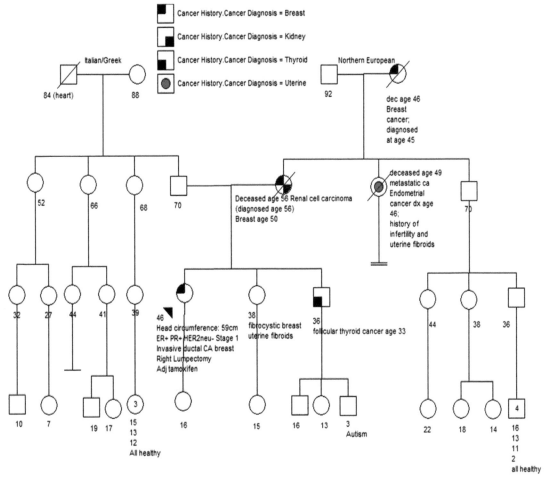

FIGURE 15.20. Four-generation pedigree suspect for an inherited cancer syndrome (Cowden's syndrome) with numerous red flags and an autosomal pattern of inheritance for breast cancer. Proband depicted by arrowhead.

family history of cancers consistent with an inherited cancer syndrome (e.g., *breast cancer, follicular thyroid cancer, endometrial cancer, and renal cancer*); (4) clinical characteristics present on the proband (*macrocephaly ≥ 97th percentile*) with positive history of confirmed breast cancer; *pathognomonic mucocutaneous lesions consistent with trichilemmomas*; and (5) endometrial disease associated with *benign uterine fibroids* and *fibrocystic disease* among family members. Many of the family members on the maternal lineage met criteria for Cowden's syndrome. These criteria included the following: *pathognomonic criteria* for Cowden's syndrome, including mucocutaneous lesions of trichilemmomas of the facial area (proband); *major criteria* for a history of breast cancer (proband, mother, maternal aunt, and maternal grandmother), epithelial thyroid cancer (brother), macrocephaly (confirmed on proband), and endometrial cancer (maternal aunt); and *minor criteria* of uterine fibroids and fibrocystic disease of the breast (Eng, 2014).

Once data collection were obtained, the information was assessed to identify if red flags were present that were suspect for an inherited cancer syndrome. The personal and family history revealed a *high probability* for Cowden's syndrome, because many of the criteria were met for the genetic autosomal disorder. Based upon the assessment data and high probability for Cowden's syndrome, *risk communication* was provided focusing on genetic education, counseling, and *PTEN* genetic testing, while also considering ethical, legal, social, and cultural issues of the individual. After informed consent, genetic *PTEN* testing was conducted that revealed a deleterious mutation for the syndrome. Post-test counseling was implemented including results disclosure, *risk management*, and family implications, including results disclosure (see Figure 15.20). The proband is currently following-up in a high risk clinic for risk management and enhanced surveillance with an interprofessional collaborative team. Table 15.9 provides additional resources that can be used to assist in the assessment process.

TABLE 15.9. *Examples of Online Resources for Understanding the Genomics of Cancer and Hereditary Cancer Syndromes.*

Online Resource	Description	Site Location
GeneReviews™ trademarks of the University of Washington, Seattle.	Expert-authored and peer-reviewed, current disease descriptions that apply genetic testing to the diagnosis, management, and genetic counseling of inherited conditions	http://www.ncbi.nlm.nih.gov/ projects/GeneTests/static/ about/content/reviews.shtml
National Cancer Institute, (NCI), National Institute of Health	A wide-range of cancer topics including hereditary cancer syndromes • *Cancer Genetics Overview*—expert information summary of hereditary cancer and an extensive list of genetics resources including information on genetic counseling, methods of genetic analysis.	http://www.cancer.gov/ http://www.cancer.gov/ cancertopics/pdq/genetics/ overview/healthprofessional
National Comprehensive Cancer Network (NCCN)®	Up-to-date guidelines on a variety of cancer topics including cancer detection, prevention and risk reduction	http://www.nccn. org/professionals/ physician_gls/f_guidelines. asp#detection
National Coalition for Health Professionals in Genetics (NCHPEG)—*Colorectal Cancer is your Patient at High Risk*	Educational program for primary care providers focuses on identification and management of patients at risk of hereditary colorectal cancer (CRC). The program focuses on risk assessment, genetic testing, risk communication, screening and surveillance, and referral.	http://www.nchpeg.org/index. php?option=com_content& view=article&id=331&Item id=223
Online Inheritance in Man (OMIM)	Comprehensive compendium of human genes and genetic phenotypes containing information on all known Mendelian disorders and over 12,000 genes. Database is updated daily and the entries contain links to other genetics resources.	http://www.ncbi.nlm.nih.gov/ omim

FIGURE 15.21. RAPID Approach to Assess Selected Case with Personal and Family History Suspect for an Inherited Cancer Syndrome (Cowden's syndrome).

15.8. REFERENCES

Aarnio, M., Säily, M., Juhola, M., Gylling, A., Peltomäki, P., Järvinen, H.J., & Mecklin, J. P. (2012). Uroepithelial and kidney carcinoma in Lynch syndrome. *Familial Cancer 11*(3), 395–401.

Aarnio, M., Sankila, R., Pukkala, E., Salovaara, R., Aaltonen, L.A., de la Chapelle, A., . . . & Järvinen, H. J. (1999). Cancer risk in mutation carriers of DNA-mismatch-repair genes. *International Journal of Cancer, 81*, 214–218.

Abbas, O., & Mahalingam, M. (2009). Cutaneous sebaceous neoplasms as markers of MuirTorre syndrome: a diagnostic algorithm. *Journal of Cutaneous Pathology, 36*, 613–619. doi: 10.1111/j.1600-0560.2009.01248.

Abdel-Rahman, W. M., Mecklin, J. P., & Peltomäki, P. (2006). The genetics of HNPCC: Application to diagnosis and screening. *Clinical Reviews in Oncology/Hematology, 58*(3), 208–220.

Agalliu, I., Gern, R., Leanza, S., & Burk, R.D. (2009). Associations of high-grade prostate cancer with BRCA1 and BRCA2 founder mutations. *Clinical Cancer Research, 15*(3), 1112–1120. doi: 10.1158/1078-0432.CCR-08-1822.

Agarwal, P., Kabir, F.M.L., DeInnocentes, P., & Bird, R. C. (2012). Tumor suppressor gene p16/INK4A/CDKN2A and its role in cell cycle exit, differentiation and determination of cell fate. In Cheng, Y. ed. *Tumor Suppressor Genes*. Croatia: InTech. Retrieved from http://www.intechopen.com/books/tumor-suppressor-genes

Agendia (2015). *Mammaprint® 70-Gene Breast Cancer Recurrence Assay*. Retrieved from http://www.agendia.com/healthcare-professionals/breast-cancer/mammaprint/

Al-Sohaily, S., Biankin, A., Leong, R., Kohonen-Corish, M., & Warusavitarne, J. (2012). Molecular pathways in colorectal cancer. *Journal of Gastroenterology and Hepatology, 27*(9), 1423–1431. doi: 10.1111/j.1440-1746.2012.07200.

Alberts, B., Johnson, A., Lewis, J., Raff, M., Roberts, K., & Walter, P. (2008a). Specialized tissues, stem cells, and tissue renewal, Chapter 25. In *Molecular Biology of the Cell*, 5thed. New York: Garland Science, Taylor & Francis Group, LLC.

Alberts, B., Johnson, A., Lewis, J., Raff, M., Roberts, K., & Walter, P. (2008b). Cancer. Chapter 20, pp. 1205–1265. In *Molecular Biology of the Cell*, 5th ed. New York: Garland Science, Taylor & Francis Group, LLC.

Alberts, B., Johnson, A., Lewis, J., Raff, M., Roberts, K., & Walter, P. (2008c). The cell cycle. pp. 1053-1114. In *Molecular Biology of the Cell*, 5th ed. New York: Garland Science, Taylor & Francis Group, LLC.[TG9]

Alberts, B., Johnson, A., Lewis, J., Raff, M., Roberts, K., & Walter, P. (2008d). Control of gene expression pp. 493-495. In *Molecular Biology of the Cell*, 5th ed. New York: Garland Science, Taylor & Francis Group, LLC.

Ali-Khan, S.E., Daar, A. S., Shuman, C., Ray, P. N., & Scherer, S. W. (2009). Whole genome scanning: esolving clinical diagnosis and management amidst complex data. *Pediatric Research, 66*(4), 357–363. doi: 10.1203/PDR.0b013e3181b0cbd8.

Ambry Genetics. (2014-2015.). Colonext. Retrieved from http://ambrygen.com/tests/colonext.

Ambry Genetics. (nd). *Hereditary Cancer Panels-Clinical Guide.* 503391463_v1.

American Cancer Society. (2015). *Cancer Facts and Figures 2015.* Atlanta: American Cancer Society.

American Cancer Society. (2014). *Cancer Facts and Figures 2014.* Atlanta: American Cancer Society.

American Cancer Society. (2012). Lifetime risk of developing or dying from cancer. Retrieved from http://www.cancer.org/cancer/cancerbasics/lifetime-probability-of-developing-or-dying-from-cancer.

American Cancer Society. Breast Cancer Facts & Figures 2013-2014. (2013-2014). Atlanta: American Cancer Society, Inc. Retrieved from www.cancer.org/acs/groups/content@research/documents/document/acspc-042725.pdf

American Society of Clinical Oncology. (2003). American Society of Clinical Oncology policy statement update: Genetic testing for cancer susceptibility. *Journal of Clinical Oncology, 21*(12), 2397–2406.

Anand, P., Kunnumakkara, A.B., Sundaram, C., Harikumar, K.B., Tharakan, S. T., Lai, O. S., . . . & Aggarwal, B. B. (2008). Cancer is a preventable disease that requires major lifestyle changes. *Pharmacology Research, 25*(9), 2097-2116. doi:10.1007/211095-008-9661-9. Retrieved from www.ncbi.nlm.nih.gov/pmc/articles/PMC2515569

Ando, Y., Fujita, K., Sasaki, Y., & Hasegawa, Y. (2007). UGT1AI*6 and UGT1A1*27 for individualized irinotecan chemotherapy. *Current Opinions in Molecular Therapy, 9*(3), 258–262.

Antoniou, A.C., Pharoah, P. D., Narod, S., Risch, H.A., Eyfjord, J. E., Hopper, J. L., . . . & Easton, D. F. (2005). Breast and ovarian cancer risks to carriers of the *BRCA1* 5382insC and 185delAG and *BRCA2* 6174delT mutations: A combined analysis of 22 population based studies. *Journal of Medical Genetics, 42*, 602–603.

Antoniou, A., Pharoah, P. D., Narod, S., Risch, H.A., Eyfjord, J.E., Hopper, J.L., ... & Easton, D. F. (2003). Average risks of breast and ovarian cancer associated with *BRCA1* or *BRCA2* mutations detected in case series unselected for family history: A combined analysis of 22 studies. American Journal of Human Genetics, 75(5), 1117–1130.

Aretz, S., Vasen, H. R. A., & Olschwang, S. (2011). Clinical utility gene card for: [TG10]Familial adenomatous polyposis (FA) and attenuated FAP (AFAP). *European Journal of Human Genetics 19.* doi:10.1038/ejhg.2011.7 (online). Retrieved from www.nature.com/ejhg/journal/v19/n7/full/ejhg20117a.html

Araghany, T., Wilson, J. D., Chu, Q., & Mills, G. (2012). Genetic alterations in colorectal cancer. *Gastrointestinal Cancer Research, 5*(1), 19–27.

Arrington, A[TG11]. K., Heinrich, E. L., Lee, W., Duldulao, M., Patel, S., Sanchez, J., Garcia-Aguilar J. & Kim, J. (2012). Prognostic and predictive roles of *KRAS* mutation in colorectal cancer. *International Journal of Molecular Science, 13*(10), 12153-12168. doi: 10.3390/ijms131012153.

Ashfaq. R. (2012). Molecular profiling for personalized care. *Clinical & Experimental Metastasis, 29*(7), 653–655. Retrieved from www.ncbi.nlm.nih.gov/pmc/articles/PMC3484311/.

Ashworth, A., Lord, C. J. & Reis-Filho, J. S. (2011). Genetic interactions in cancer progression and treatment. *Cell, 145*, 30–38.

Baba, A. I. & Câtoi, C. (2007). Comparative oncology. In Chapter 3, *Tumor Cell Morphology.* Bucharest: The Publishing House of the Romanian Academy. Retrieved from http://www.ncbi.nlm.nihgov/books/NBK9553/.

Beamer, L.C., Grant, M. L., Espenschied, C. R. , Blazer, K. R. , Hampel, H. L., Weitzel, J.N & MacDonald, D. J. (2012). Reflex immunohistochemistry and microsatellite instability testing of colorectal tumors for Lynch syndrome among US cancer programs and follow-up of abnormal results. *Journal of Clinical Oncology, 30*(10), 1058–1063. doi: 10.1200/JCO.2011.38.4719. Epub 2012 Feb 21.

Bellcross, C. A., Page, P. Z. & Meaney-Delman, D. (2012). Direct-to-consumer personal genome testing and cancer risk prediction. *Journal of Cancer, 18*(4), 293–302. doi: 10.1097/PPO.0b013e3182610e38.

Berliner, J. L., Fay, A.M., Cummings, S. A., Burnett, B., Tillmanns, T. (2013). NSGC Practice Guideline: Risk Assessment and Genetic Counseling for Hereditary Breast and Ovarian Cancer. *Journal of*

Genetic Counseling, 22(2), 155–63. doi: 10.1007/ s10897-012-9547-1. Epub 2012 Nov 28.

Bignon, Y-J. (2004). Biological basis of cancer predisposition. In Eeles, R.A., Easton, D.F., Ponder, B.A.J & Eng, C. (editors), *Genetic Predisposition to Cancer*, 2nd ed. London: Arnold.

Bisgaard, M.L., Fenger, K., Bülow, S., Niebuhr, E. & Mohr, J. (1994). Familial adenomatous polyposis (FAP): Frequency, penetrance, and mutation rate. *Human Mutation, 3*(2), 121–125.

Boland, R. C. (2007). Clinical uses of microsatellite instability testing in colorectal cancer: An ongoing challenge. *Journal of Clinical Oncology, 25*(7), 754-756.

Bolocan, A., Ion, D., Stoian, R. V. & Serban, M. B. (2011). MAP syndrome (MYH associated polyposis) colorectal cancer, etiopathological connections. *Journal of Medicine and Life, 4*(1), 109–111.

Bosserman, L. D. (2008). Genetic testing and management of patients with *BRCA1/2*-positive breast and ovarian cancers. *Community Oncology, 5*(Supplement 1), 2–7.

Bowtell, D.D. (2010). The genesis and evolution of high-grade serous ovarian cancer. Nature Reviews Cancer, 10(11), 803-808. doi: 10.1038/nrc2946.

Brand, R., Nielsen, M., Lynch, H. & Infante, E. (2012, Oct 4, Initial posting). *MUTYH-associated polyposis*. In: Pagon, R. A., Adam, M. P., Ardinger, H. H. *et al.*, eds. GeneReviews ® [Internet]. Seattle (WA): University of Washington, Seattle; 1993–2014. Retrieved from http://www.ncbi.nlm.nih.gov/books/ NBK107219.

Burt, R. W. (2003). Gastric fundic gland polyps. *Gastroenterology, 125*(5), 1462–1469.

Campbell, L.L. & Polyak, K. (2007). Breast tumor heterogeneity: Cancer stem cells or clonal evolution? *Cell Cycle, 6*(19), 2332–2338. doi:10.4161/ cc.6.19.4914.

Campisi, J. (2005). Senescent Cells, tumor Suppression, and organismal aging: Good citizens, bad neighbors. *Cell, 120*(4), 513–522.

Cankaya, A. B., Erdem, M. A., Isler, S. C., Cifter, M., Olgac, V., Kasapoglu, C. & Oral, C. K. (2012). Oral and maxillofacial considerations in Gardner's Syndrome. *International Journal of Medical Science, 9*(2), 137–141. doi: 10.7150/ijms.3989. Epub 2012 Jan 7.

Chandar, N. & Viselli, S. (2010). The eukaryotic genome. In Harvey, R. A. (series editor), *Cell and Molecular Biology*. Philadelphia: Wolters Kluwer/ Lippincott Williams & Wilkins.

Chen, H., Hardy, T.M., Tollefsbol, T.O. (2011). Epigenomics of ovarian cancer and its chemoprevention. *Frontier in Epigenomics, 2*(67) [Open access]. Retrieved from http://www.frontiersin.org/Epigenomics/10.3389/fgene.2011.00067/abstract.

Chen, S. & Parmigiani, G. (2007). Meta-analysis of BRCA1 and BRCA2 penetrance. *Journal of Clinical Oncology, 25*(11), 1329–1333.

Chen, C. S., Phillips, K. D., Grist, S., Bennett, G., Craig, J.E., Muecke, J.S. & Suthers, G. K. (2006). Congenital hypertrophy of the retinal pigment epithelium (CHRPE) in familial colorectal cancer. *Familial Cancer, 5*(4), 397–404.

Chial, H. (2008a). Proto-oncogenese to oncogenes to cancer. Nature Education, 1(1), 33. Retrieved from http://www.nature.com/scitable/topicpage/proto-oncogenes-to-oncogenes-to-cancer-883.

Chial, H. (2008b). Tumor suppressor genes (TS) and the two-hit hypothesis. (2008). *Nature Education, 1*(1) Retrieved from http://www.nature.com/scitable/topicpage/tumor-suppressor-ts-genes-and-the-two-887.

Chow, A. Y. (2010). Cell cycle control by oncogenes and tumor suppressors: driving the transformation of normal cells into cancerous cells. *Nature Education, 3*(9):7. Retrieved from http://www.nature.com/scitable/topicpage/cell-cycle-control-by-oncogenes-and-tumro-14191459.

Claes, K., Dahan, K., Teipar, S., De Paepe, A., Bonduelle, M., Abramowicz, M., Verellen, C…Kartheuser, A. (2011). The genetics of familial adenomatous polyposis (FAP) and MutYH-associated polyposis (MAP) *Acta Gastro-Enterologica Belgica, 74*(3), 421–426.

Clarke, M.F., Dick, J.E., Dirks, P.B., Eaves, C.J., Jamieson, C.H.M., Jones, D.L., . . . Wahl, G.M. (2006). Cancer stem cells—Perspectives on current status and future directions: AACR workshop on cancer stem cells. *Cancer Research, 66*; doi 10.1158/0008-5472.CAN-06-3126. [online]. Retrieved from http://cancerres.aacrjournals.org/content/66/19/9339.full.

Croce, C.M. (2008). Oncogenes and cancer. *New England Journal of Medicine, 358*, 502-311.

Culver, J., Lowstutter, K. & Bowling, L. (2006-2007). Assessing breast cancer risk and BRCA1/2 carrier probability. *Breast Disease, 27*, 5–20.

Darst, B. F., Madlensky, L., Schork, N. J. , Topol, E. J. & Bloss , C. S. (2014). Characteristics of genomic test consumers who spontaneously share results with their health care provider. *Health Communications, 23*(1). doi: 10.1080/10410236.2012.717216.

Das, P.M. & Singal, R. (2004). DNA methylation and cancer. *Journal of Clinical Oncology, 22*(22), 4632–4642.

De Abreu, F. B., Schwartz, G.N., Wells, W. A. & Tsongalis, G. J. (2014). Personalized therapy for breast cancer. *Clinical Genetics, 86*,(1), 62–67.

de la Chapelle, A. & Hampel, H. (2010). Clinical relevance of microsatellite instability in colorectal cancer. *Journal of Clinical Oncology, 28*(20): 3380–3887.

Deininger, P. (1999). Genetic instability in cancer: Caretaker and gatekeeper genes. *The Ochsner Journal, 1*(4). 206–209.

Duffy, M.J. & Crown, J. (2014). Precision treatment for cancer: Role of prognostic and predictive markers. *Informa Healthcare, 51*(1), 30–45. doi:10.310 9/10408363.2013.865700. Retrieved from http://informahealthcare.com/doi/abs/10.3109/10408363. 2013.865700.

Dutton-Regester K & Hayward, N. K. (2012). Whole genome and exome sequencing of melanoma: a step toward personalized targeted therapy. *Advanced Pharmacology, 65*, 399–435. doi: 10.1016/B978-0-12-397927-8.00013-0.

Easton, D.F., Steele, L., Fields, P., Ormiston, W., Averill, D., Daly, P.A., . . . Goldgar, D. E. (1997). Cancer risks in two large breast cancer families linked to BRCA2 on chromosome 13q12-13. *American Journal of Human Genetics, 61*, 120–128.

Edge, S. B. & Compton, C. C. (2010). The American Joint Committee on Cancer: the 7th edition of the AJCC Cancer Staging Manual and the future of TNM. *Annals of Surgical Oncology, 17*, 1471–1474.

Edwards, B.K., Noone, A-M., Mariotto, A.B., Simard, E.P., Boscoe, F.P., Henley, J., . . . Ward, E.M. (2014). Annual report to the Nation on the status of cancer 1975–2010, featuring prevalence of comorbidity and impact on survival among persons with lung, colorectal, breast, or prostate cancer. *Cancer, 120*(9), 1290–1314.

Eheman, C., Henley, J., Ballard-Barbaseh, R., Jacobs, E.J., Schymura, M.J., Noone, 1-M., Pan, L., . . . Edwards, B.K. (2012). Annual report to the nation on the status of cancer, 1975–2008, featuring cancers associated with excess weight and lack of sufficient physical activity. *Cancer. 118*(9). doi: 10.1002/cncr.27514.

Eisen, A., Lubinski, J., Klijn, J., Moller, P., Lynch, H. T., Offit, K., . . . Narod, S.A. (2005). Breast cancer risk following bilateral oophorectomy in *BRCA1* and *BRCA2* mutation carriers: an international case–control study. *Journal of Clinical Oncology, 23*(30), 7491–7496.

Eng, C. (2014, January 23 updated [initial posting November 29, 2001]). PTEN Hamartoma Tumor Syndrome (PHTS). In: Pagon, R. A., Adam, M. P., Ardinger, H. H., *et al.*, editors. *GeneReviews®* [Internet]. Seattle (WA): University of Washington, Seattle; 1993–2014. Retrieved from: http://www.ncbi.nlm.nih.gov/books/NBK1488/.

Entius, M., Keller, J., Drilenburg, P., Kuypers, K., Giardiello, F. & Offerhaus, G. (2000). Microsatellite instability and expression of *Hmlh-1* and *Hmsh-2* in sebaceous gland carcinomas as markers for Muir Torre syndrome. *Clinical Cancer Research, 6*, 1784–1789.

Evaluation of Genomic Applications in Practice and Prevention (EGAPP) Working Group. (2009). Recommendations from the EGAPP Working Group: genetic testing strategies in newly diagnosed individuals with colorectal cancer aimed at reducing morbidity and mortality from Lynch syndrome in relatives. *Genetics in Medicine, 11*(1), 35–41.

Evers, B. & Jonkers, J. (2006). Mouse models of BRCA1 and BRCA2 deficiency: past lessons, current understanding and future prospects. *Oncogene, 25*(43), 5885–5897.

Fecteau, H., Vogel, K.J., Hanson, K. & Morrill-Cornelius, S. (2014). The evolution of cancer risk assessment in the era of next generation sequencing. *Journal of Genetic Counseling, 23*(4), 633–639.

Finch, A., Evans, G. & Narod, S. A. (2012). BRCA carriers, prophylactic salpingo-ophorectomy and menopause: clinical management considerations and recommendations. *Women's Health, 8*(5), 543–555.

Finch, A., Beiner, M., Lubinski, J., Lynch, H.T., Moller, P., Rosen, B., . . . Narod, S.A (2006). Salpingo-oophorectomy and the risk of ovarian, fallopian tube, and peritoneal cancers in women with a *BRCA1* or *BRCA2* mutation. *Journal of the American Medical Association. 296*(2), 185–192.

Ford, D. Easton, D. F., Stratton, M., Narod, S., Goldgar, D., Devilee, P., . . . Zelada-Hedman, M., *et al.* (1998). Genetic heterogeneity and penetrance analysis of the BRCA1 and BRCA2 genes in breast cancer families. The Breast Cancer Linkage Consortium. *American Journal of Human Genetics, 62*(3): 676–689.

Foulkes, W. D. (2008). Inherited susceptibility to common cancers. *The New England Journal of Medicine, 359*(20), 2143–2153. doi:10.1056/NEJMra0802968.

Frank, S. A. (2007). Multistage progression. In *Dynamics of Cancer: Incidence, Inheritance, and Evolution*, Chapter 3. Princeton (NJ): Princeton University Press. Retrieved from http://www.ncbi.nlm.nih.gov/books/NBK1562/.

Frank, T.S. (2001). Hereditary cancer syndromes. *Archives of Pathology & Laboratory Medicine, 125*(1), 85–90.

Friedländer, M.R., Lizano, E., Houben, A. J., Bezdan, D., Báñez-Coronel, M., . . . Estivill, X. (2014). Evidence for the biogenesis of more than 1,000 novel human microRNAs. *Genome Biology, 15*(4). Retrieved from http://genomebiology.com/content/15/4/R57/.

Gail, M. H., Brinton, L. A., Byar, D. P., Corle, D. K., Green, S. B., Schairer, C. & Mulvihill, J. 1J. (1989). Projecting individualized probabilities of developing breast cancer for white females who are being examined annually. *Journal of National Cancer Institute, 81*(24), 1879–1886.

Gao, X. & Edwards, T.L. (2011). Genome-wide association studies: where we are heading? *World Journal of Medical Genetics, (1)*, 23–35.

Garber, J. E. & Offit, K. (2005). Hereditary cancer predisposition syndromes. *Journal of Clinical Oncology, 23*(2), 276–292.

Garnett, M.J., Edelman, E.J., Heidorn, S. J., Greenman, C.D., Dastur, A., Lau, K.W., . . . Mitropoulos, X (2012) Systematic identification of genomic markers of drug sensitivity in cancer cells. *Nature, 483,* 570–575.

Garzon, R., Calin, G. A. & Croce, C.M. (2009). MicroRNAs in cancer. *Annual Review of Medicine, 60,* 167–179.

Geiersbach, K. B. & Samowitz, W. S. (2011). MSI and colorectal cancer. *Archives of Pathology and Laboratory Medicine, 135*(10), 1269–1277. doi: 10.5858/arpa.2011-0035-RA.

GeneDx. (2014). *Breast and Ovarian Cancer—A Guide for Clinicians.* Gaithersburg, MD

Gigek, C.O., Chen, E. S., Calcagno, D. Q., Wisnieski, F., Burbano, R.R. & Smith, M.A (2012). Epigenetic mechanisms in gastric cancer. *Epigenomics, 4*(3), 279–294. doi: 10.2217/epi.12.22.

Gil, J., Stembalska, A., Pesz, K.A., Sasiadek, M.M. (2008). Cancer stem cells: the theory and perspective in cancer therapy. *Journal of Applied Genetics, 49*(2), 193–199.

Ginsburg, G. S & Willard, H. F. (2009). Genomic and personalized medicine: foundations and applications. *Translational Research, 154*(6), 277–287. doi: 10.1016/j.trsl.2009.09.005.

Goldthwaite, C. A. (2011). Are stem cells involved in cancer? In National Institute of Health Stem Cell Information. Retrieved from http://stemcells.nih.gov/info/Regenerative_Medicine/2006chapter9.htm.

Gonzalez-Angulo, A. M., Timms, K. M., Liu, S., Chen, H., Litton, J. K., Potter, J.,...Meric-Bernstam, F. (2011). Incidence and outcome of BRCA mutations in unselected patients with triple receptor-negative breast cancer. *Clinical Cancer Research. 17*(5), 1082–1089. doi: 10.1158/1078-0432. CCR-10-2560.

Graeser, M. K., Engel, C., Rhiem, K., Gadzicki, D., Bick, U., Kasl, K., . . . Schmultzer, R. K. (2009). Contralateral breast cancer risk in *BRCA1* and *BRCA2* mutation carriers. *Journal of Clinical Oncology, 27*(35), 5887–5892. doi:10.1200JCO-2008.19.9430.

Greaves, M. & Maley, C. C. (2012). Clonal evolution in cancer. *Nature, 481*(7381), 306–313.

Gruber, S. B. (2006). New development in Lynch syndrome (hereditary nonpolyposis colorectal cancer) and mismatch repair gene testing. *Gastroenterology, 130*(2), 577–588.

Gruber, S. B. & Kohlmann, W. (2003). The genetics of hereditary non-polyposis colorectal cancer. *Journal of National Comprehensive Cancer Network, 1*(1), 137–144.

Gullapalli, R. R., Desai, K. V., Santana-Santos, L., Kant, J. A. & Becich, M. J. (2012). Next generation sequencing in clinical medicine: Challenges and lessons for pathology and biomedical informatics. *Journal of Pathology Informatics, 3*(40). doi: 10.4103/2153-3539.103013. Retrieved from http://www.ncbi.nlm.nih.gov/pmc/articles/PMC3519097/.

Györffy, B., Hatzis, C., Sanft, T., Hofstatter, E., Aktas, B., & Pusztai, L. (2015). Multigene prognostic tests in breast cancer: past, present, future. *Breast Cancer Research: BCR, 17*(1), 11. doi:10.1186/s13058-015-0514-2. Retrieved from http://www.ncbi.nlm.nih.gov/pmc/articles/PMC4307898/.

Haile, R. W., Thomas, D. C., McGuire, V., Felberg, A., John, E.M., Milne, R.L., . . . Whittemore, A. S. (2006). *BRCA1* and *BRCA2* mutation carriers, oral contraceptive use, and breast cancer before age 50. *Cancer Epidemiology, Biomarkers and Prevention, 15*(10), 1863–1870.

Haidle, J. L. & Howe, J. R. (2014 last updated May 22. [initial posting 2003, May 13]). Juvenile polyposis syndrome. In: Pagon RA, Adam, M. P., Ardinger, H.E., *et al.*, editors. *GeneReviews®* [Internet]. Seattle (WA): University of Washington, Seattle; 1993–2014. Retrieved from: http://www.ncbi.nlm.nih.gov/books/NBK1469/.

Half, E., Bercovich, D. & Rozen, P. (2009). Familial adenomatous polyposis. *Orphanet Journal of Rare Diseases, 4,* 22. Retrieved from http://www.ojrd.com/content/4/1/22.

Hall, J. M., Friedman, L, Guenther, C., Lee, M.K., Weber, J.L., Black, D.M., & King, M.C. (1992). Closing in on a breast cancer gene on chromosome 17q. *American Journal of Human Genetics, 50*(6), 1235–1242.

Hampel, H., Frankel, W.L., Martin, E., Arnold, M., Khanduja K., . . . de le Chappelle, A. (2008). Feasibility of screening for Lynch syndrome among patients with colorectal cancer. *Journal of Clinical Oncology, 26,* 5783–5788.

Hampel, H., Frankel, W.L., Martin, E., Arnold, M., Khanduja, K., Kuebler, P., . . . de la Chapelle, A. (2005). Screening for Lynch Syndrome (hereditary nonpolyposis colorectal cancer). *The New England Journal of Medicine, 352*(18), 1851–1860.

Han, L., shi, S., Gong, T., Zhang, Z. & Sun, X. (2012). Cancer stem cells: therapeutic implications and perspectives in cancer therapy. *Acta Pharmaceutic Sinica B, 3*(2), 65–75.

Harfe, B. D. & Jinks-Robertson, S. (2000). DNA Mismatch repair and genetic instability. *Annual Review of Genetics, 34,* 359–399.

Hawkins, N. J. & Ward, R. L. (2001). Sporadic colorectal cancers with microsatellite instability and their possible origin in hyperplastic polyps and serrated adenomas. *Journal of the National Cancer Institute, 93*(17), 1307–1313.

Hindorff, L. A. Sethupathy, P., Junkins, H. A., Ramos, E.M., Mehtar, J.P. Collins, F. S. & Manolio, T. A. (2009). Potential etiologic and functional implications of genome-wide association loci for human diseases and traits. *PNAS Early Edition,* 1-6. Retrieved from http://www.genome.gov/Pages/About/OD/NewsAndFeatures/PNASGWASOnlineCatalog.pdf.

Hochstrasser, M. (1996). Ubiquitin-dependent protein

degradation. *Annual Review of Genetics, 30*, 405–439. doi: 10.1146/annurev.geneti.30.1.405.

Insel, R. (2011). *Director's Blog: Improving Diagnosis through Precision Medicine*. Retrieved from National Institute of Health, National Institute of Mental Health (online) http://www.nimh.nih.gov/about/director/2011/improving-diagnosis-through-precision-medicine.shtml.

Iodice, S., Barile, M., Rotmensz, N., Feroce, I., Bonanni, B., Radice, P., . . . Gandini, S. (2010). Oral contraceptive use and breast or ovarian cancer risk in *BRCA1/2* carriers: a meta-analysis. *European Journal of Cancer, 46*(12), 2275–2284. doi: 10.1016/j.ejca.2010.04.018.

Jasperson, K. & Burt, R. W. (2014,[Updated March 27, 2014]). *APC*-associated polyposis conditions. In: Pagon, R. A., Adam, M. P., Ardinger, H. H., *et al.*, editors, *GeneReviews®* (Internet). Seattle (WA): University of Washington, Seattle; 1993–2014. Retrieved from http://www.ncbi.nlm.nih.gov/books/NBK1345.

Jasperson, K., Tuohy, T. M., Nekalason, D. W. & Burt, R. W. (2010). Hereditary and familial colon cancer. *Gastroenterology, 238*, 2044–2058.

Jeschke, J., Van Neste, L., Glöckner, S.C., Dhir, M., Calmon, M.F., Deregowski, V., . . . Ahuja, N. (2012). Biomarkers for detection and prognosis of breast cancer identified by a functional hypermethylome screen. *Epigenetics, 7*(7), 701–709.

Kastrinos, F. & Syngal, S. (2012). Screening patients with colorectal cancer for Lynch syndrome: What are we waiting for? *Journal of Clinical Oncology, 30*(10), 1024–1027.

Kauff, N.D., Satagopan, J.M., Robson, M.E., Scheuer, L., Hensley, M., Hudis, C. A., . . . Offit, K. (2002). Risk-reducing salpingo-oophorectomy in women with a *BRCA1* or *BRCA2* mutation. *New England Journal of Medicine, 346*(21), 1609–1615.

King, M. C., Marks, J. H., Mandell, J. B., & New York Breast Cancer Study Group (2003). Breast and ovarian cancer risks due to inherited mutations in *BRCA1* and *BRCA2*. *Science, 302*(5645), 643–646.

King, M.C., Wieand, S., Hale, K., Lee, M., Walsh, T., Owens, K., . . . Fisher, B.. (2001). Tamoxifen and breast cancer incidence among women with inherited mutations in *BRCA1* and *BRCA2*: National Surgical Adjuvant Breast and Bowel Project (NSABP-P1) Breast Cancer Prevention Trial. *Journal of the American Medical Association, 286*(18), 2251–2256.

Knudson, A. G. (2001). Two genetic hits (more or less) to cancer. *Nature Reviews, 1*, 157–162.

Kohlman, W. & Gruber, S. B. (Updated 2014, May 22 [initial posting 2004, February 5]). Lynch Syndrome. In Pagon, R. A., Adam, M. P., Ardinger, H. H., *et al.*, editors. *GeneReviews®* (Internet): Seattle (WA): University of Washington, Seattle; 1993–2014. Retrieved from: http://www.ncbi.mlm.nih.gov/books/NBK1211/.

Kovacs, M. E., Papp, J., Szentirmay, Z., Otto, S., Olah, E. (2009). Deletions removing the last exon of TACSTD1 constitute a distinct class of mutations predisposing to Lynch Syndrome. *Human Mutation, 30*(2), 197–203.

Kramer, J. L., Velazquez, I.A., Chen, B. E., Rosenberg, P. S, Struewing, J. P. & Greene, M. H. (2005). Prophylactic oophorectomy reduces breast cancer penetrance during prospective, long-term follow-up of *BRCA1* mutation carriers. *Journal of Clinical Oncology, 23*(34), 8629–8635.

Ku, C. S., Cooper, D. N., Polychronakos, C., Naidoo, N., Wu, M. & Soong, R. (2012). Exome sequencing: dual role as a discovery and diagnostic tool. *Annals of Neurology, 71*(), 5–13. doi.10.1002/ana.22647.

Ladabaum, U., Wang, G., Terdiman, J., Blanco, A., Kuppermann, M., Boland, C. R., . . . Phillips, K.A. (2011). Strategies to identify the Lynch syndrome among patients with colorectal cancer: a cost-effectiveness analysis. *Annals of Internal Medicine, 155*(2), 69–79.

Lange, C.P., Campan, M., Hinoue, T., Schmitz, R.F., van der Meulen-de Jong, A.E., Slingerland, H.,.Laird, P.W. (2012). Genome-scale discovery of DNA-methylation biomarkers for blood-based detection of colorectal cancer. *PLoS One, 7*(11), e50266. doi: 10.1371/journal.pone.0050266. Epub 2012 Nov 28.

Le-Petross, H. T. , Whitman, G. J., Atchley, D. P., Yuan, Y., Gutierrez-Barrera, A., Hortobagyi, G. N. , Litton, J. K. & Arun, B. K. (2011). Effectiveness of alternating mammography and magnetic resonance imaging for screening women with deleterious *BRCA* mutations at high risk of breast cancer. *Cancer, 117*(17), 3900–3907. doi: 10.1002/cncr.25971.

Lee, E., Ma, H., McKean-Cowdin, R., Van Den Berg, D., Bernstein, L., Henderson, B. E., & Ursin G. (2008). Effect of reproductive factors and oral contraceptives on breast cancer risk in BRCA ½ mutation carriers and noncarriers: results from population-based study. *Cancer Epidemiology Biomarkers and Prevention, 17*(11), 3170–3178.

Lee, E., McKean-Cowdin, R., Ma, H., Spicer, D. V., Van Den Berg, D., Bernstein, L, & Ursin, G. (2011). Characteristics of triple-negative breast cancer in patients with a *BRCA1* mutation: results from a population-based study of young women. *Journal of Clinical Oncology, 29*(33), 4373–4380. doi: 10.1200/JCO.2010.33.6446.

Levitt, N.C. & Hickson, I. D. (2002). Caretaker tumor suppressor genes that defend genome integrity. *Trends in Molecular Medicine, 8*(4), 179–186.

Liede, A., Karlan, B. Y. & Narod, S. A. (2004). Cancer risks for male carriers of germline mutations in *BRCA1* or *BRCA2*: A review of the literature. *American Society of Clinical Oncology, 22*(4) 735–742.

Lièvre, A., Bachet, J.B., Boige, V., Cayre, A. , Le Corre, D., Buc, E., . . . Laurent-Puig, P. (2008). KRAS mutations as an independent prognostic factor in patients with advanced colorectal cancer treated with cetuximab. *Journal of Clinical Oncology, 26*(3), 374-379. doi: 10.1200/JCO.2007.12.5906.

Ligtenberg M. J., Kuiper, R.P., Geurts van Kessel, A. & Hoogerbrugge, N. (2013). EPCAM deletion carriers constitute a unique subgroup of Lynch syndrome patients. *Familial Cancer, 12*(2). doi: 1007/s10689-012-9591-x. Retrieved from http://download.springer.com/static/pdf/129/art%253A10.1007%252Fs10689-012-9591-x.pdf?auth66=1363810344_94351c62c106d782d8fbfc2896840a44&ext=.pdf.

Lindor, N. M., Petersen, G. M., Hadley, D. W., Kinney, A. Y., Miesfelt, S., . . . (2006). Recommendations for the care of individuals with an inherited predisposition to Lynch syndrome. *Journal of the American Medical Association, 296*, 1507–1517.

Lodish, H., Berk, A., Zipursky, S.L., Matsudaira, P., Baltimore, D., & Darnell, J. (2000). Proto-oncogenes and tumor suppressor genes, section 24.2. In *Molecular Cell Biology*, 4th ed. New York: W. H. Freeman. Retrieved from http://www.ncbi.nlm.nih.gov/books/NBK21662/.

Lowry, K. P., Lee, J. M., Kong, C.Y., McMahon, P.M., Gilmore, M.E., Cott Chubiz, J.E., . . . Gazelle, G. S. (2012). Annual screening strategies in *BRCA1* and *BRCA2* gene mutation carriers: a comparative effectiveness analysis. *Cancer, 118*(8), 2021–2030.

Lu, K. H., & Broaddus, R. R. (2005). Gynecologic cancers in Lynch syndrome/HNPCC. *Familial Cancer, 4*(3), 249–254.

Lynch, H. T., Lynch, P.M., Lanspa, S.J., Snyder, C. L., Lynch, J. F. & Boland, C.R. (2009) Review of Lynch syndrome: history, molecular genetics, screening, differential diagnosis and medicolegal ramifications. *Clinical Genetics, 76*(2), 1–18. doi: 10.1111/j.1399-0004.2009.01230.x.

Lynch, H. T. & de la Chapelle, A. (2003). Hereditary colorectal cancer. *The New England Journal of Medicine, 348*(10), 919–932.

Lynch, H. T. & Lynch, J. (2000). Lynch syndrome: genetics, natural history, genetic counseling and prevention. *Journal of Clinical Oncology, 18*, 19s–31s.

Maher, E.H. (2013). Genomics and epigenomics of renal cell carcinoma. *Seminar Cancer Biology, 1*, 10–17.

Malumbres, M. & Barbacid, B. (2007). Cell cycle kinases in cancer. *Current Opinions in Genetics and Development, 17*, 60–65.

Mavaddat, N., Barrowdale, D., Andrulis, I. L., Domchek, S. M., Eccles, D. Nevanlinna, H., . . . Antoniou, A. C., Cosortium of Investigators of Modifiers of *BRCA1/2*. (2012). Pathology of breast and ovarian cancers among BRCA1 and *BRCA2* mutation carriers: results from the Consortium of Investigators of Modifiers of *BRCA1/2* (CIMBA). *Cancer Epidemiology and Biomarkers Prevention, 21*(1), 134–147.

McGarrity, T. J., Amos, C., Frazier, M. L. & Wei, C (2013, updated July 25[initial posting 2001, Febr. 23]). Peutz-Jeghers syndrome. In: Pagon, R. A., Adam, M. P., Ardinger, H. E., *et al.*, editors, *GeneReviews*® [Internet]. Seattle (WA): University of Washington, Seattle; 1993–2014. Retrieved from http://www.ncbi.nlm.nih.gov/books/NBK1266/.

McLaughlin, J.R., Risch, H.A., Lubinski, J., Moller, P., Ghadirian, P., . . . Narod, S. A. & Hereditary Ovarian Cancer Clinical Study Group. (2007). Reproductive risk factors for ovarian cancer in carriers of *BRCA1* or *BRCA2* mutations: a case-control study. *Lancet Oncology, 8*(1), 26–34.

Meyer, L.A., Broaddus, R. R. & Lu, K. H. (2009). Endometrial cancer and Lynch syndrome: clinical and pathologic considerations. *Cancer Control, 16*(1), 14–22.

Milanowska, K., Rother, K. & Bujnicki, J. M. (2011). Databases and bioinformatics tools for the study of DNA repair. *Molecular biology International, *Retrieved from www.hindawi.co/journals/mbi/2011/475718/.

Milne, R. L., Knight, J. A., John, E.M., Dite, G. S., Balbuena, R., Ziogas, A., . . . Whittemore, A.S. (2005). Oral contraceptive use and risk of early-onset breast cancer in carriers and noncarriers of *BRCA1* and *BRCA2* mutations. *Cancer Epidemiology and Biomarkers Prevention, 14*(2), 350–356.

Minion, L.E., Dolinsky, J.S., Chase, D.M., Dunlop, C.L., Chao, E. C., & Monk, B.J. (2015). Hereditary predisposition to ovarian cancer, looking beyond *BRCA1/BRCA2*. *Gynecological Oncology, 137*(1), 86–92.

Mladosievicova, B., Dzurenkova, A., Sufliarska, S. & Carter, A. (2011). Clinical relevance of thiopurine S-methyltransferase gene polymorphisms. *Neoplasma, 58*(4), 277–282.

Mohamad, H. B. & Apffelstaedt, J. P. (2008). Counseling for male BRCA mutation carriers-a review. *The Breast, 17*(5), 441–450.

Moline, J. & Eng, C. (2013 [Updated Jan 10, 2013]). Multiple endocrine neoplasia Type 2. In Pagon, R. A. , Adam, M. P., Ardinger, H. H., Bird, T. D., Dolan, C. R., Fong, C. T., Smith, R. J. H., & Stephens, K. (eds). *GeneReviews*® (Internet). Seattle (WA): University of Washington, 1993-2014. Retrieved from www.ncbi.nlm.nih.gov/books/NBK1257/.

Nagy, R., Sweet, K & Eng, C. (2004). Highly penetrant hereditary cancer syndromes. *Oncogene, 23*: 6445–6470.

Narod, S. A., Dubé, M.P, Klijn, J., Lubinski, J., Lynch, H.T., Ghadirian, P., . . . Brunet, J. S. (2002). Oral contraceptives and the risk of breast cancer in BRCA1 and BRCA2 mutation carriers. *Journal of the National Cancer Institute, 94*(23), 1773–1779.

National Cancer Institute. (2015a). *Precision Medicine Initiative and Cancer Research*. Retrieved from http://www.cancer.gov/news-events/nci-update/2015/precision-medicine-initiative-2016.

National Cancer Institute. (2015b [January 6, 2015]). Cancer staging. *National Cancer Institute Fact Sheet.* Retrieved from www.cancer.gov/cancertopics/factsheet/detection/staging.

National Cancer Institute. (2015c). *What is Cancer?* (Updated February 9, 2015). Retrieved from www.cancer.gov/cancertopics/what-is-cancer.

National Cancer Institute, Surveillance Epidemiology and End Results (SEER). (2013a). *Previous version: SEER Cancer Statistics Review, 1975–2010 (accessible version)—United States Mortality Trends, 1950–2010.* Retrieved from http://seer.cancer.gov/archive/csr/1975_2010/.

National Cancer Institute (2013b [Updated July 2, 2013]). *FDA Approval for Cetuximab. Cancer Drug Information.* Retrieved from www.cancer.gov/cancertopics/druginfo/fda-cetuximab.

National Cancer Institute. (2012). Breast cancer risk in American women. *National Cancer Institute Factsheet.* Retrieved from http://www.cancer.gov/cancertopics/factsheet/detection/probability-breast-cancer.

National Cancer Institute. (nd). *Personalized medicine. NCI Dictionary of Cancer Terms.* Retrieved from http://cancer.gov/dictionary?CdrID=561717.

National Cancer Institute. (2011) *Breast cancer risk assessment tool.* Retrieved from http://www.cancer.gov/bcrisktool/about-tool.aspx#explaining.

National Comprehensive Cancer Network (2015b). Genetic/familial high risk assessment: breast and ovarian version 1.2015. Retrieved from http://www.nccn.org/professionals/physician_gls/pdf/genetics_screening.pdf.

National Comprehensive Cancer Network (2015b). Genetic/Familial high-risk assessment: colorectal. Version 2.2015. Retrieved from http://www.nccn.org/professionals/physician_gls/pdf/genetics_colon.pdf.

National Human Genome Research Institute (genome.gov). (2014 [Last updated October 31, 2014]). *DNA Sequencing Costs.* Retrieved from http://www.genome.gov/sequencingcosts/.

National Human Genome Research Institute (genome.gov). (2015 [Last update March 23, 2015]. *A Catalog of Published Genome-Wide Association Studies.* Retrieved from http://www.genome.gov/page.cfm?pageid=26525384&clearquery=1#result_table.

National Institute of Health (2015 [Last reviewed February 9]). *Precision Medicine Initiative.* Retrieved from http://www.nih.gov/precisionmedicine/goals.htm.

Nussbaum, R.L., McInnes, R. R., & Willard, H.F. (2007). Cancer genetics and genomics. Chapter 16. In *Thompson & Thompson Genetics in Medicine,* 7th ed. Philadelphia, PA: Saunders Elsevier.

Obermair, A., Youlden, D. R., Young, J.P., Lindor, N.M., Baron, J. A., Newcomb, P., . . . Jenkins, M.A. (2010). Risk of endometrial cancer for women diagnosed with HNPCC-related colorectal carcinoma, *127*(11), 2678–2684. doi: 10.1002/ijc.25501.

Oliveira, A.M., Ross, J.S. & Fletcher, J.A. (2005). Tumor suppressor genes in breast cancer: the gatekeepers and caretakers. *American Journal of Clinical Pathology, 124,* Suppl: S16–S28.

OncotypeDX Breast Cancer Assay. (2004-2015a). *The Oncotype DX®* Breast Cancer Assay. Retrieved from http://www.oncotypedx.com/en-US/Breast/HealthcareProfessionalsInvasive.

OncotypeDX Breast Cancer Assay. (2004-2015b). Recurrence Score Result. Retrieved from http://breast-cancer.oncotypedx.com/en-US/Professional-Invasive/WhatIsTheOncotypeDXBreastCancerTest/Recurrence%20Score%20Result.aspx

OncotypeDX Colon Cancer Assay. (2004-2015). Overview—Addressing an Unmet Need in the Treatment of Colon Cancer. Retrieved from http://colon-cancer.oncotypedx.com/en-US/Professional/WhatIsTheColonCancerTest/HowTheColonCancerTestWorks.aspx.

Online Mendelian Inheritance in Man, OMIM®. McKusick-Nathans Institute of Genetic Medicine, Johns Hopkins University (Baltimore, MD) (2015; [Updated March 28, 2015]. Retrieved from http://omim.org/.

Paik, S., Tang, G., Shak, S., Kim, C., Baker, J., Kim, W., . . . Wolmark, N. (2006). Gene expression and benefit of chemotherapy in women with node-negative, estrogen receptor-positive breast cancer. *Journal of Clinical Oncology, 24*(23), 3726–3734.

Palma, M. D., Domchek, S.M., Stopfer, J., Erlichman, J., Siegfried, J.D. Tigges-Cardwell, J., . . . Nathanson, K.L. (2008). The relative contribution of point mutations and genomic rearrangements in *BRCA1* and *BRCA2* in high-risk breast cancer families. *Cancer Research, 68*(17), 7006–7014. doi: 10.1158/0008-5472.CAN-08-0599.

Pancione, M., Remo, A & Colantuoni, V. (2012). Genetic and epigenetic events generate multiple pathways in colorectal cancer progression. *Pathology Research International.* doi: 10.1155/2012/509348. Retrieved from http://www.ncbi.nlm.nih.gov/pmc/articles/PMC3409552/.

Passaperuma, K., Warner, E., Causer, P. A. , Hill, K. A., Messner, S., Wong, J. W., . . . Narod, S. A. (2012). Long-term results of screening with magnetic resonance imaging in women with BRCA mutations. *British Journal of Cancer, 107*(1), 24–30. doi: 10.1038/bjc.2012.204.

Peltomäki, P. (2005). Lynch syndrome genes. F*amilial Cancer, 4*(3), 227–232.

Pino, M. S. & Chung, d. L. (2010). The chromosomal instability pathway in colon cancer. *Gastroenterology, 136*(6), 2059–2072.

Plass, C. (2002). Cancer epigenomics. *Human Molecular Genetics, 11*(20), 2479–2488.

Rainville, I. R. & Rana, H.Q. (2014). Next-generation sequencing for inherited breast cancer risk: counseling through the complexity. *Current Oncology Reports, 3*, 371. doi. 10.1007/s11912-013-0371-z.

Rakha, E. A., Reis-Filho, J. S. & Ellis, I. O. (2008). Basal-like breast cancer: A critical review. *Journal of Clinical Oncology, 28*(15), 2568–2581. doi:10.1200/JCO.2007.13.1748.

Rebbeck, T.R, Levin, A.M, Eisen, A., Synder, C., Watson, P., Cannon-Albright, L., . . . Weber, B. L. (1999) Breast cancer risk after bilateral prophylactic oophorectomy in *BRCA1* mutation carriers. *Journal of the National Cancer Institute, 91*(17), 1475–1479.

Rebbeck, T. R. (2002). Prophylactic oophorectomy in *BRCA1* and *BRCA2* mutation carriers. *European Journal of Cancer, 38*(Suppl. 6), S15–S17.

Rebbeck, T. R., Kauff, N. D. & Domchek, S. M. (2009). Meta-analysis of risk reduction estimates associated with risk-reducing salpingo-oophorectomy in *BRCA1* or *BRCA2* mutation carriers. *Journal of National Cancer Institute, 101*(2), 80–87.

Richards, S., Aziz, N., Bale, S., Bick, D., Das, A., Gastier-Foster, J., . . . Rehm, H.L., on behalv of the ACMG Laboratory Quality Assurance Committee. (2015). Standards and guidelines for the interpretation of sequence variants: A joint consensus recommendation of the American College of Medical Genetics and Genomics and the Association for Molecular Pathology. *Genetics in Medicine.* DOI: 10.1038/GLM.2015.30. Retrieved from www.acmg.net/docs/Standards_Guidelines_for_the_Interpretation_of_Sequence_Variants.pdf.

Risch, H.A., McLaughlin, J.R., Cole, D.E., Rosen, B., Bradley, L., Kwan, E., . . . Narod , S. A. (2001). Prevalence and penetrance of germline *BRCA1* and *BRCA2* mutations in a population series of 649 women with ovarian cancer. *American Journal of Human Genetics, 68*(3), 700–710.

Roberts, M.E., Riegert-Johnson, D. L., Thomas, B. C., Thomas, C. S., Heckman, M. G., Krishna, M., . . . Cappel, M. A. (2012). Screening for Muir-Torre syndrome using mismatch repair protein immunohistochemistry of sebaceous neoplasms. *Journal of Genetic Counselors, 3*, 393–405. doi: 10.1007/s10897-012-9552-4.

Robson, M.E., Storm, C. D., Weitzel, J., Wollins, D. S., Offit, K. & American Society of Clinical Oncology (2010). American Society of Clinical Oncology policy statement update: genetic and genomic testing for cancer susceptibility. *Journal of Clinical Oncology, 28*(5), 893-901. doi: 10.1299/JCO.2009.27.0660. Retrieved from http://jco.ascopubs.org/content/28/5/893.full.pdf+html.

Rodriguez-Bigas, M.A., Lin, E. H. & Crane, C. H. (2003) Genetic pathways in colorectal cancer. In Kufe, D. W., Pollock, R. E. Weichselbaum, R. R. *et al.*, (eds.) *Holland-Frei Cancer Medicine*, 6th edition. Hamilton (ON): BC Decker. Retrieved from http://www.ncbi.nlm.nih.gov/books/NBK12839/.

Ronen, A. & Glickman, B. W. (2001). Human DNA re-

pair genes. *Environmental Molecular Mutagenesis, 37*(3), 241–283.

Roy, R., Chun, J., & Powell, S.N. (2011) BRCA1 and BRCA2: different roles in a common pathway of genome protection. *Nature Reviews Cancer, 12*(1), 68–73. doi:10.1038/nrc3181.

Saijo, N. (2012). Critical comments for roles of biomarkers in the diagnosis and treatment of cancer. *Cancer Treatment Reviews, 38*(1), 63–67. doi: 10.1016/j.ctrv.2011.02.004.

Saslow, C., Boetes, C., Burke, W., Harms, S., Leach, M. O., Lehman, C. D., . . . Russell, C. A. & American Cancer Society Breast Cancer Advisory Group. (2007). American Cancer Society guidelines for breast screening with MRI as an adjunct to mammography. *CA: A Cancer Journal for Clinicians; 57*(2), 75–89.

Scully, R. (2000). Role of BRCA gene dysfunction in breast and ovarian cancer predisposition. *Breast Cancer Research, 2*(5), 324–330.

Shalin, S. C., Lyle,S., Calonje, E. & Lazar, A. J. F. (2010). Sebaceous neoplasia and the Muir–Torre syndrome: important connections with clinical implications. *Histopathology, 56*(1), 133–147. doi: 10.1111/j.1365-2559.2009.03454.x.

Sherr, C. J. (1996). *Cancer cell cycles. Science, 274*, 1672–1676.

Simmons, D. (2008). Epigenetic influences and disease. *Nature Education, 1*(1). Retrieved from http://www.nature.com/scitable/topicpage/epigenetic-influences-and-disease-895.

Sinha, A., Tekkis, P. P., Gibbons, D. C., Phillips, R. K. & Clark, S. K. (2011). Risk factors predicting ntussus occurrence in patients with familial adenomatous polyposis: a meta-analysis. *Colorectal Disease, 13*(11), 1222-1229. doi: 10.1111/j.1463-1318.2010.02345.x.

Slodkowska, E. A. & Ross, J. S. (2009). MammPrint 70-gene signature: another milestone in personalized medical care for breast cancer patients. *Expert Review of Molecular Diagnostics, 9*(5), 417–422. doi: 10.1586/erm.09.32.

Smits, V. A. J & Medema, R. H. (2001). Checking out the G2/M transition. *Biochimica et Biophjysical Acta (BBA)—Gene Structure and Expression, 1519*(1-2), 1–12.

Spannhoff, A., Sippl W. & Jung, M. (2009). Cancer treatment of the future: inhibitors of histone methyltransferases. *International Journal of Biochemical Cell Biology, 41*(1), 4–11.

Stadler, Z.K, Thom, P., Robson, M.E., Weitzel, J.N., Kauff, N.D., Hurley, K. E., . . . Offit, K. (2010). Genome-wide association studies of cancer. *Journal of Clinical Oncology, 28*(27), 4255–4267.

Sturt, N. J. & Clark, S. K. (2006). Current ideas in desmoid tumours. *Familial Cancer, 5*(3), 275–285; discussion 287–288.

Su, P. (2013). Direct-to-consumer genetic testing: A comprehensive view. *The Yale Journal of Biology and Medicine, 86*(3), 359–365. Retrieved from www.ncbi.nlm.nih.gov/pmc/articles/PMC3767220/.

Thompson, E. R, Doyle, M. A., Ryland, G.L, Rowley, S. M. , Choong, D. Y., Tothill, R. H., . . . Campbell, I. G. (2012). Exome sequencing identifies rare deleterious mutations in DNA repair genes FANCC and BLM as potential breast cancer susceptibility alleles. *PLoS Genetics, 8*(9) e1002894. doi: 10.1371/journal.pgen.1002894. Retrieved from http://www.ncbi.nlm.nih.gov/pubmed/23028338.

Thompson, D., Easton, D. F. & Breast Cancer Linkage Consortium. (2002). Cancer incidence in BRCA1 mutation carriers. *Journal of the National Cancer Institute, 94*(18), 1358–1365.

Trojan, A., Vergopoulos, A., Breitenstein, U., Tausch, C., Seifert, B., & Joechle, W. (2013). CYP2D6 phenotype indicative for optimized antiestrogen efficacy associates with outcome in early breast cancer patients. *Cancer Chemotherapy and Pharmacology, 71*(2), 301–306. doi: 10.1007/s00280-012-2003-y. Epub 2012 Oct 26.

Tuna, M. & Amos, C. I. (2012). Genomic sequencing in cancer. *Cancer Letters, 340*(2), 161–170. doi: 10.1016/j.canlet.2012.11.004.

Tung, N., Battelli, C., Allen, B., Kaldate, R., Bhatnagar, S., Bowles, K., . . . Hartman, A. R. (2015). Frequency of mutations in individuals with breast cancer referred for *BRCA1* and *BRCA2* testing using next-generation sequencing with a 25-gene panel. *Cancer, 121*(1), 25–33.

Umar A., Boland, C. R., Terdiman, J. P., Syngal, S., de la Chapelle, A., Rüschoff, J., . . . Srivastava, S. (2004). Revised Bethesda Guidelines for hereditary nonpolyposis colorectal cancer (Lynch syndrome) and microsatellite instability. *Journal of the National Cancer Institute, 96*(4), 261–268.

United States Department of Health and Human Services (2014 [Updated July 16]). *HealthyPeople.gov—Genomics*. In *Healthy People 2020*. Retrieved from http://www.healthypeople.gov/2020/topicsobjectives2020/objectiveslist.aspx?topicId=15.

United States Department of Health and Human Services, U.S. Food and Drug Administration. (2013). 23andMe, Inc. 11/22/13. In Inspections, Compliance, Enforcement, and Criminal Investigations. Retrieved from www.fda.gov/iceci/enforcementactions/warningletters/2013/ucm376296.htm.

Warshawsky, D. (2006). Carincogens and mutagens. In Warshawsky, D & Landolph, J.R. *Molecular Carcinogenesis and the Molecular Biology of Human Cancer* pp 6–24. Boca Raton, Florida: CRC Press Taylor & Francis Group.

van Asperen, C. J., Brohet, R.M., Meijers-Heijboer, E. J., Hoogerbrugge, S., Verhoef, S., Vasen, H.F., . . . Netherlands Collaboration Group on Hereditary Breast Cancer (HEBON). (2005). Cancer risks in *BRCA2* families: estimates for sites other than breast and ovary. *Journal of Medical Genetics, 42*(9), 711–719.

van der Groep, P., van der Wall, E., & van Diest, P. J. (2011). Pathology of hereditary breast cancer. *Cell Oncology, 34*(2), 71–88. doi:10.1007/213402-0010-3.

Vasen, H. F. A., Blanco, I., Aktan-Collan, K., Gopie, J. P., Alonso, A., Aretz, S., Berstein, Inge, . . . Möslein, G. (the Mallorca group). (2012). Revised guidelines for the clinical management of Lynch syndrome (HNPCC): recommendations by a group of European experts. *Gut*. doi:10.1136/gutjnl-2012-304356. Retrieved from http://gut.bmj.com/content/early/2013/02/20/gutjnl-2012-304356.long.

Vasen, H. F., Stormorken, A., Menko, F. H., Nagengast, F. M., Kleibeuker, J. H., Griffioen, G., Taal, B. G., Moller, P. & Wijnen, J.T (2001). *MSH2* mutation carriers are at higher risk to cancer than MLH1 mutation carriers: a study of hereditary nonpolyposis colorectal cancer families. *Journal of Clinical Oncology, 19*(20), 4074–4080.

Vasen, H. F., Hendriks, Y., de Jong, A. E. , van Puijenbroek, M., Tops, C., Bröcker-Vriends, A. H., Wijnen, J. T. & Morreau, H. (2004). Identification of HNPCC by molecular analysis of colorectal and endometrial tumors. *Disease Markers, 20*(4-5), 207–213.

Vasen, H. F., Watson, P., Mecklin, J. P. & Lynch, H. T. (1999). New clinical criteria for hereditary nonpolyposis colorectal cancer (HNPCC, Lynch syndrome) proposed by the International Collaborative group on HNPCC. *Gastroenterology, 116*(6), 1453–1456.

Venkitaraman, A. R. (2001). Functions of *BRCA1* and *BRCA 2* in the biological response to DNA damage. *Journal of Cell Science, 114*(Pt20), 3591–3598.

Vogelstein, B., Sur, S. & Prives, C. (2010). p53: The most frequently altered gene in human cancers. Nature Education, 3(9): 6. Retrieved from www.nature.com/scitable/topicpage/p53-the-most-frequently-altered-gene-in-14192717.

Vogt, S., Jones, N., Christian, D., Engel, C., Nielsen, M., Kaufmann, A., . . . Aretz, S. (2009). Expanded extracolonic tumor spectrum in MUTYH-associated polyposis. *Gastroenterology, 137*(6), 1976–1985 E10.

Wang, G., Kuppermann, M., Kim, B., Phillips, K.A. & Ladabaum, U. (2012). Influence of patient preferences on the cost-effectiveness of screening for Lynch syndrome. *Journal of Oncology Practice, 8*(3S), e24s–e30s. doi:10.1200/JOP.2011.000535.

Wang, H., Luo, T., Liu, W.Q., Huang, Y., Wu, X. T. & Wang, X. J. (2011). Clinical presentations and surgical approach of acute intussusception caused by Peutz-Jeghers syndrome in adults. *Journal of Gastrointestinal Surgery, 15*(12), 2218–2225. doi: 10.1007/s11605-011-1724-2.

Warner, E., Foulkes, W., Goodwin, P., Meschino, W.,

Blondal, J., Paterson, C., . . . Narod, S. (1999) Prevalence and penetrance of *BRCA1* and *BRCA2* gene mutations in unselected Askenazi Jewish women with breast cancer. *Journal of the National Cancer Institute, 91*, 1241–1247.

Warshawsky, D. (2006). Carcinogens and mutagens. In Warshawsky, D. & Landolph, J. R. Jr. (editors) *Molecular Carcinogenesis and the Molecular Biology of Human Cancer*, Chapter 1). Boca Raton, FL: CRC Press Taylor & Francis Group., LLC.

Weissman, S. M., Burt, R., Church, J., Erdman, S., Hampel, H., Holter, S., . . . Senter, L. (2012) Identification of Individuals at Risk for Lynch Syndrome Using Targeted Evaluations and Genetic Testing: National Society of Genetic Counselors and the Collaborative Group of the Americas on Inherited Colorectal Cancer Joint Practice Guidelines. *Journal of Genetic Counseling 21*(4) 484–493.

Weissman, B. E. (2006). Tumor suppressor genes. In Warshawsky, D & Landolph, J.R. Molecular *Carcinogenesis and the Molecular Biology of Human Cancer* pp 6–24. Boca Raton, Florida: CRC Press Taylor & Francis Group.

Weitzel, J. N., Clague, J., Martir-Negron, A., Ogaz, R., Herzog, J., Ricker, C.,... Larson, G. P. (2013). Prevalence and type of BRCA Mutations in Hispanics undergoing genetic cancer risk assessment in the Southwestern United States: A report from the Clinical Cancer Genetics Community Research Network. *Journal of Clinical Oncology, 31*(2):210-216. doi: 10.1200/JCO.2011.41.0027.

Weitzel, J. N., Blazer, K. R., MacDonald, D. J., Culver, J.O., & Offit, K. (2011). Genetics, genomics, and cancer risk assessment—State of the art and future directions in the era of personalized medicine. *CA: A Cancer Journal for Clinician, 61*(5), 327–259.

Weitzel J. N., Lagos, V., Blazer, K. R., Nelson, R., Ricker, C., Herzog, J., McGuire, C., & Neuhausen, S. (2005). Prevalence of *BRCA* mutations and founder effect in high-risk Hispanic families. *Cancer Epidemiology Biomarkers & Prevention, 14*(7), 1666–1671.

Whittemore A. S., Gong, G. & Itnyre, J. (1997). Prevalence and contribution of BRCA1 mutations in breast cancer and ovarian cancer: result from three U.S. population-based case-control studies of ovarian cancer. *American Journal of Human Genetics, 60*(3), 496–504. Retrieved from: www.ncbinlm.nih.gov/pmcarticles/PMC1712497/.

Wingo, P. A, Ory, H. W., Layde, P. M. & Lee, N. C. (1988). The evaluation of the data collection process for a multicenter, population-based, case-control design. *American Journal of Epidemiology, 128*(1), 206–217.

Wood, R. D., Mitchell, M. & Lindahl, T. (2005). Human DNA repair genes, 2005. *Mutation Research, 577*, 275–283.

Wooster, R., Neuhausen, S. L., Mangion, J., Quirk, Y., Ford, D., Collins, N., . . . Averill, D., *et al.* (1994). Localization of a breast cancer susceptibility gene, BRCA2, to chromosome 13q12-13. *Science, 265*(5181), 2088–2090.

World Health Organization (2013). Breast cancer prevention and control—breast cancer burden. Retrieved from http://www.who.int/cancer/detection/breastcancer/en/index1.html.

World Health Organization. (2009). Women's health. Retrieved from http://www.who.int/mediacentre/factsheets/fs334/en/.

Yoon, Y.S., Yu, C. S., Kim, T. W., Kim, J. H. , Jang, S. J., Cho, D. H. , Roh, S.A. & Kim, J. C. (2011). Mismatch repair status in sporadic colorectal cancer: immunohistochemistry and microsatellite instability analyses. *Journal of Gastroenterology and Hepatology, 26*(12), 1733–1739. doi: 10.1111/j.1440-1746.2011.06784.x.

You, J.S. & Jones, P.A. (2012). Cancer genetics and epigenetics: Two sides of the same coin? *Cancer Cell, 22*(1), 9–20. doi.org/1-.1016/j.ccr.2012.06.008.

Young, S. R., Pilarski, R.T., Donenberg, T., Shapiro, C., Hammond , L. S., Miller, J., . . . Narod, S. A. (2009). The prevalence of BRCA1 mutations among young women with triple-negative breast cancer. *BMC Cancer, 9*, 86. Published online. doi: 10.1186/1471-2407-9-86. Retrieved from: http://www.ncbi.nlm.nih.gov/pmc/articles/PMC2666759/.

Young, R. H. (2005). Sex cord-stromal tumors of the ovary and testis: their similarities and differences with consideration of selected problems. *Modern Pathology, 18*, Supplement 2, S81–98.

Zarbl, H. (2006). Cellular oncogenes and carcinogenesis. In Warshawsky, D & Landolph, J.R. *Molecular Carcinogenesis and the Molecular Biology of Human Cancer* pp 103–129. Boca Raton, Florida: CRC Press Taylor & Francis Group.

Zhang, W., Dahlberg, J.E. & Tam, W. (2007). MicroRNAs in tumorigenesis—A primer. *The American Journal of Pathology, 171*(3), 728–738.

Zhu, J. (2006). DNA methylation and hepatocellular carcinoma. *Journal of Hepatobiliary Pancreatic Surgery, 13*(4), 265–274.

Chapter 16

Genomics in Nursing Education, Research, Leadership, and Practice

SUSAN T. TINLEY, Ph.D, CGC, RN (RET)
QUANNETTA T. EDWARDS, Ph.D, FNP-BC, WHNP, AGN-BC, FAANP
ANN H. MARADIEGUE, Ph.D, FNP-BC, FAANP
DIANE C. SEIBERT, Ph.D, ARNP, FAANP, FAAN

16.1. INTRODUCTION

This book was envisioned as a resource for nurses enrolled in a graduate program or already working at the graduate level in nursing and it uses the *Essential Genetic and Genomic Competencies for Nurses with Graduate Degrees* (Greco, Tinley, & Seibert, 2012) as an organizing framework. Most of the content deals with what is known about genes and disease, so the vast majority of the book is clearly applicable to nurses who provide direct patient care. Nurse executives, nurse educators, nurse researchers, and nurse informaticians may wonder why they should invest the time and effort to learn the content of this book because at first glance, it may not appear to be relevant to their practice settings. The purpose of this chapter is to link the genomic concepts to the practice of nursing leaders who, while no longer providing direct patient care, greatly influence the overall quality of healthcare. Educators obviously need to be able to teach the content. Researchers will find an increasing applicability of genomics to many areas of nursing research, such as described in the chapter on symptomatology. All nurses, regardless of their position, play pivotal roles in preparing patients and systems for a genomic future, because nurses touch the lives of more individuals, families, and communities than any other health care profession.

16.2. NURSING EDUCATION

There has been a call for the inclusion of genetics in the nursing curriculum since the senti-nel article by Brantl and Esslinger appeared in the literature over four decades ago (1962). Despite this promising early start, for the next 20 years, almost nothing was published in the nursing literature addressing the importance of including genomic content in nursing curriculum. This dearth of attention to genetics education by nursing was reflected in a study that revealed that nurses from a variety of educational backgrounds had little to no knowledge of basic genetics (Cohen, 1979). Beginning in the early 80's, more publications began appearing in the nursing literature related to the use of genomics in practice settings, but there was very little progress made to integrate genetics into nursing education (Anderson, 1996).

A 2005 study that examined nurse practitioner (NP) student knowledge and comfort with genetics found most were uncomfortable with their ability to construct a pedigree or talk with patients or families about a genetic condition (Maradiegue, Edwards, Seibert, Macri, & Sitzer, 2005). The authors stressed the need to integrate genetics into graduate nursing programs and acknowledged that the primary hurdles to be overcome were the lack of faculty who were comfortable teaching genomics, insufficient time in the curriculum to add genomics, and a lack of consensus on the importance of genetic content. A subsequent publication by the same research team (Edwards, Maradiegue, Seibert, Macri, & Sitzer, 2006) examined NP faculty perceptions of their personal knowledge of genomics and if there was genomic content in the curriculum, how they taught the content (e.g., free standing genetics course, integration into the basic sciences, etc.). They found that NP faculty, like their students, reported poor understanding of genomics, and they were not certain about the best way to integrate this content in the NP curriculum. Although they believed genomics was important, faculty reported major barriers, such as lack of knowledge and time. More than 90% reported minimal to no discussion of basic genomic concepts, such as common inheritance patterns, and 75% did not teach students how to collect a detailed three generation family health history.

Seeing little progress with the efforts to increase the genetic literacy, a nursing task force was formed to identify the steps needed to develop a knowledgeable work force. The task force report called for "(a) broadening the focus of education and training from genetics to genomics, (b) providing faculty training with clinical application-based genomic education models, and (c) including adequate knowledge of human genetics and genomics in accrediting, licensure, and certification" (Health Resources and Services Administration and the National Institutes of Health, 2000). The same call for genetics in accreditation criteria and licensure and certification examinations was reiterated by Williams, Skirton, & Masny six years later (2006). A literature review provided substantial evidence of the relevance and importance of genetics to nursing practice (Burke & Kirk, 2006), and integration of genetics education across both academic and continuing education settings was identified as essential. A call was made for research into the most effective educational methods of achieving a genetics literate nursing workforce.

16.2.1. Educating Faculty

Although nursing education has not yet advanced as far as nursing leaders would have hoped, the end of the 20th and beginning of the 21st centuries seem to represent a turning point for genetics education in nursing. Several programs to educate nursing faculty such as The Genetics Interdisciplinary Faculty Training (GIFT) project, which ran from 2001 to 2004, were developed specifically to improve the genomic competency of nursing faculty. GIFT was an intense, one week educational program for teams composed of graduate nursing and physician assistant faculty and a genetic counselor to help

them develop strategies for integrating genomics into the curriculum. In total, 28 teams completed the program during the 3 years that GIFT ran, and after completing the project, each team was provided with a stipend to help initiate and sustain an integration or education project at their college (Turner, Strand, & Speer, 2006).

Another notable project is the highly acclaimed Genetics Program for Nursing Faculty (GPNF) initiated at the University of Cincinnati in 1997, with the purpose of increasing nursing faculty knowledge about genomics and to promote the addition of genomics content into bachelor of nursing (BSN) programs. In 2002, the program was transformed to an 18-week interactive online course and is now known as the Web Based Genetic Institute http://www.cincinnatichildrens.org/education/clinical/nursing/genetics/cont/web-genetics/ (Prows, Hetteberg, Hopkin, Latta, & Powers, 2004).

Another ongoing education initiative to prepare nurse leaders is the National Institute of Nursing Research (NINR) Summer Genetics Institute (SGI), an intensive 4 week course focused on molecular genetics for graduate students, faculty, and practitioners.

SGI objectives include the following:

- "Increase knowledge in molecular genetics for use in research, teaching, and clinical practice.
- Gain ability to use molecular genetics methods for biobehavioral research.
- Evaluate families with genetic problems and make appropriate referrals to genetic and community resources.
- Analyze strategies used for genomic-based therapies and trends in molecular therapeutics.
- Identify the strengths, weaknesses, and applications of genetic tests and inaccuracies that can be introduced during the testing period.
- Analyze ethical and legal issues related to genetic testing and genetic counseling and implications for practice and research." https://www.ninr.nih.gov/training/trainingopportunitiesintramural/summergeneticsinstitute#.VedPL_lVhBc

Upon successful completion, every graduate of the SGI is awarded eight graduate college credits

(NINR, 2015), and to date, over 350 nurses have completed the SGI, including many faculty who have returned to their universities to integrate genetics into their curricula.

The call to add genomic content to program accreditation criteria were heard in the 2008 revision of the American Association of Colleges of Nursing (AACN) Essentials for BSN programs (American Association of Colleges of Nursing, 2008) and again in the revision of the Masters' essentials in 2011 (American Association of Colleges of Nursing, 2011). These essentials documents provide the standards for nursing education by which the Commission on Collegiate Nursing Education assesses and accredits educational programs; the inclusion of genomic content in the essentials language has been a major step forward in encouraging educational programs to add genomics content to their curricula.

16.2.2. Essential Competencies for Genetics and Genomics

The first document to articulate the expectations for genetic and genomic practice by professional nurses was developed in 2006 by the Consensus Panel on Genetic/Genomic Nursing Competencies (2006). The 2nd edition of the *Essentials of Genetic and Genomic Nursing Competencies, Curricula Guidelines, and Outcome Indications* (Consensus Panel on Genetic/Genomic Nursing Competencies, 2009) expanded the initial competencies, adding curricular guidelines and practice indicators to facilitate the development of curriculum. This offered a framework to assess the genetic and genomic competencies among nurses. In addition, the 2009 competency document provided a roadmap for faculty to achieve the AACN accreditation criteria while preparing students for safe and competent practice in the genomic era.

While acknowledging the value of minimum genetic essentials for nursing practice, faculty teaching in graduate level programs began requesting an expanded set of competencies that would meet needs of nurses with advanced degrees. In 2009, a team began developing a new set of essential genetic and genomic competencies for nurses prepared at the graduate level (Greco, Tinley, & Seibert, 2012). This set of advanced competencies includes 28 competencies applicable to all nurses practicing at the graduate level regardless of practice setting, and 10 competencies that apply specifically to nurses with advanced practice degrees.

16.2.3. Suggestions for Integration and Leveling

Recent surveys have confirmed ongoing deficiencies in genomic literacy among nurses and acknowledge the need for nurses to be prepared for and involved in providing genomic healthcare (Calzone *et al.*, 2012; Calzone *et al.*, 2011). All nursing faculty are responsible for incorporating genomics into their courses, whether that's accomplished through the creation of a dedicated genetics and genomics course or through integration into existing courses (Williams *et al.*, 2011). Ideally, genomics should be integrated and leveled throughout the curriculum along with other aspects of health, illness, and nursing care. The placement of some genomic content, such as carrier, prenatal, and newborn screening, is easily identifiable, and many programs have already integrated it into their curriculum. Other content, such as genomic risk assessment tools or interpretation of a family health history, may be less likely to be included.

Genomic content can be ranked to meet the learning needs of nursing students. For example, undergraduate nursing students might be provided with general information about pharmacogenomics in a pharmacology course, which would then be reinforced in the clinical area. Content for Nurse Practitioner students would expand to include where to obtain information about recommendations for genomic testing prior to prescribing certain medications, how to access that testing, and how to explain it to their clients. Undergraduate students could be taught to obtain a three generation family history and construct a pedigree using standardized symbols in an undergraduate assessment course; the skills could be reinforced and applied in clinical courses throughout the remainder of the student's education. Content for graduate nursing students would include analysis of the pedigree, conducting a targeted physical examination, collecting a comprehensive health history inclusive of environmental and behavioral factors, obtaining radiological or laboratory evaluations, and interpreting the results of all the data to identify genetic or genomic risk.

Courses outside of what are traditionally considered "core" nursing curriculum could also incorporate some genomic content. The explosion of knowledge coming out of genomic research makes it impractical for professionals outside of a genetics specialty to remain current with the domain, but courses focused on information technology could introduce students to high quality genomic resources and teach students how to access current, accurate evidence for themselves and their patients. In evidence based practice and research courses, students could be asked to evaluate the state of genomics knowledge and how this emerging information could be translated into clinical practice. Ethics courses could offer students an opportunity to discuss some of the challenges encountered when obtaining informed consent for genetic testing or the privacy issues that emerge when some family members want genetic information and others do not. Every faculty group needs to examine their curricula for opportunities to add genomic content, and once those areas have been identified, the content can be woven into the courses. Many faculty are surprised to discover that adding genomic content can be done without adding a significant amount of additional lecture or clinical instruction time. There are several excellent resources for faculty to improve their own genomic knowledge, and others specifically developed to facilitate the integration of genomic content (see Table 16.1).

16.3. NURSING RESEARCH

Since the completion of the Human Genome Project in 2003, research has continued to pour out of laboratories around the globe, continually reshaping the understanding of genomics and moving the health care community closer toward the dream of personalized medicine. Genomic discoveries have impacted an enormous range of health care areas, affecting screening, diagnosis, treatment, and prevention (Jenkins, Grady, & Collins 2005; National Human Genome Research Institute 2013). Over the past three decades, nurse researchers have played an ever increasing role in the genomic research revolution and promise to continue being a major force in genomic science in the future. In the spring of 2013, an advisory panel was charged with the task of developing a blueprint for genomic nursing research mapped to the strategic goals of the NINR. The Genomic Nursing State of the Science Advisory Panel (Calzone *et al.*, 2013) developed and published a blueprint for nursing research that centered around four themes: (1) *health promotion and disease prevention* (risk assessment, communication, and decision support studies); (2) *quality of life* (the family context, symptom management, disease states and self-management); (3) *innovation* (emerging technology, informatics systems and environmental influences); and (4) *training* (capacity building and education). The panel also identified two additional themes important to genomic nursing research; *client focused* research (health

TABLE 16.1. Examples of Genetic Educational Resources for
Nursing Research, Practice, Leadership and Education.

Genetics/Genomics Competency Center (G2C2)	Links the minimum essential competencies and outcome indicator with educational resources and assessments.	http://www.g-2-c-2.org/
CDC's Office of Public Health Genomics (OPHG)	Information on translation of genomics research into population health.	http://www.cdc.gov/genomics/default.htm
Cincinnati Children's Hospital Medical Center: Genetics Education Program for Nurses	Provides continuing education and instructional resources in genetics and genomics for nurses and nursing faculty.	http://www.cincinnatichildrens.org/education/clinical/nursing/genetics/default/
Evaluation of Genomic Applications in Practice and Prevention (EGAPP)	Reviews CDC-commissioned evidence reports, highlights knowledge gaps, and provides guidance on the use of genetic tests.	http://www.egappreviews.org/
Global Genetics and Genomics Community G3C	Bilingual collection of unfolding genetic/genomic case studies.	http://g-3-c.org/en

disparities, cost) and research that examines the *context* (policy and public education) in which health care is delivered.

The panel stated that nurse researchers should "focus on conducting research that produces clinically relevant evidence" (Calzone *et al.*, 2013, p. 4), using diverse methodologies and measurement strategies. The panel recommended that nurse researchers work toward building an evidence base to facilitate the integration of genomics into nursing practice and regulation while simultaneously improving health outcomes (Calzone *et al.*, 2013). More information on the Genomic Nursing State of Science Research Recommendations can be found on the national Human Genome Research Institute web site located at http://www.genome.gov/27549398 (National Human Genome Research Institute, 2013).

One of the key roles nurses play in the health care system is to help patients and families manage symptoms such as fatigue and pain caused by disease or disease treatments. To answer some of these important questions, the NINR Division of Intramural Research has developed a program dedicated to supporting nurses conducting basic and clinical research, focusing on improving the understanding of molecular mechanisms and environmental influences associated with symptom manifestations (National Institute of Nursing Research [NINR], 2014). NINR funding support has produced new evidence advancing the understanding of the biological mechanisms, molecular-genetic biomarkers, and morphologic changes associated with small nerve fibers and neuropathic pain; the creation of new tools to measure the relationship between pain and sleep disruption; the effectiveness of clinical interventions focused on reducing symptoms; the molecular pathways activated in response to cellular damage; and sleep and circadian rhythm changes in patients undergoing treatment for prostate cancer (NINR, 2014). More information on the NINR, Division of Intramural Research and specific branches of NINR can be found by navigating the NINR web site at www.ninr.nih.gov/researchandfunding/dir.

The NINR also supports intramural training to increase the research capability in biomedical research through the SGI. The goal of the SGI is to increase genomic research capability among nursing graduate students and faculty, with a secondary goal of expanding genomic clinical competency among nurse clinicians. The program provides attendees with instruction in molecular genetics so that these research tools can be used in research studies, but as mentioned above SGI graduates also use the information in education and in their clinical practice. The NINR also sponsors extramural research funding for a wide range of research opportunities, including genomic studies and career development awards given to nurses to expand clinical skills or enhance scientific career. More information on the NINR and its impact on genomic research can be found through navigating the NINR website at http://www.ninr.nih.gov/

Support for nurses interested in conducting genomic research is not limited to NINR. Nurses have received funding through private foundations such as the Cystic Fibrosis Foundation and the Foundation for Sickle Cell Disease Research (FSCDR), as well as professional organizations such as Sigma Theta Tau, Tri-Service Nursing Research Program (available to active duty and retired military nurses), and the Agency for Healthcare Research and Quality (AHRQ).

16.4. NURSING LEADERSHIP

Nurses working in senior leadership roles, such as senior nurse executives, play a pivotal leadership role in facilitating the incorporation of genomic practices within their organization to attain the best patient outcomes. The American Organization of Nurse Executives (AONE) have a Manager Inventory Tool (2004) that includes the following key concepts: financial management, human resource management, performance improvement, foundational thinking skill, technology, strategic management, and appropriate clinical practice knowledge, which will be used as the framework to demonstrate how nursing leaders can support the integration of genomics into their health care systems.

Financial management addresses health care economics, budgetary and policy issues, inclusive of institutional Joint Commission accreditation. Nurse administrators are responsible for understanding health care economics and policy regulations as they apply to the delivery of patient care, which includes genomics. Budget categories should address mechanisms for reimbursement of genomics care, including Medicaid, Medicare, and third party payers. Understanding regulations is important, because these regulations can have an immediate impact with measureable outcomes on patient care and the delivery of services (Calzone *et al.*, 2013; Institute of Medicine [IOM], 2013).

Human resource management includes an understanding of the scope of practice laws and licensure requirements, as well as developing plans to address changes in roles, and a professional development plan for each employee. As noted in the previous chapters, genomics is affecting the way nurses practice and it is therefore incumbent upon the nurse administrator to mentor and support the training of other nurses. Current initiatives with State Boards of Nursing will aid in bringing genomics to the bedside (Caskey, 2013). In the near future, the basic professional NCLEX exams for nurses will include genomic content, making it imperative for new graduates to understand this content. Scope of practice laws are driven by the evidence and nurses' competency in genomics at the bedside (Calzone *et al.*, 2013). Additionally, the American Nurses Credentialing Center (2015) is offering genetic credentialing for advanced practice nurses (APRNs) (http://www.nursecredentialing.org/Advanced-Genetics), providing another tool for nurse administrators to address the development and performance improvement of their nursing staff.

Performance improvement includes patient and medication safety, which will include measures driven by pharmacogenomics. Nurse administrators can facilitate the delivery of safe, effective, genomic care (Kirk, Calzone, Arimori, & Tonkin, 2011) by monitoring drug reactions, utilizing pharmacogenomics drug strategies, and identifying the patient's genomic risk in order to monitor and deliver safe patient care. Understanding and implementing organizational and regulatory requirements to include genomic care is part of the nurse administrator's responsibility. An example would be understanding that gene expression in chronic wounds can expedite impact wound healing and guide treatment plans (Tomic-Canic, Ayello, Stojadinovic, Golinko, & Brem, 2008).

Organizational behaviors and leadership includes *foundational thinking skills* as an approach to analysis and decision-making, problem solving skills, and navigating change. Use of

evidence based models, such as the three-generation pedigree, integrating genetic services into plans of care, and an eye to the future direction of genomics as part of the health system is an important function of the nurse administrator as change agent. Data driven models may include contracts to allow for genetic testing with certified laboratories or partnering by smaller entities with larger medical centers that offer these services. Planning for sophisticated whole genome sequencing (WGS) as part of patient care will require strong leadership skills to work with hospital administration and other disciplines. Care at this level, provided throughout the life span, requires work with an interdisciplinary team to examine genomic high impact priority problems for the public's health that can be translated to the bedside (Calzone *et al.*, 2013; IOM, 2013).

Understanding *information technology* and the effect on patient care is critical to the delivery of patient care. The nurse administrator has a unique opportunity to impact the way electronic medical records (EMRs) are utilized in the clinical setting. Currently biobanks are being linked to medical records data for genomic studies in clinical centers (McCarty *et al.*, 2011). Using EMRs, the nurse administrator should assess ways to maintain privacy and Health Insurance and Portability Accountability Act (HIPAA) regulations regarding DNA test results and WGS. Another important role for EMRs is the inclusion of structured three-generation pedigrees as a key step for disease identification (Hoffman, 2007). The APRN should be part of the team to evaluate the utilization and implementation of EMR systems within organizations, as well as assisting with technology that will affect care at the unit and system level.

Strategic management includes the development of strategic and operational plans to move the organization forward. Development of programs that include genomics to move the health care organization forward include programs that will easily fit into all of the existing health programs. Genomics pain programs, sleep disorders/management, depression identification/prevention, and cancer care are broad areas that will fit into many existing health initiatives and impact the level of care given within the institution.

Clinical practice knowledge is a required skill for all nurse administrators. A practice that is founded on established genomic principles of care will improve outcomes for the patients, families, and communities (Calzone *et al.*, 2013; IOM, 2013). The nurse administrator will need to understand the leveling of competencies specific to staff nurses (Consensus Panel Genetic/Genomic Nursing Competencies, 2009), APRNs, and all graduate nurses (Greco *et al.*, 2012).

16.5. NURSING PRACTICE

Advances in genomic science have arguably had the biggest impact on APRNs. This book is particularly relevant for nurse practitioners, nurse midwives, nurse anesthetists, and clinical nurse specialists. Professional APRN organizations have also begun to acknowledge the importance of genomics to clinical practice, as evidenced by the recent infusion of genomic competencies into some community practice standards (Expert Panel for Adult-Gerontology Clinical Nurse Specialist Competencies, 2010; NONPF Population-Focused Competencies Task Force, 2013). The Essential Genetic and Genomic Competencies for Nurses with Graduate Degrees (Greco *et al.*, 2012) provides a framework with detailed information about exactly what APRNs should know about genomics to provide the high quality care that the public has come to expect. Although the majority of the competencies apply to all nurses prepared at the graduate level, 10 in particular apply to nurses in direct patient care settings.

As a profession, nurses are trained to tailor health information to meet the needs of individuals with diverse educational levels and learning needs. Providing effective education about genomics can be particularly challenging because the science is new, complex, and often requires the educator to communicate using statistical probabilities. When caring for an individual or family with a genomic concern, APRNs should have a good understanding of the disorder (or know where to get reliable information about the condition), collect and interpret a detailed three-generation Family Health History (FHH), recognize genetic red flags (see Chapter 2) in the FHH or targeted physical examination, explain the mode of inheritance, estimate recurrence risks, generate referrals, order and interpret genetic and non-genetic diagnostic test results, and evaluate the effectiveness of genomic interventions.

APRNs should also be familiar with the clinical condition to fully discuss the benefits, risks, and limitations of a particular test and do all of this while assessing the impact of genomic information on family coping, communication, and functioning and while navigating the difficult family discussions that may arise when family members have different goals, attitudes, values, and/or beliefs. Finally, APRNs should also be prepared to collaborate with genetic professionals to develop management plans, incorporating genomic information and technology as appropriate. To provide effective, high-quality health care, APRNs need more than a basic understanding of genomics; they must also be capable of applying that knowledge at the point of care.

16.6. REFERENCES

American Association of Colleges of Nursing. (2008). The essentials of baccalaureate education for professional nursing practice. Retrieved from http://www.aacn.nche.edu/education-resources/BaccEssentials08.pdf

American Association of Colleges of Nursing. (2011). The essentials of masters education in nursing. Retrieved 11 November 2013 from http://www.aacn.nche.edu/education-resources/MastersEssentials11.pdf

Amercian Nurses Credentialing Center. (2015). Advanced Genetics Nursing. Retrieved from http://www.nursecredentialing.org/AdvancedGenetics

American Organization of Nurse Executives (AONE). (2004). Manager Inventory Tool. Retrieved 14 Feburary 2014 from http://www.aone.org/search?q=Manager+Inventory+Tool&site=AONE&client=AONE_FRONTEND_1&proxystylesheet=AONE_FRONTEND_1&output=xml&filter=0&oe=UTF-8

Anderson, G. (1996). The evolution and status of genetics education in nursing in the United States 1983–1995. *Image: Journal of Nursing Scholarship, 28*(2), 101–106.

Brantl, V. M., & Esslinger, P. N. (1962). Genetics implications for the nursing curriculum. *Nursing Forum, 1*(2), 90–100.

Burke, S., & Kirk, M. (2006). Genetics education in the nursing profession: literature review. *Journal Advanced Nursing, 54*(2), 228–237. doi: 10.1111/j.1365-2648.2006.03805.x

Calzone, K. A., Jenkins, J., Bakos, A. D., Cashion, A. K., Donaldson, N., Feero, W. G., . . . Webb, J. A. (2013). A blueprint for genomic nursing science. *Journal of Nursing Scholarship, 45*(1), 96–104. doi: 10.1111/jnu.12007

Calzone, K. A., Jenkins, J., Yates, J., Cusack, G., Wallen, G. R., Liewehr, D. J., . . . McBride, C. (2012).

Survey of nursing integration of genomics into nursing practice. *Journal of Nurings Scholarship, 44*(4), 428–436. doi: 10.1111/j.1547-5069.2012.01475.x

Calzone, K. A., Jerome-D'Emilia, B., Jenkins, J., Goldgar, C., Rackover, M., Jackson, J., . . . Feero, W. G. (2011). Establishment of the genetic/genomic competency center for education. *Journal of Nurings Scholarship, 43*(4), 351–358. doi: 10.1111/j.1547-5069.2011.01412.x

Caskey, S. (2013). Expanding RN Scope of Practice: A method for introducing a new competency into nursing practice (MINC). *Competency Focus, 7*(1).

Cohen, F. (1979). Genetic knowledge possessed by American nurses and nursing students. *Journal of Advanced Nursing, 4*, 493–501.

Consensus Panel on Genetic/Genomic Nursing Competencies. (2006). *Essential genetic and genomic nursing competencies, curricula guidelines, and outcome indicators.* Silver Spring, MD: American Nurses Association.

Consensus Panel Genetic/Genomic Nursing Competencies. (2009). *Essentials of genetic and genomic nursing competencies, curricula guidelines, and outcome indicators.* Silver Spring, MD: American Nurses Association.

Edwards, Q. T., Maradiegue, A., Seibert, D., Macri, C., & Sitzer, L. (2006). Faculty members' perceptions of medical genetics and its integration into nurse practitioner curricula. *Journal of Nursing Education, 45*(3), 124–130.

Expert Panel for Adult-Gerontology Clinical Nurse Specialist Competencies. (2010). Adult-Gerontology Clinical Nurse Specialist Competencies. Retrieved from http://www.aacn.nche.edu/geriatric-nursing/adultgerocnscomp.pdf

Greco, K. E., Tinley, S., & Seibert, D. (2012). *Essential genetic and genomic competencies for nurses with graduate degrees.* Silver Spring, MD: American Nurses Association and International Society of Nurses in Genetics.

Health Resources and Services Administration and the National Institutes of Health. (2000). *Report of the Expert Panel on Genetics and Nursing:Implications for Education and Practice.* Retrieved from: http://archive.hrsa.gov/newsroom/NewsBriefs/2002/geneticpanel.htm

Hoffman, M. A. (2007). The genome-enabled electronic medical record. *Journal of Biomedical Inform, 40*(1), 44–46. doi: 10.1016/j.jbi.2006.02.010

Institute of Medicine. (2013). The Economics of Genomic Medicine: Workshop Summary. Washington, DC: National Academies Press.

Jenkins, J., Grady, P. A., & Collins, F. S. (2005). Nurses and the genomic revolution. *Journal of Nursing Scholarship, 37*(2), 98–101.

Kirk, M., Calzone, K., Arimori, N., & Tonkin, E. (2011). Genetics-genomics competencies and nursing regulation. *Journal of Nursing Scholarship, 43*(2), 107–116. doi: 10.1111/j.1547-5069.2011.01388.x

Maradiegue, A., Edwards, Q. T., Seibert, D., Macri, C., & Sitzer, L. (2005). Knowledge, perceptions, and attitudes of advanced practice nursing students regarding medical genetics. *Journal of American Academy of Nurse Practice, 17*(11), 472–479. doi: 10.1111/j.1745-7599.2005.00076.x

McCarty, C. A., Chisholm, R. L., Chute, C. G., Kullo, I. J., Jarvik, G. P., Larson, E. B., . . . & eMERGE Team. (2011). The eMERGE Network: a consortium of biorepositories linked to electronic medical records data for conducting genomic studies. *BMC Medical Genomics, 4*(13). doi: 10.1186/1755-8794-4-13

National Human Genome Research Institute. (2013). Genome Nursing State of Science Research Recommendations. Retrieved from www.genome.gov/27549386

National Institute of Nursing Research. (January 21, 2015). Summer Genetics Institute (SGI) program description. Retrieved from https://www.ninr.nih.gov/training/trainingopportunitiesintramural/summergeneticsinstitute#.VagjqbdOUdU

NONPF Population-Focused Competencies Task Force. (2013). Population-Focused Nurse Practitioner Competencies. Retrieved from http://www.nonpf.org/?page=14

Prows, C. A., Hetteberg, C., Hopkin, R. J., Latta, K. K., & Powers, S. M. (2004). Development of a web based genetics institute for a nursing audience. *Journal of Continuing Eduation in Nursing, 35*(5), 223–231.

Tomic-Canic, M., Ayello, E. A., Stojadinovic, O., Golinko, M. S., & Brem, H. (2008). Using gene transcription patterns (bar coding scans) to guide wound debridement and healing. *Advances in Skin & Wound Care, 21*(10), 487–492. doi: 10.1097/01.ASW.0000323563.59885.1c

Turner, B. S., Strand, J., & Speer, M. C. (2006). Genetics Interdisciplinary Faculty Training (GIFT): integrating genetics into graduate nursing curricula. *Annual Review of Nursing Education, 4*, 23.

Williams, J. K., Prows, C. A., Conley, Y. P., Eggert, J., Kirk, M., & Nichols, F. (2011). Strategies to prepare faculty to integrate genomics into nursing education programs. *Journal of Nursing Scholarship, 43*(3), 231–238. doi: 10.1111/j.1547-5069.2011.01401.x

Williams, J. K., Skirton, H., & Masny, A. (2006). Ethics, policy, and educational issues in genetic testing. *Journal of Nursing Scholarship, 38*(2), 119–125.

Chapter 17

Genomic Technologies

YVETTE P. CONLEY, Ph.D

Objectives:

- Describe three different genomic technologies currently available and their clinical utility.
- Identify the challenges surrounding current genomic technologies.
- Summarize the role of future genomic technologies and the potential impact on personalized care.

17.1. INTRODUCTION

Technologies that more thoroughly, quickly, and accurately evaluate the genome are instrumental to increasing the utility of genomic data in the health care setting. This chapter discusses three key genomic technologies that are contributing to our understanding of the genomic underpinnings of health-related phenotypes and are increasingly being used for clinical decision making. These technologies are Next Generation Genome Sequencing, Gene Expression Profiling, and Epigenomics. Readers are cautioned that genomic technologies and their utility change very quickly and for this reason, online resources are supplied throughout this chapter to supply the reader access to reliable, updated information over time. The online resources are also useful for the reader who would like more in-depth information about any of the described technologies. Two additional online resources that provide general information include the National Human Genome Research Institute talking glossary that defines frequently used genetic terms (www.genome.gov/glossary) and Online Mendelian Inheritance in Man (OMIM), which provides a clinically relevant catalog that can be searched using the condition or gene of interest to attain up to date information within a genetic context (www.ncbi.nlm.nih.gov/OMIM).

17.2. NEXT GENERATION GENOME SEQUENCING

Sequencing provides information about the order of nucleotides (G, A, T, and C) in DNA, which can provide data on mutations and polymorphic variation in the genome. DNA sequencing is not a new technology. However, the rate that sequence data can be collected has increased significantly through techniques called next generation or massively parallel sequencing, which now allow DNA molecules to be sequenced in a parallel manner instead of one molecule at a time. In the past, clinical sequencing focused on small segments of the genome that usually involved interrogation of a specific gene or small panel of genes. With next generation sequencing, it is possible to answer clinical questions by sequencing much larger segments of the genome, including whole genome sequencing and whole exome sequencing. Whole genome sequencing interrogates the entire genome supplying nucleotide sequence data for all aspects of the genome, and includes all genes, as well as noncoding regions such as introns and regulatory regions. Whole exome sequencing collects nucleotide sequence data only for the coding regions of the genome, called the exome. Whole exome sequencing is more rapid and cheaper than whole genome sequencing, because it interrogates only about 1% of the genome; however that 1% is estimated to contain the majority of DNA variability contributing to health-related phenotypes (Choi *et al.*, 2009).

Clinical utility of next generation sequencing is gaining momentum and provides opportunities along with challenges, demonstrated by the ClinSeq project (Biesecker, 2012). The goals of the ClinSeq Project (www.genome.gov/205193550) are to enroll 1,500 participants to see how genomic variability relates to health, evaluate how best to return results to participants, and generate new ways to manage and analyze the large amount of DNA sequence data generated. Participants in the ClinSeq Project not only have their genomes sequenced, but also provide family and personal medical histories and undergo clinical and biochemical laboratory tests. In the past, DNA sequencing for clinical purposes focused on segments of the genome chosen, because they were implicated with a phenotype presenting in an individual or family. This approach is very useful for monogenic conditions, but less useful for more complex conditions that might be impacted by many genomic changes or monogenic conditions in which genomic variability outside the gene of interest impacts clinical presentation. Next generation sequencing addresses the issue of needing more coverage of the genome but brings with it some challenges. Exemplar challenges include how to handle the extensive variability in the genome when most of it is likely to be benign and how to handle incidental findings. Filtering variability in the data generated from whole genome or whole exome sequencing is necessary because some of the variability will impact an individual's health while most will not. Interestingly, as we learn more about variability in the genome and its clinical impact, what is considered clinically relevant versus benign will be a moving target. Therefore evaluation of a patient's genomic variability for clinical utility will not be a static evaluation, but one that requires revisiting, further emphasizing the need for ways to store and manage these data in a manner that facilitates clinical utility. Incidental findings within the context of genome sequencing occur when abnormalities in the DNA are uncovered that are known to impact health; however, that information was not anticipated by the patient. Examples of unintentional findings that could be

uncovered while conducting genome sequencing include mutations in cancer susceptibility genes and repeat mutations in a disease causing size range such as those known to cause Huntington disease. Health care professionals have to be prepared for communications with patients about incidental findings, including the patient's desire to have this information communicated to them, how best to deliver the information, and whether additional counseling may be indicated. How to deal with incidental findings stemming from genomic technologies is a timely, dynamic topic (Black *et al.*, 2013; Krier & Green, 2013; Wolf *et al.*, 2012).

An additional challenge worth noting is error rate and data quality of data generated through next generation sequencing (Su *et al.*, 2011). It is reasonable to think that error rates will decline and data quality improve over time as data collection platforms and data evaluation software for high throughput sequencing improve. However, it will always be important for health care providers who will rely upon the data to be able to evaluate the information provided in the report. A laboratory report, that should be generated using data collected in a Clinical Laboratory Improvement Amendments (CLIA) certified laboratory or stemming from genome or exome sequencing should have information related to coverage and quality of data. Genes or regions of the genome not covered because of technical difficulties or data quality concerns is an important piece of information for health care providers to have when assessing the results for a particular patient. Additionally, resequencing or otherwise confirming findings that will be used to make health care decisions is prudent.

17.3. GENE EXPRESSION PROFILING

Evaluation of gene expression provides information on the extent that a gene is actively transcribed (expressed) in a particular tissue of interest. DNA sequence provides the information that is used to code for messenger RNA (mRNA) through a process called transcription, which is a necessary step in the process to producing proteins in our cells. It is the mRNA that is assessed in a gene expression evaluation. Gene expression evaluations provide important information because although all genes are present in the DNA of all cells, all genes are not active to the same extent in every cell. Under normal circumstances genes are active in cells where the gene product is supposed to be made. Some health-related phenotypes are known to be due to a gene being expressed that should not be (e.g., expression of a proto-oncogene in a cell where it has long been inactivated results in it acting like an oncogene), or a gene not being expressed or expressed to a lesser extent than is should be (e.g., a tumor suppressor gene). Gene expression evaluation is not a new technology; however, the increased number of genes, including those that code for microRNAs (miRNA) (Ryu *et al.*, 2011), that can be simultaneously evaluated along with the increased sensitivity of newer technologies have resulted in greater clinical applicability of gene expression data.

Gene expression data collection can focus on one gene, a pathway of related genes, a specific group of genes validated for a phenotype, or all genes within the genome at once. Whole genome expression evaluation is also termed transcriptome evaluation. More information is available from the Transcriptome Fact Sheet (www.genome.gov/13014330) that is sponsored by the National Human Genome Research Institute.

Although whole genome gene expression studies have great utility for researching the biological underpinnings of health-related phenotypes, clinical utility of gene expression profiling currently involves interrogation of a group of genes that have been validated for a phenotype. For example, gene expression profiling has revolutionized care of the patient diagnosed with breast cancer. Breast cancer at the cellular level is very heterogeneous, and as a result, one size fits all prognoses and treatments are not optimal. Tailoring recurrence risk and optimized treatment regimens that are based on gene profiling of the breast cancer cells from the patient has resulted in individualizing the intensity of therapy and therapies targeted toward the biological abnormalities specific to the patient's cancer. Researchers initially found genes that were over- or under-expressed in breast cancer cells versus normal surrounding breast cancer cells from the same individual using whole genome expression evaluations. These studies utilized predesigned panels, using technology often referred to as microarrays, which allowed for all genes in the genome to be evaluated simultaneously. After replication and validation of the findings from these studies, expression levels of a group of genes appeared to be sensitive and reliable enough to use in clinical trials designed to individualize treatment regimens for women with early stage breast cancer. Many of the genes found to exhibit increased or decreased expression in early stage breast cancer cells were, not surprisingly, oncogenes, tumor suppressor genes, and genes that otherwise play a role in cell cycling. The use of gene expression profiling to assist in treatment decision-making for early stage breast cancer is now standard of care in most settings. To facilitate the utility of these profiles, several commercial testing options exist. Options that are currently available include, but are not limited to, Oncotype DX® (www.oncotypedx.com/) and MammaPrint®, which is now integrated with other genomic profiling assays into a suite of profiles called Symphony™ (www.agendia.com/). However, it should be noted that there are changes made to the profiles as our knowledge of how these genes impact patient outcomes and response to therapy expands, and companies offering the commercially available profiling are subject to change. Therefore, these examples are offered just as an exemplar of current commercial offerings; readers are encouraged to visit the online resources to attain more recent information about the utility of gene expression profiling for breast cancer. Additionally, although breast cancer is used as an example, the clinical utility and validity of gene expression profiling has extended to other cancers and research continues that will extend gene expression profiling to noncancer phenotypes.

17.4. EPIGENOMICS

Epigenomics refers to the chemical modifications to DNA or the packaging of DNA that impact gene regulation and gene expression. Epigenetics is the focus on one gene of interest, whereas epigenomics is the focus on many genes or the entire genome simultaneously. In this chapter, the term epigenomics is used to encompass both. It is important to point out that although the material interrogated for epigenomic evaluations is DNA, the sequence of nucleotides and the variability inherent in DNA are not the target of these evaluations. Epigenomics consists of molecular modifications to the DNA that impact whether a gene or genes will be expressed, without changes to the nucleotides of the DNA. Although epigenomics is not a new field of inquiry, it may appear to be because our understanding of these modifications, our ability to assess them, and the clinical applications of the modifications have recently evolved so rapidly. The current field of epigenomics focuses mainly on four dynamic molecular mechanisms (Diamandis, Sidransky, Laird, Cairns, & Bapat, 2010): histone modification, chromatin remodeling, microRNA (miRNA), and methylation of DNA (http://www.ncbi.nlm.nih.gov/epigenomics). Post translational modifications of proteins that interact with DNA, known as histones, impacts the ability of these proteins to package DNA and, therefore, whether a gene will be expressed or not. The combination of DNA plus proteins related to its packaging is called chromatin. Tightly packaged chromatin results in genes within that region of genome being down-regulated (lower or no gene expression), whereas more loosely packaged chromatin results in genes within that region being up-regulated (higher gene expression). Micro RNA, mentioned briefly in the section on gene expression profiling, are short

pieces of RNA that interact with corresponding messenger (mRNA) so that the specific template of mRNA is not available for protein production. This ultimately results in that gene being down-regulated. Interestingly, miRNAs are coded for by genes that themselves are epigenetically regulated, adding to the complexity of gene regulation. DNA methylation is a chemical modification to the DNA that involves adding methyl groups to cytosines (Cs) within cytosine-guanine (CG) rich regions of DNA known as CpG islands. Genes are down-regulated when DNA is hypermethylated while active genes reside in regions of hypomethylated DNA. More information is available from the Epigenomics Fact Sheet (www.genome.gov/27532724) that is sponsored by the National Human Genome Research Institute.

Although all of the previously mentioned epigenomic mechanisms have the potential to impact health related phenotypes and provide potential therapeutic avenues, DNA methylation is the mechanism that has received the most attention and is experiencing the most clinical utility to date. As mentioned above in the section on gene expression profiling, genes are often turned on when they are not supposed to be and are turned off when they are supposed to be active, and this

TABLE 17.1. Examples of Genetic/Genomic Technology Tools and Resources.

Resources	Purpose	Website
Government Sponsored Clinical Trials	Clinical Trials funded by NIH	www.clinicaltrials.gov
ClinSeq Project	Clinical Trial—How genomic variability relates to health	www.genome.gov/205193550
ColoVantage® test	Quest Diagnostics test for individuals who are non-adherent to traditional colorectal screening methods	http://www.questdiagnostics.com/home/physicians/testing-services/by-test-name/colovantage/about
Epigenomics Fact Sheet	Epigenomic Mechanisms	www.genome.gov/27532724
Epigenomic Mechanisms	Explore genome-wide maps of DNA and histone modifications from database	http://www.ncbi.nlm.nih.gov/epigenomics
Online Mendelian Inheritance in Man	Provides a clinically relevant catalog that can be searched using condition or gene of interest to attain up to date information within a genetic context	www.ncbi.nlm.nih.gov/omim
Oncotype DX®	Gene expression profiling to assist treatment decision for early stage breast cancer	www.oncotypedx.com
Symphony™	Gene expression profiling to assist treatment decision for early stage breast cancer	www.agendia.com
Talking Glossary	Defines frequently used genetic terms	www.genome.gov/glossary
Transcriptome Fact Sheet	Whole genome expression evaluation	www.genome.gov/13014330

can result in abnormal phenotypes. A mechanism that can account for the abnormal gene expressions that result in abnormal phenotypes is DNA methylation, in which hypermethylation of a gene turns off a gene that is supposed to be active (e.g., a tumor suppressor gene) or hypomethylation turns on a gene that is supposed to be inactive (e.g., an oncogene) (Fernandez *et al.*, 2012; Feinberg & Tycko, 2004; Fraga *et al.*, 2004; Lujambio *et al.*, 2008; Su *et al.*, 2012). Like gene expression profiling, epigenomics can evaluate DNA methylation patterns across the entire genome, which is very valuable to researchers attempting to understand the biological underpinning for a phenotype. However, clinical utility of DNA methylation involves evaluation of DNA methylation for one gene or a small group of validated genes (Ned, Melillo, & Marrone 2011), and similar to clinical utility of gene expression profiling, much of the clinical utility of DNA methylation assays are focused on cancer-related phenotypes. Exemplar DNA methylation based assays are those that have great potential for colorectal cancer screening. One example assay assesses the methylation pattern of the vimentin gene from DNA extracted from stool (ColoSure™) and another assesses the methylation pattern of the septin9 gene from DNA extracted from a blood sample (ColoVantage®) (Ned *et al.*, 2011; Warren *et al.*, 2011). Of interest, the ColoVantage® test has been licensed and is offered by Quest Diagnostics, with the focus of the test on individuals who are nonadherent to traditional colorectal screening methods (www.questdiagnostics.com/home/physicians/testing-services/by-test-name/colovantage/about.html).

17.5. CONCLUSION

The three genomic technologies discussed in this chapter represent state of the science approaches for research that are becoming more commonly used in health care settings. Health care providers should have a basic understanding of these technologies as more applications are emerging. Readers are encouraged to visit www.clinicaltrials.gov and search using key words such as DNA methylation, gene profiling, and genome sequencing to get an up-to-date idea of the number of clinical trials using these emerging technologies. Given the number of clinical

trials currently underway, there is great potential for these technologies to continue to impact how health care is delivered in the future.

17.6. REFERENCES

Biesecker, L. G. (2012). Opportunities and challenges for the integration of massively parallel genomic sequencing into clinical practice: lessons from the ClinSeq project. *Genetics in Medicine, 14*(4), 393–398. doi:10.1038/gim.2011.78.

Black, L., Avard, D., Zawati, M.H., Knoppers, B.M., Hebert, J., & Sauvageau, G. (2013) Funding considerations for the disclosure of genetic incidental findings in biobank research. *Clinical Genetics 84*(5), 397–406. doi: 10.1111/cge.12190.

Choi, M., Scholl, U. I., Ji, W., Liu, T., Tikhonova, I. R., Zumbo, P., . . . Lifton, R.P. (2009). Genetic diagnosis by whole exome capture and massively parallel DNA sequencing. *Proceedings of the National Academy of Science USA, 106*(45), 19096–19101. doi:10.1073/pnas.0910672106.

Diamandis, E. P., Sidransky, D., Laird, P. W., Cairns, P., & Bapat, B. (2010). Epigenomicsbased diagnostics. *Clinical Chemistry, 56*(8), 1216–1219. doi:10.1373/clinchem.2010.148007.

Feinberg, A. P., & Tycko, B. (2004). The history of cancer epigenetics. *Nature Reviews Cancer, 4*(2), 143–153. doi:10.1038/nrc1279.

Fernandez, A. F., Assenov, Y., Martin-Subero, J. I., Balint, B., Siebert, R., Taniguchi, H., . . . Esteller, M. (2012). A DNA methylation fingerprint of 1628 human samples. *Genome Research, 22*(2), 407–419. doi:10.1101/gr.119867.110.

Fraga, M. F., Herranz, M., Espada, J., Ballestar, E., Paz, M. F., Ropero, S., . . . Esteller, M. (2004). A mouse skin multistage carcinogenesis model reflects the aberrant DNA methylation patterns of human tumors. *Cancer Research, 64*(16), 5527–5534. doi:10.1158/0008-5472.CAN-03-4061.

Krier, J. B. & Green, R. C. (2013). Management of incidental findings in clinical genomic sequencing. In *Current Protocols in Human Genetics*, 9.23.1–9.23.13, Supplement 77. doi: 10.1002/0471142905.hg0923s77.

Lujambio, A., Calin, G. A., Villanueva, A., Ropero, S., Sanchez-Cespedes, M., Blanco, D., . . . & Esteller, M. (2008). A microRNA DNA methylation signature for human cancer metastasis. *Proceeding of the National Academy of Science USA, 105*(36), 13556–13561. doi:10.1073/pnas.0803055105.

Ned, R. M., Melillo, S., & Marrone, M. (2011, March). Fecal DNA testing for Colorectal Cancer Screening: the ColoSure test. *PLoS Currents, 3*. doi:10.1371/currents.RRN1220. Retrieved from: http://www.ncbi.nlm.nih.gov/pmc/articles/PMC3050633/

Ryu, S., Joshi, N., McDonnell, K., Woo, J., Choi, H.,

Gao, D., . . . Mittal, V.(2011). Discovery of novel human breast cancer microRNAs from deep sequencing data by analysis of pri-micro RNA secondary structures. *PLoS One, 6*(2):e16403. doi: 10.1371/journal. pone.0016403. Retrieved from http://www.plosone. org/article/info%3Adoi%2F10.1371%2Fjournal. pone.0016403

Su, P. H., Lin, Y. W., Huang, R. L., Liao, Y. P., Lee, H. Y., Wang, H. C, . . . Lai, L.C. (2012). Epigenetic silencing of PTPRR activates MAPK signaling, promotes metastasis and serves as a biomarker of invasive cervical cancer. *Oncogene.* doi:10.1038/ onc.2012.29.

Su, Z., Ning, B., Fang, H., Hong, H., Perkins, R., Tong, W., & Shi, L. (2011). Next-generation sequencing and its applications in molecular diagnostics. *Expert Review of Molecular Diagnostics, 11*(3), 333-343. doi:10.1586/erm.11.3.

Warren, J. D., Xiong, W., Bunker, A. M., Vaughn, C. P., Furtado, L. V., Roberts, W. L., . . . Heichman, K.A. (2011). Septin 9 methylated DNA is a sensitive and specific blood test for colorectal cancer. *BMC Medicine, 9* (133). doi:10.1186/1741-7015-9-133.

Wolf, S.M., Crock, B.N., Van Ness, B., Lawrenz, F., Kahn, J.P., Beskow, L.M., . . . Wolf, W.A. (2012). Managing Incidental findings and research results in genomic research involving biobanks and archived data sets. *Genetics in Medicine, 14*(4), 361–384, doi: 10.1038/gim.2012.23.

Chapter 18

Genomics and Symptomatology

QUANNETTA T. EDWARDS, Ph.D, FNP-BC, WHNP-BC, AGN-BC, FAANP
SUSAN T. TINLEY, Ph.D, RN, CGC (RET)
DIANE C. SEIBERT, Ph.D, ARNP, FAANP, FAAN
ANN H. MARADIEGUE, Ph.D, FNP-BC, FAANP

Objectives:

- Discuss the impact of genomics on cancer related fatigue.
- Discuss the genes associated with pain.
- Explain the role of nursing regarding genomics and symptomatology.

18.1. INTRODUCTION

An individual's genome impacts the trajectory of their health and illness throughout life. Thus far, the focus of this book has been on the impact of genomics as it relates to an individual's response to drugs, their risk for developing diseases based on their family history, or as a result of shared genetic and environmental factors. Beyond health, illness, and the effectiveness of drugs, genomics also influences how an individual experiences a particular disorder—or the *symptomatology* of that condition. Research examining the genetics of common symptoms offers the promise of reducing adverse symptoms and improving quality of life, which is particularly important, because symptom management is a key function for nursing.

In this chapter, brief overviews of two common symptoms are discussed These symptoms are *cancer-related fatigue* and *pain*, as each of these symptoms have been shown to be influenced by genomic discoveries. The role of genomic variants (i.e., single nucleotide polymporphisms [SNPs]) influencing the onset, duration, or severity of symptoms, as well as how they influence therapeutic responses in preventing, alleviating, or eliminating patient's symptoms, will be discussed. Where applicable, other influences that may potentiate the effects of genomic variants in symptom manifestation and treatment

will be described. Genomic advances in symptom management will help ensure that the right person receives the right therapy (personalized or precision health care), will reduce adverse effects, and will improve both quality of life and overall health outcomes.

18.2. GENOMICS AND CANCER-RELATED FATIGUE

Fatigue is a symptom manifested in patients that is associated with a wide range of diseases and syndromes that often affect individual's physical, social, and mental functioning (Landmark-Hoyvik *et al.*, 2010). It is also one of the most commonly reported symptoms in individuals diagnosed with cancer, often resulting in increased stress and anxiety and other health-related quality of life issues including, but not limited to, impaired physical performance, inactivity, helplessness, sleep disturbances, lack of appetite, and/or depression (Escalante, Kallen, Valdres, Morrow, & Manzullo, 2010; Horneber, Fischer, Dimeo, Ruffer, & Weis, 2012; Saligan & Kim, 2012). *Cancer-related fatigue* (CRF) is defined as a "distressing, persistent, subjective sense of tiredness or exhaustion related to cancer or cancer treatment that is not proportional to recent activity and interferes with usual functioning" (National Comprehensive Cancer Network (NCCN), 2015m p. MS-3). The symptoms of

CRF can occur during and after treatment of the cancer and are often attributed to treatment regimens, such as cytotoxic chemotherapy, radiation therapy, or other biological treatments. However, CRF can vary, occurring any time in the course of disease, and may be self-limiting or persisting for many years even after treatment (Bower *et al.*, 2006; Horneber *et al.*, 2012). For example, in one longitudinal study of breast cancer survivors, approximately 34% of the participants reported fatigue 5 to 10 years after diagnosis (Bower *et al.*, 2006). Similar effects regarding fatigue persistence after diagnosis and treatment have been reported (Husson *et al.*, 2013; Hwang *et al.*, 2014).

Fatigue among patients with cancer can be associated with multifactorial etiologies and manifest in a myriad of clinical features (Horneber *et al.*, 2012; NCCN, 2015). Contributing factors to fatigue include pain, emotional distress, sleep disturbances, and co-morbidities such as anemia; poor nutrition; physical inactivity; medication side effects; alcohol and/or substance abuse; therapeutic management with cytotoxic, biologic, or radiation therapy; or other medical conditions (National Cancer Institute, 2013; NCCN, 2015). However, the diagnostic criteria for CRF include fatigue, distress, or impairment due to fatigue, etiology related to cancer or cancer treatment, and the exclusion of underlying psychiatric or medical disorders. CRF is common, with studies revealing varied prevalence estimates ranging from 25% to 99% of patients with cancer experiencing this symptom, depending on the population and type of assessment (Bower, 2007). Most common clinical manifestations of CRF are focused on fatigue, lack of energy, exhaustion, or impaired physical function that can affect physical or psychosocial well-being of the individual (Horneber *et al.*, 2012).

The exact biological mechanisms of CRF are unknown; however, some proposed mechanisms associated with the symptom include 5-HT3 neurotransmitter deregulation, disturbances in hypothalamic regulation, dysregulation in circadian rhythm, skeletal muscle wasting, pro-inflammatory cytokines, or dysregulation of inflammatory cytokines (Barsevick *et al.*, 2013; Bower & Lamkin, 2013; Horneber *et al.*, 2012; NCCN, 2015; Ryan *et al.*, 2007). Genomic factors associated with inflammation have been linked to CRF prior

to, during, and after treatment, particularly in the pro-inflammatory cytokine network (Bower & Lamkin, 2013). Molecular-genetics, particularly gene polymorphisms, have shown to possibly play an important role in the mechanism of CRF. One example is that of proinflammatory cytokine SNP that influences interleukin (IL) and/or tumor necrosis factor (TNF) genes (i.e., *IL1B; IL-6; TNFα*) and is associated with CRF both during and after treatment (Aouizerat *et al.*, 2009; Bower, 2007; Bower & Lamkin, 2013; Miaskowski *et al.*, 2010). Alteration in pro-inflammatory cytokine production of *IL6* and other inflammatory markers has been linked with persistent fatigue among breast cancer survivors (Bower *et al.*, 2006; Collado-Hidalgo, Bower, Ganz, Cole, & Irwin, 2006). Persistent CRF among patients with breast cancer has also been found to be associated with increased activity of pro-inflammatory transcription factors NF-κB activity and decreased expression of glucorticoid receptor anti-inflammatory transcription factors (Bower, Ganz, Irwin, Arevalo, & Cole, 2011). The association with CRF and cytokines, the proteins that mediate cell-to-cell communication, may be due to dysregulation of cytokines often attributed to cancer and cancer treatments that increase plasma levels of many cytokines, particularly the *TNF-α* and certain *IL* genes (Ahlberg, Ekmanb, Gaston-Johansson, & Mock, 2003; Ryan *et al.*, 2007). Cytokines are important for the development and functioning of the immune response, and aberrant expression from genetic polymorphisms have been associated with overall disease and functionality (Smith & Humphries, 2009). Pro-inflammatory cytokines, particularly *IL-1B, IL-6* and *TNF-α*, are thought to induce symptoms of fatigue via signaling of the central nervous system through varied somnogenic influence (Weschenfelder, Sander, Kluge, Kirkby, & Himmerich, 2012).

The nuclear factor NF-κB, pro-inflammatory transcription factor, for example, is activated by the cancerous tumor microenvironment (Aggarwal, 2004) and, thus, pretreatment CRF may be due to tumorigenesis (Bower & Lamkin, 2013). Fatigue often occurs also during treatment, particularly due to chemotherapy or radiation therapy; this effect has been associated with elevations in inflammatory markers secondary to the therapeutic intervention. For example, in one study, changes in inflammatory markers, including C-reactive protein and IL1 receptor antagonist, were found to be associated with fatigue symptoms among certain individuals with breast and ovarian cancer (Bower *et al.*, 2009). CRF has been found to occur years after completion of therapy in breast cancer survivors and alterations in proinflammatory markers also have been found among these individuals (Collado-Hidalgo *et al.*, 2006; Orre *et al.*, 2009).

Besides pro-inflammatory genes, other genomic factors are currently being studied to determine their impact on fatigue among cancer patients. For example, the relationship between dysfunction in certain mitochondrial genes has been found among prostate cancer patients receiving external beam radiation (Hsiao, Wang, Kaushal, & Saligan, 2013). Advances in genomic technologies will certainly change the face of understanding the molecular impact of genetics and CRF that will enhance predicting and managing the symptoms and improving outcomes.

18.2.1. Future Implications—Cancer Related Fatigue and Genomics

Although many studies have shown an association with varied inflammatory markers and CRF among patients with cancer, causality has not been established and gaps in knowledge continue, warranting further research in this area (Saligan & Kim, 2012). Specifically, problems exist regarding measurement of CRF, exact understanding of the underlying biology of the symptom, and clinical trials targeted towards CRF (Barsevick *et al.*, 2013). However, future links between CRF and inflammatory markers may be a means to provide personalized/precision medicine as a prognostic biomarker for fatigue among cancer patients or genetic predictors of fatigue for therapeutic management (Collado-Hidalgo *et al.*, 2006; Jim *et al.*, 2012), as well as future development of effective treatments such as cytokine antagonists targeting CRF (Bower & Lamkin, 2013). Further, because fatigue is a complex symptom with phenotypic heterogeneity, the inclusion of biobehavioral research of fatigue may provide clarity and contribute to the understanding of CRF and to future development of genetic/genomic interventions (Lyon, McCain, Pickler, Munro, & Elswick, 2011). The international and interdisciplinary *GeneQoL Consortium* is one means to improve patient outcomes regarding issues that impact quality of life, including that of fatigue (GeneQol Consortium, 2015; Sprangers *et al.*, 2009). This consortium was established to investigate genetic disposition of patient-reported quality-of-life outcomes in order to gain insight on the impact of disease and treatment on patient outcomes (GeneQol Consortium, 2015). Clinical implications of the consortium are based on obtaining genetic knowledge, including understanding biological pathways that may impact quality of life (GeneQol Consortium, 2015), and incorporating understanding of the biological and genetic mechanisms of CRF (Barsevick, Frost, Zwinderman, Hall, & Halyard, 2010).

18.3. GENOMICS AND PAIN

Pain is universal and has been described since antiquity, and yet the biochemical pathways and pathophysiologic underpinnings of pain are only now beginning to be unraveled. An excellent review of the history of pain and pain management can be found in the article by Meldrum (2003). Despite the lack of understanding and effective therapies to manage pain, helping patients and families cope with the manifestations of pain has been a central feature and core mission area for nurses since at least the 19th century, when Florence Nightingale discussed pain management in "Notes on Nursing" (Nightingale, 1860). Since then, many resources have been developed to improve nursing competency in pain management, including a pain management nursing certification awarded by the American Nurses Credentialing Center; establishment of the American Society for Pain Management Nursing (ASPMN) in 1991, which publishes a journal dedicated entirely to nursing management of pain; and nursing competencies focused on pain management (http://mbon.maryland.gov/Documents/pain_management.pdf).

Over 100 million Americans suffer from pain every year (Institute of Medicine ([U.S.] Committee on Advancing Pain Research, 2011), and a recent study estimates that chronic pain is more expensive than cancer, heart disease, and diabetes, costing up to $635 billion a year (i.e., up to $300 billion in direct costs and $334 billion in lost productivity) (Gaskin & Richard, 2012). Pain, a very important signaling mechanism in animals, plays a significant role in survival, because it forces the animal to protect an injury until it heals. Pain becomes chronic when the noxious stimuli persists after healing is complete, evolving into pain without a purpose. The *experience* of pain is highly variable; some people who experience acute pain from a noxious agent will develop chronic pain whereas others, exposed to the same causative agent, will not (Mogil, 2012). The *perception* of pain is highly individualized and subjective as well, as indicated by pain rating scores used in research and clinical settings. Finally, there is marked individualized variability in *response to analgesics*, with some people responding to very small doses and others requiring much larger doses to feel an effect (Aubrun, Langeron, Quesnel, Coriat, & Riou, 2003). All of this variability raises questions about the possibility that genetic factors could influence the experience of pain. More than 350 candidate genes have been associated with variability in pain sensitivity, and twin studies have clarified the heritability of pain in several specific conditions; however, to date, there are still many unanswered questions related to the basic genetic underpinnings of pain (Smith & Muralidharan, 2012).

Several classification systems have been developed to guide pain assessment and management. Some of the most common categorization systems include stratifying pain as acute or chronic, based on the length of time it has been present, or by intensity (mild to moderate, or severe). Numeric pain scales were developed to attempt to capture pain intensity. Physiologic changes (nociceptive, neuropathic, and inflammatory) and manifestations based on the affected tissue types (skin, muscles, viscera, joints, tendons, and bones) have also been used to categorize pain. Some diseases have classic pain characteristics; therefore, pain has been clustered by syndrome (cancer, fibromyalgia, migraine, etc.) (University of Wisconsin, 2014). This chapter reviews just a few of the areas being explored in the genomics of pain.

A few rare single gene disorders are associated with alterations in pain sensation, such as paroxysmal pain or a complete inability to feel pain. Although at first glance the genes appear to involve seemingly unrelated functional protein classes, on closer inspection, almost all the pathways involve the *SCN9A* gene in one way or another (Mogil, 2012). *SCN9A* encodes for the alpha subunit of the NaV1.7 sodium channel, expressed primarily in peripheral sensory nerves that transmit pain, touch, and smell signals to the central nervous system (Mogil, 2012). The role that *SCN9A* plays in more common pain responses is less clear (Young, Lariviere, & Belfer, 2012). Some studies have shown that variations in *SCN9A* alter pain responses (e.g., individuals with a G allele on *SCN9A* report lower pain scores compared with individuals having the less common A allele); other studies have been unable to consistently replicate those findings (Starkweather & Pair, 2013)

Genome wide association studies (GWAS) are changing the landscape of genomic research. GWAS tools such as computerized databases containing the reference human genome sequence, a map of human genetic variation, and new analytic technologies that can cheaply, rapidly, and accurately analyze whole-genome are making it possible to locate the genes associated with common diseases, such as asthma, diabetes, and heart disease. Once a new gene has been located, new strategies to detect, prevent, and/or treat a particular disorder can be developed.

Despite the rapid advances made in fields such as cardiology, oncology and hematology using GWAS, research into the genes associated with pain has lagged for several reasons. Reasons include the subjective nature of pain, relatively low funding levels, and associated lack of interest from researchers (Mogil, 2012). More recently, however, more research has been done to examine the genetic underpinnings of pain associated with diseases such as migraine headaches, osteoarthritis, endometriosis, Crohn's disease, and temporomandibular disorder (TMD) (Young *et al.*, 2012). Some of the genes found in these studies include a mutation in *ZNF429* and a gene upstream of the *RHBDF2* gene, whose function is currently unknown. Although no polymorphisms have been found in any of the known opioid receptor genes, ethnic differences appear to play an important role, because the strongest effect in one study was country of origin (Mogil, 2012). Despite the progress that has recently been made in understanding the genes associated with pain response, significant hurdles remain, such as technology and data analysis limitations, explaining phenotypic heterogeneity, and the costs associated with conducting GWAS, which typically involve genotyping large numbers of people (Young *et al.*, 2012).

18.3.1. Epigenetics and Pain

As scientific understanding of epigenetic processes has increased over the past decade, there has been a concurrent surge of research exploring epigenetic mechanisms involved in regulating the nervous system, particularly the epigenetic processes associated with memory and synaptic plasticity (Denk & McMahon, 2012). Recent studies have found that epigenetic control is particularly important in three distinct areas: peripheral inflammation, pain processing, and plasticity.

When the body is exposed to a physical, chemical, or biologic insult, an inflammatory response develops rapidly to remove or destroy the injurious material, setting the stage for tissue repair and healing. Inflammation is commonly associated with pain, redness, heat, and swelling, which have been shown to increase healing, either because the injured person protects that area or because inflammatory cells, such as macrophages, produce high levels of insulin-like growth factor-1 (IGF-1), which increases the rate of healing and muscle regeneration (Lu *et al.*, 2011). The inflammatory response is highly complex, involving genes involved in a number of different processes, such as antimicrobial defense, immune response, tissue repair, and remodeling. Epigenetic changes in genes regulating macrophage function may play a particularly important role in inflammatory response, because they help macrophages change in response to different infectious organisms (Bayarsaihan, 2011). Epigenetic changes in T cells and monocytes, transcription factors found in several protein families (NF-κB, FOXP3, IRF, STAT), RE1silencing transcription factors (REST), and histones (i.e., histone H4 hyperacetylation) have all been shown to regulate inflammatory response (Bayarsaihan, 2011; Selvi, Mohankrishna, Ostwal, & Kundu, 2010).

Inflammation persisting beyond the normal healing period is considered "chronic inflammation" characterized by chronic infiltration of mononuclear immune cells and low antioxidant and high free radicals levels, creating an environment in which tissue healing is occurring at the same time tissue is being damaged, become a self-perpetuating cycle of injury, repair and usually, pain (Khansari, Shakiba, & Mahmoudi, 2009). Identifying the epigenetic mechanisms associated with the development of chronic pain may open the door to much needed advances in pain management (Denk & McMahon, 2012; Mogil, 2012). Epigenetic regulation of tissues in the nervous system is of particular interest, because these are the cells that generate and transmit pain signals, but also because the regeneration rate of individual neurons in the nervous system is very slow. The same neuron is likely to survive for decades, and because DNA is very resistant to change, epigenetic adjustments that occur over the life of the cell may be critical as they continually adapt to environmental stressors (Seo *et al.*, 2013). A neuron's use of epigenetics to adapt to the environment is particularly important because such changes are reversible; therefore, if pain develops because of an epigenetic change, a drug that chemically "resets" the neuron to its normal state might be a powerful therapeutic tool (Seo *et al.*, 2013). Although there is evidence from animal studies to demonstrate that it is possible to modify epigenetic mechanisms with drugs (Geranton, 2012), more research needs to be done before human studies can begin to ensure that the drugs do not alter epigenetic mechanisms in other tissues (Crow, Denk, & McMahon, 2013).

Reinforcing the idea that epigenetics plays an important role in the development and perception of pain, data from genomic studies examining pain response is often contradictory. For example, *ORPM1*, a common m-opioid receptor variant, has been shown to increase ben-dorphin binding and activation of g-proteins in some studies, but this effect is not found in all studies on a consistent basis. Similarly, in some studies, individuals with *COMT* variations were found to have greater sensitivity to pain, but the same association has not been seen in other studies (Bond *et al.*, 1998; Kim *et al.*, 2004; Zubieta *et al.*, 2003). These inconsistencies suggest that factors, such as epigenetics, may play an important role in pain phenotypes (Seo *et al.*, 2013)

Opioids are used to treat pain on a routine basis, and many opioids are now approved for use, each of which has different efficacy and adverse response profiles based on the individual. If an individual has a poor response to one opioid, another is usually tried in a trial and error fashion until the most effective drug is found. Because this random approach exposes individuals to adverse effects and decreases quality of life, as the search for an effective analgesic agent continues, there has been considerable interest in finding the genetic factors that explain the variability in response to opioids (Branford, Droney, & Ross, 2012).

Several studies have found an association between the *A118G* SNP in *OPRM1* and opioid dosing (Chou *et al.*, 2006a; Chou *et al.*, 2006b; Reyes-Gibby *et al.*, 2007), but similar to the issues with *OPRM1* mentioned above, a meta-analysis of genetic association studies concluded that the *A118G* SNP is inconsistently associated with pain-related phenotypes (Walter & Lotsch, 2009). It is becoming clear that the genes associated with pain relief are not the same genes that influence the development of adverse effects, highlighting the need to carefully choose and define the phenotype being studied. It is also very likely that interactions among multiple genetic and environmental factors are playing important roles in the phenotype (Branford *et al.*, 2012).

Acute pain transforms into chronic pain in a complex series of discrete pathophysiologic and histopathologic steps involving more than 2000 gene changes in over 400 candidate genes. Broadly, the process involves neurons that abandon the normal "modulated" response to pain (reversible activation of intracellular signal-transduction cascades) and adopt a more persistent "modified" response involving relatively permanent changes to neuron activation (Voscopoulos & Lema, 2010). A growing body of evidence suggests that nociceptor modifications can occur in response to psychological triggers, further complicating research efforts (Diatchenko, Fillingim, Smith, & Maixner, 2013).

Understanding the genomics of individual variability in pain sensitivity, analgesic response, adverse reactions, and triggers that transform acute to chronic pain is still in its infancy. Once the genomic roadmap has been created, the highly complex interactions between the environment and the human genes that regulate the pain re-

sponse can then be explored, leading to a more effective and safe personalized approach to pain management.

18.4. NURSING ROLE AND SYMPTOMATOLOGY

Symptom management applies to nurses prepared at every level and practicing in virtually every setting—from nurses providing direct care to patients in inpatient and outpatient settings to conducting genomic research and to nursing faculty and nurses leading the largest health care systems. Nurses working at the point of care should be familiar with the emerging genetic information that helps support decisions that can improve the care of an individual patient, the goal of precision and personalized care. Nurses in faculty roles are responsible for ensuring that students entering nursing are well informed about genetics and are prepared to use emerging genomic information to improve patient outcomes. Nurse researchers might want to focus their scientific efforts on exploring the biological and behavioral aspects of symptoms such as pain and fatigue, with the goal of developing new knowledge and new strategies for improving patient health and quality of life (National Institute of Nursing Research, nd). Nurse administrators play a critical role, because they serve in key leadership roles as systems begin to integrate genomic discoveries into clinical settings in a meaningful way. Their support can accelerate nurses' use of genomic information as it continues to emerge from large population based studies.

18.5. REFERENCES

Aggarwal, B. B. (2004). Nuclear factor-kappaB: the enemy within. *Cancer Cell, 6*(3), 203–208. doi: 10.1016/j.ccr.2004.09.003

Ahlberg, K., Ekmanb, T., Gaston-Johansson, F., & Mock, V. (2003). Assessment and management of cancer-related fatigue in adults. *The Lancet, 362*(9384), 640–650. doi: 10.1016/S0140-6736(03)14186-4

Aouizerat, B. E., Dodd, M., Lee, K., West, C., Paul, S. M., Cooper, B. A., . . . & Miaskowski, C. (2009). Preliminary evidence of a genetic association between tumor necrosis factor alpha and the severity of sleep disturbance and morning fatigue. *Biol Res Nurs, 11*(1), 27–41. doi: 10.1177/1099800409333871

Aubrun, F., Langeron, O., Quesnel, C., Coriat, P., &

Riou, B. (2003). Relationships between measurement of pain using visual analog score and morphine requirements during postoperative intravenous morphine titration. *Anesthesiology, 98*(6), 1415–1421.

Barsevick, Frost, M., Zwinderman, A., Hall, P., & Halyard, M. (2010). I'm so tired: Biological and genetic mechanisms of cancer-related fatigue. *Quality of Life Research, 19*(10), 1419–1427.

Barsevick, A. M., Irwin, M. R., Hinds, P., Miller, A., Berger, A., Jacobsen, P., . . . & National Cancer Institute Clinical Trials Planning, M. (2013). Recommendations for high-priority research on cancer-related fatigue in children and adults. *J Natl Cancer Inst, 105*(19), 1432–1440. doi: 10.1093/jnci/djt242

Bayarsaihan, D. (2011). Epigenetic mechanisms in inflammation. *J Dent Res, 90*(1), 9–17. doi: 10.1177/0022034510378683

Bond, C., LaForge, K. S., Tian, M., Melia, D., Zhang, S., Borg, L., . . . & Yu, L. (1998). Single-nucleotide polymorphism in the human mu opioid receptor gene alters beta-endorphin binding and activity: possible implications for opiate addiction. *Proc Natl Acad Sci USA, 95*(16), 9608–9613.

Bower, J. E. (2007). Cancer-related fatigue: links with inflammation in cancer patients and survivors. *Brain Behav Immun, 21*(7), 863–871. doi: 10.1016/j.bbi.2007.03.013

Bower, J. E., Ganz, P. A., Desmond, K. A., Bernaards, C., Rowland, J. H., Meyerowitz, B. E., & Belin, T. R. (2006). Fatigue in long-term breast carcinoma survivors: a longitudinal investigation. *Cancer, 106*(4), 751–758. doi: 10.1002/cncr.21671

Bower, J. E., Ganz, P. A., Irwin, M. R., Arevalo, J. M., & Cole, S. W. (2011). Fatigue and gene expression in human leukocytes: increased NF-kappaB and decreased glucocorticoid signaling in breast cancer survivors with persistent fatigue. *Brain Behav Immun, 25*(1), 147–150. doi: 10.1016/j.bbi.2010.09.010

Bower, J. E., Ganz, P. A., Tao, M. L., Hu, W., Belin, T. R., Sepah, S., . . . Aziz, N. (2009). Inflammatory biomarkers and fatigue during radiation therapy for breast and prostate cancer. *Clin Cancer Res, 15*(17), 5534–5540. doi: 10.1158/1078-0432.CCR-08-2584

Bower, J. E., & Lamkin, D. M. (2013). Inflammation and cancer-related fatigue: mechanisms, contributing factors, and treatment implications. *Brain Behav Immun, 30 Suppl*, S48–57. doi: 10.1016/j.bbi.2012.06.011

Branford, R., Droney, J., & Ross, J. R. (2012). Opioid genetics: the key to personalized pain control? *Clin Genet, 82*(4), 301–310. doi: 10.1111/j.1399-0004.2012.01923.x

Chou, W. Y., Wang, C. H., Liu, P. H., Liu, C. C., Tseng, C. C., & Jawan, B. (2006a). Human opioid receptor A118G polymorphism affects intravenous patient-controlled analgesia morphine consumption after total abdominal hysterectomy. *Anesthesiology, 105*(2), 334–337.

Chou, W. Y., Yang, L. C., Lu, H. F., Ko, J. Y., Wang, C. H., Lin, S. H., . . . Hsu, C. J. (2006b). Association of mu-opioid receptor gene polymorphism (A118G) with variations in morphine consumption for analgesia after total knee arthroplasty. *Acta Anaesthesiol Scand, 50*(7), 787–792. doi: 10.1111/j.1399-6576.2006.01058.x

Collado-Hidalgo, A., Bower, J. E., Ganz, P. A., Cole, S. W., & Irwin, M. R. (2006). Inflammatory biomarkers for persistent fatigue in breast cancer survivors. *Clin Cancer Res, 12*(9), 2759–2766. doi: 10.1158/1078-0432.CCR-05-2398

Crow, M., Denk, F., & McMahon, S. B. (2013). Genes and epigenetic processes as prospective pain targets. *Genome Med, 5*(2), 12. doi: 10.1186/gm416

Denk, F. & McMahon, S. B. (2012). Chronic pain: emerging evidence for the involvement of epigenetics. *Neuron, 73*(3), 435–444. doi: 10.1016/j.neuron.2012.01.012

Diatchenko, L., Fillingim, R. B., Smith, S. B., & Maixner, W. (2013). The phenotypic and genetic signatures of common musculoskeletal pain conditions. *Nat Rev Rheumatol, 9*(6), 340–350. doi: 10.1038/nrrheum.2013.43

Escalante, C. P., Kallen, M. A., Valdres, R. U., Morrow, P. K., & Manzullo, E. F. (2010). Outcomes of a cancer-related fatigue clinic in a comprehensive cancer center. *J Pain Symptom Manage, 39*(4), 691–701. doi: 10.1016/j.jpainsymman.2009.09.010

Gaskin, D. J., & Richard, P. (2012). The economic costs of pain in the United States. *J Pain, 13*(8), 715–724. doi: 10.1016/j.jpain.2012.03.009

GeneQol Consortium. (2015). GeneQol Consortium –Genetic research into quality of life (home page). Retrieved July 16, 2015, from http://www.geneqol-consortium.org/

Geranton, S. M. (2012). Targeting epigenetic mechanisms for pain relief. *Curr Opin Pharmacol, 12*(1), 35–41. doi: 10.1016/j.coph.2011.10.012

Horneber, M., Fischer, I., Dimeo, F., Ruffer, J. U., & Weis, J. (2012). Cancer-related fatigue: epidemiology, pathogenesis, diagnosis, and treatment. *Dtsch Arztebl Int, 109*(9), 161–171; quiz 172. doi: 10.3238/arztebl.2012.0161

Hsiao, C. P., Wang, D., Kaushal, A., & Saligan, L. (2013). Mitochondria-related gene expression changes are associated with fatigue in patients with nonmetastatic prostate cancer receiving external beam radiation therapy. *Cancer Nurs, 36*(3), 189–197. doi: 10.1097/NCC.0b013e318263f514

Husson, O., Nieuwlaat, W. A., Oranje, W. A., Haak, H. R., van de Poll-Franse, L. V., & Mols, F. (2013). Fatigue among short- and long-term thyroid cancer survivors: results from the population-based PROFILES registry. *Thyroid, 23*(10), 1247–1255. doi: 10.1089/thy.2013.0015

Hwang, I. C., Yun, Y. H., Kim, Y. W., Ryu, K. W., Kim, Y. A., Kim, S., . . . Sohn, T. S. (2014). Factors related to clinically relevant fatigue in disease-free stomach cancer survivors and expectation-outcome consistency. *Support Care Cancer*. doi: 10.1007/s00520-013-2110-2

Institute of Medicine (US) Committee on Advancing Pain Research, C., and Education,. (2011). *Relieving Pain in America: A Blueprint for Transforming Prevention, Care, Education, and Research*. Washington, DC: National Academies Press (US) Retrieved from http://www.ncbi.nlm.nih.gov/books/NBK92514/.

Jim, H. S., Park, J. Y., Permuth-Wey, J., Rincon, M. A., Phillips, K. M., Small, B. J., & Jacobsen, P. B. (2012). Genetic predictors of fatigue in prostate cancer patients treated with androgen deprivation therapy: preliminary findings. *Brain Behav Immun, 26*(7), 1030–1036. doi: 10.1016/j.bbi.2012.03.001

Khansari, N., Shakiba, Y., & Mahmoudi, M. (2009). Chronic inflammation and oxidative stress as a major cause of age-related diseases and cancer. *Recent Pat Inflamm Allergy Drug Discov, 3*(1), 73–80.

Kim, H., Neubert, J. K., San Miguel, A., Xu, K., Krishnaraju, R. K., Iadarola, M. J., . . . Dionne, R. A. (2004). Genetic influence on variability in human acute experimental pain sensitivity associated with gender, ethnicity and psychological temperament. *Pain, 109*(3), 488–496. doi: 10.1016/j.pain.2004.02.027

Landmark-Hoyvik, H., Reinertsen, K. V., Loge, J. H., Kristensen, V. N., Dumeaux, V., Fossa, S. D., . . . Edvardsen, H. (2010). The genetics and epigenetics of fatigue. *PM R, 2*(5), 456–465. doi: 10.1016/j.pmrj.2010.04.003

Lu, H., Huang, D., Saederup, N., Charo, I. F., Ransohoff, R. M., & Zhou, L. (2011). Macrophages recruited via CCR2 produce insulin-like growth factor-1 to repair acute skeletal muscle injury. *FASEB J, 25*(1), 358–369. doi: 10.1096/fj.10-171579

Lyon, D. E., McCain, N. L., Pickler, R. H., Munro, C., & Elswick, R. K., Jr. (2011). Advancing the biobehavioral research of fatigue with genetics and genomics. *J Nurs Scholarsh, 43*(3), 274–281. doi: 10.1111/j.1547-5069.2011.01406.x

Meldrum, M. L. (2003). A capsule history of pain management. *JAMA, 290*(18), 2470–2475. doi: 10.1001/jama.290.18.2470

Miaskowski, C., Dodd, M., Lee, K., West, C., Paul, S. M., Cooper, B. A., . . . Aouizerat, B. E. (2010). Preliminary evidence of an association between a functional interleukin-6 polymorphism and fatigue and sleep disturbance in oncology patients and their family caregivers. *J Pain Symptom Manage, 40*(4), 531–544. doi: 10.1016/j.jpainsymman.2009.12.006

Mogil, J. S. (2012). Pain genetics: past, present and future. *Trends Genet, 28*(6), 258-266. doi: 10.1016/j.tig.2012.02.004

National Cancer Institute (2013). Fatigue (PDQ®). Causes of Fatigue in Cancer Patients. Retrieved from http://www.cancer.gov/cancertopics/pdq/supportivecare/fatigue/Patient/page2

National Comprehensive Cancer Network. (2015). Cancer-Related Fatigue (Version 2.2015). Retrieved July 16, 2015, from http://www.nccn.org/professionals/physician_gls/pdf/fatigue.pdf

National Institute of Nursing Research. (nd). Spotlight on symptom management research. Retrieved July 16, 2015, from https://www.ninr.nih.gov/research-andfunding/symptommanagement#.Uy9VJvtiKM0

Nightingale, F. (1860). *Notes on nursing what it is, and what it is not* (New ed.). London: Harrison.

Orre, I. J., Murison, R., Dahl, A. A., Ueland, T., Aukrust, P., & Fossa, S. D. (2009). Levels of circulating interleukin-1 receptor antagonist and C-reactive protein in long-term survivors of testicular cancer with chronic cancer-related fatigue. *Brain Behav Immun, 23*(6), 868–874. doi: 10.1016/j.bbi.2009.04.003

Reyes-Gibby, C. C., Shete, S., Rakvag, T., Bhat, S. V., Skorpen, F., Bruera, E., . . . Klepstad, P. (2007). Exploring joint effects of genes and the clinical efficacy of morphine for cancer pain: OPRM1 and COMT gene. *Pain, 130*(1-2), 25-30. doi: 10.1016/j.pain.2006.10.023

Ryan, J. L., Carroll, J. K., Ryan, E. P., Mustian, K. M., Fiscella, K., & Morrow, G. R. (2007). Mechanisms of cancer-related fatigue. *Oncologist, 12 Suppl 1*, 22-34. doi: 10.1634/theoncologist.12-S1-22

Saligan, L. N. & Kim, H. S. (2012). A systematic review of the association between immunogenomic markers and cancer-related fatigue. *Brain Behav Immun, 26*(6), 830–848. doi: 10.1016/j.bbi.2012.05.004

Selvi, B. R., Mohankrishna, D. V., Ostwal, Y. B., & Kundu, T. K. (2010). Small molecule modulators of histone acetylation and methylation: a disease perspective. *Biochim Biophys Acta, 1799*(10-12), 810–828. doi: 10.1016/j.bbagrm.2010.09.005

Seo, S., Grzenda, A., Lomberk, G., Ou, X. M., Cruciani, R. A., & Urrutia, R. (2013). Epigenetics: a promising paradigm for better understanding and managing pain. *J Pain, 14*(6), 549–557. doi: 10.1016/j.jpain.2013.01.772

Smith, A. J., & Humphries, S. E. (2009). Cytokine and cytokine receptor gene polymorphisms and their functionality. *Cytokine Growth Factor Rev, 20*(1), 43–59. doi: 10.1016/j.cytogfr.2008.11.006

Smith, M. T., & Muralidharan, A. (2012). Pharmacogenetics of pain and analgesia. *Clin Genet, 82*(4), 321–330. doi: 10.1111/j.1399-0004.2012.01936.x

Sprangers, M. A., Sloan, J. A., Veenhoven, R., Cleeland, C. S., Halyard, M. Y., Abertnethy, A. P., . . . Zwinderman, A. H. (2009). The establishment of the GENEQOL consortium to investigate the genetic disposition of patient-reported quality-of-life outcomes. *Twin Res Hum Genet, 12*(3), 301–311. doi: 10.1375/twin.12.3.301

Starkweather, A. R., & Pair, V. E. (2013). Decoding the role of epigenetics and genomics in pain management. *Pain Manag Nurs, 14*(4), 358–367. doi: 10.1016/j.pmn.2011.05.006

University of Wisconsin, S. o. P. H. (2014). Pain Magement: Classification of Pain. Retrieved 17 March 2014, from http://projects.hsl.wisc.edu/GME/Pain-Management/session2.4.html

Voscopoulos, C., & Lema, M. (2010). When does acute pain become chronic? *Br J Anaesth, 105 Suppl 1*, i69–85. doi: 10.1093/bja/aeq323

Walter, C., & Lotsch, J. (2009). Meta-analysis of the relevance of the OPRM1 118A>G genetic variant for pain treatment. *Pain, 146*(3), 270–275. doi: 10.1016/j.pain.2009.07.013

Wang, X. S., Zhoa, F., Fisch, M. J., O'mara, A. M.,

Cella, D., Mendoza, T. R., & Cleeland, C. S. (2013). Prevalence and characteristics of moderate to severe fatigue. *Cancer, 2*, 425–432. doi: doi 10.1002/cncr.28434

Weschenfelder, J., Sander, C., Kluge, M., Kirkby, K. C., & Himmerich, H. (2012). The influence of cytokines on wakefulness regulation: clinical relevance, mechanisms, and methodological problems. *Psychiatria Danubina, 24*(2), 112–126.

Young, E. E., Lariviere, W. R., & Belfer, I. (2012). Genetic basis of pain variability: recent advances. *J Med Genet, 49*(1), 1-9. doi: 10.1136/jmedgenet-2011-100386

Zubieta, J. K., Heitzeg, M. M., Smith, Y. R., Bueller, J. A., Xu, K., Xu, Y., . . . Goldman, D. (2003). COMT val158met genotype affects mu-opioid neurotransmitter responses to a pain stressor. *Science, 299*(5610), 1240–1243. doi: 10.1126/science.1078546

Index